textiles: origins to usage

textiles: origins to usage

DR. JULES LABARTHE

professor of textile technology

carnegie institute of technology

pittsburgh, pennsylvania

the macmillan company

collier-macmillan limited, london

Fifth Printing, 1969

Library of Congress catalog card numbers 64–12169

THE MACMILLAN COMPANY
COLLIER-MACMILLAN CANADA, LTD., TORONTO, ONTARIO

Printed in the United States of America

The purpose of this book is to provide information leading to the best use of textile products by the consumer in terms of his own particular pattern of needs. If it leaves the student unsatisfied, then so much the better, if by unsatisfaction is meant that the reader's interest has been stirred to such an extent that he wishes to know more about some phase or other—perhaps on the technical development, maybe from the historical point of view, or the economic—but at any rate, that student will wish to explore further and read more in the field. It is hoped that it will help the home economist in business, the extension worker dealing with adult groups, and store salespeople, even though it is intended primarily for students of Home Economics and perhaps as a very preliminary introduction into textile chemistry.

Research workers in science are agreed that the intensified application of research in any field of scientific endeavor during a year of war is equivalent to many more years of research under peacetime conditions. Whether the increase in progress is at a rate of five to one or ten to one is relatively unimportant. The facts are that researches for survival result in a flood of new discoveries applicable to everyday life. Many changes in our textiles have resulted from the research efforts during two world wars. From the textile product point of view, after World War I the United States emerged as one of the great powers in industrial-chemical research. From World War II was won the position as one of the leaders in polymer research leading to new fibers, new knowledge of old fibers, the engineering ability to blend and manipulate these for specific end-use

v

applications, and at last, the expanded knowledge of how best to finish and dye these goods for ultimate consumer satisfaction.

Even more amazing and useful to the consumer has been the quickening of all means of communication and of transportation. Store buyers visit all the great markets of the world, not once a year as was customary for some of the larger stores, but perhaps several times a year even for stores of moderate size. Goods may be transported not in weeks or even in days but in a matter of hours. The consumer watching television at home has as good a seat at the grand opening of world-famed couturiers' new lines for the seasons as do the buyers who have traveled to New York, to Paris, to Rome, and to other style centers to view these first offerings. Shopping itself is more comfortable now for the consumer than ever before. They are no longer dependent upon the mail order catalogue or upon trips to the big downtown stores to view their merchandise. They can select their purchases just as easily in the shopping centers growing so rapidly around the periphery of our large cities. These magnets draw customers from the city to the outskirts and from the countryside around into the city border for shopping.

Where we fall behind is in our efforts to communicate the facts about these wonderful new achievements. Thus, many of our customers are somewhat sceptical about the real place of synthetic fibers in the textile picture. There still persists some confusion between rayon and acetate, simply because they were for a time mistakenly grouped together under the so-called Rayon Rules. It has become necessary to clarify the new fiber names under the Textile Fiber Products Identification Act and to define the textile nomenclature for all fibers as had been done by the Wool Products Labeling Act for wool and wool derivatives and the Fur Products Labeling Act for garments of animal fur fibers. Though these laws identify textile products in advertising and selling, the facts are still of limited use to the consumer unless he knows much more about the background and the individual properties of all these new materials. Similarly, much of the effort of the manufacturers of these new textile fibers, of the weavers, of the creators of new textile constructions and textures, and of the creators of dyes and finishes giving these products new and unusual physical and service properties, are wasted on a non-understanding public. Informative labels, textile standards developed for the consumer by the efforts of the American Standards Association, and all the many elements of the textile industry remain unused through lack of understanding. At every professional level, chemists, engineers, physicists, biologists, and other technically trained persons devoting their lives to careers in the textile industry are not only trying constantly to improve textile products they make but also trying to communicate with the consumer through the development of better and more realistic test methods, more closely compared wih use experience than with laboratory machines; thus, the American Association of Textile Chemists and Colorists is responsible for most of the testing and analytical techniques dealing with the chemical properties of textile fibers and fabrics, while the American Society for Testing Materials devotes its attention to the physical testing. Interlocking committees between the societies and work with the government in the commercial standards programs all are further efforts devoted to finding means of communication with the consumer. In reaching the consumer, one must first reach the consumer's contact with the store—the salesperson. How to create an eagerness for knowledge in the sales-people so that they can take the enthusiasm of the buyer who has made a selection in the market and present it in all its exciting details to the customer on the other side of the counter is a constant challenge.

The textbook should not simply be a collection of facts, no matter how informative and useful they may be. Textiles have a thrilling history, and if we are to understand and appreciate the natural fibers, we should know something of their background, the part each fiber has played at one time or another in the politics of the country in which it was created or in which it was of major importance in relations, both political and economic, between countries. The constant shuffling of position between one fiber and another in various end uses excites the onlooker. What is the responsibility of the informed consumer with regard to choice of merchandise today? How much of a factor is the textile industry of Europe going to be in the American consumers' buying life as the Common Market expands its fiber and fabric names into the United States in competition with ours? For trade is a two-way matter—we cannot export and not import—but what and how much are for the economists to decide. Yet, each consumer can determine where his own best interests lie in comparing the qualities of American goods with those of Europe or those from Japan or Hong Kong.

There are undoubtedly ideas and conclusions expressed in several parts of this book which will be in disagreement with the opinions of some of the teacher readers. I hope this is true, because on disagreement depends progress in ideas. I am sure that the experiences leading to these ideas were somewhat different from those of the writers of most textbooks on textiles.

Prior to accepting a professorship in Textile Technology at Carnegie Institute of Technology in 1958, I headed an Industrial Fellowship at Mellon Institute maintained for 27 years by the Kaufmann Department Store of Pittsburgh. This was the laboratory of the store but was located in this research institute instead of being within the store itself. Like most retail store laboratories, we were called upon for the testing, evaluation, and analysis of almost every kind of merchandise sold by the establishment, but textiles predominated, just as they do in the sales of any large department store. Some 15,000 consumer complaints dealing with textiles were examined and reported to the store during this period of time. (It must be emphasized that in all evaluations of new merchandise, the products were received in the laboratory in the ready-to-be-used condition.) Therefore, it was inevitable that the store laboratory technicians of the Kaufmann Fellowship quickly developed the consumer's point of view. We were concerned with how the material or article was going to function in use; or in the case of a complaint, we were charged with trying to find out why it did not perform as expected, and, almost always, a new article was submitted for test or comparison with the consumer's article. Thus, through my career and through working on committees of the American Standards Association and the National Retail Merchants Association's Technical Committee and Consumers Goods Committee, together with testing program studies of various technical committees of the AATCC and ASTM Committee D-13, it was the consumer's point of view I tried to express.

During my five years of teaching classes in Textiles at Carnegie Institute of Technology, as well as at several summer schools and Home Economics Workshops at other institutions, parts of several chapters of this book have been used, revised, and used again. But one cannot simply go on revising and changing, no matter how much improvement is made. The less technical portions of the chapters on the various fibers have been thoroughly adequate for introducing textiles to freshman students in Home Economics. For more advanced students in textile chemistry, these same chapters have been used in their entirety. A graduate course in Textile Consumership drew heavily on the last four chapters in this book, following an abbreviated orientation on the present status of textile fibers and fabrics.

I am indebted to my many friends in the textile industry who have given me advice and encouragement, to my students who have been test subjects, to my friends in Home Economics and in Extension Service for advice and enthusiasm, to my typists, Miss Pearl Izbrand, Mrs. Carroll Labarthe, and Miss Rena B. Zeffer, and most of all to my wife, to whom these several years of preparation were longer even than to me.

J. L.

contents

why study textiles

The housewife of today has a unique relationship with the businesses of manufacturing and selling goods. This is especially true in the case of textile products. At no previous time in history since man first began to clothe himself has the user of clothing materials been so dependent on manufactured goods and on what the manufacturer and the retailer say about them; at no time has man had so wide a choice.

THE DEPENDENT CONSUMER

It is common practice to refer to the purchaser of goods as "she," because the woman of the household makes most of the actual purchases; indeed, some estimators say that 85 per cent of retail purchases are made by women. It is more accurate, though, to make clear that the purchaser is first a **customer** and then a **consumer.** All of us are customers while we are making our purchases of clothing, furniture, food, automobiles, cosmetics, or whatever else it may be. We are consumers during the entire period of time in which we are using these things. As customers we are guided in our selection by experience and knowledge, by the effectiveness of the advertising of the product, by the representation made by the sales person, by the impression made by the package and label, and by the price of the article. As consumers we more or less unconsciously weigh the satisfaction the product has given us as compared with our expectations.

The informed, intelligent consumer is the desirable kind of customer because she best knows what to expect of the articles she buys and how to care for them. Informed customers don't just grow; they develop through practical consumer education and buying experience until they achieve skills in buying all types of goods. The intelligent selling of goods to customers requires the same education. Too many sales people are poor at their jobs because they lack interest in and knowledge of what they are selling.

HOW TEXTILE KNOWLEDGE CAN HELP

It is so evident that textile knowledge, such as familiarity with the kinds of products, their anticipated performance, and their ease of care, will help all young people, both men and women, when they become shoppers for their own homes, that the point need not be emphasized. Where, however, in the well-balanced Home Economics curriculum can a course in textiles be of help professionally as well as personally?

Actually the usefulness is as wide spread as the possible employment fields open to the Home Economics graduate with a solid college background with chemistry, textiles, and clothing as a major. It can also widen the opportunities for one wishing to enter into late study as an adult, preparatory, perhaps, to re-entering a professional field after one's children are on their own.

Suppose, then, we group these job opportunities into the various segments of the textile industry.

1   Production (Development)
2   Distribution
3   Consumption

production

Research of a fundamental technical nature rarely calls upon a graduate in Home Economics because the technical fields of fiber study, dyes, synthetics, and finish development and application require more intensive chemistry as a background. However, in the **development** of new products and the researches into their application and performance, the laboratories of textile mills, chemical processing agents for textiles, detergent producers, government laboratories (such as the Agricultural Experiment Stations), and various colleges and universities need help. **Field tests** of new products and the **evaluation of consumer reaction** to these textiles are essential to fiber and fabric producers, the textile servicing industries, commercial testing laboratories, and some universities. Eventually this new knowledge will help the consumer. **Testing** of fabrics is another technical field for students of textiles. This involves both physical and chemical evaluation procedures and may be correlated with field or use tests previously mentioned. In production, these procedures may be a part of **quality control** of the product, the comparison with the properties of competitors' goods, or the perfection of a product for new uses and markets. It may be carried out in the laboratory of the producer or in a commercial testing laboratory.

distribution

Testing and chemical analysis of textile products are usually the main activities of laboratories maintained by individual stores, buying organizations, or commercial testing companies. The semi-technical bulletins and reports of consumer advisory organizations, such as Consumers Research and Consumers Union, require technicians and writers familiar with textiles and other consumer goods. The results from laboratories of certain lay reader publications, such as Good Housekeeping Magazine, also benefit the consumer of textiles.

Many girls skilled in textiles are employed by stores as **buyers, assistant buyers, heads of stock, or salespeople.** Others go into **fashion design, style coordination, interior display,** employee **training,** and other services. Prominent in the positions open at the distribution level are the **public relations** positions presenting new fibers, special finishes, and laundry and care demonstrations in behalf of producers before store salespeople and large meetings of consumers. Many home economists in business represent the appliance and chemical industries in providing public information and help.

consumption

Though difficult to categorize, probably the technical staffs of the textile service industries, such as the American Institute of Laundering and the National Institute of Dry Cleaning, best serve their member business firms and their customers by the propagation of information in the care of delicate or easily damaged, hard-to-clean textile products. Knowledge of textiles is mandatory if dependable conclusions are to be drawn. Much of this work handled by chemists and home economists is educational. Of future value to consumers, or perhaps it might be put as being of value to future consumers, is the teaching of textile facts in the high schools and colleges. Still another aspect of **teaching** is the work done by the home economists in the Extension Service of the U.S. Department of Agriculture, whether in food and nutrition or textiles and clothing. Educational, too, is the **technical writing** in the daily press and in magazines.

Quite apart from these reasons to study fabrics and their properties, and even apart from its practical contributions in the future, when one must shop not only for oneself but for a family, a textile textbook can suggest through collateral reading many fascinating chapters in the development of textiles.

1   The arts in textile construction and decoration, as shown in museums and books, with comparisons of ancient civilizations with the handcraft and power-produced goods of today.

2   The history and intrigue involved in the gradual spread of silk, wool, and cotton from one country to another.

3 The Industrial Revolution following the application of power and inventive genius to the textile trade of England and Europe.

4 The inevitable disturbance, both economic and social, when a cheaper new fiber displaces the older one for an important product.

5 The part played by cotton in United States history.

6 The search for fur fibers for the hat-trade of Europe, which led to the opening of our Western states.

7 The range wars between cattleman and sheepherder.

8 The black days of child labor and the succession of laws for the betterment of working conditions in textile mills.

9 The great scientists and inventive geniuses of the textile and allied industries.

10 The constant problem of foreign trade balances in textile products.

plain, twill, and satin—
the basic ABC weaves

When a customer enters a store to buy a dress or a suit, the fabric of which the garment is made attracts her interest. The texture, color, feel, draping quality, handle, and brightness—all are important elements entering into her selection. Indeed, the fabric is still on trial when the article is worn, washed, or cleaned. Is it not true that the texture and color of the dress must be attractive; that the apparent warmth of the blanket and its depth of nap are important elements in its selection; that the firmness and springiness of the material in a man's suit constitute some of the factors governing his selection; or that the permanence of absorbency in a toweling is one quality a customer will consider? These and many other appearance and serviceability factors are, of course, influenced by the type of textile, by the size, twist, and composition of the individual yarn. It is equally true that the quality of dyeing and finishing applied to the fabric largely determines both its initial attractiveness and its potential serviceability. But it is the fabric the customer buys; therefore, it is logical that we begin our discussion of textiles from the standpoint of the fabric and then go back to determine the significance of fiber, yarn, finish, dyestuff, and other processing mechanisms and materials which enter into our finished textile product—the fabric.

FORMING THE FABRIC

The most important method of forming fabrics by mechanical means is **weaving,** which is the interlacing of two sets of yarns at right angles by means of a loom. The yarns in the lengthwise direction of the bolt of fabric, and generally of the garment also, are known as the **warp** (from the term **warp ends**). The crosswise yarns are called **filling** yarns or **picks.** These are the terms most frequently used at the consumer level—warp and filling yarns. At various production stages in the textile industry, the terms **ends** and **picks** are used.

If the fabric is formed by a succession of loops, each row interlocking with the one below it, the cloth is made by **knitting.** Both weaving and knitting may be done at home, on a hand loom or with knitting needles, respectively.

A third method of textile product formation of increasing interest to the consumer is the **non-woven** fabric, which is much like paper and in which the individual fibers have been laid down in a random or disordered fashion to form a sheet structure. Wool and fur fibers may be formed into an interlocked fibrous structure called a **felt**. Felting of wool probably is the oldest of all textile-producing methods.

outline of weaving

The fact that primitive man understood the principles of weaving is shown in his crude baskets and mats, drawings and fragments of which have come down to us through thousands of years. (The products made by some of our western Indian tribes are already museum pieces.) Primitive man used twigs and grasses for his baskets. These, of course, were long fibers, and at a later date, man learned how to twist together hair, wool, cotton, or other short fibers and eventually developed the mechanical appliance known as the hand loom. All that was required of the first crude loom was a method of fastening the warp ends so that they lay parallel and were fairly rigid or firmly held in position at both ends. Weighted warp yarns, suspended from a horizontal branch, or warp yarns held rigidly between two sticks have been described in ancient writings or have been depicted in crude drawings. One or more inventive geniuses built the first of the rigid wood frames, the **warp beam,** made to hold the warp yarns in a crude loom.

Doubtless the filling threads or yarns were first passed under and over successive warp yarns in a slow laborious fashion, using a pointed stick or a bone as a needle to pry apart the alternate warp yarns to give the under-and-over weave of the cloth. It became apparent that weaving could be made somewhat easier if all the alternate warp threads were raised or lowered simultaneously, permitting the fillings to be shot through quickly clear across the width of the fabric. We recognize this technique in the harness looms of today, not only in the simple hand looms or home industry looms, but also in the large industrial appliances. The separation is carried out by means of a **harness** or frame holding a series of wires each having a needle-eye and referred to as **heddles**. The process by which one harness, or collection of heddles each holding a warp yarn, is raised, permitting the shuttle carrying the filling yarn to be shot through the open angle between the two sets of warp yarns, is called **shedding.** Next, the harnesses are reversed; the harness which had been down is raised, and the

Fig. 2-1 Operation of a loom: High-speed photography stops action of shuttle to illustrate the principles of weaving. In the upper left-hand corner, we see the harness frames. Some have been raised in the loom and others have been lowered to form the shed or funnel through which the shuttle has just passed, leaving a filling pick in its wake.

The reed through which the threads are seen to pass has begun its movement forward to the solid cloth on the right, beating up the pick that the shuttle has just delivered. The reed will pound this pick firmly against the cloth. It then swings back to the left, and the harness frames in the upper left-hand corner change position to form a new shed of threads, and this time the shuttle will be shot from the left side of the reed to the shuttle box on the right-hand side, leaving a new pick as it goes. (*Reproduced through the courtesy of The Wool Bureau, Inc.*)

other is lowered for the return trip of the shuttle through the shed. More complex looms may have as many as twelve harnesses, thus permitting the weaving of complex yarn combinations and patterns which could only be achieved on the hand loom through painstaking care and many hours of demanding labor and attention.

fundamental steps in weaving

It is not necessary to go into full details with regard to the appearance or operation of a loom. Our references will be made to collateral reading. However, the fundamental steps should be summarized for clear understanding.

1　After the **warp beam** has been set up, by winding around the wood spool the desired number and lengths of warp yarns, and all of the warp ends passed through their individual heddles on the loom harness, one or more sets of the warp ends are lifted or separated by a foot **treadle** or other mechanism (depending upon whether it is a **true harness** loom, such as a hand-operated type, or a more complex machine-operated high-speed loom) in the process of shedding.

2　The shuttle carrying the filling yarn, or pick, is shot through the shed. The term pick persists from the early weaving operations when the alternate warp threads were picked or lifted individually for the insertion of the filling yarn.

3 After each filling yarn has passed through the shed, it is **battened,** or pushed up against the previous filling thread, by the **reed** in order to give a uniformly packed fabric. The reed consists of a frame with wires set in vertically, with a wire between each pair of warp yarns.

4 When the desired length has been woven, the warp yarns are released from the warp beam, and the length of finished cloth is taken up or wound on the **roll,** or merchandise beam. This is called letting off and taking up. At the same time, the additional lengths of warp yarn extending from the piece of fabric are attached to the heddles, and the weaving operation is continued until the full length of cloth corresponding to the length of warp yarns originally twisted has been produced. Sometimes additional warp yarns are individually tied to these warp ends so that additional yardage may be produced.

the selvage

If we were to depend upon the warp yarns alone to keep a fabric firm during all the processes through which it must go before it reaches the consumer, the edges would be ragged and raveled without some kind of reinforcement by mechanical finishing or self-edging. These edges are called **selvages** and are usually made with somewhat heavier and more closely packed warp yarns than those used in the rest of the cloth. In dress goods and suitings, these selvages are generally quite narrow, varying from about one-quarter to one-half inch in width. Fabrics requiring a considerable amount of wear and abrasion during use and which are not used as components of garments must have the maximum of selvage strength. Therefore, such items as towels, bed sheets, tablecloths, draperies, curtains, and upholstering materials generally have tape selvages, which are firmer and stronger than plain selvages.

NUMBER OF YARNS

In some fabrics the size or diameter of the yarn used in the warp and in the filling are the same, but this need not necessarily be the case. It is also common for the warp to have more yarns to the inch than the filling, because the weaving operation itself imposes more strain on the warp yarns. One has only to compare the density of a percale sheeting with the open structure of a voile to see the different degrees of compactness which can be achieved even on a simple loom. For maximum durability and ability of the fabric to hold its shape and dimension, it is logical to expect better service from a more closely and firmly woven fabric than from one which is extremely open in texture. This degree of closeness of the weave is measured by the **count** of the cloth. This is literally a count of the number of warps and fillings to the square inch. This count is customarily made using the help of a small pocket magnifying glass having beneath it an exact square of one-half or one-inch sides and marked off in sixteenths of an inch, similar to the markings on a ruler. Because this glass was first used in the linen industry, it is sometimes referred to as a **linen tester**. If the cloth is fairly open, it is very easy to set one edge of the opening in the base against a warp yarn and then count the number of warp yarns in a quarter of an inch and multiply by four to give the full count per inch, or preferably to count clear across the one-inch span; this process should then be repeated with the filling yarns. The count is expressed as e.g., 60 × 40, if the warp yarns count is 60 and the filling yarns 40, the warp count always being given first. If the fabric structure is made obscure either because of a more compact weave or the finishing process, it is sometimes simpler to pull out a few yarns from the warp and a few from the filling, leaving a short fringe along two sides, the ends of which can then be counted under the glass with the aid of a pin or textile pick to separate the fringe for better visibility.

If the count is the same in both warp and filling, as is the case in a very common cloth known as print cloth, having 80 warp threads and 80 filling threads, such a cloth is referred to as an 80-square. Muslin sheeting standards[1] call for two counts, or types: Type 128 and Type 140. These figures refer to the total warp and filling threads in a square inch of the muslin. These fabrics would have their greatest durability if they were evenly balanced, that is, with a 64-square count for the Type 128 and a 70-square for the Type 140. Generally, however, there will be more warp threads than filling threads. The differences may be of the order of 10 per cent or slightly more. Thus, a 77 × 63 count muslin sheet could be called a Type 140, but it would not be as strong a fabric in the filling direction as in the warp. It must be remembered, however, that from the practical point of view the greatest strain on a bed sheet is in the warp direction, both during the weaving operation and also in placing the sheet on the bed. Before the adoption of these standards, very cheap bed sheets could be found with counts as low as 50-square, the openings being filled in with clay, starch, or some other inert material to give the appearance of a lustrous, compact sheeting—until the first laundering.

One of the hazards of using low-count fabrics in wearing apparel is the tendency of the materials to ravel at the seams. More compact and firm cloths are more resistant to this raveling, especially in the case of the man-made and synthetic fibers, which are generally more slippery than the natural fibers due to their smooth outer surfaces. A clue to this tendency to ravel or to shift under strain can be had by a simple hand test. If the fabric is gripped between the thumb and forefinger of each hand with the thumbs close and parallel and then if both thumbs are pressed down firmly, the fabric may split if the yarns in that direction (warp or filling) are weak, or the fabric may open up into a crescent or elliptical shape as a result of yarn slippage or shifting. In the one case, the fabric would

[1] American Standard, L4. 1-1948 American Standards Association.

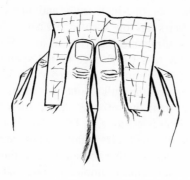

a. Grip fabric between thumbs and fore-fingers.

b. Roll thumbs back-to-back, applying tension on fabric.

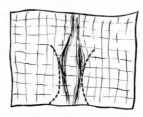

c. Opening in fabric due to tension; dash lines show position of thumbs.

Fig. 2-2   Thumb-slip test for shifting.

not be durable enough for use without splitting; in the other, openings might be expected to form during wearing when the fabric was subjected to a sudden strain, and the seams would be very likely to ravel and open unless very firmly reinforced during the sewing operation.

balance of the cloth

By **balance** of a cloth is meant the proportion of warp threads to filling threads. Generally a cloth is considered to be in balance or to have good balance if there is not more than 10 yarns' difference between the two. We refer again to the case of the 77×63 count Type 140 muslin sheet. This would not have good balance; however, a 75×65 would be reasonably good. Similarly, a gauze with a count of 28×24 is in good balance, but one of 34×18 would be poor. If there are insufficient filling threads to give a firm structure, then shifting and slipping are sure to occur.

A cloth can also be out of balance if the yarns in one direction are much heavier than those in the other. For example, in a print cloth of 80-square, there might be much finer warp yarns than filling, and the fabric would actually be unbalanced as far as durability is concerned. On the other hand, one might have a cotton broadcloth of what seems to be a count far off-balance, such as 144 × 72. In this case, if the filling yarns are about twice the diameter of the warp yarns, we could have a dense, compact fabric having a ridged surface effect. A noteworthy fabric of this general type having balance achieved through a much heavier filling yarn was a combination fabric popular for dress goods in 1957. This fabric was called a **combination fabric** because it had a different kind of fiber in the warp than it had in the filling. In this case, the very fine warp yarns had a count of approximately 140 and were of nylon. The filling yarns, much larger in diameter, had a count of only 20 and were of cotton. The result was a ridged fabric of interesting texture and apparently in balance as far as compactness was concerned. Nevertheless, the material proved to be a great disappointment when the consumer first tried to iron it. Although the cotton yarns were outnumbered 140 to 20, cotton was the principal fiber, for the heavier cotton filling yarns accounted for 65 per cent of the actual weight of the cloth. Thus, pressing the cloth required the use of an iron at the cotton setting in order to remove wrinkles. This setting was too hot for the nylon, and the very fine nylon yarns were melted. To iron it at a lower temperature for the nylon would not remove the wrinkles from the cotton. Thus, we see that the count and balance, though important to the ultimate serviceability and durability of the cloth, cannot give the whole answer when it comes to combinations of two or more kinds of fiber in the same fabric.

THE ABC WEAVES

It is in the weave and the method in which the filling yarns are enmeshed with the warp yarns that man has his first opportunity to develop novelty and distinction in appearance of a cloth. Weaves are named in accordance with the design followed in interlacing these yarns. The ten most important weaves to be discussed are:

1	Plain	6	Dobby
2	Twill	7	Leno or Gauze
3	Satin	8	Swivel
4	Pile	9	Lappet
5	Jacquard	10	Clip-Spot

The first three are the fundamental or ABC weaves, the middle four are pattern weaves, and the last three provide embroidered effects.

plain weave

The plain weave is the most common of all cloth weave constructions and accounts for about 80 per cent of all woven goods. In this plain weave, the filling passes over one warp yarn, under the next, over the third, under the fourth, and

11

so on across the cloth from selvage to selvage. The second time across, the filling yarns go under each yarn over which the previous filling yarn passed and over each yarn under which the filling had passed on the previous passage. This is repeated so that each odd-numbered filling yarn travels the same path as the first; each even-numbered filling yarn passes in the manner of number two. It is strong cloth and its threads are interlaced tightly because the over-and-under passages on alternate yarns give rigidity and firmness. Figure 2-3 shows the plain weave drawn first as the yarn structure and second as a designer's graph or point-paper pattern. This kind of pattern is useful in sketching out intricate designs on paper before they are set up in a more detailed pattern for the loom. We should visualize the black squares in this plain-weave graph paper design in the following manner:

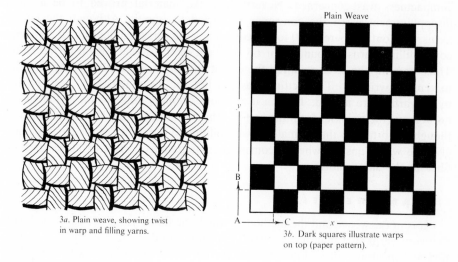

3a. Plain weave, showing twist in warp and filling yarns.

Plain Weave

3b. Dark squares illustrate warps on top (paper pattern).

Fig. 2-3   The plain weave.

The vertical squares represent the warp. The black shows where each warp yarn passes over the filling. The squares in the horizontal position represent the filling yarns, and, on the face of the fabric, the light squares show where the filling yarn is on top. This diagram can show equally well the appearance of the back, or the wrong side, of the cloth. Again, the black shows where that particular yarn is on the surface. On the back, we would begin in the lower left-hand corner, for we would then consider the filling or horizontal yarns first. The black squares on the wrong side would represent where the filling yarns passed over the warps. If we let (A) represent the point at the corner, (B) the width of the square in the vertical, or Y axis, and (C) the width of the square along the horizontal, or X axis, then the diameter or width of the warp yarns would be the distance (AC), and the diameter of the filling yarns would be the distance (AB). If a cloth is in perfect balance and in a plain weave, then these figures would be squares, and the two yarns would have almost the same diameter.

The plain weave is sometimes referred to as the taffeta or the tabby weave. It is also known generally as the cotton weave.

Among the important cloths made in the plain weave are the following: made from cotton: batiste, broadcloth, cambric, calico, chambray, cheesecloth, chintz, crash, cretonne, dimity, flannel, lawn, muslin, nainsook, organdy, poplin, voile, sheeting, tarlatan, balloon cloths, scrim, bunting, buckram, canvas, flannelette; made from linen: crash, dress linen, handkerchief linen, butcher's linen, art and pillowcase linen, toweling, cambric, airplane linen; made from woolens and worsteds: albatross, balmacaan, broadcloths, challis, flannel, home-spun, nun's veiling, georgette, some tweeds; made from silk (also from rayon, acetate, and synthetics): taffeta, organza, voile, canton crepe, flat crepe, georgette, chiffon, pongee, shantung, top silk, broadcloth, habutai, crepe de Chine, mogadore, moiré, ninon, pucker prints, and some plaids.

The plain weave is an uninteresting fabric in texture and appearance even when the warp and filling yarns are of different colors. Mention has already been made of the desire for balance in plain weave fabrics, but indeed, unbalanced fabrics are very often made in order to produce materials of greater attractiveness and consumer demand. Vertical ribs appearing at regular intervals may be produced in the plain weave by using a much heavier warp yarn at regular intervals across the harness of the loom; with a periodic heavy warp yarn con-trasting with a succession of fine warp yarns, a rib or heavy stripe, such as in striped dimity or corded madras, may be produced. Heavier ribs and cords in the filling direction may be produced in such fabrics as dimity, faille, bengaline, and certain broadcloths. Heavy yarns may be used in both directions to create cross-bar effects. It must be kept in mind that the surface wear of the fine crosswise yarns resting along the top surface of a heavy rib yarn makes such fabrics lower in durability, especially in resistance to abrasion or rubbing. The cutting action of one yarn against another is also a factor in these deliberately unbalanced fabrics.

Oxford cloth for men's shirtings and dress fabrics represents another method of creating surface interest in the square weave. One type of Oxford cloth common to men's shirtings is called a 2 × 1 basket weave. In such a fabric, a single heavy filling yarn passes alternately over and under two warp yarns, each of which is exactly one-half the diameter of the filling yarn. If this size ratio is not exact, the fabric would develop an oblong rather than a square effect. This basket weave can be extended to cover other geometrical combinations of yarns. For example, a 3 × 2 basket weave (a common dress material of Oxford cloth) has two fillings passing over and under three warps. An interesting fabric of long-standing popularity as a drapery material is monk's cloth. This is available in several different weights of basket-weave construction, varying from 2 × 2 to

4×4 and even 8×8 combinations in which two fillings pass alternately over two yarns in the first fabric, four fillings over and under four warps in the second, and eight fillings over and under eight warps in the third. Monk's cloth is a somewhat open weave fabric; hence, it is likely to shrink in washing, and it will ravel at the seams unless very carefully reinforced. This kind of fabric in a synthetic fiber might be expected to scuff up and to pill rather badly when abraded or rubbed.

The plain weave lends itself to other textural and appearance effects by the use of random or hit-or-miss heavy yarns combined with fine ones, or with yarns deliberately made thick and thin, or with heavy slubs, such as characterized by some of our coarser linen fabrics and dress fabrics of shantung silk. Reference to thick and thin yarns will be made in the chapter on yarns (Chapter 7). Variations in twist are characteristic of these slubbed yarns and other novelties. Texturized yarns, stretch yarns, and tightly twisted yarns producing a crimped or a crepe effect are all modifications deliberately introduced in order to give style and interesting texture to the fabric.

Other modifications already briefly referred to may be achieved by using two colored filling yarns in combination with white warps or vice versa, or by introducing combinations of colors in one or both directions. Similarly, unusual effects can be achieved by the use of different fibers in the yarns of the two directions. We have already seen one case in which heavy cotton filling was used in combination with a very fine nylon warp. Combinations of natural fibers with synthetics or with rayon and acetate are very common. Indeed, several of our most popular crepes for women's blouses—alpaca and ratiné, for example—are actually combinations of rayon and acetate yarns plied together (twisted together) to produce a heavier yarn with interesting variations of shiny viscose yarns showing in contrast to the dull acetate. The use of luster adds to the attractiveness of textiles and is, of course, highlighted through the use of metal yarns (Chapter 15, page 231), or of heavy monofilament yarns of a shiny synthetic contrasted with dull yarns in the other direction.

Variations may be created by the method of finishing (reference to these will be made in Chapter 5, pages 95–98), but it is at once evident that even the basic mechanical processes for the removal of short fibers from the somewhat dull and lifeless-looking cotton gray goods, followed by bleaching, mercerizing, and pressing, will enhance the brightness and uniformity of the material, making it a much more saleable piece of goods. A three-dimensional or puffy effect can be given this same piece of material if it is printed with a strong alkali, such as is used in mercerizing, thus producing a shrinking and lustering in the printed areas. Some seersuckers are created by this method.

the twill weave

The outstanding characteristic of the **twill** weave is a woven diagonal line pattern to give fabrics an interesting surface appearance. The twill weave is extremely durable in both abrasion resistance and breaking strength.

Virtually all textile fibers may be found in fabrics of twill-weave construction: made from cotton are: doeskins, drills, twill cloth, ticking, denims, gabardine, linings, galatea, uniform goods, Canton flannel, institution fabrics, and jeans; made from linen are: some of the bird's-eye materials, tickings, and towelings; made from woolens and worsteds are: cassimere, cavalry twill, cheviot, covert, doeskin, elastique, flannel, gabardine, checks, serge, and a few novelty dress woolens; made from silk are: twill foulard, serge, surah, and titan silk; made from rayon, acetate, and synthetic fibers are: foulards, gabardines, plaid cloths, serges, surah, and novelty goods.

The diagonal lines in twills are often referred to as **wales.** They are formed by interlacing the warp and filling threads as shown in Figure 2-4, which illustrates a right-hand twill in which the diagonals extend from the lower left to the upper right-hand corner of the illustration. Left-hand twills have the wales pass from the upper left to the lower right-hand direction of the cloth. The modification of the twill construction in which the wales appear to run in both directions is called a **herringbone twill,** a very popular suiting fabric in wool worsted for men and women. In an even twill, the filling yarns will pass under and over the same number of warp yarns, that is, under two, over two, or under three, over three, etc. These are identified by having the wale or raised diagonal of the same width as the valley or indentation line on the face of the cloth. In uneven twills, the filling yarns may pass under two, over three, under two, over three, etc., or it may be a combination of under one, over two, under one, over two. In

Fig. 2-4A Showing right-hand even twill. Heavy lines show *first repeat* of pattern. Shaded squares show warp yarns on top.

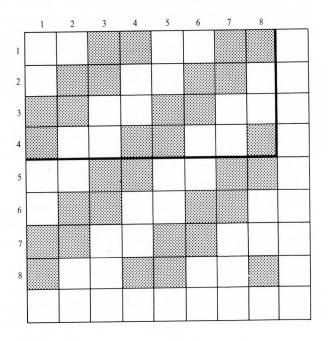

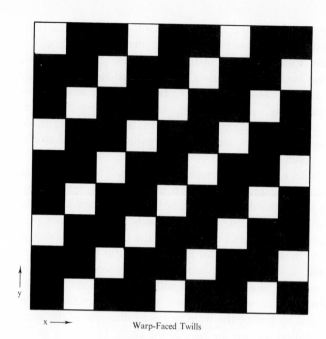

Fig. 2-4B Uneven warp-faced twill over y and under x.

y

x ⟶ Warp-Faced Twills

coarser uneven twill, longer floats, or lengths of yarn passing over the warp, may be used. In order to understand more clearly the way in which twills are formed, considering the even right-hand twill, paper-designed pattern in Figure 2-4a as representing a small section of eight warp and eight filling yarns; we will number the warps one to eight inclusive, and the rows of filling yarns also one to eight. The warp shed used to form such a twill would be set up so as to lift alternate pairs of warp yarns to permit the shuttle carrying the filling yarn to pass through the following order:

In the top row, warps three and four, seven and eight.
In the second row, warps seven and six, three and two.
In the third row, warps one and two, five and six.
In the fourth row, warps nine, eight, five, four, one.
In the fifth row, repeat first row order.

It would seem, therefore, that it takes four rows or picks to complete a design of this even twill. Thus, four series of warp combinations must be lifted, and four harnesses will be used on the loom. The fabric is, therefore, called a **four-shaft twill.** The shaft number is quickly determined by adding together the number of warp yarns the filling goes over and under in forming the summit of one ridge and one valley for a single unit in the twill construction. In this case, the filling went over two and under two for a total of four.

Right-hand twill   Reversal point   Left-hand twill

Fig. 2-5   Herringbone twill.

In the herringbone pattern, the twill runs in both directions in the cloth; however, Figure 2-5 shows the pattern for an even herringbone weave in which the herringbone is a right-hand twill for a certain distance, then reverses and becomes a left-hand twill. The effect resembles the backbone of a fish, as the name implies. In order to create this reversal, there must be a variation in the weave at the apex or point of the inverted V in order to reverse the wale direction. In the fabric portrayed, the two over two, the pattern is broken at this apex by passing under one warp, over the next, then under two, over two, under two, and so on, to change the direction from lower left to upper right into a ridge running from upper left to lower right. Intricate geometrical designs can be made in twills, forming diamonds and other figures in some fine suiting cheviots. Changing the twist, modifying the thickness of the yarn, and using combinations of dyed warp and filling yarns produce many of the novelty effects which make the twill weave so popular.

The general characteristic of twills is their density. These fabrics are generally closer in texture than plain weaves; thus, they are heavier in weight and are stronger. The twill weave may be referred to as the backbone fabric construction for men's outer clothing and for uniform fabrics in which extreme

17

durability is one of the most important considerations. They require somewhat more intricate loom setting or shedding, and this adds somewhat to the cost; plus the fact that being heavier, they have a greater weight of natural textile fiber per square yard than the usual plain weave.

the satin weave

The characteristic of the **satin weave** is an apparent absence of surface pattern. This is accomplished by having long floats passing over several yarns before interlacing with a single yarn, followed by another long float. These floats may be from four to as many as twelve yarns long. In fact, the satin or sateen weave is a highly unbalanced twill designed to highlight or to emphasize the shine and smoothness of silk, rayon, acetate, mercerized cotton, and the lustrous synthetics, and to give the illusion of a perfectly smooth, shiny-surfaced material without any pattern.

Among the satin-weave materials made from silk, rayon, acetate, and synthetics are: brocade, brocatel, crepe, damask, dress silk, duvetine, slipper satin, stripings, tablecloth and napkin fabrics, tapestries, tie fabrics, and upholsteries; in cottons and linens: damask tablecloths and napkins, and sateens.

In **satins,** the long floats on the right side of the material are the warp direction. Thus the fabric feels more slippery when rubbed in the lengthwise direction. On the reverse side of the fabric, the floats would then be predominantly in the filling direction. If on the right side of the fabric, the filling direction shows the predominance of floats, and its slipperiness is in the widthwise direction, the fabric is called a **sateen.** Generally in sateens, the floats are shorter than in satin.

Figures 2-6 and 2-7 show the typical interlacings for a short- and long-float satin weave.

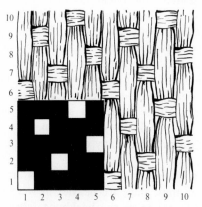

Fig. 2-6 Short float satin weave.

Warp-face satin; 5-harness base (or counter) of 2, showing the first repeat as a paper pattern, the rest with sketches of woven yarns.

Fig. 2-7 Long float (8-shaft) satin.

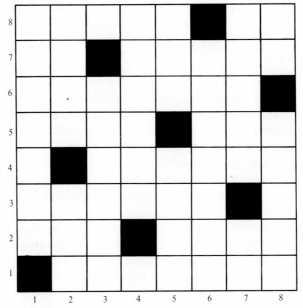

Showing first repeat. 8-harness, base of 3 (7-over, 1-under). *Note:* No. 1 filling is up. The next filling, in row 2, if the base or counter is **3**, would be over the **3**rd warp to right, or No. 4; in the **3**rd row, again 3 to the right, or No. 7. In row 4, the repeat boundary requires the use of warp No. 2 (1 to the right to the boundary, then to the extreme left and 2 more to the right.

The smooth, lustrous, dense appearance of satins suggests reasonably good service in use. However, the long floats are subject to damage from abrasion or rubbing, and the longer the float the more easily the surface can be scarred by cutting or chafing the floating fibers. The short-float fabrics are more durable than the long, but they do not have the luster or brilliance. These fabrics make excellent materials for coat linings because they can be so easily slipped on and off. They generally shed dirt well, but spots and stains are as visible as smudges on a mirror.

The complexity of the harness set-up of the loom for long-float satins adds considerably to the cost of production. For example, in a sateen in which the filling passes over four and under one warp, five shafts are required (one plus four equals five); and in a twelve-float satin, the filling would be under twelve and over one, requiring thirteen shafts.

Modifications in twist will provide variety in surface appearance. A high-sheen satin is produced when the warp yarns are very low in twist. A more tightly twisted warp in a shorter float fabric would produce a softer luster. Combinations of tightly twisted filling with loosely twisted warps will produce crepe-backed satins called **satin crepe.** Combinations of fibers may be used: a silk warp on the face, rayon or cotton on the back. Nylon, Orlon, and Dacron may likewise be used in these various satin constructions for novelty effects.

THE IDENTIFICATION OF FABRICS

The three basic weaves—plain, twill, and satin—are relatively easy to identify as to warp and filling direction and for the right and wrong faces for the purpose of using these fabrics in garments. In the yard goods department, of course, it is easy to determine the direction of warp and filling when the whole bolt can be examined or the selvage seen in a small sample. The warp yarns, of course, are parallel with the selvage. If, on the other hand, the customer has but a small sample, it is sometimes more difficult to know which is the warp and which is the filling.

Because the warp, or lengthwise direction, must withstand the greatest amount of pulling during manufacturing and processing, and because most of the pull in natural use is likewise in the length direction, the warp usually has more yarns than does the filling in a sample of material. Therefore, in plain weaves, the higher count generally indicates which direction is the warp. In the case of a square-count cloth such as the common 80-square print, the strength of the yarns is the best indication. This can be estimated by raveling out a few yarns from each direction; then with a pull between the fingers, the stronger direction can be ascertained. This usually will be the warp. In basket weaves, the warp is the more tightly twisted yarn. In unbalanced fabrics, particularly those with a large yarn in one direction and numerous finer yarns in the other, the warp will be the direction of the finer yarns and the more bulky crosswise yarn will be the filling. In case of other novelties in plain weave, such as the thick and thin or the nubby yarns of pongee and shantung, the irregular yarns are usually in the warp.

identifying the right face of a fabric

In using a piece of cloth, it is, of course, customary to have the right face forward. Fabrics are generally folded or rolled on a bolt with the right side protected against accidental soiling and abrading. In the case of a small sample, it is sometimes difficult to tell which is the right side and which is the wrong side of the material. Usually the brighter, shinier surface will be the right side, the one intended to be seen. If the weave characteristics are more distinct and the pattern more attractive on one side than the other, then the more attractive face is the right side. It is usually much simpler to determine this in the case of prints, because the print will be more vivid and clear on the right side of the material. Some woolens and wool-synthetic fiber combinations in suitings and coatings are napped on one face. This is usually on the right side, the side to be exposed to the onlooker. Twill weaves are sometimes more obscure, but if the small sample is held in such a way that the wales run either from lower left to upper right or from upper left to lower right, the warp yarns will then be in the vertical direction and the filling yarns in the horizontal. The warp yarns will probably be more tightly twisted (if there really is a difference in twist), and when yarns are pulled out in either direction, those which stay straighter and show the least amount of waviness will be the warp yarns which have been made somewhat more rigid by strains imposed upon them. The filling yarns, on the other hand, will show more of the waviness put into the yarns as they pass over and under the warp.

With the very smooth, lustrous fabric characteristics of the satin weave, it is easy to determine the direction of the floats, and knowing this and the identity of the fiber, conclusion can be reached as to which is the right side. For example, if the fabric is of silk, rayon, acetate, or synthetics alone or in combination, the weave is satin and the floats are in the warp direction. If the fabric is all cotton, the float is usually fillingwise in the sateen construction. There is one exception, however, and that is in an all-cotton material called farmers' satin which is used for coat linings. This is a warp-float cotton.

QUESTIONS

1 Why are plain, twill, and satin regarded as the basic textile weaves?

2 How do they compare in: (a) compactness, (b) durability, (c) luster, and (d) pattern?

3 How does a satin weave differ from a twill?

4 What is meant by a left-hand twill? A herringbone twill?

5 How does satin weave differ from sateen?

6 What does balance mean in a fabric?

7 Could a 120 × 60 count cloth ever be balanced? If so, how?

8 Discuss various ways to give surface interest to a plain weave fabric.

9 What is a basket weave?

10 How many harnesses or shafts are required for the plain weave?

novelty weaves

The simple harness loom may be equipped with special attachments for the weaving of novelty or fancy fabrics with a woven-in pattern. Special looms and weaving operations must be called upon for the more intricate fabrics, including such things as rugs and carpetings; velvets; patterned brocades for furniture coverings or for other decorative textiles; and even for such utilitarian end-use products as terry towels or Bird's-eye diaper cloth. These operations are slower than those of the conventional loom and are consequently more costly. Fully as important to the quality and durability of these fabrics are a firm construction and the use of first-quality dyestuffs and finishing agents.

FABRICS WITH A PILE WEAVE

By a pile weave is meant a fabric one face of which has soft, clipped fiber ends called the **pile.** Some pile-woven fabrics have the face of the fabric covered with loops of pile yarns; examples of this are the twist carpet fabrics and terry toweling. In the case of terry towels, the loops are commonly found on both faces of the cloth. The back of pile-woven fabrics generally shows that the basic structure is a twill weave; however, woven in are extra yarns forming the loops which then may be cut or left uncut, depending on the desire of the manufacturer.

There are five common methods of weaving these pile fabrics:

1   *The Filling Pile Method.* Often used for such wearing apparel fabrics as corduroy, plushes, and velveteens.

2   *Double-cloth Method.* Used for wearing apparel such as transparent velvets and millinery velvet. It is applicable also to some types of blankets.

3   The Terry-weave Method. Used for terry cloth towels and for bathroom and some cotton throw rugs.

4   The Wire Method. May be applied to such fine fabrics as velvets for wearing apparel or for upholstery plush fabrics and for such heavier fabric structures as carpets and rugs, particularly of the Wilton and Axminster types (see Chapter 27, "Rugs and Carpets"). A fabric rather widely used for upholstery material some years ago but not now particularly high style is Friezé made by this method.

5   The Rug Method. This incorporates several techniques and has several applications, including hooked rugs, tufted patterned rugs, and chenilles (see Chapter 27).

filling pile method

The filling pile method requires extra filling yarns which float over four to five warp yarns. These floating yarns are cut accurately in the center so that the ends are even in height over the entire surface of the fabric. Sometimes a clipping or evening process with rapidly revolving sharp-edged knife blades is necessary to make the surface perfectly smooth. Corduroy is characterized by having vertical stripes formed by the raised and cut pile the full length of the goods. This raised figure is called a **wale.** Alternate extra filling yarns are not cut, so that the fabric shows the series of hills and valleys characteristic of the corduroy structure. Corduroys vary in fineness from so-called wide-wales, with five wales or fluffy ridges to the inch, down to pin-wale corduroys in which there may be as many as 23 wales to the inch. Corduroys may further be described as V- or W-loop construction. Figure 3-1 shows that the V-construction corduroy has the cut-

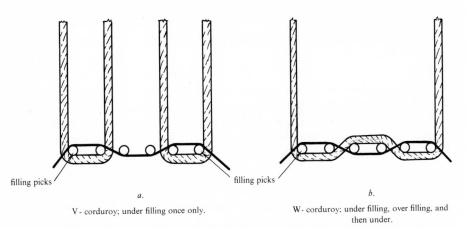

filling picks   filling picks

a.   *b.*

V - corduroy; under filling once only.   W - corduroy; under filling, over filling, and
                                                 then under.

Fig. 3-1   Showing interlacing of two pile loops in adjacent ribs of V- and W-construction corduroys.

pile loop held by only one warp yarn, whereas the W-construction corduroy has the loop passing under one, over one and under a third warp. The second construction is a much more durable structure.

Velveteen has an all-over pile construction, and heavy plush fabrics for upholstery material likewise have the texture of an over-all nap-like effect. These fabrics, including corduroy, are very resistant to wear against the pile loop ends, that is, they are very wear-resistant on the right side of the fabric. However, moderate rubbing will very often pull the pile loops through from the back, and corduroys and velvets can become totally denuded of their pile when severely abraded on the wrong side. The W-construction corduroy is, of course, more resistant to this pulling out of the loops.

double-cloth method

As the name implies, this construction is of two layers of cloth woven face to face, using two sets of warps and two sets of fillings, each pair of which forms one of the fabric layers. An extra set of warp yarns binds these two together. The individual cloths may be woven in any of the conventional plain weaves. Figure 3-2 shows the method of construction of such a **double cloth.** The figure shows that two shuttles are required, one for each of the two cloths. The filling threads attached to each are woven into their respective warps. The extra warp yarns holding the two fabrics together are later cut apart with a sharp knife, and the ends projecting on the right face of each layer then make up the pile surfaces. This method is used for delicate transparent velvets and for velvet and velveteen fabrics for the hat industry.

Not all double-cloth fabrics are cut apart. This method is used today to construct reversible coating material, one surface of which may be a plain fabric, the other a gay plaid or patterned material. Matelassé crepe for women's dresses is woven double, the inner fabric being a rather tightly-woven plain weave, the outer one a heavy crepe. When heavy crepes first came on the market some years ago, they were known as **moss crepe.** They lacked a backing fabric, and the crepes stretched so badly during wearing that it was sometimes necessary to clip off as much as three inches from the bottom of the dress after it had been worn to a dance. Stores selling these dresses were unable to hang them for display. They had to be kept in drawers to avoid this growing or stretching. The double-cloth construction makes these crepes dimensionally stable.

terry weave

The terry weave may be carried out on a conventional loom with four harnesses, two for warp yarns held taut and making up the ground, or base fabric structure. The other two harnesses carry warp yarns which are allowed to relax by having the tension released at intervals, at which time they are pushed forward by the reed, thus forming the loops. They are then caught and held in

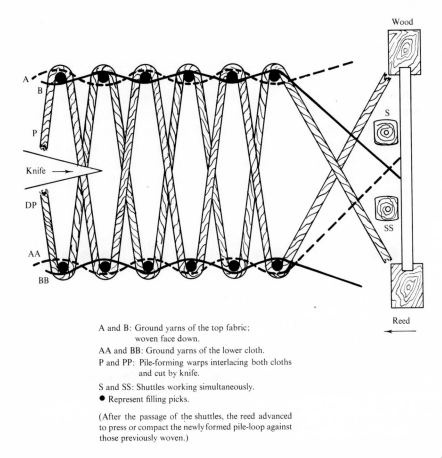

A and B: Ground yarns of the top fabric;
        woven face down.
AA and BB: Ground yarns of the lower cloth.
P and PP: Pile-forming warps interlacing both cloths
         and cut by knife.
S and SS: Shuttles working simultaneously.
● Represent filling picks.

(After the passage of the shuttles, the reed advanced
to press or compact the newly formed pile-loop against
those previously woven.)

Fig. 3-2   Showing construction of a pile fabric by the double cloth method.

position by the filling yarns shot through a shed made of the taut ground fabric warps. In one common terry construction, the pile or loop warps are raised in the first shed through which are shot two fillings; when the loop warps are lowered and the third filling has been shot through, all three are battened back together, thus sealing the loops. This is known as the three-pick terry because three picks, two under and one over, constitute the basic unit. A characteristic of terry is that the loops are generally alternating, first on one face, then on the other. Variations in figures are possible by weaving terry fabrics on dobby and Jacquard looms to form patterns. In most terry fabrics, water absorption is one of the principal characteristics desired; therefore, the warp yarns used in the terry loops are generally of low twist to permit as much water absorption as possible.

the wire method

The wire method for constructing pile fabrics uses an extra warp to form these pile yarns. As in the case of terry, one set of warps interlaces with the filling to form the ground or base fabric. This may be a plain weave or a twill. The other set forms the pile. When the harness carrying the pile-warp yarns is raised to form the shed, instead of a shuttle bearing a filling yarn being shot through, a wire is inserted. The diameter of the wire determines the height of the pile, and when the harness is lowered, the pile-warp yarns wrap over this wire, and the loop is held in place by the filling yarns battened against the base of the wire on either side. The wire is then withdrawn; the ground fabric is woven for a number of fillings or picks to hold the loops before another loop is

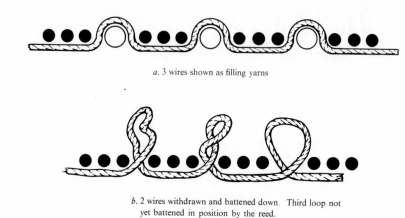

a. 3 wires shown as filling yarns

b. 2 wires withdrawn and battened down. Third loop not yet battened in position by the reed.

Fig. 3-3   The wire method of loop-pile formation.

formed and so forth through the length of the fabric. If it is a cut pile, the wire used has at its end a sharp knife, and when the wire is withdrawn, this knife cuts each loop across the width of the goods. In order to obtain absolutely even pile height over the whole length of fabric, it may be sheared with a device something like an electric razor. If the pile is to be of loop or uncut type, then, of course, the smooth wire is withdrawn, leaving the loops intact.

rug method of forming pile fabrics

The rug method of forming pile fabrics depends upon the type of rug. The various methods are described in Chapter 27, and the quality of the fabric produced varies from velvets woven on the conventional loom with cut pile of wool or synthetic fiber on a base fabric of jute and cotton to chenilles, Axminsters, and Wiltons, which are generally woven on Jacquard looms or, in the case of chenille, on a double-loom set-up.

characteristics of pile fabrics

The primary esthetic qualities are, in the case of cotton piles, softness to the touch and richness and warmth of color without luster or shininess. To aid in achieving dullness in wearing apparel, it is customary to cut the fabric so that the pile runs in the vertical direction. Thus, when viewed by the wearer, she looks downward into the depth of the fabric, and the richness of color is emphasized without luster. In this position also, any friction or rubbing tends to be against the lay of the pile fibers; thus matting is reduced. Most pile fabrics are subject to spots and stains which produce shiny marks where the pile may be flattened by the staining liquid as it dries. The garment may be steamed to remove these unsightly spots after the staining material has been removed by conventional methods. Pile is greatly improved in appearance and service life by frequent brushing with a soft brush, working first against the lay of the pile, then parallel to it. These fabrics are very sensitive to wear and abrasion on the inner surface, because the cut pile may be plucked and pulled through by catching the loop where it is interlaced with the filling yarn.

pile fabrics in decorative fabrics

Pile fabrics in household decoration, such as upholstery coverings (friezé, for example) or carpets and rugs, depend very largely upon the quality of construction for their durability. Again, one of the primary considerations is wear. Rubbing on the face of such fabrics usually does not seriously damage them. There is a tendency, however, for cut-pile carpets and rugs in fibers other than wool to show traffic lanes where the fiber ends tend to flatten out under prolonged compression. Wool has a greater resilience, and these fibers will come erect more readily. It is primarily due to this traffic-lane problem that most of the synthetic fiber rugs are in uncut pile or loop construction which does not crush down as does cut pile.

JACQUARD METHOD

No one fails to marvel at the beautiful and often intricate patterns woven into the finest of linen table **damasks.** Similarly, the delicate and precise colored patterns woven into upholstery damasks of silk or synthetic fibers, the beautiful brocades, and the intricate colorings in rugs—all these are beyond the capacity of the conventional harness loom. If the pattern is especially complicated or if the **repeat** is large, that is, greater than about 12 to 16 picks in height along the length of the goods, a Jacquard loom is used. A less expensive dobby loom may be used for the shorter repeats. In both of these, the control is not of groups of warp yarns but of the movement of each individual yarn.

There is no standard Jacquard weave, for this loom is capable of weaving plain, twill, satin, and combinations, due to the control of the individual warps. It was invented by a Frenchman, Joseph Marie Jacquard, in 1801. Jacquard refers to the method of weaving.

It often requires months to set up a Jacquard loom for a particularly elaborate pattern. The pattern is first sketched and all the colors decided upon. The sketch is then transferred to the conventional point-paper pattern. However, instead of setting up the warps in the colors desired along a harness beam, a series of paper-pattern punch cards is prepared. There is a punch card for every filling yarn to be used in each repeat, and on each card, there is a space for a punch hole to be inserted for each warp yarn across the width of the loom. A hole is punched in the appropriate place on each card for every warp yarn which is to be raised when that filling yarn is shot through. Each warp yarn to be passed over by that pick has its pattern spot on the card intact. In a sense, then, each of these paper-pattern cards actuates the warps to be raised in a similar fashion as the old-fashioned pianola record, on which holes were punched in the paper roll, caused certain piano keys to respond. It is obvious why this setting-up operation is laborious, because the repeat may have as many as four or five thousand picks. This means four or five thousand cards, and the fabric width may be such that five thousand warp ends are used. For each of these, there must be an identical possible hole position on every card. These cards are then laced together in order, and they pass successively over a long oblong cylinder near the top of the loom. Each warp yarn is threaded through an eye at the lower end of a fine steel wire which hangs by a cord, the upper end of which is attached to a horizontal wire called a needle. Thus, there is a needle for each of the warp yarns. When a shed is to be formed, all the needles press forward against the card which is in place. Those needles opposite holes in the card press through, and the pull on these cords lifts the wires and thus raises the warps to form a shed through which the shuttle passes. The oblong cylinder then makes its next turn, placing the second card in position as the first one drops down. The operation is then repeated with another set of warps forming the shed until the pattern or repeat has been completed. When the cards have all been used once, they are re-positioned for the next repeat of the pattern. Some Jacquard looms weave the pattern on the down face of the fabric in the loom; in this operation, the shed is formed by a down-thrust of the wires.

The motion of the loom is slow compared with the ordinary harness type, and the price of the fabric is necessarily high. Every attempt is made at economy through the re-use of old pattern cards. Indeed, some of the patterns now being used in fine table damask are similar to those of heirloom pieces. If a pattern is a staple which can be used again and again, great savings are effected by simply tying a new set of warp yarns onto the old, so that, in a sense, the patterned goods will be virtually endless as the cards are used many times. In fine damask, the design stands out clearly, because it is often a sateen figure with long floats in the filling direction contrasting against the background fabric having a satin weave with the luster in the warp at a 90-degree angle to the design.

Fig. 3-4　The Jacquard Loom: The fabric being woven requires six stacks of pattern cards for control of the warp yarns. (*Courtesy of Mohawk Mills and the Hoover Company.*)

A few years ago, the author had occasion to visit "The Breakers," the Newport, Rhode Island, home of the Vanderbilt family. This palatial estate represents an era of society now gone from the United States, and the house with all its furnishings is a most fascinating museum. During the tour through this beautiful home, it was noted that in various rooms some of the silk brocade draperies appeared new; others had been faded and weakened by prolonged exposure to light and to the sea air. Similarly, the tapestry-covered chairs in various rooms, such as the music room and the large formal dining room, were in tattered, used condition; others were new. When questioned about this, the guide explained that shortly after World War II, some of the U.S. troops quartered near a small French textile mill found a large stock of used cards, including the original Jacquard pattern cards for the fabrics used in this home when first built at the turn of the century. The cards appeared to have been unused in the nearly fifty years which had elapsed. Soon afterward, replacement of the old covers and decorative pieces was undertaken, and, as a chair tapestry is finished or drapery is completed, it is shipped to The Breakers and is put on a piece of furniture to replace the one which is most worn. The same textile fibers are being used, silk, wool, linen, and cotton in the same patterns and the same colors, so that eventually these articles will all be new.

THE DOBBY WEAVE

The **dobby** attachment may be put on a harness loom to weave small designs. Strips of wood take the place of the cards of the Jacquard loom. These strips are plaited together in a chain, and in each strip of wood, pegs are inserted to indicate the pattern. There is a strip of wood for each pick in the design or repeat, and there is a peg position for each warp to be lifted to form the shed with any pick. Thus, the patterns are generally small. One of the most common fabrics produced by this method is the Bird's-eye weave in diaper cloth. The dobby attachment can control about 25 harnesses. Because the limitation as to frequency of repeat, usually not more than sixteen rows, is also made by an American device called the **head-motion attachment,** both are usually referred to as the dobby weave.

Huck toweling is another fabric frequently made by this method of weaving. Honeycomb and waffle cloth are other household textiles introduced by the dobby method. In wearing apparel, such as men's suitings, the so-called sharkskin, which has much the same figure as Bird's-eye, is a dobby weave product. Small figures on men's shirtings and dress goods, such as the figured Madras or the "white on white" patterns, are dobby products.

THE LENO WEAVE

The **leno** weave produces a plain, lace-like, open construction; marquisette curtains are generally made by the leno weave. It is produced by a special attachment which twists adjacent warp yarns around each other, and the filling

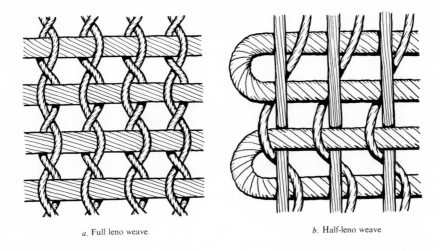

a. Full leno weave.   *b.* Half-leno weave

Fig. 3-5   The leno weaves.

passes through the eye formed by the twist (see Figure 3-5). In some marquisettes, the two warps are in equal tension, and the loop then is fairly round; in other constructions, one may be kept taut and the other then twisted around it, producing what is known as the gauze construction. It must be distinguished, however, from plain-weave gauze which is used in bandaging and as an interliner. The leno weave is more resistant to shifting or sliding of yarn under tension than is a plain weave in a similarly thin fabric. Numerous members of the man-made fibers are used in this construction, such as curtains of nylon, Dacron, Orlon, Fiberglas, rayon, and others. Mosquito netting used so widely in the tropics is also of a leno weave. Some nettings have occasional heavy yarns inserted in order to give greater strength. It is usually heavily sized in order that it stay firmly and stiffly in position and not sag down over the sleeper in use. **Sizing**, though primarily a finishing process to stiffen and strengthen yarns by adding gums, waxes, or starches, also helps prevent soiling and reduces the tendency of mildew growth in extremely humid conditions.

APPLIED PATTERNS

Although more and more of the fabrics resembling dotted Swiss and other minute tufted effects are being applied by means of loose flock fibers glued to the surface of the fabric, there are still many fine fabrics in which we have a simulated embroidery actually woven into the goods. Some of these ornamental effects are the swivel, lappet, clip-spot, and Schiffli designs. The characteristics of these designs are that they are not an integral part of the ground fabric and unlike the pattern figures in the Jacquard or dobby woven goods, which are permanent, these embroidered effects can be pulled out simply by pulling on an end of the figure on the reverse side of the cloth.

swivel design

In the **swivel** design, extra filling yarns are carried on extra shuttles at regular intervals. These extra filling yarns are carried several times around the group of warp yarns, giving them the appearance of being tied together. However, this design, made of one thread only, is clipped and loose at each end, that is, the ends are not knotted to the fabric. Unless these ends are pulled or the fabric abraded on the reverse side, they wear quite satisfactorily. This construction is sometimes applied to marquisette for a figured curtain in small

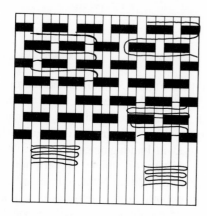

Fig. 3-6 The swivel weave: Swivel weave as seen on the wrong side of the fabric to show the interlacing of the pattern filling yarns.

dots or very small oblong figures. Generally, cotton is used on this design because it is less slippery than any of the man-made fibers; thus, the design stays in place. Some of the best of the dotted Swiss imported from Europe is of swivel design.

lappet design

Lappet also is formed from extra yarns. These, however, are in the warp direction. In this case, the yarns are threaded through needles which are set in front of the reed, but they do not pass through the reed. By moving these needles from side to side, they engage with the filling yarns, but with the pattern in the direction of the warp. Lappet yarns are not clipped; thus the back of the cloth has rather long floats of waste material between patterns, following one another in the lengthwise direction of the material. Such fabrics are more durable when they have a backing to prevent these long floats from being caught or pulled; also it is more wasteful of the embroidery yarn than is the swivel design.

Fig. 3-7   Lappet design figure.

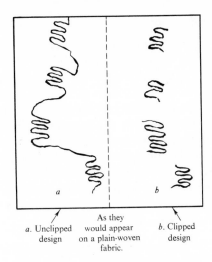

a. Unclipped   As they   *b.* Clipped
design   would appear   design
on a plain-woven
fabric.

clip-spot design

Clip-spot is another design resembling embroidery and utilizing an extra filling yarn, usually of a different size or color than that used in the regular fabric filling yarn. This colored or textured filling yarn is shot through at intervals and floats between the designs, that is, it is continuous clear across the width of the goods. However, after the cloth has been woven, shearing knives cut the floated yarns in a manner somewhat similar to the cutting of corduroy but giving a small fluffy spot with the fiber ends on the right side of the fabric.

Fig. 3-8 Clip-spot design: Clip-spot as viewed from the wrong side or back of fabric and showing the floats of filling yarns between pattern areas. Magnified section in lower left corner shows the interlacing filling yarns.

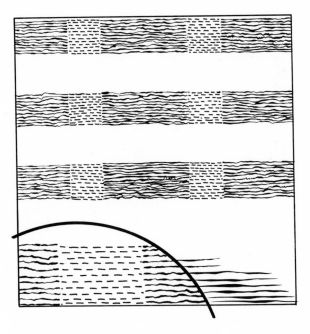

schiffli design

The **Schiffli** machine was developed in St. Gall in Switzerland. The word means "little boat," and, indeed, the shuttle somewhat resembles a little boat, producing lace or embroidery in widths up to fifteen yards and on any kind of fine material, such as batiste, lawn, or organdy. It makes a machine embroidery resembling hand work. The design is controlled by cards similar to those used in the Jacquard loom, but the machine applying the lacy embroidery to finished goods has from 682 to 1020 needles capable of producing intricate appliqués on lingerie fabric and other fine textile products. Although the products from this machine closely resemble lace, it is not a lace machine and hence is more properly described as producing an ornamental effect.

QUESTIONS

1 Describe four methods of making pile-weave fabrics.

2 Identify at least two fabrics made by each method and describe their use.

3 Compare the durability of V- and W-construction corduroy.

4 How should velvet be cared for?

5 Describe the operation of the Jacquard loom.

6 In what ways can the cost of setting up the Jacquard loom be lowered?

7 Distinguish between swivel, lappet, Jacquard, Schiffli, dobby, and clip-spot fabrics.

8 What is the difference in durability between ornamental woven-in patterns and those glued on?

9 Define double cloth.

10 What advantages does the dobby weave have over the Jacquard weave?

knitted fabrics and miscellaneous special constructions

Numerous articles of wearing apparel have long been of knitted construction. Hosiery, sweaters, underwear, and some types of lingerie are knitted because elasticity, wrinkle resistance, comfort, and porosity features are of primary importance to the consumer of those garments. This type of construction is rapidly increasing in volume in both outer wear and in home furnishings. The principal reasons are that it is lower in price, because the knit goods can be made two to five times faster than woven types, the physical characteristics of knitted fabrics are increasingly popular for sportswear, and the natural disadvantages of this construction, such as excessive stretch and shrinkage and a tendency to snag and run, are being overcome.

Knitted fabrics are composed of rows of loops with each row caught into the row previously formed. It is due to the ability of these loops to stretch when pulled by a stress that the knitted hosiery or other close-fitting clothing adapts itself to the changing shape of the moving body or portion thereof. Its comfort is remarkably superior to the relatively rigid woven fabric structure. The movement of these knitted yarn loops helps also in pumping air through close-fitting garments, thus removing body heat. Loosely fitting, bulky fabrics, such as sweaters, have a high dead-air content and are good insulators against cold except in strong wind conditions.

An English curate, the Rev. William Lee, invented in 1589 the first machine which could knit stockings. It was virtually unchanged for 200 years, an amazing invention long in advance of the Industrial Revolution.

There are two basic types of knit construction, but each has several modifications. Although **warp knitting** is becoming increasingly popular, by far the greater volume of knit goods is of the **weft knit** construction, the two types of which are better known as the **flat knit** and **circular knit,** respectively. The essential difference between warp knitting and weft knitting is that the former uses many parallel yarns which are carried by as many needles in a vertical direction; the latter usually uses one yarn in a crosswise direction, but since, for example, in sweaters, as many as 84 yarns must be used, thus, 84 courses are knitted at once. Diagrams may appear complex at first, but further study will emphasize the essential difference between them.

Circular-knit nylon hosiery, and most sweaters, bathing suits, and undershirts, are examples of weft-knit items which are formed in a continuous tube. Usually, except in hosiery, the tube is split open and then cut into the pieces from which the article is to be made.

The knit fabrics formed by flat machine knitting are generally known as full-fashioned. In this construction, the yarn or yarns travel back and forth, and the lengthwise edges are narrow selvages. It is a slower method of construction but permits the accurate shaping required in full-fashioned hosiery and full-fashioned sweaters. The garments produced by this method are, therefore, higher-priced. This structure can only be made by machine.

Warp knitting uses as many yarns as there are needles, and these yarns travel in a vertical direction. For that reason, the fabrics are firmer than the weft-knit types and will not stretch appreciably in length. This makes them snag resistant and particularly suitable for women's gloves, silk, rayon, or nylon jersey, hosiery, and lingerie.

Each of these constructions permits the production of numerous surface textures, depending on the yarn, type of stitch, and kind of finish.

Among the various stitches to be found in garments are the following:

I. *Weft-Knit Fabrics*
  A. *Flat Stitch* or *Plain Circular Knitting.*
  B. *Run-Resist Knit.* A variety of plain knitting.
  C. *Purl Stitch* or *Link and Link Stitch.*
  D. *Rib Stitch.* This is characterized by the alternation of the wales on front and back: single front and back wales alternated in 1 × 1 rib and two of each in the 2 × 2 rib, or Swiss Rib.
  E. *Accordion Rib.* This is a combination of 1 × 1 and 2 × 2 construction.
  F. *Panel Rib.* This fabric uses a 1 × 1 rib to form a pattern.
  G. *Tuck Stitch.* The gather of two or three yarns on one needle with either a plain stitch or rib stitch.

Fig. 4-1 The flat knit construction and showing wales and courses.

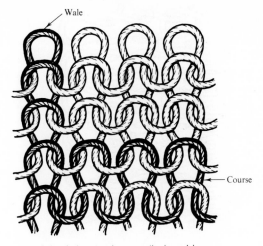

A *wale* (vertical row) and a *course* (horizontal loop row) in a plain-knit fabric.

Fig. 4-2 Circular knit construction, a type of run-resistant knitting.

Fig. 4-3 The purl or link and link stitch: This has the same appearance on both sides.

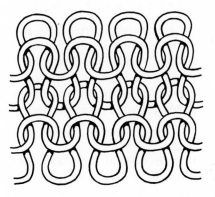

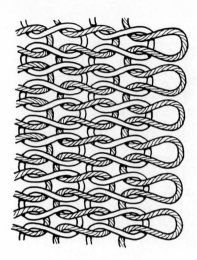

Fig. 4-4   Plain circular knit.

H. *Cardigan Stitch.* A tuck stitch on a 1 × 1 rib base. The full cardigan has equal-size wales on each side; the half cardigan has closer wales on the face and resembles a 1 × 1 rib.
I. *Rack Stitch.* A variation of the half cardigan and identified by a herringbone pattern on the face.
J. *Double Knitting.* The use of a second yarn either to provide a pattern, extra thickness, or a napped fleece.

II. *Warp-Knit Fabrics*
A. *Tricot.* Tricot shows lengthwise rows of loops on the face and horizontal loops on the back. If two sets of yarns are used, it is a 2-bar tricot and is runproof. The lengthwise rows of loops are called **wales.** The crosswise rows of loops are referred to as **courses.**
B. **Milanese.** Each of the many threads moves diagonally from one side to the other. It is run-resistant.

THE FIBERS USED IN KNITTING

Wool, silk, cotton, rayon, hair, rubber, textured and stretch synthetics, and metal yarns can be used in knitted fabrics. Linen is rarely knitted because of its cost. These various fibers may be used alone or in combinations to produce fabrics of different textures. The natural texture of the knitted merchandise may be modified by means of a finishing process such as bleaching, dyeing, or napping. Most knitted garments are formed from dyed yarns.

wool

It is with woolen yarns and blends of wool with synthetics that home knitting is chiefly concerned. Much commercially knitted merchandise likewise is knitted from similar yarns.

Purchasers of knitted woolen articles are now well protected against false labeling and misleading advertising. Manufacture of garments using knitted or woven yarns of wool must conform to the following standard:[1, 2]

1   "All," "Pure," "100 per cent," and similar terms used in connection with woolen or worsted yarns or garments are synonymous and may be used only if the fiber content is actually 100 per cent wool (a two per cent tolerance is permitted).

2   "Wool," "Woolen," "Worsted," and similar terms with the expressions "decorated with silk," "with rayon decorations," and the like, signify 95 per cent wool (a two per cent tolerance is permitted).

3   If the wool content is less than 95 per cent by weight, the guaranteed percentage of wool must be given, e.g., "80% Wool," and the blended fiber type must be named and per cent content disclosed.

Thus, it is clear that wool and part-wool articles conform to the Wool Product Labeling Act of 1939 (page 508), and all others must be labeled according to the Textile Fiber Products Identification Act (page 509).

There are numerous descriptive terms applied to knitted wool fabrics and garments. These terms describe the origin of the fiber, the quality of the fiber, and the type or kind of yarn. Some of the terms are confusing because they have become corrupted to such a point that they are actually deceptive. The basic knit stitch is the jersey, especially for outer wear.

Among the descriptive terms applied to knitted woolen merchandise and to yarns are the following:

1   *Angora wool* is the hair of the Angora goat. It is more generally described as mohair. Angora rabbit hair is combed from a special breed of rabbits, the best of which is the French Angora. The rabbit hair may be combined with wool to produce a warm, soft, wooly yarn much used in fine wear for infants, such as mittens, and in novelty sweaters and wraps and similar luxury merchandise. The rabbit hair seems to grow as it gradually pulls out from the combined yarn and sheds. Angora knitting yarn is usually of this combination type.

2   *Australian wool* is imported for use in the finer goods of knit underwear and for infants' wear because of its warmth and softness.

3   *Camel hair* is sometimes used in sweaters. It should mean the soft hair of the Bactrian camel. When used in small amounts with wool, it should be described as "Wool and Camel Hair."

4   *Cashmere* or *Kashmir* should refer only to the soft, fine hair of the Kashmir or Tibetan goat of the Himalayan Mountains or to fabrics made from that hair. Many of the Cashmere sweaters sold in the United States contain mixed

[1] *Recommended Commercial Standard for Wool and Part-wool Fabrics,* C.S.65-38 (Washington, D.C.: U.S. Gov't. Printing Office). U.S. Bureau of Standards, National Association of Wool Manufacturers.

[2] *A Guide for Retail Advertising and Selling,* Second Edition (New York: National Association of Better Business Bureaus, Inc., 1938), p. 37.

yarns of wool and Cashmere and are more properly labeled "Wool and Cashmere."

5   *Merino* should be used only to designate an all-wool fabric or yarn derived from the merino sheep. It is sometimes wrongly applied to mixed yarns of wool and cotton.

6   *Mohair* is the fine, lustrous hair of the Angora goat. The fibers are smooth and wiry, and, therefore, in order to make a durable knitting yarn, they are combined with cotton or wool. The term used alone should refer to an all-mohair fabric or yarn. Mohair yarns and part-mohair yarns are usually loosely spun and are suitable for light-weight sweaters. Kid mohair is softer and finer than ordinary mohair.

7   *Ply-yarn,* referring to a yarn made up of two or more yarns spun separately and then twisted together, indicates extra strength and durability.

8   *Rabbit hair,* where used to describe sweaters, refers to the sheared hair of domestic rabbits which is mixed with wool.

9   *Shetland wool* should designate an article or yarn made up of this Scottish wool. It may be soft or harsh in texture. The imported Shetland sweaters and the fine lacy scarfs are made from the soft type of Shetland wool. Imitations are made of soft woolen yarns or of mixtures of wool and mohair.

10   *Woolen yarn,* or wool yarn, is made from carded fibers and is usually rather loosely spun. It produces a warm, thick, soft-knit garment.

11   *Worsted yarn* is made from combed wool fibers. It is smoother, stronger, and thinner than a woolen yarn and produces a finer and more expensive knit garment. Three principal types of worsted yarn are:

A. *English* or *Bradford* spun yarn, which is strong, firm yarn used in men's sweaters and recently in outer wear, such as knitted topcoat materials.

B. *French* spun refers to a type of spinning rather than the place of origin. This yarn is softer and uses shorter wool fiber than is required for the English spun yarn. It is used principally for women's sweaters and for infants' wear.

C. *Zephyr* is applied to the fine quality, soft worsted yarn used in knitting by hand. A long wool fiber and special spinning methods are required to give a soft, full feeling yarn without sacrificing strength.

12   *Virgin wool* designates new, unused wool.

silk

The principal use of silk in knitted merchandise is in fabrics for dresses and fine lingerie. Weighted silk is rarely used in knitting.

cotton

Knit underwear for men and boys is commonly made from cotton yarns. Other uses are for hosiery, balbriggan sportswear, women's underwear, sport shirts, novelty sweaters, ski pajamas, and numerous other kinds of merchandise.

Several descriptive terms are applied to cotton yarns. Among the most common are the following:

1   Carded cotton refers to yarns spun from the shorter grades of cotton fiber which have simply been carded into a semblance of order while removing short fibers and waste. These inexpensive yarns are used in underwear and produce an absorbent and soft fabric.

2   Combed cotton is produced from previously carded cotton of longer staple length. The shorter fibers have been eliminated, and the cotton fibers are nearly parallel. When spun, combed cotton produces a fine, smooth, strong yarn well suited for use in such knitted fabrics as hosiery, women's underwear, sport shirts, and the like.

3   Lisle thread is a two-ply combed cotton yarn. It is tightly twisted and is singed to remove loose fiber ends. The fine, smooth-appearing yarn has great strength and is widely used in the better grades of men's, women's, and children's hosiery, in the top and foot of some nylon hose, and in women's underwear.

4   Mercerized yarn is a combed cotton yarn which has been given added luster, increased strength, and greater absorbency by dipping in strong alkali under tension and carefully controlled conditions. **Durene** is a trademarked combed, two-ply cotton yarn which has been mercerized under special conditions.

rayon

The rayon fibers produced by the cellulose acetate, viscose, and cuprammonium processes have been important in knit goods. The principal application has been in lingerie, inexpensive hosiery, and knit underwear. The *continuous filament* type of yarn is that most widely used, but *spun* rayon or cut filament spun yarn is becoming important in sweaters, knitted shirts, and other outer wear.

In describing the rayon yarn used in knit underwear, it is helpful to indicate the kind of rayon by process name or by a trade name. The number of filaments in the yarn helps to show its quality, a multi-filament yarn being stronger and smoother but more expensive. The size of the yarn or denier should also be expressed. The finer 100-denier yarn produces a better-appearing garment than does the usual 150-denier.

synthetic yarns

Although all the synthetic yarns, acrylics, polyesters, nylons, and others, are found in knit wear, especially in sweaters, nylon is by far the most commonly used of these fibers. Nylon tricot has become almost a standard fabric construction for women's sleepwear and for the finest of lingerie. In the soft-textured, elastic tricot structure, nylon has been found to be satisfactorily comfortable. It has no tendency to bind, it is comfortable even in warm weather, due to its pumping action carrying away body moisture and heat, and it washes and dries so easily that its use is growing steadily. In Chapter 7 dealing with Bulk and Textured Yarns, reference is made to the wide use of these products in sweaters, especially with the popularity of the bulky sweater texture beginning in 1960. These specialty yarns are currently made more from nylon than from any other synthetic fiber, and this, again, gives nylon a tremendous share of the sweater business. Textured nylon is used also in the stretch pants and leotards so popular with young women. Orlon was the most common synthetic fiber in sweaters until the entry of textured yarns.

rubber

"Spun rubber" yarns are round extruded rubber filaments around which are twisted yarns of silk, rayon, cotton, nylon, or wool. These covered rubber yarns are knitted into garments to give them even more elasticity than is normally produced by the knitted construction. The principal application is to underwear, foundation garments, surgical bandages and hosiery, and bathing suits. Spandex fibers have largely replaced the rubber threads in foundation garments (see page 344).

metal yarns

Threads made from narrow, flat strips of colored aluminum can be sandwiched between two sheets of Mylar or other clear plastics; some novelty garments are given a luster by this decorative yarn.

combining fibers

Thus far, the combination of fibers in knitting yarns has been only briefly mentioned. There are several ways of combining fibers in yarns to produce different effects or to provide a cheaper or a stronger product. These fibers may differ in identity, size, grade, or color.

The mixed yarn may be produced by one or by a combination of two or more of the following methods:

1 Before spinning, the fibers may be simply mixed or blended together. This method is useful for mixing two or more dyeings of the same fiber; to combine shorter wool fibers with cotton, Dacron or other synthetics, staple rayon, or staple silk; to combine various grades of wool fibers; or to combine rarer fibers, such as camel hair, with wool and then to blend by spinning into one yarn any of the above-desired combinations.

2 Spinning each kind or color of fiber into an individual yarn permits the application of different mixing methods before knitting.

    A. The individual yarns may be twisted into ply yarns.

    B. Several different yarns may be knitted together as a unit but without twisting or definitely joining them together before knitting.

    C. One thread may be wound around another, as in core yarns, metal yarns, rubber yarns, bouclé, and other novelty yarns.

3 During the knitting operation, several methods of combination may be used.

A. Multiple feed.

B. Double knitting and tuck stitch to throw a desired yarn on the outer surface.

C. Plating, which is a method in which a desired yarn is thrown to the face surface and the other to the back of the fabric. Almost any desired combination of yarns can be used. One which is widely applied in men's rayon and nylon hosiery is to throw the nylon onto the outer surface at wear areas, such as heels, etc. Some low-priced hose is actually such a plated fabric.

FINISHING PROCESSES

The common finishing processes used in woven goods can be applied to knitted fabrics also. No details as to bleaching, dyeing, cross-dyeing, printing, pre-shrinkage, moisture repellency, moth repellency, or other routine textile-finishing processes will be elaborated on, because they are discussed in the several chapters dealing with the finishing of textiles.

With the increased use of knitted constructions in outer wear, sweatshirts, and blankets, and the desire for the brushed surface effect in some sweaters and the fleeced surface in some lingerie, napping of knit fabrics is of great importance. Napping is simply the controlled scuffing of the surface by means of burrs or fine wire brushes to produce a uniformly flat-appearing surface of loose filament ends. The fleecy surface of some sweatshirts and the suede finish on knitted rayon gloves are similarly produced.

KNITTING FINENESS

The degree of fineness of a knitted cloth cannot be expressed in terms of yarns per inch. Instead, there is a count of the number of loops, or **wales,** per inch. The fineness is expressed as the gauge of the knitted article, although only in hosiery is the gauge generally given on labels or printed on the article. The openness or compactness of the knitted article is usually expressed in terms of **gauge,** and the number refers to the number of **wales** or of needles used in one and one-half inches of space in the needle bar (for full-fashioned) or cylinder (for circular-knit). The thickness or width of the needle is dependent largely upon the size of yarn being processed. Thus, in sweaters generally 15- to 20-gauge would be as fine a yarn as could be accommodated. In knitting nylon hosiery, 45-gauge is one of the standard constructions. This means there would be 45 needles used in 1.5 inches of needle bar, which is 14 inches wide for a full-fashioned stocking. Needle count is two-thirds of the gauge value, and some manufacturers refer to gauge in terms of number of needles per inch; thus,

45-gauge, that is, 45 wales for 1.5 inches, would be equivalent to 30 needles per inch; 51-gauge, 60-gauge, and 72-gauge are increasing degrees of fineness in nylon hose of the full-fashioned, or warp-knit, type. In circular-knit hosiery, it was customary to express the fineness in terms of the total number of needles used in knitting such hose. Circular-knit hosiery knitted with 400 needles was of the same wale count as 51 gauge. Since 1949 the F.T.C. has permitted the term gauge to be applied to circular-knit hosiery, but the label must indicate by the equally conspicuous words "circular-knit," "no seam," or "seamless" that the hosiery is not full-fashioned.

KNITTED PILE FABRICS

Imitation fur material or simulated fur garments have grown rapidly in importance since 1955.[1] In that year, 750 thousand coats of this type were produced; in 1960, over one million units utilizing some six million pounds of synthetic fiber were produced by ten different mills. Most of these coats are produced from Orlon-Dynel mixtures, usually 65 per cent Orlon and 35 per cent Dynel. Acrilon, Creslan, and Zefran have also been used during the last two years. Knitted fabric has been found to be much more comfortable and to have a much more natural drape than coat bodies of woven structures. One of the reasons for the use of Dynel is to reduce the hazard of flammability in these dense pile textiles. The construction of these fabrics is complicated and is a relatively slow procedure. According to Reichman,[2] on whose section on Knitted Pile Fabric many of these details are based, the oldest method is called the sliver-and-backing-yarn method. Recently, two somewhat faster methods have been announced: one is a cut-loop-and-ground-yarn principle, using a circular knitting machine, and the other is a cut-pile-and-ground-yarn method on a raschel knitting machine.

In the conventional machine the pile sliver is fed into the knitting cylinder and is locked in by a jersey construction using a heavier base yarn. The mixed staples to form the pile, that is, the blend of Orlon and Dynel or other fiber combinations, are carded and the sliver placed on the feed roll, which is taken by the worker, who places it on the main carding cylinder to be straightened. As the knitting operation begins, the knitting needles seize the staple in the small hooks near the needle head, and as the knitting operation proceeds, this staple is firmly caught into the jersey base, where it is locked into place by the yarn structure. The depth of the pile is determined by the length of the staple selected for the fabric and may then be sheared to make it absolutely even in height. Machine production is at the rate of about five yards per hour. If the sheared fabric is ¾-inch staple, the weight of imitation fur is approximately five-

---

[1] J. J. Press (ed.), *Man-made Textile Encyclopedia* (New York: John Wiley & Sons, Inc., 1959.
[2] *Ibid.,* pp. 434–35.

eighths of a pound per square yard. In order to simulate more closely the beauty and luster of natural furs, these coat materials must go through the following steps:

1   Heat setting to shrink the cloth lengthwise to a stable position and also to expand the diameter of the individual fibers.

2   Tigering, which is a heavy brushing operation with wire brushes, the purpose of which is to ease out any loose fibers from the staple which may not have been completely held in place by the knitting operation.

3   Rough shearing, a mowing-type operation carefully regulating the height of the pile.

4   Electrofying, a combing operation with an electrically heated cylinder, on the surface of which are a series of polishing helixes or grooves. This is to polish and add high luster to the pile.

5   Wet application, intended to add to the luster of the fibers. With Orlon and Dynel mixtures, alcohol and water may be used. If the imitation fur contains quantities of wool, then acetic acid, formaldehyde, and alcohol and water may be called upon. In the case of wool, one of the objectives is to remove crimp so that the fibers will stay at a uniform height throughout the wear life of the garment. Following this, there is a second **electrofying** and a second and final **shearing operation.**

QUESTIONS ON KNITTED FABRICS

1   How does knitting differ from weaving?

2   Explain weft knitting.

3   Explain warp knitting.

4   How do these two differ in the properties of the fabrics produced?

5   What are the principal advantages of the purl stitch, of the plain stitch, of ribbed stitches?

6   What is tricot? What fibers are most commonly made with tricot knit?

7   How do the properties of flat-knit fabrics differ from those which have been circular-knit?

8   How should knitted articles be cared for?

9   What is meant by the gauge in knitted hose? Define gauge.

10   Define courses.

11   How are simulated fur fabrics most commonly made?

12   Through what final finishing processes must such fabrics go before being cut into garments?

LACES

Probably most customers today believe that lace is still a handcraft product. As early as 1813, John Leavers made the first commercially efficient lace machine, using the conventional weaving loom with some modifications. Then a few years later, a Jacquard motion was employed, and machine-made lace was here to stay. The modern machines based on **Leaver's** principle can produce lace webs ten yards wide. These machines are very large; they may be as much as eighty feet in length. Basically, the motion of the lace machine can be described as follows:

In the operation of the lace machine, the odd-numbered threads can be moved sideways to the right and left, whereas the even-numbered ones move only at right angles to these, that is, they move toward and away from a person standing in front of the machine. By controlling this movement so that the odd-numbered threads pass each other sideways in front of the even forward-moving threads, and then pass in the opposite direction behind the even-numbered threads again as they move backward, the final effect is that the machine forms a whole series of lacy geometrical figures across the full width of the goods. The exact pattern depends upon the distance apart and the plan of engagement for each of the odd-numbered pairs.

Another important type of lace machine is the **Nottingham,** used principally in coarse lace tablecloth structures and for curtains of synthetic fibers. The **Schiffli** operates like a multiple sewing machine in its needle-and-shuttle action. Several hundred needles are controlled simultaneously by a punch-card system rather similar to the Jacquard used on the Leaver machine. One application of this Schiffli machine is in the knitting of imitation fur products. The **Bobbinett** machine utilizes two sets of yarns, each supplied by two sets of bobbins, and produces a hexagonal net. This is used as a base for appliqué work, and it can be cut and sewn to form durable, no-run net hosiery. It is also used extensively for veiling and millinery. A modification of this is the new Bobbin lace machine, producing a heavy-textured, uniform-count yarn but not used for fine lace work.

types of laces

Among the more common types of lace are the following:

Alençon. This is a heavy outline cord or cordonnet lace of floral design and a fine net background. It is named for the town of Alençon, France.

Carrickmacross. Obviously Irish by name, this has a heavy outline with a solid motif of fine lawn on which is developed a rather coarse pattern.

Chantilly. A very fine ground net with shaded designs and only slightly enlarged outline cords. Named after Chantilly, France. In finer qualities the individual threads connecting the parts of the design may be ripped out, leaving the figures independently held in place for emphasis. It is one of the most elaborate lace designs.

Cluny. An open coarse lace similar to crochet work.

Lille. Resembles Valenciennes but hexagonal in figure.

Valenciennes. Named for the town in France, this lace usually has a round or diamond-shaped hole with floral design but with little emphasis on the figured outlines. It is probably the most widely used type, both from beauty and from moderate price.

Venetian. This coarse lace, generally used for edges and insertions, has no net background and was first made by needlepoint. Today a bobbin is used in Flat Venetian Point.

non-woven textiles

Felted wool was doubtless one of the earliest of textile materials formed by man for protection of the wearer or to provide a blanket-like shelter. In the presence of alkalies or acids and with the application of moisture, heat, and pressure, wool fibers will move in the direction of their roots. When there is agitation, such as stirring or tumbling, the somewhat softened and swelled fibers tend to cling together and then to become enmeshed firmly both by the crimp of the wool and the catching together of the scales. This is true felting, as contrasted to the matting together of fibers to produce blotting paper or a mass of fiber to be used in heat insulation.

Some of the synthetics have a tendency to felt together as a result of heat softening, but, when cool, these materials are hard and useless for most textile applications.

N O N - W O V E N S

The non-woven fabrics, though they include felts, are described in the following manner:[1]

1   Non-woven textiles of ½- to 5-inch fibers are formed into a dry web by one of several methods and made to adhere tightly. This group offers the greatest potential commercial value.

[1] D. V. Probasco, Chapter on Non-woven Materials, in J. J. Press (ed.), *Man-Made Textile Encyclopedia*, (New York: John Wiley & Sons, 1959), pp. 480–491.

Fig. 5-1 Diagramatic sketches of woven or reinforced felts used in the pulp and paper industry and wherever durability is required: Note that these weaves resemble those in woven textiles but are more open so as to hold the wool fibers. (*Courtesy of the Albany Felt Company [Albany, N.Y.].*)

STRAIGHT TWILL WEAVE

Straight Twill Weave
In Finest Grade of Felt

DUPLEX WEAVE

Duplex Weave
Gives Heavy, Bulky Felt.

PLAIN WEAVE

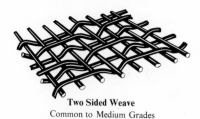

Plain Weave
Stable and Durable;
Used in Coarser Felts
and Where Speed Is Needed.

TWO-SIDED WEAVE

Two Sided Weave
Common to Medium Grades

SATIN WEAVE

48

Satin Weave
for Unusually Smooth Felts

2   Wool-blend felts are made from the same fiber lengths but depend on wool or other animal hair to bind together two or more thin sheets.

3   Needled and shrunk felts use a mixture of non-shrinkable and shrinkable fibers which can be made to move about by chemical or heat applications until a web is formed. They may then be needled or stitched one web layer to another and made to shrink to the desired firmness.

4   Papers are made from very short fibers by a wet process, followed by chemical bonding to a firm mass.

5   Battings are low-density dry fiber masses which may be bonded.

They are defined by Committee D-13 of A.S.T.M. as follows: "Non-woven fabrics are a structure of fibers held together with a bonding material." The actual material may be applied to the fiber mat by a painting, spraying, coating, or printing operation.

Major producers of these textiles are:

1   American Felt Company
2   Star Woolen Company
3   Pellon Corporation
4   The Visking Corporation
5   Minnesota Mining and Manufacturing Company
6   Avondale Mills
7   Raybestos-Manhattan, Inc.
8   C. H. Dexter and Sons
9   Chicopee Mills

METHODS OF BONDING

Three principal methods are used: resin bonding, thermoplastic fiber bonding, and stitch-through bonding. There may be combinations of these. To confuse one still further, most of the resins used are thermoplastic.

In the resin bonding method, the manner of resin application depends on the end use and may be a bath, spray, or paint. The web is then dried and heat-cured at temperatures of 200° F. to 400° F., depending on the materials used.

In thermoplastic fiber bonding a small percentage of a thermoplastic fiber is added to the higher melting, or non-thermoplastic, web materials. When such a web is **calendered** or pressed by passage between hot rolls, the lower melting fibers, generally 10 to 30 per cent by weight of the fabric, seal themselves into the web structure. The newest fibers to be used are the acrylics, for they give webs of high strength and durability, limited washability and re-use, good light fastness, and fair solvent resistance.

In the stitch-through operation, the laminated webs may be basted together. A thermoplastic thread would respond to heat treatment by shrinking as it softened to give a more compact structure.

COMMERCIAL PROPERTIES OF NON-WOVEN

At a symposium, "Non-woven Fabrics Today and Tomorrow," MacIlroy[2] reported ten primary properties more or less identified with non-woven fabrics. The author pointed out that these varied properties have been developed through the last 20 years, and although many of them are not exclusive to non-wovens, their range is more characteristic of the non-woven family than of other textile structures. The marketing strategy of the industry is based largely upon these properties, which are:

1 Opacity—providing the covering power of sheeting at a lower price per yard.

2 Absorbency—capacity, speed, and dispersion.

3 Variable Range—densities may vary from high to low; texture, from soft to stiff; pliability, from rigid to resilient.

4 Softness—can rival original textile textures.

5 Drapeability—shapes, drapes, and conforms to surface outlines as do textiles of woven type.

6 Vehicle—can carry or be coated with adhesives, chemicals, and pharmaceuticals, all of which may be applied during the process.

7 Porosity—high, free air flow with low back pressure afforded by the great percentage of continuing voids.

8 Retention—fiber structure retains solids.

9 Dimensional stability—no thread or yarn distortion; controlled shrinkage; edges resist curling.

10 Ease of handling—will not ravel or drop out individual filaments; no yarns or threads on face or edges to ravel or catch.

Admittedly, these non-wovens would find a greater market if some of their physical disadvantages could be improved. Among these are improvement in tear strength and tensile strength, a somewhat higher resistance to abrasion, and improved stretch memory.

The current success of these fabric structures was shown by Shearer[3] at this same symposium.

The non-wovens referred to in Table 5-1 are those of a fibrous web nature held together with a bonding medium which imparts to the composite structure certain woven-fabric-like qualities desired for similar kinds of use. This definition of Shearer's then goes on to explain that it does not limit the web in its density, whether high or low; whether it is bonded by like or unlike materials; or whether the web be formed wet or dry; but it does exclude such things as felts,

[2] John V. MacIlroy, "Marketing Non-woven Fabrics," *American Dyestuff Reporter*, 51 (August 20, 1962), pp. 51–52.

[3] Howard E. Shearer, "Fibers Used in the Production of Non-woven Fabrics," *American Dyestuff Reporter*, 51 (August 20, 1962), pp. 44–46, Table 1.

waddings, paper, and heavy glass mat, as used in molded glass-plastic articles as a reinforcement.

TABLE 5-1 / ESTIMATED CURRENT ANNUAL RATE OF CONSUMPTION OF FIBERS IN NON-WOVEN FABRICS

Category of Use	Millions of Lbs.	Principal Fiber
Abrasives (coated discs, pads, fabric, etc.)	3	nylon, rayon
Apparel (interlinings, inner and outer wear, etc.)	14	rayon, nylon, acetate
Coated fabrics (automotive, furniture, wall covering, shoes, rug backing, tentage, etc.)	12	cotton, rayon, acetate
Filters (milk, chemical, air, oil, etc.)	14	rayon, glass, acetate
Laminated plastics (overlay sheets, electronic quilting, high and low pressure)	3	rayon, cotton, glass, acrylic
Sanitary and medical (hospital and doctor supplies, diapers, bandages, face masks, etc.)	35	rayon, cotton
Tapes and ribbons (decorative and industrial)	21	cotton, rayon, acetate, Dacron
Wiping cloths (dusting, polishing, shining, mopping)	8	cotton, rayon
Miscellaneous household (towels, napkins, drapes, shades, etc.)	8	rayon, cotton, acetate
Miscellaneous small items (casket linings, hair waving, bookbinding, headers, etc.)	5	all types
	123	

Note: These estimates are those of the writer and in no way reflect the position one way or another of the company by which he is employed.
Reprinted from *American Dyestuff Reporter*, 51, No. 17 (August 20, 1962), p.44, Table 1. Courtesy *American Dyestuff Reporter*.

Cotton and rayon were the fibers first used in these structures, and generally two types of web were produced: 1) the web laid down by the cotton carding machine was oriented, that is, the fibers all lay in approximately parallel position, and 2) the web produced by the woolen card was more random in fiber direction; such a web has more uniform strength in all directions. Randomness or a 90-degree cross-ply structure may be produced by laying oriented webs one on another at various angles.

Table 5-1 shows the fibers most commonly found in non-woven fabrics. Generally, the fibers are selected because of their various properties, which are given below:

1 Cotton (unbleached)—good wet strength and opacity, but color may not be clear. Bleached cotton is more expensive than rayon but gives good color, opacity, and strength.

2   Rayon (viscose)—excellent whiteness, good dry strength, but water-sensitive, fabric has papery feel.

3   Acetate—equal to viscose in color and opacity; has less papery feel.

4   Nylon—excellent in color and strength; good resilience; is expensive and has poor opacity.

5   Wool—gives good hand and drape, high bulk, good resilience, but low strength.

6   Glass fibers have high strength, but adhesion is poor.

7   Other fibers—it is reasonable to assume that all fibers will be tried out from time to time, and any one may be found to be superior for certain types of webs.

Russell[4] reports the following cost per pound for the fibers most commonly used in these non-woven fabrics.

Fiber	Cents/Lb. (approx.)
Acetate	36
Cotton Comber*	22
Nylon, Type 100	120
Rayon, Viscose, first grade	33
Rayon, Viscose, "B" grade	25

* Low middling 1-in. cotton was 32 cents; middling 1-in. was 37 cents (1959).

USES

Products made of non-wovens were initially introduced as semi-disposable items, and that still is one of the objectives in many cases. To be used a few times at most and then discarded, the products should then be less expensive than a conventional fabric. This relatively new use, however, is not to be supplied with waste or scrap fibers. Quality non-wovens require fibers as good and as clean as those for other textile formations.

medical and sanitary

In the following items non-wovens have already been found to be highly desirable:

Bandages   Covers for tables, trays, dressers
Bed pads and sheets   Dressings
Bibs   Tissues

They could also go into nurse's caps, wash cloths, and hand towels.

[4] C. W. Russell, *Cotton in Non-woven Fabrics* (Memphis, Tenn.: National Cotton Council, 1959), p. 8.

apparel

Rather wide use, especially when traveling, is made of these materials in disposable items. Among these are diapers, face cloths, bibs, and foundation garments. Semi-disposable underwear, blouses, collars, and shirts have not yet appealed to the public. Stiff interlining materials are popular in girls' dresses and in many apparel items. Other uses are:

Aprons and bibs	Paddings
Facings	Work clothes
Findings in garment construction	Caps and sport hats

home furnishings

Many uses are found for these fabrics in many weights, textures, and degrees of stiffness. For the most part, the products are disposable after one use, although their length of service may vary from a few minutes for a disposable dish cloth to a year for a pair of draperies.

Dish cloths	Tablecloths	Place mats
Draperies	Cleaner bags	Tissues
Dust cloths	Shelf covers	Towels
Sheeting	Doilies	Vacuum cleaner bags
Napkins	Pads	Window shades

industrial

These uses often affect the home; the modern tea-bag, for example, is made of a non-woven fabric. Polishing and wiping cloths of non-wovens are superior to the pick-up apparel scraps used in most homes. Other uses are:

Filters of all kinds	Insulation
Backing fabrics	Laminated products
Wrapping materials	Packaging

When non-woven fabrics are as soft and pliable as woven or knit goods, their market in protective clothing of semi-disposable types will grow. The new synthetics with their chemical resistance could make much cheaper laboratory coats and aprons. However, the factors of comfort and mobility require roomy sleeves and armscyes. These in turn cause too many accidents, such as catching apparatus with sleeve cuff or, in industry, having a too roomy garment catch in moving machinery.

textile fibers: general properties

The fiber is a very fine, hair-like material of almost infinite length compared with its diameter. The fiber must be long enough to be twisted with other fibers to form a yarn which, in turn, must have sufficient flexibility, softness, and strength to be woven into a fabric. Finally, the fabric must be capable of being colored and finished to an acceptable degree of beauty and attractiveness and to be fashioned into a garment, or drapery, or other kind of household textile product.

The fiber identification labeling law passed by the Senate and signed by President Eisenhower on September 2, 1958, placed additional significance upon the identity of the fibers in a vast number of textile products. The law became effective on March 2, 1960, with the Federal Trade Commission responsible for the definitions, rules, and regulations affecting the administration of the law. (See Chapter 29, p. 508.) The classification of the common fibers is given in Table 6-1.

TABLE 6-1 / TEXTILE FIBER CLASSIFICATION

Natural Fibers	Man-Made Fibers Non-thermoplastic	Man-Made Fibers Thermoplastic
Cellulosic (vegetable)	Alginate	Cellulosic
cotton	alginate	**acetate or triacetate**
linen	Cellulosic	acetate
minor fibers	**rayon**	Arnel*
abaca	Avril*	Non-cellulosic

Natural Fibers	Man-Made Fibers Non-thermoplastic	Man-Made Fibers Thermoplastic
coir	Avlin*	**acrylic**
hemp	Corval*	Acrilan*
jute	Fiber E*	Courtelle*
kapok	Fiber SM27**	Creslan*
kenaf	Fiber 500**	Orlon*
milkweed	Fortisan*	Zefran*
ramie, rhea, grass linen	rayon	**modacrylic**
sisal	cuprammonium	dynel
Mineral	viscose	Verel*
asbestos	Topel*	**nylon**
Protein (animal)	Zantrel*	Caprolan*
silk	Mineral	nylon
wool	**glass**	**nytril**
minor fibers	Fiberfrax*	Darvan*
alpaca	Fiberglas*	**olefin**
angora (rabbit)	Garan*	Boltathene*
camel	Modiglass*	DLP*
cashmere (goat)	Pittsburgh*	Firestone*
cow hair	PPG*	Olane*
fur fibers (mink, beaver, etc.)	Unifab*	Pex*
guanaco	Uniformat*	Polyarns*
horsehair	Unirove*	Prolene*
llama	Vitron*	Reevon*
mohair (goat)	**metallic**	Royalene*
qiviut (musk ox)	aluminum	Velon LP*
rabbit	Alustran*	Wynene*
vicuna	Durastran*	**polyester**
feathers	Chromflex*	Dacron*
	Fairtex*	Fortrel*
	Lurex*	Kodel*
	Malora*	Vycron*
	Metlon*	**rubber**
	Nylco*	Lastex*
	Reynolds*	**saran**
	Reymet*	Rovana*
	Lamé*	saran
	copper	**spandex**
	gold	Lycra*
	silver	Vyrene*
	Protein	**vinal**
	azlon	vinylon
	Ardil* (peanut)	**vinyon**
	casein (milk)	Avisco Vinyon*
	Aralac*	tetrafluoroethylene
	chicken feather	Teflon*
	cottonseed	
	soybean	
	Vicara* (corn)	

* Fiber trademark names. Trademarks and companies to whom assigned are given in the sections where fiber groups are discussed.

** Trademark names have not been announced.

Taken from: Evelyn E. Stout, *Introduction to Textiles* (New York: John Wiley & Sons, Inc., 1960), p. 10, Table 3. With permission.

WHAT IS A TEXTILE FIBER?

The definition of a fiber is not precise, and, in fact, textile terminology often makes no clear distinction between hair and fiber. In a general sense, a fiber may be defined as the raw material used in the manufacture of textiles. Thus it may be partly described as being a slender filament or fine strand of sufficient length, pliability, and strength to be spun into yarns and woven into cloth. Even with this definition, individual fibers vary greatly in appearance and length, from the almost endless filaments produced by the man-made fiber industry making rayon and acetate to the short, hollow, twisted tubes identified as cotton fibers, the relatively stiff monofilaments of Saran and certain other synthetic fibers, or the soft, silky hair fiber of the angora rabbit. All are textile raw materials. Technologists sometimes differentiate three classifications of textile "fibers" on the basis of length. A **fibril** is a very small cell or a component of a fiber cell wall and is customarily measured in microns or millimicrons (one micron is 0.001 millimeters). A **fiber** is customarily measured in inches. A **filament** is a spun or extruded fiber of continuous length most conveniently measured in yards or meters. Silk is a natural filament, whereas rayon and acetate are man-made.

If a fiber is to qualify for the textile industry, three basic requirements must be met:

1 It must be available in sufficient quantity.
2 It must be economical in cost or have excellent relative value for use in certain textiles.
3 It must have satisfactory fineness to be readily spinnable into a yarn.

The man-made and synthetic fibers face two other requirements for successful marketing in competition with the natural fibers:

4 Costly chemicals and solvents must be recoverable for re-use.
5 By-products must be marketable and waste must be disposable at low cost.

To a lesser degree, these same additional qualifications must be faced by the natural fibers, for waste and by-products are found in the waxes, oils, and gums in cotton, wool, and silk, for example. Then, too, contaminants, such as sand, burrs, leaves, and tangled fibers called **neps,** are found in wool and other animal fibers. Contaminants of an organic nature are the waxes, gums, and woody materials in the stems of such fibers as flax and ramie.

FIBER PROPERTIES

The spinnability of a fiber depends very largely upon its physical properties. These properties will be dealt with more fully in the chapters devoted to the individual fibers themselves and in discussion of the textile materials made from them. However, a brief reference to the physical and chemical properties is appropriate as laying a groundwork for rather general definitions of these physical terms.

fiber length

A fiber must be sufficiently long if it is to be successfully spun into a yarn. Generally, a fiber must be at least 100 times as long as it is wide to be spinnable. Many fibers exceed this minimum by a very large amount. Natural fibers vary in length from approximately one-half inch to forty inches or more. Very fine, soft fibers such as kapok and milkweed fiber are too short for making a yarn, because the limit for economical spinning is approximately 0.20 of an inch. The longer the fiber, the stronger the yarn and the more uniform its diameter. Generally, fibers should be relatively even in length in any spinning mixture. The spinning process may require fibers of certain lengths; for example, the cotton system used almost all over the world operates best when the cotton fibers are about one and one-half inches in length. In the worsted fabrics produced by the Bradford system, the optimum length for wool is four to eight inches. In the spun silk system, the long silk filaments are cut to fiber lengths of eight to fourteen inches.

color

Most natural fibers have some **color.** For example, silk is yellow to tan; wool has a brownish tint; cotton is a creamy white or brown; most of the synthetic fibers, too, have a slight creamy or yellowish color. Fibers must, therefore, be bleached, boiled, or stripped of their color by some chemical process in order to produce as white a fiber and yarn as possible. This is necessary not only for white fabrics but also for a more even dyeing of the fabrics for consumer use.

fineness or diameter

The **fineness** or diameter of fiber is commonly expressed in microns, one micron being 0.001 millimeters. Rarely are fibers perfectly round in cross-section; therefore, the geometrical cross-section wall thickness and the diameter of the **lumen** or hollow center (if present) should be calculated if the fineness is to be determined with extreme accuracy for research or if precise grading problems are involved. The natural fibers vary greatly in fineness from place to place on an individual fiber. The synthetic fibers and rayon and acetate are much more uniform in cross-section and fineness due to their method of extrusion through a metallic orifice, or spinneret.

crimp

Crimp is the waviness of a fiber. It is a natural quality in merino wools. Fine wools usually have many fine waves. Coarse wool is more definitely curled rather than crimped. Crimp is often put into fibers for specific end-uses; for example, carpet viscose rayon is given a permanent crimp in order to provide a more lofty or vertically piled carpeting. The synthetic fibers, being thermoplastic or heat-softened, can be given a more permanent crimp; this is a characteristic of some of the so-called **textured yarns,** giving unusually soft and bulky yarns for sweaters, socks, and suitings. Crimp is measured by the difference between the length of the crimped fiber lying at rest and of the same fiber stretched gently until it is perfectly straight. Crimp is expressed as the percentage of the stretched fiber length.

spinnability

This term, **spinnability,** includes several physical properties, each having an effect upon the ability of the fibers to be spun into yarn. For example, staple fibers must be capable of taking a twist, they must have a certain degree of friction against one another so as to stay in place when pull is applied to the yarn, and they must be able to take and hold special finishes for the purpose of lubrication during spinning or of providing additional surface resistance to soiling or abrasion. With fabric and yarn strength depending so much upon the fiber-to-fiber contacts and friction effects, the strength of the individual fibers is also of importance.

tensile strength

Fiber **tensile strength** is the ability to resist breakage as a result of stress. Generally, it is expressed in terms of the force per unit of cross-sectional area, that is, kilograms per square millimeter or pounds per square inch (p.s.i.). Another term for fiber and yarn strength is **tenacity,** which is the strength per unit number, indicating the fineness of the fiber or yarn, for example, where the yarn number is expressed as a weight per unit length, such as grams per denier. The terms **tensile strength** and **tenacity** are not the same, but there is a method of getting one from the other[1] (Appendix, p. 546).

Wet strength is often an important characteristic, particularly in the vegetable fibers, which have a higher wet strength than their dry breaks, and in the protein fibers and rayon, which characteristically have lower strengths when wet than when dry.

density

Density is the mass or weight of material per unit volume generally expressed in grams per cubic centimeter. The **specific gravity** or **specific weight** of a material is the ratio of the mass weighed in air to the mass of an equal volume of water at 4° C. Because the exact volume is affected by the porosity,

[1] J. M. Matthews and H. R. Mauersberger, *Textile Fibers,* 5th ed. (New York: John Wiley & Sons, 1947), p. 36.

resulting from surface cracks, the diameter of the lumen, and the amount of crystallinity in certain sections of the individual fibers, the true density is very difficult to determine, and the specific gravity is generally the preferred method of expressing the weight of a textile fiber. In Table 6-2 are given the specific gravities of the principal textile fibers, beginning with the synthetics, which are the lightest, to asbestos and glass, the heaviest fibers.

TABLE 6-2 / SPECIFIC GRAVITIES OF FIBERS

Fiber	Specific Gravity	Fiber	Specific Gravity
Polyethylene	0.95	Ardil	1.31
Polystyrene	1.05	Wool	1.32
Nylon 6	1.14	Acetate	1.33
Nylon 66	1.14	Silk (raw)	1.33
Orlon 42	1.14	Vinyon HH	1.34
Orlon 81	1.14	Verel	1.37
Zefran	1.15	Dacron	1.38
Acrilan	1.17	Cotton	1.50
Creslan	1.17	Cuprammonium rayon	1.52
Darvan	1.18	Fortisan	1.52
Kodel	1.22	Fortisan 36	1.52
Vicara	1.25	Viscose rayon	1.52
Silk (boiled off)	1.25	Saran	1.70
Fibrolane	1.29	Velon	1.70
Merinova	1.29	Asbestos	2.10–2.80
Vinylon (Kuralon)	1.30	Teflon	2.30
Arnel	1.30	Fiberglas	2.56
Dynel	1.31		

From J. J. Press (ed.), *Man-made Textile Encyclopedia* (New York: John Wiley & Sons, Inc., 1959), p. 145, Table II.

elasticity

The elasticity of the various textile fibers will be discussed in detail in the chapters dealing with these materials. However, the definition of several of the terms should be given here. The **elasticity** of a fiber is the property by which the fiber tends to recover its original length upon removal of a stress causing deformation or stretch. Vulcanized rubber is an outstanding example of a highly extensible or elastic material and recovers almost immediately its original form and length when the load is released. Under certain conditions of heat and moisture, wool also shows considerable elasticity, as does silk. On the other hand, certain of the cellulose fibers show so little extensibility as to be classed as brittle. Numerous research chemists probing into the structure of such high **polymers** or giant, chain-like molecules with repetitive simple chemical units serving as the links, as, for example, rubber, nylon, the acrylic fibers, cotton, and wool, are in substantial agreement that the key to differences in elasticity between fibers is linked with the chain structure of the various polymers and the cross-linkages existing between chains. The **elastic limit** is the maximum load or stress to which a fiber or yarn can be subjected without the formation of a permanent set when the load is removed. This property affects the setting of crimp or curl in synthetic fibers.

plasticity

Plasticity is the property of a solid by which, under certain conditions of temperature or pressure, it may be made to take on the shape of any mold and to retain this shape after cooling. The synthetic fibers, being thermoplastic materials, are all heat plastic in nature. The heat-setting of nylon hosiery to predetermined size is an example of this phenomenon. The stretch yarns, many of which are of nylon but which may be of other thermoplastic materials, are other examples of plasticity applied to fibrous materials. Under certain conditions, wool becomes somewhat plastic, so that a wool suit can be shaped or molded under the influence of steam and pressure to give a smooth-fitting shoulder or lapel.

resilience

Resilience is the springing back or recovery of a fiber mass when it is released from a compression load. This is a desirable attribute in carpeting materials, for it enables the indentations from chair and table feet to disappear when the furniture has been moved. Resiliency is also a desirable property in pillows and mattresses and in some types of wearing apparel.

absorbency

Because most textile fibers **absorb moisture** from the air, it is important that the purchaser of fibers and yarns know what the moisture content is so that he is not paying fiber prices for water. The amount of moisture present is expressed as a percentage of the original weight of the material or of its oven-dry weight. In the first case, it is expressed as the per cent of moisture in the textile material as received; in the second case, it is referred to as the **moisture regain,** or moisture absorbed from a standard atmosphere (usually 70° F. and 65 per cent relative humidity) after exposure of the oven-dried sample. Storage conditions play a very significant part in the amount of moisture a fiber will absorb.

In Table 6-3 are given the moisture regain data of various fibers at standard conditions, 65 per cent relative humidity and constant temperature of 70° F. This table demonstrates that the amount of moisture regain from a zero content depends upon the kind of fiber, the ambient or external temperature, the amount of moisture in the air, and, of course, the compactness of the bale or package of fiber. The more dense the pack, the more difficult it will be for the air to enter. Certain moisture regain values are accepted by other trades as the regain to be used in calculating a legal weight of shipment of any specific textile fiber. Various countries are not in complete agreement as to these regain figures;

however, this is just one of the textile properties being standardized by the International Standards Organization (see Chapter 29 on Standards).

TABLE 6-3 / MOISTURE REGAIN OF TEXTILE FIBERS

Test Procedure: A carefully selected specimen of the fiber to be tested† is placed in an uncovered, tared weighing can and dried in an oven at 220° F. for two hours. A tared cover is placed on the can which is then removed from the oven, allowed to cool in a desiccator, and weighed to determine the dry net weight of the specimen. The dried specimen is then conditioned in the uncovered can at 70° F., 65 per cent R.H. for 24 hours, re-covered, and re-weighed to determine the conditioned net weight of the specimen. The moisture regain of the fiber is calculated from the following formula.

$$\frac{\text{Moisture regain}}{\text{(in per cent)}} = \frac{\text{Net weight of conditioned specimen} - \text{Net weight of dried specimen}}{\text{Net weight of dried specimen}} \times 100$$

	Fibers	Moisture Regain at 70° F., 65 Per Cent R.H.†† (per cent)
Man-made		
Acetate	Secondary (ACELE*)	6
	Triacetate ("Arnel")	4
Acrylic	All (including ORLON* and ORLON SAYELLE**)	1.5 to 2.5
Modacrylic	"Dynel"	0.4
	"Verel"	—
Nylon	Nylon 6 and nylon 6-6 (including ANTRON*** and DU PONT Type 501)	4 to 5
Nytril	"Darvan"	2 to 3
Olefin	Polyethylene, polypropylene	none
Polyester	All (including DACRON*)	0.2 to 0.8
Rayon	All	11 to 14
Saran	All	none
Spandex	LYCRA*	1.3
	"Vyrene"	—
Natural		
Cotton	All (including mercerized and not mercerized)	7 to 11
Flax	Bleached	8
Silk	Boiled-off	10 to 11
Wool	Cashmere, mohair, and regular (Merino)	about 15

* Du Pont's registered trademark.
** Du Pont's registered trademark for its bi-component acrylic fiber.
*** Du Pont's registered trademark for its trilobal multifilament nylon.
† In general, this test is not suitable for yarns spun from a blend of fibers or for fabrics made from such yarns.
†† These are actual regains and in many cases are different from commercial regains. The latter are the accepted values for determining the commercial weight of fibers, and for calculating the fiber content of textile products for labelling purposes.

capillarity or porosity

These two terms express properties which have simultaneous influence upon the ability of a textile fiber or yarn to accept and hold a dye, a finish, a lubricant, or even a resin in order to increase the wrinkle resistance of a fabric or to give it a "wash-and-wear" finish. Liquids pass rapidly through small cracks or breaks in the outer surface of a fiber, bringing about absorption of a dye or finish or other liquid through **porosity.** In the case of the passage of these liquids through the hollow center, or lumen, in cotton or through small voids on the surface of a wool fiber, it is usually regarded as the effect of **capillarity.** In either case, it is important that the desired material absorbed should then be retained in the fiber permanently.

cohesion

Cohesion is the property of clinging or sticking together in a mass. Usually the more rigid the fiber, the lower its cohesion. Lack of cohesion on the part of one fiber will often make the uniform blending of this and a more cohesive fiber somewhat uncertain. Usually it is assumed that a rather high degree of frictional resistance plays a part in cohesiveness. It is certain that external scales or neps (wool and flax, respectively) or the twists and irregularities in diameter of cotton will contribute to the ability of fibers to hold together and with other fibers blended with them in the spinning operation. Smooth-textured uniformly-surfaced fibers, such as most of the synthetics, do not possess this phenomenon of cohesion unless specially treated.

luster

Generally, a certain amount of **luster** is desirable in a fabric, for it tends to show off to advantage any woven-in or printed pattern on the textile goods. It is an ornamental or an esthetic property rather than a necessity. Sometimes fibers have too much luster or brightness. Thus, in the middle 1920's, when rayon and acetate first came on the market, there was great objection to their appearance because they were so lustrous as to appear shiny and almost metallic as compared with the warmer, more subtle luster of silk, for example. Many of our man-made fibers, including rayon and acetate but also a great many of the synthetics, are found on the market as bright, semi-dull, and dull textured fibers, filaments, yarns, and fabrics. A common dulling agent is titanium dioxide, TiO_2, which is also used today in most of our white paints.

flammability

Flammability will be discussed in detail in the chapter on finishes (p. 109), but as a general fiber property, the mineral fibers, such as glass, asbestos, and mineral wool, do not burn. Dynel is also nonflammable, and undyed nylon is generally regarded as a nonflammable fiber. With these exceptions, all other textile fibers burn, some of them being highly combustible. Because fibers are so very fine and because a mass of fibers, unless very tightly packed, contains abundant air, they are readily ignited and burn fiercely. The cellulosic fibers, cotton and rayon, are readily flammable in fabrics having a napped or raised surface and in extremely sheer nets. The Flammable Fabrics Act (Public Law 88) was passed by the 83rd Congress and signed by President Eisenhower on June 30, 1953, and became effective July 1, 1954. This act applied specifically to textiles used in wearing apparel and is discussed in greater detail in Chapter 9.

static electrical properties

The phenomenon of **static electricity** creates a problem in the spinning and other processing of textile fibers, especially in rooms with very low relative humidity. The problem is much more severe in the case of synthetic fibers, which have extremely low **electrical conductivity** and which generally absorb too little moisture to provide a path whereby the static charge can be carried away. Static electrical properties create problems in the packaging, in the sewing, and in the wearing of many of these textile products. The problem of static electricity will be discussed in Chapter 9.

QUESTIONS

1 Describe a textile fiber.

2 Textile fibers have been grouped into generic types in this chapter. List them.

3 Within each category, what are the similarities of the numerous fibers?

4 List the various essential requirements that must be met by new material in order to qualify commercially as a textile fiber source.

5 List at least ten important properties a successful textile must have.

6 Define moisture regain.

7 Explain the difference between density and specific gravity of a fiber.

8 Distinguish between elongation and elasticity of a fiber.

9 Of what importance is porosity in a fiber?

10 What other properties of a fiber depend largely upon its moisture absorbency?

yarns

Yarns have already been referred to in Chapter 2, on Fabric Constructions, for yarns are the sinews of fabrics. It is the yarn, the individual fibers collected into a strand and then twisted for greater compactness and strength, that is woven or knitted into a fabric structure. Some of the properties of the individual fibers carry over into the performance of the yarns and fabric during service. This is particularly true of the **chemical properties;** that is, the resistance of the individual fibers to acid, alkali, bleach, sunlight, excessive heat, and other destructive agencies will be equally damaging to the yarns and the fabrics fashioned therefrom. On the other hand, the **physical properties** of fibers, such as their tenacity, elasticity, specific gravity, cross-section, and other measurable properties, become somewhat masked or less clear and distinct when fibers are formed into yarns and fabrics. Thus, it is evident that yarn properties are as important as fiber properties. These yarn properties depend very largely upon the amount of twist imparted into the yarn in the spinning and the effect of various finishing agents on the yarns and the fabrics. Not all fabrics require yarns as an intermediate step; non-wovens, for example. Nevertheless, a definition for yarn has been agreed upon by the Textile Committee of the American Society for Testing Materials, Committee D-13, as:

A generic term for continuous strands of textile fibers or filaments in a form suitable for knitting, weaving, or otherwise intertwining to form a textile fabric. It may comprise: a) a number of fibers twisted together; b) a number of filaments laid together without twist (a O-twist yarn); c) a number of filaments laid together with more or less twist; or d) a single filment with or without twist (a monofilament).[1]

Subsequent references to specific fibers will deal with the individual requirements of these various fibers, leading to the preparation of a satisfactory yarn. One would expect that the natural fibers would be subject to contamination by foreign substances, such as dirt, fragments of plants, and other solid material caught in the mass of fiber, and would require greater care and many extra steps in the purification and cleaning operation leading to a clean fiber to be spun into a yarn. Natural fibers, such as cotton, wool, and linen, also contain various oils and other materials associated with the growing and maturing of the fiber, and these, too, must be removed. Some of the extra operations required in the preparation of natural fibers are as follows:

COTTON   The baled raw cotton may still contain portions of leaves and twigs; the removal of these and the numerous steps required to straighten and to form cotton into a spinnable shape are described in Chapter 10, Cotton, pages 130 to 141.

FLAX FIBER OR LINEN   These also require special operations, such as retting to loosen the woody constituents of the stems and scutching to break down and remove mechanically the last traces of woody stem material prior to spinning.

RAW WOOL   Wool as it arrives at the mill contains a variety of foreign substances which the sheep may have snarled into the fleece during grazing. Thus, burrs, dirt, branding paint for the identification of the animal, chemicals remaining from dipping the animal for control of ticks and other insects, together with natural contaminants, **wool grease,** or **suint,** and other substances, may have to be removed.

SILK   Silk is usually purchased in the raw state and has simply been reeled from the cocoons onto a skein or other transportable holder and still contains the natural silk gum, **sericin.** Silk is already a long fiber and does not require any of the operations required to form a workable strand as is the case in the short fibers, cotton, linen, and wool, unless, of course, a staple fiber has been made out of silk for spun yarns.

Thus, it will be seen that the man-made fibers have a great advantage at the very beginning, for they generally arrive at the mill in a condition ready for spinning into a yarn. They are free from contaminants and dirt; thus, they do not require any of these pre-spinning operations.

[1] American Society for Testing Materials, Committee D-13 on Textiles, *Standard Definitions of Terms Relating to Textile Materials* (1960), ASTM Designation D-123-59.

METHODS OF SPINNING

The actual spinning of the yarn may be done by the mills specializing in this process. Such mills might produce neither fiber or fabric, simply supplying spun yarns for the textile trade. Other mills may spin their own yarns and weave them.

cotton spinning methods

The cotton system refers to one or another of several types of spinning frame by which a fine **roving** or loose plait of cotton can be formed into a satisfactory yarn for weaving. It must be remembered that the cotton fiber generally regarded in the United States as spinnable varies in fiber length from ⅞- to about 1½-inches. This cotton system can produce yarns of a wide variety of sizes and **counts,** and, of course, the fineness depends largely upon the fineness of the roving; also, showing the count of the roving in the cotton system, the count refers to the number of 840-yard hanks, or loops, of yarn or roving, respectively, needed to make one pound. Thus, when we speak of a fabric containing 40's cotton warp yarn, it means that 40 hanks of 840-yards each total one pound. The higher the count, the finer or thinner the yarn. Generally, the cotton system is used in spinning other fibers with cotton, because the fiber lengths should be approximately the same in each of the two different fibers, and this system spins shorter fibers than can be accomplished by other mechanical methods.

the american system

The American System is a modified cotton system spinning frame which has been developed from early attempts with cotton machinery to use heavier weights and larger rolls in order to process not only cotton but worsted yarns. On this, it is possible to spin fibers from the longer staple cotton with other fibers, up to about 5-inch fibers; thus, this system is being widely used today for most staple yarn fabrics made of the man-made fibers, rayon, acetate, and the synthetics, alone or blended with one another or with wool or cotton.

Prior to spinning, of course, these staple yarns must go through the preliminary stages such as complete mixing, carding, drawing, and roving. Because the public has grown to expect a more uniform quality of weave from the manmade fibers than from natural fibers, the presence of irregularities, slubs, thick and thin spots, and all other surface-defacing spots must be avoided. This is particularly true in the very lightweight fabrics if the individual fibers have a very low denier. The texture of the fabric can be altered considerably by using a heavier denier fiber and spinning longer fibers in the yarns. These two factors generally produce a crisp, firm, and somewhat more resilient fabric. However, many quality mills have found that it is more satisfactory in the long run for them to produce a standard cloth, keeping the denier, the blend, and the fiber length constant, and depending upon the textile finish to give the particular texture desired by the garment manufacturer. For uniformity of fabric, many

Fig. 7-1   Cotton roving. (*Courtesy Pepperell Manufacturing Company.*)

spinners feed in a roving from at least 10 different fiber sources or lots, so that the resultant yarn will be as uniform as possible. These precautions are taken in spite of the uniformity one associates with the man-made fibers, because one lot of viscose rayon, for example, may dye slightly differently than another lot. Similarly, different batches of nylon or Dacron or acetate may differ somewhat in their ability to pick up dyes in certain shades resulting from slight differences in fiber absorbency on one hand and the difference in size of different dye molecules on the other.

There are certain practical limits to the fineness of yarn one can spin. According to Johnson,[2] the theory is that it is not wise to produce yarns with fewer than 77 fibers per cross-section. If a mill is producing yarn from a strong fiber, the temptation may be to produce a finer yarn, one with fewer fibers in the cross-section. To have done so has been reported to result in less yarn cohesion, or ability to stay together, and a greater tendency for neps or irregularities to appear. A formula is given for calculating the number of fibers per cross-section in spun synthetic yarns. This is as follows: there are 4,465,528 yards of one-denier yarn in one pound. There are eight hundred and forty yards of 1's yarn in one pound. Therefore, 4,465,528 divided by 840 equals 5,314, the total denier in a 1's yarn. The total denier divided by denier per filament in the yarn equals fibers per cross-section in the yarn. Therefore, if, for example, it was desired to know the number of fibers per cross-section in a 20's yarn made of three-denier staple viscose, 5,314 divided by 20 equals 265.7, and 265.7 divided by 3 equals 88.6 fibers per cross-section in the 20's yarn.

the worsted system

This was intended originally to spin carded and combed wool fibers into worsted yarns. This system is being used for many other fibers as well, many, of course, in blends with wool. If the yarn is completely of man-made fibers, some of the preliminary steps required for the removing of contaminants from wool sliver can be omitted, but the carding and combing must be similar to those of wool worsted fabrics of similar fineness. The upper limit of fiber length is seven inches; however, the process is used most commonly on fibers of 1¾ to 2½ inches. The amount of twist is generally lower than that in worsted fabrics because the synthetic fibers are generally stronger than wool and do not require as tight a twist in order to give a strong, easily handled yarn.

woolen system processing

This is the system used for woolen fabrics and soft textured fabrics, such as dress goods, blanketings, materials for robes, and flannels. It is referred to at some greater length in the chapter on Wool. In the case of blends of wool with synthetics or man-made fibers blended together, the relative cleanliness of man-made fibers makes many of the original preliminary steps unnecessary. In general, fibers of approximately the same degree of fineness and length will be the most compatible and uniform in spinning. Russell L. Brown[3] gives the following

[2] F. M. Johnson, "Chapter V-4," in J. J. Press (ed.), *Man-made Textile Encyclopedia* (New York: John Wiley & Sons, Inc., 1959), p. 193.

[3] Russell L. Brown, in J. J. Press (ed.), *Man-made Textile Encyclopedia* (New York: John Wiley & Sons, Inc., 1959), p. 199.

tabular data comparing the uniformity of wool fibers with synthetics in terms of the two definitions for wool quality, the blood designation and the English number, and the denier terminology applied to man-made fibers.

TABLE 7-1 / WOOL FINENESS AND SYNTHETIC FIBER DENIER

WOOL QUALITY		
Blood	English No.	Approx. Denier
Fine	70's	4
Fine	64's	4.5
½	60's	6
⅜	56's	7.5
¼	50's	9

The numbers system for fineness of wool is not the same as that for the fineness of cotton, that is, 40's for wool and 40's for cotton would not be the same. In the case of wool, the figure refers to the number of 560-yard hanks of wool yarn to weigh one pound; the higher the number the finer the wool yarn.

Fig. 7-2 Testing uniformity of wool yarn: The yarn is wound on a black card. The distance between strands is carefully controlled, so that when the sample card is completed, the inspector can judge the evenness of the yarn. (*Courtesy of The Wool Bureau, Inc.*)

In the formation of wool and man-made fiber blends, the carding operation causing the fibers to lie more parallel and at the same time mixing the two or more different kinds of fibers intimately must be carefully carried out if the yarn is to be uniform. The fact that the wool fiber is naturally crimped and somewhat more resilient than the man-made fibers may cause the wool to wrap itself around the nearby fibers of synthetic or man-made origin. If this happens, the spun yarn gradually develops a cord effect, with the man-made fibers more or less concentrated in the center and with the wool fibers wrapped around them. This, of course, is not a uniform yarn, and even color in dyeing might be a problem. The wear pattern also would vary in different portions of the garment, depending upon concentration of core regions compared with very uniform mixtures in the same or adjacent yarns.

STEPS LEADING TO SPINNING

Brief mention should be given to certain preliminary procedures and the several methods of spinning yarns, some of which are applicable also to the man-made fibers. These several steps are as follows:

1. *Blending.* Blending is the mixing together of the desired quantities of two or more different fibers. Even the man-made fibers may have been formed into rather compact masses or balls in the bag or sack in which they were shipped. These large clusters of fiber must be broken up. This is called **opening.** The various containers of cotton, wool, rayon, or synthetic fiber are weighed to give the desired composition. Generally the two component kinds of fiber are blended by layering one kind of fiber on top of the other in a loose mat, or the two types may be placed in a mixing device in which the fibers are blown and rotated until the mixture is as uniform as possible.

2. *Tinting.* A temporary dyestuff may be added to one of the fiber types by using a dye which will color only one fiber and not the other. This enables the inspector to determine the uniformity of the mixture and also gives him a quick measure of the fiber or fibers remaining in the waste, that is, short lengths which may be separated out from the mass as it proceeds through the various steps to the spinning frame. These dyes are removed about the time for the bleaching of the goods prior to dyeing in the desired shades for commercial use.

3. *Cleaning.* This step is not necessary in the case of man-made fibers, but it is in blends of man-made with natural fibers. It is at this point that the final cleaning of foreign material from the fibers is accomplished. The mass of cotton and other fibers is repeatedly picked up and dropped by mechanical fingers tearing the clotted or matted portions apart so that any foreign material may fall free.

4. *Carding.* This is a **combing** procedure by which the individual fibers are separated from each other and laid in a relatively parallel condition. As **carding** proceeds, the sheet becomes thinner and thinner, and it finally passes as a flat

sheet on a moving belt through a funnel-like device, causing it to form into a soft strand approximately one inch in diameter. This is called the **card sliver.** This carding operation carries away the last of the broken and loose fibers and tangled masses which become attached to the card teeth. These are known as the **noils** and make up the greater part of the processing waste. Here, too, the tinting identifies the fibers which are being removed and indicates how closely the remaining blend compares with the composition as first mixed.

5. *Combing.* This process is required only for extremely fine fabrics. It is used, for example, in worsteds, and it is this additional paralleling process which readily differentiates between worsteds and woolens. It is used to remove further quantities of short fibers. The sliver from the combing device is more lustrous and is finer than that from the card, largely because of the additional reflected surface as the individual fibers have become more closely parallel.

6. *Spinning.* Spinning generally includes several processes, **drying, spinning,** and **winding.** In order to have as intimate a mixture as possible, numerous (that

Fig. 7-3 The operation of spinning yarn: Front View of a Spinning Frame. At the top we see the large wool spool giving off the individual ends of roving as it rests on a fluted roller. Immediately after the fluted rollers we see the feed rolls and one may trace the end as it passes through the eyelets down through the delivery rolls. These delivery rolls revolve at a greater speed than the feed rolls and in this manner draw out the roving to reduce its bulk. After the roving leaves the delivery roll it passes through the eyelet directly above each spindle and is then twisted and wound onto the bobbin on the upright spindle as yarn. (*Courtesy of The Wool Bureau, Inc.*)

is, six to ten) combed slivers, whichever it may be, are fed into the machine together in order to bring about further blending and greater uniformity in the final product. Rollers rotating at different speeds tend to draw out the strand formed from the several slivers and to give it a degree of stretching. This operation makes the rovings more and more thin; when this very thin strand is put on the spinning frame, it is given a slight twist, enough to hold the fibers together. From the spinning frame, the yarns pass onto the hardware on which they are to be marketed, that is, in the form of bobbins or spools or other kinds of holders.

These yarns may then be further processed for the particular purpose they are to fulfill in the weaving operation, whether they are meant to be used for filling yarns or for warp yarns.

CONTINUOUS FILAMENT YARNS

These have been by-passed thus far because they do not require any of the mechanical operations leading up to the spinning frame. The procedure by which the number of filaments required to produce the desired yarn size are collected together and twisted loosely to give a strand is called **throwing.** Thus, throwing includes all the elements of drying, spinning, and winding. The continuous filament yarns are then wound onto the holders on which they are to be used or marketed. A lubricant may be added if the yarn is to be a warp yarn; some filling yarns likewise are lubricated. In the case of synthetic fibers, it is rather common to treat them with an anti-static agent, so as to reduce the flying about of yarns and fiber ends during the weaving operation. Generally, too, synthetic fibers, whether spun or filament, are better handled in a relatively high humidity condition in order to reduce the static electrical effects. Warp yarns sometimes need extra strength and firmness; this may be given by a sizing agent, such as a synthetic or natural gum, or by a soap or starch.

YARN NOMENCLATURE AND MEASUREMENT

yarn twist

Yarns may be twisted either clockwise or counter-clockwise. These are usually designated as S and Z twist, respectively. Figure 7-5 shows the S and Z twist. It will be noted that the slant of the stem of the letter corresponds to the direction of twist in the yarn. As a general rule, warp yarns are given a higher twist because they must withstand the stresses of weaving and also be as free of friction as possible so that the shuttle may be passed through the shed easily and without binding. The filling yarns are given varied degrees of twist, depending upon the characteristics of the cloth. If the surface is to be lustrous, as in the case of satins and some brocades, there may be no twist whatever. Another reason for low twist of the filling is in fabrics in which the surface is to be raised,

Fig. 7-4 Indicating the direction of yarn twist.

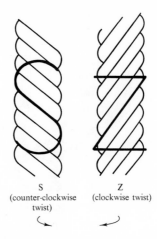

S
(counter-clockwise twist)

Z
(clockwise twist)

such as napped blankets and flannels. On the other hand, extremely high twist, great enough to cause distortion and knotting of the filling yarns, is characteristic of many crepes. Generally, the yarns in both warp and filling are given a relatively high twist in the case of worsted fabrics from wool yarns, whereas woolen fabrics have a low twist in both directions.

yarn classification

When fibers have been twisted together to form a yarn, such a yarn is called a single-ply or usually a singles yarn. Such a yarn may be a monofilament, a cluster of fibers with little or no twist, or one with a tight twist. Whatever twist is present is always in one direction, either S or Z. Often we have multiple yarns, that is, yarns made up of more than one twisted unit or **ply.** When such a yarn is untwisted, the individual plies separate into singles, which, in turn, may be untwisted to form fibers. If two or more plies are twisted together, the unit formed is called a **cord.** Figure 7-6 shows the progression from fiber, to singles, to ply-yarn, and finally to cord. Generally, textile fabrics for wearing apparel are of singles. Ply yarns are used in heavier fabrics in which greater durability is required. This would be in work clothing and industrial fabrics, or for some sheers, such as voiles, in which the yarns are so fine that a ply is required to give greater strength per unit cross-section. Similarly, cord yarns are used in extra-heavy industrial fabrics, such as heavy belting material for conveyor or automobile tire use, and, as a contrast, for ultra-fine sheer materials.

yarn uniformity

Uniformity in a yarn may be evaluated either as to its physical appearance and texture, that is, whether it is uniform throughout its length or whether it is characterized by irregularities, surface effects, color variations, etc.; or also

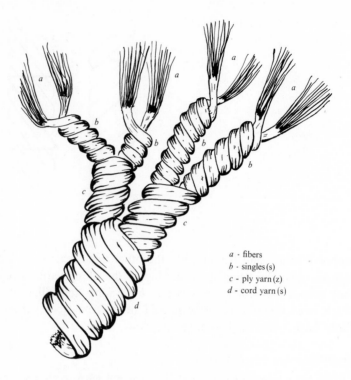

a - fibers
b - singles (s)
c - ply yarn (z)
d - cord yarn (s)

Fig. 7-5   The three textile sinews.

by its composition, that is, uniformity of the individual fibers in size, shape, or identity.

Generally, the very uniform yarn is termed "a simple yarn" and is characterized by uniform twist throughout its length, by a very uniform diameter, and by the fact that only one type of fiber is customarily used. A blended yarn may have two or more different kinds of fiber blended together in the same color; it may be cross-dyed, with each fiber being a different color; on the other hand, one fiber may be colored and the other left white.

Novelty yarns are those of complex or irregular structure. Some of these are singles in which neps or small tangles of fibers (usually immature cotton fibers); thick areas, such as slubs; or complex effects such as loops and curls, as in bouclé, are formed. There are also the spiral yarns; covered, coated, or striped yarns; ratiné; and yarns with other irregular configurations. In general, the purpose of these novelty yarns is to give either the woven or knitted fabric an irregular surface appearance to impart a three-dimensional effect and thus make the fabric more interesting. It has been shown that yarns may vary greatly in their diameter or fineness. They may vary also in their compactness, which

Fig. 7-6 Taslan yarn: Fine denier Taslan textured nylon yarns showing that the waviness of fiber loops and snarls do not affect the uniformity of the yarn. (*Courtesy of Chemstrand Corporation.*)

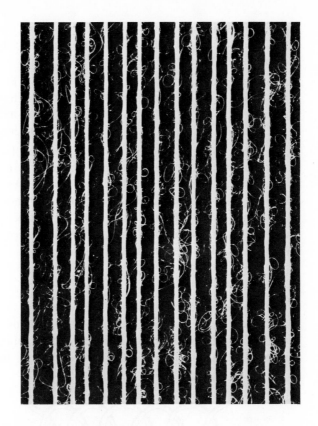

perhaps one may better state as their linear density, that is, roughly, their weight per unit of length. Through historical development, tradition, and habit, each textile fiber has brought with it its own yarn number system, which is still used in most mills. Thus, we have one system based on the weight per unit of length, and the other based on the length per unit of weight. To complicate things still further, the units of weight and of length vary.

The system using weight per unit of length is called **direct** system. This is the one used traditionally for silk and some jute fibers and has been carried over into all man-made fibers in both the filament and spun or staple yarns. These numbers are based on the **denier** system, that is, the number of grams (deniers) weighed by 9000 meters of yarn. (For convenience in measuring and weighing, both the weight and length are commonly divided by 20. Under this system, denier is the number of 0.05 grams that a 450-meter length of yarn weighs.) As the yarn becomes coarser or greater in diameter, the number increases; thus, denier is a direct measure.

The length per unit weight is an **indirect** system in which the number designation decreases as the diameter of the yarn becomes greater. This system, with different units used for wool, cotton, linen, glass, and asbestos, is based on the number of units of constant yardage (but with the constant varying depending on the fiber) required to weigh one pound.

For cotton and spun silk	840-yard hanks to weigh one pound
linen and woolen yarns	300-yard hanks to weigh one pound
worsted	560-yard hanks to weigh one pound
glass	100-yard hanks to weigh one pound

It is not to be wondered at, therefore, that laboratories and the several technical societies are interested in a common system applicable to all fibers. Such a system being promoted actively by the American Society for Testing Materials is the TEX System, in which the yarn numbers for all fibers are the weight in grams of 1000 meters of yarn. This is being applied gradually in this country and abroad, but mill men, being rather steeped in tradition, have been slow to respond to a more simple system.

TEXTURED YARNS

As a matter of convenience, two types of so-called textured yarns are grouped together; one class is the **bulk yarns,** the other, the **stretch yarns.** Although any thermoplastic or heat-set yarn or fabric can be used, the greater number of the textured yarns are of nylon. There are several reasons for this:

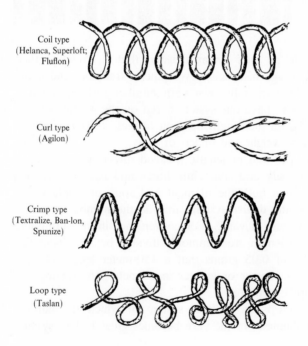

Coil type
(Helanca, Superloft; Fluflon)

Curl type
(Agilon)

Crimp type
(Textralize, Ban-lon, Spunize)

Loop type
(Taslan)

Fig. 7-7 Textured yarns.

first, nylon is produced in both filament and staple form in a very wide variety of denier or degrees of fineness; second, nylon is the strongest of the synthetic fibers in commercial production, and it has a relatively high softening temperature and a good retentive memory, causing it never to go back to its original form; third, there are more commercial producers of nylon than of any other synthetic fiber.

Bulk yarns are generally continuous filament yarns which have been crimped or repeatedly folded back and forth on themselves in order to give greater bulk per unit length of the yarn after modification. They are stretchable to the limit of the crimping or folding.

Stretch yarns are more often of staple construction and have been looped or coiled. They have considerably higher elongation than the bulk yarns, recover rapidly, and are generally used in garments in which the wearer wants stretch rather than coverage, such as sweaters and other knitted articles. Their growth has been phenomenal, however, from approximately 2 million pounds in 1950, 5 million pounds in 1954, 30 million pounds in 1958, 45 million pounds in 1960, to a forecast of 75 million pounds in 1962. Taking the principal trademarks alphabetically, the following are the most important:

Agilon—Deering-Milliken Research Corporation
Fluflon—Marionette Mills, Inc.
Helanca—Heberlein Patent Corporation
Saaba—Universal Winding Company
Spunize—Spunize Company of America, Inc.
Super-Loft—Universal Winding Company
Taslan—E. I. du Pont de Nemours & Company, Inc.
Textralized—Joseph Bancroft and Sons Company
Tycora—Textured Yarn Company, Inc.

Helanca was the first of the commercial yarns of bulk nature to be introduced into the United States. Coming from Switzerland in 1950, it became important primarily in stretch socks. This promotion made it possible for a manufacturer to knit but two sizes, large and small. Stretchiness, bulk, and softness of the yarn gave comfort to all who wore them. It proved an aid in the inventory of the retail establishment. Helanca stretch socks and the Uni-sized socks however, introduced a psychological problem in some homes, in which fathers and sons could probably wear the same size of stretch sock, and civil war might break out if the favorite pair should appear on the feet of another person in the household. The wear-resistance and strength of nylon, together with its low moisture regain, assure good durability and satisfactory washing. These high-bulk yarns are relatively free from pilling; however, there is some tendency for them to pick up lint and dust through electrostatic attraction.

Agilon is a curled-type static or non-torque stretch yarn developed by Deering-Milliken Research Corporation. The yarn generally has two com-

Fig. 7-8   Various Bulky yarns. (*Courtesy of Chemstrand Corporation.*)

7-8a Superloft, 70 denier nylon stretch yarn.

7-8b Fluflon, 2-ply, 7 denier nylon filament stretch yarn.

7-8c Agilon,   (stabilized) type nylon yarn.

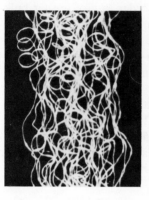

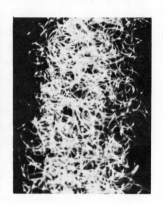

7-8d Spunize, (R) textured yarn of Chemstrand nylon.

7-8e Whitin A.R.C.T., 2-ply, 70-denier–34 filament of Chemstrand nylon.

7-8f Saaba, 2-ply, 70-denier–34 filament textured nylon yarn.

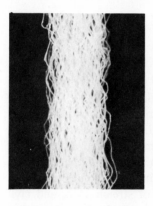

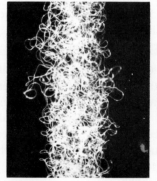

7-8g Agilon, crimped type, stretch nylon yarn.

7-8h Agilon, typical monofilament stretch yarn.

7-8i Helanca, conventional yarn of Chemstrand nylon.

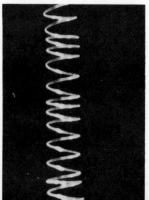

ponents, one an S twist, the other a Z, combined to form a non-twisting yarn. The continuous filament yarn is heated just to the softening point and is then rubbed along a knife edge which deforms the filaments by giving them a slightly flat surface plane replacing a small arc of the circumference. This flat plane twists slightly around the fiber, causing it to spiral (somewhat the same principle as drawing a knife edge along the flat side of a ribbon in order to curl it on a gift wrapping). Sometimes a monofilament yarn is used instead of the multifilament. In either case, the yarn is suitable for seamless full-fashioned stockings, sweaters, knitted outer wear, underwear, and even for carpets, and is now a strong market force. **Helanca NT** (non-torque) stretch yarn can be given a false twist on a machine to give a grooved or knit single yarn without distortion. These are widely used in sweaters and underwear. **Chadalon** and **shape 2 U** are other curl-type yarns.

Ban-lon and **Textralized** are products of the Joseph Bancroft and Sons Company. Other firms have been licensed to produce these yarns on a quality control basis. The various steps are: 1) crimping by compressing the yarn into a metal stuffer box, causing the individual filaments to fold or bend at a sharp angle; when heat-set during compression, crimping occurs; 2) the yarns are then cleared of broken filaments or any imperfections; 3) slight lubricating aids in the process of fabrication; 4) although nylon is the principal fiber used for Ban-lon and Textralized, there is considerable variation in the types of nylon and their denier, in other words, from 30- to 200-denier find practical use in these yarns, and often they are three to five-ply in order to prevent broken ends; 5) after they have been plied and twisted, the textured yarn is lubricated and wound on cones. Some of the finer of the denier yarns have been named Textralized; for others, the term Ban-lon is still used. The characteristic figure for these yarns is a zig-zag crimp, providing unusually soft hand, high bulk, an increase of 200 to 300 per cent in volume, sufficient elasticity to permit comfortable fit, and a somewhat increased moisture absorption for additional comfort.

Super-Loft and **Fluflon** are so-called false-twist methods of producing a bulk and stretch-type yarn. In the Super-Loft, the thermoplastic yarn is taken from the package, twisted, heat-set with direct contact heat, untwisted, and then taken up again on a cone in loose form for further processing. The use in Fluflon of radiant heat at a constant tension during heating is the principal difference. There may be some variability among different packages of yarns produced by this method, due to slight differences in the amount of twist, the temperature of setting, and the amount of tension applied. Thus, these yarns may sometimes be found to be relatively stiff and other times soft, loose, and bulky. Either of these may then be given an additional treatment, under controlled temperature and heating time, with the tension modified so as to remove some of the stretch previously put in the Super-Loft and Fluflon yarns, but retaining the bulk. Yarns so modified by one producer as to give high bulk as their primary characteristic are known as **Saaba.** These yarns are particularly good for knitted under-wear, swim wear, hosiery, warp-knit fabrics, industrial fabrics, webbings, braids, and girdles.

Spunize is another bulky yarn developed by the stuffer-box technique to induce crimp in the yarn, utilizing heat setting in an autoclave. It is very largely given to filaments of rather heavy denier, and these bulky yarns are excellent for rugs, carpets, and upholstery fabrics.

Taslan has a characteristic loop structure and the technique of its formation can be applied to any continuous filament, that is, the filament need not be thermoplastic. It is produced in a more random manner by feeding nylon, Dacron, viscose, or other filaments through a spinneret into a turbulent air jet. The strand of filaments is fed out at a rate faster than it is taken up on the rolls; thus, there are loose loops and curls blown in the individual filaments as they flow out into a rather bulky mass of loose fiber instead of remaining close together in a con-ventional type of spun nylon monofilament yarn. As these yarns are wound on the pickup rolls, many little loops are left loose both inside and outside the yarn. Possibly 20 per cent of the yarn length is lost by this bulking; but the volume of the yarn increases anywhere from 50 to 100 per cent, depending upon the jet force and the speed of take-up. Taslan yarns do not stretch but retain a permanent bulk. American Enka Corporation has a similar yarn called **Skyloft.**

Tycora is the yarn name of the Textured Yarn Company and designates a source of manufacture but not the method, because Tycora's producers utilize a wide variety of procedures to produce yarns of a bulking or stretching nature.

Q U E S T I O N S

1 What is a yarn?

2 Describe single, ply, and cord yarns.

3 For what purposes is each of these three types of yarns used?

4 What are the four principal spin-ning methods for yarn production used in the United States?

5 What are the preliminary steps prior to the spinning of a yarn?

6 How is yarn uniformity achieved?

7 Compare in size a 30's cotton and a 30's wool.

8 What is the TEX yarn classifica-tion system?

9 Draw the S and Z twist. Why do we have two different directions of twist?

10 What is a textured yarn? Dis-tinguish between a textured yarn and a novelty yarn.

11 Why are warp yarns custom-arily lubricated prior to the weaving operation?

12 Describe the appearance of four textured yarns.

13 What is the difference between a bulk yarn and a stretch yarn?

dyeing and printing

The application of color as adornment may actually pre-date the use of clothing. Color was applied to the skin of many primitive peoples, including the ancestors of the American Indians and the natives of Africa. Daubs of color were usually applied to the skin as a part of the observance of ceremonials as well as for man's enjoyment.

Color is an important economic factor in the modern textile industry, and it is difficult to imagine in this day of color-wealth that only a few generations ago the available dyestuff colors for textile decoration were so limited in variety and brightness.

COLOR AND LIGHT

Color and light are both physical phenomena. Without light we are unaware of the presence of color, and the brighter the light by which we view a colored surface, the brighter the colors seem to be.

Light is radiant energy and is composed of electromagnetic rays. These radiations advance like the waves produced by throwing a stone in a still pond. There is a characteristic wave length (distance from wave crest to wave crest or from trough to trough) for each type of radiation. The longest wave length, that of the radiations used in radio and wireless telegraphy, is 10 quadrillion times as long as the shortest, the Gamma rays. Between these limits are X-rays, light rays, heat waves, and many others.

According to one group of scientists, a substance which reflects all the rays of the spectrum in their proper proportion is white. White light is broken into its spectrum, or components, by means of a glass prism. A substance which reflects no light is black. A black object absorbs both color and heat rays. Other substances have a selective reflectivity, the color reflected—the color of the substance—being the complement of the color rays absorbed. The color deepens as the wave length of the absorbed rays increases.

This classification would define green as the deepest color, followed by blue, violet, red, orange, and yellow, because green is the visible color produced when its complement, red, is absorbed, and Table 8-1 shows red to have the longest wave length of the colors of the spectrum. The wave lengths of the various radiations are listed in Table 8-1.

T A B L E   8 - 1

Kind of Radiation	Millimicrons	Centimeters
Gamma Rays	0.01	0.000000001
X-Rays	0.1	0.00000001
Shortest Ultra-violet	60.	0.000006
Transmitted by Quartz	200.	0.00002
Shortest Solar Waves which Can Pass through Atmosphere	300.	0.00003
Shortest Visible Rays	370.	0.000037
Maximum Chemical Effect (Solar Radiation)	400.	0.00004
Violet	400.	0.00004
Blue	460.	0.000046
Green	520.	0.000052
Yellow	560.	0.000056
Orange	600.	0.00006
Red	670.	0.000067
Red (Longest Visible Waves)	760.	0.000076
Limit of Solar Spectrum	5300.	0.00053
Longest Heat Waves	314000.	0.0314
Shortest Hertz Waves	2000000.	0.2
Hertz Waves in Practical Use (Wireless)	100 to 10,000 meters	

In the selection of textile products, the color or **hue** is the first quality to catch the eye. It must be recognized, however, that the same color or hue may vary in **value,** in other words, will have a light value or a dark value. Furthermore, the value is affected by the amount of light reflected by the fabric or other substance. An ensemble which is in good harmony by daylight may not be harmonious in artificial light and vice versa. Such is the trickery of light and color. The person buying a suit or a dress should view the color under daylight as well as the artificial light in the store.

D Y E I N G

The application of design and color to fabrics is classed as one of the permanent finishing processes. As far as consumer use of the fabric is concerned, however, the permanence is relative and not absolute. The serviceability of the dye depends upon the type of dyestuff, its method of application, and the service to which the fabric is put in use. Although its effect is a physical phenomenon, the dyestuff is a chemical compound, and its application and performance in use are generally chemical processes.

the dyestuff

Fabrics may be colored red, blue, green, yellow, or any combination of colors by impregnating the fibers or by covering the surface of yarns or fabrics with a coloring substance known as a **dyestuff.**

Throughout the entire history of fabrics until 1856, when William Henry Perkin discovered the first artificial dyestuff, fabrics were colored by dyes obtained from the products of nature. Many of these natural materials are now synthesized in chemical plants and laboratories; others have been abandoned as synthetic dyestuffs of superior quality have been perfected to produce better and more permanent colors. Some idea of the variety of sources for the older coloring materials may be had from the following list of common natural dyestuffs. These materials only suggest the enormous amount of experimental work which early dyers of cloth must have done to collect, try, perfect, and prepare these coloring materials.

The principal colors used by the textile workers of ancient China and India were **Indigo,** a blue dye obtained from a plant, and **Kermas,** a red color obtained from the dried bodies of a species of insects.

An ancient Egyptian papyrus termed *Papyrus Graccus Hornkensis* preserved in the museum in Upsala, Sweden, gives seventy recipes dealing with the cleaning, mordanting, and dyeing of wool. (A **mordant** is a chemical pre-treatment sometimes needed to improve the dyeability of a fabric.) In it are mentioned the following dyestuffs known to the ancient Egyptians: Alkanova (red), Safflower (yellow and red), Kermas (red), Madder (red), and Woad (blue). The methods of applying the color were basically the same as those used in dyeing today.[1]

The dye, *Purple of Tyre,* is still associated with the ruling families of the Roman Empire. This dyestuff was probably obtained from a sea snail. Even earlier in history Alexander the Great was said by Pliny to have brought from India to Greece the art of dyeing such colors as green, black, and yellow. The dyers of Oriental rugs, as late as a century ago, kept secret the methods of dyeing certain colors. Families were skilled in making certain sun-fast and water-fast dyes, the secret of which was handed down from father to son.

The peoples living around the Mediterranean Sea became skilled in the art of dyeing with the colors known to them. Secrets of formulation and methods of dyeing were jealously guarded. The discovery of America brought to Euro-

[1] W. Von Bergen and H. R. Mauersberger, *American Wool Handbook* (New York: John Wiley & Sons, Inc., 1938), p. 573.

pean dyers many new dyestuffs, principally dyewoods. Among them were **Logwood, Redwood, Quercitron,** and **Fustic.** The most important of these and the only one still used commercially is Logwood. The dye is extracted from the blood-red wood of the Campeach, a large tree native to the West Indies and Central America. The Spaniards found a valuable scarlet red dye in Mexico. This was **Cochineal,** a dyestuff extracted from the insect of the same name and which replaced Kermas red. Most of these "new world" dyestuffs were used by the Inca and Aztec Indians in South and Central America for dyeing wool and cotton.

FIRST SYNTHETIC COLOR   The art and science of dyeing were completely changed by Perkin. Perkin was working with a coal tar derivative, aniline, and discovered a dyestuff which he called **Mauve,** a word derived from the French name for the Mallow flower. The immediate result of this discovery was a determined study of other derivatives of coal tar and their allied compounds and the manufacture of a vast variety of dyestuffs from these materials. Prior to and during World War I, Germany was pre-eminent in the dye production industry. Many German patents became available to the American chemical industry when they were seized by the Alien Property Custodian and released to the public. This fact and the great growth of industrial chemistry in the United States since 1920 continued to raise this country to the top in the tremendously profitable dyestuff industry. Although new and improved coloring materials are constantly being discovered and developed, most of the attention of the great manufacturers of dyestuffs during recent years has been devoted to the standardization of dyeing procedure and to the fastness properties of the color produced in the cloth. New challenges to the ingenuity of the dyers and the producers of chemical colorants came about with the synthetic fiber industry, especially since the middle '40's. Each new fiber type has required new dyes and new methods of application.

Approximately 4000 dyes are produced. According to their method of application, all dyestuffs are classified in the following eight groups:

Acid dyes	Direct colors
Basic dyes	Sulfur dyes
Mordant and chrome colors	Naphthol or azoic dyes
Vat dyes	Developed dyes

The acid dyes have as their chief chemical constituent an acid group, and basic dyes have salts of color bases or alkaline groups. Both the acid and basic dyestuffs can be applied directly to animal fibers. In order to color vegetable fibers with these dyestuffs, it is necessary to give the fibers a preliminary treatment with a **mordant,** a chemical which has an affinity both for the dye and the fiber. Thus, for a basic dyestuff an acid mordant is used, and vice versa. Despite the fact that dyestuffs are chemical compounds just as are the textile fibers themselves, the exact mechanisms of dyeing are not clearly understood by scientists. There is some evidence, especially in wool dyeing, that the dyeing process is chemical in nature. On the other hand the physical theory of absorption has strong adherents. Synthetic fibers demonstrate still other properties.

ACID DYE   Acid dyes are commonly used for wool, especially for brightly colored sweaters, women's clothing, upholstery yarns, bathing suits, and other fabrics. The dyeing is usually done in a solution of a neutral sodium salt and an acid to set the dye.

MORDANT AND CHROME COLORS   These colors are used most frequently for wool, principally for men's clothing. The colors are more fast but less brilliant than the acid dyestuffs. In addition to the salt and acid bath, a metal salt is required to fix the dye in the wool to produce the desired shade. This metal salt, or *mordant,* is commonly a chrome salt, hence the name *chrome color* for that particular group. The theory of this method of dyeing is that the acid combines with the wool, making it more absorptive to the dyestuff. The metal salt is then added and converts the acid-wool color compound into an insoluble metal *color lake* which is firmly and chemically united with the fiber.

VAT DYES   Many fabrics are labeled "vat dyed," and to most customers this connotes the highest quality in serviceability.

This class of dyestuffs can be used for wool, cotton, rayon, linen, and silk. Vat colors can produce the greatest color fastness to sunlight, washing, and other service conditions. They are especially useful for shirtings, uniforms, draperies, and other fabrics which must be both durable and color fast. The most famous vat dye is indigo, which is widely used for men's work clothes and for blue denims for boys' wear.

Vat dyes are insoluble in water. They are coloring substances which can be reduced to alkali soluble leuco compounds and are fixed in this form into the fiber. Exposure to the air oxidizes these leuco compounds into an insoluble color compound, thus producing color in the cloth. The strongly alkaline bath required for this process must be diluted in dyeing silk to prevent chemical damage to the fiber. The principal difficulty in vat dyeing, and a very important one, is that of matching colors. The dyer has no idea what the shade is going to be until the color is actually developed when the cloth is dried. This is much different from exposing a fabric to a dye bath until the desired shade is developed.

BASIC DYES   Basic dyes may be used to color cotton, silk, or wool. They are seldom used on wool, however, because of the superior fastness of acid dyes. This class of dyestuffs was the first to be discovered, and even now they are often referred to as **aniline** colors because the first few were derived from that compound by Perkin and his immediate followers. Silk and wool may be dyed directly with these dyestuffs, but it is necessary to fix the colors in cotton by means of a mordant. It is customary to dye cotton with some other type of coloring material and then to *top* or brighten the color by means of an application of a basic dyestuff. A brilliant color is given silk fabrics with these colors. Basic dyes have rather poor color fastness to washing, sunlight, and perspiration. **Naphthol** dyes, a modification of basic dyestuffs, are used almost exclusively in coloring and printing cotton piece goods.

DIRECT COLORS   Although these dyestuffs may be used for silk and wool, they are generally regarded as cotton dyes. No mordant is required for coloring cotton by means of these dyes, but the colors are generally dull and require brightening. They may be used for wool yarns and shoddy. They give excellent fastness, especially with wool and silk.

SULFUR DYES   Sulfur dyes are used on vegetable fibers. They may be used for wool and silk with fair color fastness when a small amount of glue is used in the dye bath. Although these colors as a class have good fastness to light and washing, certain ones, such as the yellows, are fugitive. Sulfur black has good light fastness, but prolonged sun exposure weakens the fabric because of the gradual oxidation of the sulfur compound into sulfuric acid. For this reason the black stripes in awnings are usually the first places where breaks occur during use and exposure.

ACETATE DYES   Regenerated cellulose rayon can be dyed with all the classes of colors applicable to cotton. The vat dyestuffs and the direct dyes are commonly used for rayon. Cellulose acetate, being chemically different from other textile fibers, requires an entirely different group of dyestuffs. These special dyes may be derived from basic dyes, developed dyes, water soluable dyes, or a type classed as dispersed dyes. The cross-dyeing of acetate rayon mixed fabrics offers interesting effects. Arnel, cellulose tri-acetate, may be dyed with these same dyestuffs.

PIGMENT DYES   These colors are new. Pigments are very finely ground colors, insoluble in the dye bath and fiber but carried in by the liquid medium in emulsion form and fixed by a resin or other binder. They are applicable to almost any fiber and especially useful for spun or staple yarn fabrics. These colors are generally padded on the goods passing rapidly through the color box and then a series of squeeze rolls.

methods of dyeing

The actual application of color to textile fibers is performed by highly technical operations. A review of some of the more common dyeing methods follows:

1. DYEING THE RAW FIBERS   By this method the fibers are dyed before they are carded or combed. It is often utilized in coloring wool fibers, and fabrics dyed by this method are referred to as "dyed in the wool." This method gives a uniform and very fast color. The interesting mixtures found in fine suitings for men and women are formed by mixing colored fibers from different dye baths.

2. DYEING THE SLIVER   Some fibers are dyed in the slub or sliver, the smooth rope of roughly paralleled fibers formed by the carding or combing machines. The sliver may be dyed all one color, or it may be differently colored or printed at intervals. When the latter sliver is drawn and spun, interesting mixtures are produced. The method is used for wool mixtures, and good dye fastness is obtained because the absence of twist permits rapid and uniform dye absorption by all fibers.

3. DYEING THE YARN   All textile yarns may be dyed. The fabrics woven from yarn-dyed fibers are usually colored more deeply and richly than those dyed in the piece after weaving. The dye penetration is deeper in yarn-dyed cloths, and when a yarn is unravelled, it does not show a varying depth color toward the core of the yarn as is often found in piece-dyed cloth. Plaid fabrics are good examples of yarn-dyed cloths. In hosiery, the term *ingrain* is synonymous with *yarn-dyed* and the term *dipped* corresponds to *piece-dyed*.

4. DYEING THE FABRIC   When the woven fabric is dyed, it is termed *piece-dyed*. The quality of the dyeing varies more widely when done by this method than by any other. The reason is that it is more difficult to obtain deep and uniform dye penetration after the fabric has been woven. This method is economical for the manufacturer of hosiery and of woven goods, because he can store up stocks of knitted or woven goods in the gray and then have them dyed to order. This is especially advantageous to hosiery manufacturers because of the rapid changes in the color fashion for women's hosiery. Many women of fashion are wearing nylon hose of the same hue as the dress or suit being worn.

5. CROSS-DYEING   Cross-dyeing is based on the fact that the different textile fibers do not have the same affinity or speed of dye penetration. When a cloth is composed of a mixture of animal and vegetable fibers, or natural fibers and synthetics, it is possible to produce interesting effects by proper selection of the dyestuff or of the conditions in the dye bath. The dye may color one fiber and leave the other undyed or colored to a lesser degree. The fabrics known as **unions** often contain mixtures of wool and cotton. Almost any combination of fibers may be mixed in the yarns to form a blend, or the warp yarns may be one fiber and the filling another to form a combination fabric. Proper selection of dyestuff, usually the acid type, will color the wool and leave the cotton white. By other methods of dyeing, both fibers may be colored to the same depth. Similar effects can be produced in suitings composed of wool and cotton or wool and rayon fibers. Two dyestuffs of different color, such as blue and red, can be mixed in the same dye bath, and a fabric composed of regenerated cellulose rayon and cellulose acetate will be found to have the rayon fibers dyed one pure color and the acetate fibers the other. This effect is less common in the synthetics, because they are more difficult to color by conventional methods.

Cross-dyeing may be described as a resist-printing operation which depends upon the natural resistance of one of the textile fibers to the dyestuff used.

P R I N T I N G [2]

Just as the origin and history of the first natural dyestuff extracted from bark, berries, fruits, roots, insects, and other products of nature available to early man are lost to us, so too is the development of the art of combining colors and using two or more dyestuffs to produce figures and designs in fabrics or garments. No actual specimens of these earliest attempts at printing exist today, for the organic elements of nature have gone back to the soil through the actions of mildew, bacterial decomposition, sun rotting, and gradual solution in water. The archeologists in their explorations of the tombs of royal personages in Egypt and other countries of the Near East have disclosed in the details of paintings and statuary that designed fabrics were worn, at least by the royalty of early Egypt, in about 2100 B.C. The writings of Indian scholars record that the technique of resistant dyeing and printing was known to textile artists of India many years before the birth of Christ. It is known, too, that resist printing had been practiced by other civilizations around the Caspian Sea as early as 600 B.C. In the other parts of the world, such as Indonesia and Peru, this method of textile coloring appears to have been known at an early date. Now, about 4000 years later, some of the early methods of printing have changed little; some of those used today have been reported in the hoistories of many nations whose textile industries achieved fame and whose products were carried all over the known world.

Basically, printing is simply the controlled application of color to selected areas or figures on the cloth. It is obvious that dyestuff in liquid form is too fluid and uncontrollable for such precise figure coloring; thus most printing employs the dyestuff in the form of a paste which will color the fabric area to which it is exposed but will not flow beyond the prescribed borders.

block printing

Block printing may well have been one of the very first attempts to produce figures on fabric, and it is still one of the most popular handcraft methods of producing design on fabric and on paper. Its origin as an art medium for textiles is lost in antiquity. There are records of this method having been used by the Chinese and by the Egyptians long before 1000 B.C. The cutting away of the surface of a block of hard wood to leave raised areas or lines to be reproduced as a print on the fabric or paper is still in use. Indeed, many of the other printing methods, including high-speed roller printing, are simply more sophisticated and faster developments of this early principle. The colored paste or stiffened ink is smeared on the face of the block, which is then applied firmly to the surface of the cloth or paper on which the colored design is thus reproduced. Other blocks with different patterns of surfaces and lines related to the

---

[2] Much of this section drew upon *Encyclopedia of Textiles* (Englewood Cliffs, N.J.: Prentice-Hall, 1960), Chapters on Printing.

picture desired may be used to apply other colors within the picture area. One to three colors are generally the limit for most of these block prints. However, some, even of ancient origin, have been found which are extremely intricate both in number of colors and in fineness of detail.

stenciling

Differing slightly from this method of printing is the art of **stenciling.** In this method the area to be colored by any one stencil is cut out, and the paste or ink is brushed or smeared on and a complicated and elaborate figure may be developed by the use of many stencils, one for each color to be applied. The Chinese were the earliest to develop this into a fine art. It is still one of the most prized art forms in the Indian textile industry and is the basis for the modern screen printing of today.

These textile art forms were the foundation of the textile industry of the European countries by the 17th century, when they became imperiled by the importation of Indian cottons by the East India Company. These prints became so popular that the manufacturers of cottons and woolens in European countries sought government prohibition against them. In 1686 in France, the Edict of Kings not only imposed restrictions on importations and domestic manufacture but even private use of printed cotton was banned.[3] These calicos then became one of the most popular of the articles smuggled into Europe, and, of course, even then there were imitators, who in France and other European countries copied, with some success, the Indian imports. Prohibition was impossible, and by the middle of the 18th century, the printing of cottons all over Europe began the romantic age of printing. Paintings from museums were reproduced by skilled artists in printed form, known as Toiles de Jouy. These elaborate designs, developed through the printing genius of Christophe Philippe Oberkampf, became the vogue not only in textiles but also in house furnishings. Even today **Toiles-**decorated trays, boxes, and knick knacks are found in nearly every home. The direct vertical printing of one color after another requires great skill and patience, and although Oberkampf has been credited with some early experimentation in the use of roller printing, a Scotsman named Bell had earlier developed a flat-bed press for printing textiles from engraved copper plates and is credited with the first successful roller printing machine. The control of fabric movement and of roller accuracy and precision has been so improved that today as many as sixteen colors can be applied on modern machinery to produce printed fabrics at the rate of 200 yards a minute.

resist printing

Other ancient methods of dyeing employ one or another of the techniques associated with resist printing, or dyeing by which it is made difficult or im-

[3] *American Fabrics,* No. 52 (Spring, 1961), p. 58.

possible for protected areas to be exposed to the dye bath, in this case a liquid. The Far East employed a tie-and-dye method, called **Plangi.** Certain portions of the cloth were covered with wax, or little, puffs or balls were tied with waxed threads and plunged into the dyestuff. The unprotected part of the textile was colored; the waxed portion remained white, and, in the case of the little tied-dyed puffs, white rings appeared on the surface of the cloth where the wax threads had lain. Rib-and-stitch figures could be produced also by means of sewing or stitching with a wax thread prior to dyeing.

One form of the wax resist method, known as **Batik,** is still used by the native craftsmen of Java and to some extent some other countries of the Indies. The design is covered with wax, after which the fabric is dipped in dye to provide the background with color. The wax is then removed by boiling water or by means of a suitable solvent, and the design portion appears white. In the case of a multiple-color Batik—some have been known to contain as many as 16 different colors—the wax is carefully removed bit by bit to expose those portions of the design which are to be colored by the next dye bath.

Another form of resist printing, so-called warp prints, is referred to by the Japanese as **Kasuri** and by the Indonesians as **Ikt,** and is a predecessor of today's modern space dyeing with warp yarns. In the case of this old process, warp yarns are tie-dyed before being placed on the loom. Sometimes the filling yarns are likewise tie-dyed. When the cloth is woven, colored areas appear at fixed intervals. Modern adaptation of this mode of printing is accomplished by either the drum method or the roller method. The drum method is sometimes used for printing the pile warp yarns in velvet tapestry rugs. The ends are wound onto a huge drum and printed with all the colors to be used in the pattern. The drum has numerous squares or guides for registering the color areas, so that when the yarn is fed into the loom, the design appears as it is woven. The roller method prints the yarns after they have been wound on the warp beam and in the same way as woven cloth is printed. The designs are elaborate but rather subtle in effect, because they are broken up with the unprinted filling yarns as the cloth is woven.

discharge printing

The reverse of these resist-printing methods is the modern **discharge print.** In this method, the fabric is dyed throughout with the chosen background color. It is then printed with a bleach which removes the color to form the white pattern. Generally, these fabrics are found to be white on a ground color, but by means of roller printing with varying strengths of bleach, it is possible to get two or more intermediate shades between the ground color and the white. Careful washing is required to remove all of the reacting chemical, and, in general, when these fabrics begin to fail in use, after many washings or exposure to the sun, it is the bleached portion which first breaks, due to its reduced strength as a result of exposure to the chemical solutions.

madder printing

Madder printing, associated with the beautiful British tie silks, is the modern application of the Mordant printing technique. Today's method using mordant colors was known as early as the 5th century B.C.; the writings of Pliny, the Greek historian, describe the printed garments worn by inhabitants of the Caucasus Mountains. The Egyptians used a somewhat similar process a short time later. So-called Indian chintzes were forerunners of this type of printing operation. The technique involved the covering of the cloth with mordants or binders rather than with a color, using different mordants which would react differently with the same dye bath; varying colors could be produced in the same bath with a single dye-bath exposure. This could be combined with the wax resist process or with tie-and-dye for more intricate results. The British tie silks originally used madder as a dyestuff, but it has since been replaced by a synthetic and by other of the coal tar dyes. Basically, the fabric is still printed first with the mordant and then those different colors from the single dye bath. To fix the colors after dyeing, the most effective manner is still the primitive one of passing the fabric through a solution of cow dung.

screen printing

Screen printing today is still done by hand for many fabric applications. It can also be done automatically. It is essentially a rather slow and tedious method, but it has the virtue of a true handicraft appearance, and since it requires far less equipment than any roller method, it lends itself to experimental, creative design; indeed, exclusive designs developed by recognized artists and creators of textile design provide interior decorators and manufacturers of high-priced furniture with their exclusive patterns.

The screen today is generally of nylon or sometimes of silk or a fine metal. This fine fabric screen is then covered with a film. A frame is laid on the fabric; the color may be sprayed, painted, or squeegeed on. A separate screen is required for each color to be applied to the pattern. Texstyle Creators of New York are using a special grade of silk screening stretched over wooden frames for their silk screening operation. The silk is given two coats of a gelatin compound containing ammonium bichromate. The designs are painted on translucent acetate sheets, one design sheet for each color in the print. The sheets are placed on a glass-topped frame, and each screen to be developed is laid over it in succession. Under the frame is a bank of fluorescent lights. When turned on, these lights insolubilize the gelatin bichromate mixture. After sufficient exposure, the screen is taken up and washed in water. Areas protected from light dissolve out. The screen is ready to use after it is dried and the printing color passes through the open areas developed by the light and colors the fabric stretched below the silk screen.

Thus, automatic screen printing is possible with electronic control over both the pattern selection and the dye to be used. Today two men can do the work formerly done by at least 15. Generally, the machine has eight frames, each of which may apply a different color, using different screens. As the machine is running, all the frames operate simultaneously, the cloth simply moving forward one frame width between each application of color. It is, therefore, equivalent to printing eight colors at one time. When the fabric leaves the last frame on the printing table, it goes into a drying box in which the paste colors are dried in place.

roller printing

Roller printing is the process by which most cloth is printed today. Essentially, it is the same process by which a newspaper is printed. The original design is etched into copper rollers, which are then covered with dye; as the fabric and roller come in contact, the design is transferred to the fabric. Many intermediate steps requiring great accuracy are involved.

1. MAKING THE REPEAT   The original artist's drawing is made into a repeat, so that it can be reproduced over and over again as the roller and fabric come in contact.

2. PHOTOGRAPHING THE DESIGN   Every design element representing a single color is photographed onto a sensitized copper plate, each color requiring a different copper plate.

3. PAINTING THE PLATE   The artist paints in the pattern from the traced outline of the original drawing, transferring it to the roller using a pantograph. The engraver traces the lines of the design as they appear on the flat plate, but they are automatically transferred to the curved surface of the roller.

4. PAINTING THE ROLLER   A chemical resistant is painted over the color areas of the design on the roller preliminary to etching the roller. Wherever the chemical resistant has been applied, the lines are protected. Everywhere else, acid etches the copper surface. The small hollows and indentations are not reached by the dye when the roller is locked in the printing machine; these indentations appear uncolored as the fabric leaves its contact with the roller.

5. PHOTO ENGRAVING   Rollers may also be engraved by a photochemical process which reproduces the detail and shading of the photograph. This type of roller printing is popular in decorative fabrics and in wallpaper.

6. HAND ENGRAVING   A skilled artist duplicates the design or pattern, and it is reproduced on copper plates, each etched to imprint one color to the fabric. An engraver goes over each copper plate with a fine needle or awl to remove any loose fragments of copper which might mar the clarity or perfection of the design.

Each roller, with its copper plate securely locked in place, passes through its own color tank or bath from which it picks up the dyestuff. Before the fabric comes in contact with it, a doctor knife or squeegee scrapes away the excess dye from the roller, so that a clear, even print is made. The cloth, therefore, passes in regular turn through all of the rolls and emerges with the completed print clearly transferred. Machines can print up to sixteen colors at one time and at the rate of 150 to 200 yards a minute. The colors are then set by heat for permanence against bleeding or fading when washed or exposed to sunlight.

In any printing operation, the value of the final product lies in the accuracy and perfection of the work and the avoidance of overprinting with shady edges or of white breaks where exact placement of the block or roll was faulty.

7. AIR BRUSHING   A mechanized air brush, guided by hand, may be used to blow the dye into the cloth. This method produces a blended, shadowy pattern and is used principally on smooth-surfaced silks, such as brocades, taffetas, and Jacquard designs.

8 DUPLEX PRINTING   This is simply a double printing on both sides of the cloth so that the pattern outline will coincide on each face of the fabric to simulate a woven pattern. The cloth is first printed on one side and then on the other. It is a necessary operation if the cloth is intended to be reversible.

QUESTIONS

1   What is color?

2   Define white! Black!

3   What is a dyestuff?

4   List six products of nature which once served as dyes.

5   Who was Perkin?

6   How do acid dyes perform? For what fibers are they used?

7   How do basic dyes perform? For what fibers are they used?

8   How do pigment colors differ from dyes?

9   What is printing?

10   Name six methods of printing.

11   Compare screen and roller printing.

12   How do printed designs differ from those which are woven in?

finishing fabrics

The customer who is accustomed to examine critically those lustrous, vivid rayon prints does not know how unappealing the fibers and fabrics were before they were subjected to various finishing processes. Likewise, the sheer hose, beautiful worsted suitings, sheer organdies, lustrous table linens, and even the glamorous fur coats were not nearly so attractive originally. They have all been **finished.** The actual finishing of fabrics is performed by an industry of middle-men known as **converters,** who take the goods from the mills and give them the specific finishing processes required and thus enhance their beauty and sale-ability.

The goods as they leave the mills in which they were woven are said to be **in the grey (or greige).** This term does not refer to the color of the fabric.

There are two types of finish applied to fabrics. One is to supply the esthetic appeals of appearance, drape, handle, and texture—the features attracting customer attention. The other group of finishes includes the functional or special service features affecting the consumer.

ESTHETIC   FINISHES

.1   To impart luster or brightness to the cloth. The beauty of table linen is greatly enhanced by imparting additional luster through finishing.

2   To improve the feel or **handle** of a cloth by increasing its weight or

improving its draping quality. Silk fabrics may be **weighted** to make them heavy and firm.

3 Finishing operations are employed to stiffen sheer organdies; other fabrics, such as linen suitings, are given a finishing process to keep them smooth.

No fabric is given only one finishing process. The sales appeal of a fabric depends to a great degree upon the way it has been processed after weaving. Bleaching and dyeing are properly included in any listing of permanent finishes. Each textile fiber undergoes a series of finishing processes which are characteristic of the cloths made from it.

cotton

Cotton fabrics are given the following finishing processes, usually in the order of their listing.

BRUSHING   If a cotton cloth such as a percale or a gingham is to have a smooth surface, it must be brushed and sheared. The cloth is rubbed by means of revolving brushes which raise the fuzz and loose ends in the yarns so that they can be **sheared** off by knives.

GASSING   The cloth is quickly passed through gas flames or over very hot copper plates to burn off any remaining fuzz. These two processes are known as **gassing** and **singeing**. The cloth is prevented from burning by passing it through a water bath to quench any smoldering flames in the fibers. The singeing may be on only one or on both sides, depending upon the degree of fabric smoothness desired.

BLEACHING   If the cotton yarns have not been **bleached,** the cloth as it comes from the loom will be dull and will be a grayish-brown or yellow color.

Cottons must be boiled in large tanks called kiers to remove the natural gum from the fibers. Cheap cloths, such as some muslins and those for bags, are sometimes sold as unbleached. If the cotton fabric is to be bleached in the piece after weaving, it is commonly prepared for kier boiling and for bleaching by carefully controlled baths with one or more chemicals including alkali, sulfites, chlorine, etc. This cycle may be repeated to make the fabric more receptive to the bleaching with Javelle water or bleaching powder. This same chemical, a hypochlorite solution, is commonly known in homes as chlorine bleach. Excessive bleaching and careless pre-treating may seriously weaken the fabric.

MERCERIZATION   Like bleaching, the **mercerizing** process can be performed either in the yarn stage or on the woven fabric.

This process is named after its discoverer, John Mercer. Briefly, the treatment of the cotton fiber by caustic soda solution causes it to lose its natural twist and increases both its luster and its tensile strength. Later, H. Lowe, an English chemist, modified and controlled the process by keeping the cloth under tension in the caustic solution. A wide variety of fine cotton cloths are now mercerized to enhance their luster until it actually rivals that of silk.

The longer staple cotton fibers are used in the yarns of fabrics which are to be mercerized. Because the visible effect of mercerization is a lustrous and smooth surface, it is important that the preliminary treatments should insure as smooth a surface as possible before the cloth is mercerized. These processes are careful combing of the fibers composing the yarn, singeing, and bleaching. The fabric is then mercerized.

DYEING AND PRINTING   The coloring of cotton cloth is discussed in more detail in Chapter 8. These coloring operations are an integral part of the finishing and may be done on both bleached and mercerized cloths. The latter have better absorptive power and take the dye more readily. If the cloth is to be **dyed** all one color, it is not necessary to bleach it before immersing it in the dye-bath. If one or more colors are to be **printed** onto a cloth, it is necessary to singe, bleach, and perhaps mercerize it. More permanent dyeing is accomplished by dyeing the yarn before weaving, but this yarn-dyeing is not classed as a finishing process, for that term, as it is commonly used, applies only to processing the cloth.

SIZING   **Sizing** or **dressing** is an operation to increase the weight or to improve the texture of a cloth. The stiffening of organdy, mosquito netting, and other sheer cloths, and the crispness of dimity and marquisette are typical results of sizing. The bleached, mercerized, or dyed cloth is passed between two rollers, one of which dips into the sizing mixture. Sizing may be of vegetable origin, such as a type of starch or flour paste; it may be inorganic, such as clay, magnesium chloride, or magnesium sulfate; it may be of animal origin, such as mucilage; or resin finishes may be applied. The stiffness imparted by the sizing is often modified and given a better handle by the use of oils, greases, waxes, or resins. The use of organic sizing agents makes cotton more susceptible to the attack of mildew, and an antiseptic solution such as formaldehyde or zinc chloride may be added to the sizing to prevent damage caused by mildew.

Excessive sizing can be recognized by rubbing two layers of the cloth together and noting whether small particles flake off. Scraping the fabric with a knife or one's fingernail or tearing it will also produce these fine flakes of sizing material. A dyed cloth which has been excessively sized may show **crocking,** or rubbing off of the dye when it is rubbed against a white cloth.

NAPPING   Cotton fabrics may be given a fuzzy surface closely resembling that of wool. This raised surface or **nap** is imparted mechanically by rubbing the woven fabric with stiff brushes or bristles mounted on cylindrical rolls, much as blankets are napped. For greatest ease in napping, it is necessary that the fabric be a rather open weave of loosely twisted yarns made from short staple cotton fibers. Typical napped fabrics are outing flannels, cotton blankets, and flannelette and similar materials. The nap differs from the raised pile surface formed by weaving.

GLAZING   A stiff, lustrous surface is given cotton by means of **glazing.** The stiff surface is achieved by means of starches, glues, shellacs, and resins which are given a high polish by smooth, hot rollers called calenders. Chintzes for upholstery and draperies are given this glazed finish. They shed dirt readily because of the smooth surface. A great improvement has been made in recent years, and some of these glazed fabrics, such as **Everglaze,** the trademarked product of Joseph Bancroft and Sons Co., can be washed successfully.

CREPEING   The most permanent crepe texture is given to fabrics in the weaving by using alternate filling yarns of right- and left-hand twist. It is possible, however, to impart a **crepe texture** by finishing processes. Two common methods are as follows.

1. The cloth is passed between hot rollers in the presence of steam. The rollers are indented so as to produce puckered figures in the cloth corresponding to the indentations in the rollers. The method is inexpensive, but the crepe will wash and iron out.

2. Seersucker and serpentine crepe are much more permanent crepey cloths made by the caustic soda method. A caustic soda paste is rolled onto the cloth in stripes or figures. When the fabric is washed, causing the parts to which the paste is applied to shrink the rest of the cloth puckers or crepes. Sometimes the reverse treatment is used: the cloth is given a caustic resistant paste finish in all spots and areas where crepeing is not desired, the whole cloth is then immersed in the caustic solution, it shrinks wherever the cloth is unprotected, and the rest puckers or crepes. Crinkled bed spreads are made in this manner.

BEETLING AND EMBOSSING   Heavy cottons can be given a linen-like finish by **beetling.** This finishing process is applied after the cloth has been bleached and printed. The cloth is slowly passed between rollers which subject the fabric to blows from tiny hammers. The cloth becomes compact and leathery because of the flattening of the yarns. Genuine linen fabrics are usually beetled also.

Embossing is the process of imprinting or engraving a pattern onto cheap cotton tablecloths to simulate the figures woven by the Jacquard loom. The designs are engraved on copper rolls, and the combination of steam and high temperature imprints the design on the cloth. The finish is not permanent to laundering.

CALENDERING   The final finish given to the surface of cotton cloth is that of **calendering,** or polishing. The cloth is passed between hot, smooth rollers to iron out wrinkles and to impart a sheen to the cloth. The luster is increased by sizing it before calendering or by several passages through the rollers. The principle of calendering is duplicated in the home when smooth cottons are ironed.

TENTERING   This is a mechanical process to even or straighten the width of the cloth. All fabrics have to be tentered in order to straighten the selvage. The tentering frame resembles a horizontal runway, holds the selvages, and pulls sideways jerkily. The method of pulling is to advance alternately each side a few inches by means of a chain drive and to stop it while the other side is advanced. This gives the cloth a series of slanting jerks over its entire length.

A source of steam is located under the frame so that the cloth is easily shrunk or stretched until the edges are straight, and the cloth is dried in this condition.

IMITATIVE FINISHES   The techniques of cotton finishing have brought about a wider field of usefulness for cotton. It is becoming a more important style fiber, since finishing methods have increased the luster, softness, and draping quality of these fabrics. Wash-and-wear finishes (page 111) enable cotton to resist wrinkles to a degree comparable with synthetics. The low cost of cotton fabrics has also contributed to an increased popularity for this fiber during recent years.

Cotton can be made to resemble linen, wool, and even silk. The use of nubby yarns produces a fabric closely resembling linen. Napping gives a wool-like texture to cotton cloths. Mercerizing gives a silky sheen to cotton fabrics.

finishing of linen

BLEACHING   The natural color of the linen or flax fiber is a tan or grayish tan. It is necessary, therefore, to bleach linen for fine white fabrics.

The methods of bleaching flax have been summarized in Chapter 11, but a brief summary of the processes may be given as follows:

Grass Bleaching: This method is still common in Ireland, and it is believed by many that the natural action of moisture, air, and sunlight produces the loveliest silvery color and strongest fiber.

Chemical Bleaching: The use of chemicals is becoming increasingly common in the bleaching of linen and has largely replaced the secret "father to son" methods of the crofters, or bleachers of Ireland. The grass method may require weeks or months to effect full bleaching, whereas by the modern method it is a matter of hours because the fiber is made more receptive to bleaching. The principal steps are as follows:

1   Boiling with a lime solution to remove wax and other impurities.
2   Rinsing and treating with dilute hydrochloric acid.
3   Rinsing and boiling in a caustic soda solution.
4   Bleaching with a chlorine-containing powder or by the grass method.

Chemically bleached linens are a dead white and lack the silvery luster of grass-bleached fibers. Over-bleaching weakens the flax fiber, and full-bleached linens are weaker than quarter-, half-, or three-quarter-bleached fabrics. It is advantageous to purchase linen towels and other durable linens only partially bleached. As these fabrics are repeatedly laundered, they will become whiter, and their initial strength is considerably greater than that of a full-bleached cloth.

Dyeing and Printing: Natural linens are printed without bleaching, but if a white background is desired, the linen must be bleached before printing. Solid-color linens are usually vat-dyed either in the yarn or the piece. Linen shows relatively poor dye absorption, and it is difficult to obtain a piece-dyed fabric the yarns of which have a uniform depth of color throughout.

OTHER PROCESSES   **Beetling** has been described in the section on cotton finishing. The uneven diameters of linen yarns and the usual irregularity of the weave cause openings in the fabric structure. The beetling to a firm, leathery texture makes the fabric weave compact and dense, desirable features in linens, especially table damasks.

Linens are **calendered** to flatten the yarns and to impart a more glossy finish. The firmness, glossy beauty, and characteristics drape of fine table linen is unmistakeable. A linen expert can instantly detect on a motion picture screen whether the banquet cloth used in a regal setting is linen or cotton.

Like all fabrics, linens must be **tentered** to straighten the selvages.

Dress linens and linen suitings are given a crease-resistant finish similar to that of cotton cloth in order to make them neater and less likely to wrinkle.

The natural characteristics of linen make mercerizing, singeing, and sizing unnecessary. The flax fiber is long and non-elastic; hence linens are never napped. These same properties make the spinning difficult enough so that linen is not given any crepe effects.

finishing of rayon

The rayon fabric produced by the weaver is almost ready for the consumer. The most common practice is to dye the rayon yarn; as a matter of fact, rayon is rarely bleached in the piece. Peroxides and chlorine bleaches may be used if the fabric is to be white or dyed a delicate shade. Rayon may be piece-dyed or printed, much as is the practice for cottons. Some rayons are filled by means of resins in order to make them resistant to crushing or to give them an improved handle and greater weight. Rayons which have been subjected to an excessive and deceptive weighting will often lose much of this filler when washed.

All rayons are **tentered.** Those which are to have a smooth, lustrous surface are **calendered**. A distinction is made between spun rayons and continuous filament rayons. The spun rayons are often **napped,** are usually given a **wrinkle-resistant** finish, and may be finished with oils, waxes, or resins to give an improved softness and handle. Rayon velvets are tentered and steamed.

EMBOSSING   A rayon fabric may be given a figured surface resembling a woven design by **embossing.** The cloth is passed between steam-heated rollers which imprint the roller design on the cloth. This finish is not permanent, nor can the fabric be sponged off unless it has been given a water-resistant finish. A somewhat similar finish may be given to acetate or silk, called **moiréing.** A cloth with a filling-wise rib weave is passed in double thickness between rollers, one of which may be engraved in wavy lines. This moiré figure is a watered effect. Only in the case of cellulose acetate can the moiré finish or the embossed figures be washed. In the acetate fabric, the lustrous, watered lines have been made permanent by the combination of moderate heat and great pressure.

PRE-SHRINKING   Rayons are generally pre-shrunk by a chemical impregnation. The fibers are swelled by a caustic solution, after which the chemical or resin is more easily introduced into the fiber. An important rayon pre-shrinking process is **Avcoset**.

finishing of silk

BLEACHING   Sometimes silk may be woven with yarns from which the **sericin** or gum has not been removed. Such silks must be boiled in soap solution to de-gum them. Wild silks need not be bleached if the cloth is to be sold as having the "natural" color. These silks are bleached if they are to be dyed, and the cultivated silks are bleached if they are to be printed of if they are to be pure white. The boiling-off of the gum often removes enough of the natural yellow color of the silk fiber. For more complete bleaching, hydrogen peroxide or sodium peroxide may be used, or the fabric may be exposed to the fumes of burning sulfur.

PRINTING AND DYEING   The dyeing characteristics of silk are given in detail in Chapter 14. Silk fabrics may be printed, yarn-dyed, or dyed in the piece. Delicate silk fabrics, such as georgettes, satins, and velvets, are hooked by their selvages onto hollow reels or rollers, allowing about an inch between successive folds of the fabric, and immersed in the dye bath. Crepes and other more durable cloths may be passed through the dye bath on smooth metal rolls. After dyeing, the cloth is rinsed and sprayed with water and may be given a mild acid bath in a dilute organic acid, such as aceticacid, to increase the color brilliance.

STRETCHING   Smooth-textured cloths may be stretched by passing them over rollers revolving at increasing speeds as the fabric passes from one to another. This tends to smooth the fabric and to increase its luster.

CALENDERING   As in the other fabrics previously discussed, calendering, or passing the fabric through heated, polished rollers, imparts a luster to silk cloths. No fabrics are more greatly improved by calendering than are satins. Satins may be given a very smooth and lustrous surface by using hydraulic presses in addition to the rollers.

OTHER FINISHES   All silks must be tentered, and they may be embossed or moiréed. The weighting of silk has been discussed in Chapter 14. This weighting is primarily for the purpose of replacing the sericin removed in de-gumming, but it may also be used to give a flimsy silk cloth a false appearance and feel suggesting strength and durability. The weight and compactness of a loosely woven silk can also be increased by sizing with gums, waxes, resins, glue, mucilage, or a variety of other organic materials. The formation of water spots may betray the presence of sizing if a water-soluble compound or mixture has been used.

finishing of wool

The finishing of wool goods depends on whether it is a worsted or a woolen. The distinction between the two has been described in Chapter 12. Worsteds

Fig. 9-1 Inspection and Repair of Wool Fabric Defects: Final inspection perches on which women inspectors look for possible defects in the woven woolen cloth. These include shadings, knots, uneven yarns, dye spots, etc., many of which are repaired at this point. *(Courtesy of The Wool Bureau, Inc.)*

are practically finished when they leave the loom, and their beauty depends to a great degree upon the clearness and compactness of the weave. The surface is firm and flat (except for unfinished worsteds). The beauty of woolens, on the other hand, lies in their softness and handle.

finishing woolens

The goods taken from the loom are spread out over a horizontal beam or rack and examined for defects in the yarns or the weave. Skilled needle workers repair most of these faults. This is called **perching. Mending, burling, specking, and crabbing** (holding the cloth under tension in alternate hot and cold baths to set the weave) are special wool finishes. Worsted and other clear-finished cloths are singed.

DYEING   Wool is usually bleached prior to weaving. The process may take place either in the fiber or the skein stage. It is often dyed in one or the other of these stages, or the woven fabric may be dyed. Only in the latter case is dyeing classed as a finishing process. Wool takes dye readily either in the fiber, yarn, or piece.

FELTING, or FULLING   In order to make a woolen cloth more compact and **thick,** the cloth is processed by a method variously known as **felting, milling,** or **fulling.** The woolen is immersed in a warm soap suds and is pounded and twisted in order to cause it to shrink a desired amount. Wool owes its characteristics felting behavior to the structure of the fiber (Chapter 12).

NAPPING   Many woolen coatings and suitings are **napped** in the same way as blankets are finished to give them their fuzzy surface. The fulled fabric is rinsed, dried, and tentered, after which it is passed over cylinders, the surface of which is covered with fine wire bristles. These bristles pull and raise individual wool fibers from the yarns to give a fuzzy surface. Natural plant burrs, especially the teasel, are often used to produce a softer nap and with less physical damage to the yarns. Napping with teasel burrs is often referred to as **gigging**. The nap is sheared to a uniform length. Fragments of burrs may be removed by **carbonizing** or treating with sulfuric acid to char the cellulose.

OTHER FINISHES   Woolens are sheared, steamed, pressed, and sponged. Woolens may be given a false appearance of weight by **flocking** or by **loading**. It is possible to force loose wool fibers from sheared cloth or shoddy fibers into the back of a cloth by steaming. This is considered legitimate practice if it is not over-done and if it is not for the purpose of covering up defects. The loose balls of wool which sometimes form in the pockets' of men's and boys' coats are an indication of flocking. The presence of these fibers can be shown by briskly brushing the back of a cloth with a stiff brush.

Wool is naturally hygroscopic and can absorb a large amount of water without feeling wet. Loading is a practice of sharp and unscrupulous manufacturers, wherein the cloth is treated with a hygroscopic, or water-absorbing salt, such as magnesium chloride. The woolen then can be made to absorb even more than its usual water content.

finishing of worsteds

The finishing of worsteds is relatively simple and usually consists of the following steps:

1   *Inspection* and repairing of defects.
2   *Dyeing* in the piece if the yarns have not already been dyed.
3   *Fulling* is seldom performed except to soften some worsted fabrics.
4   *Napping* is rarely done to worsteds and never beyond a slight raising of the surface.
5   *Brushing,* sponging, and pressing complete the finishing.

Fig. 9-2   Carbonizing Wool Fabric: Carbonizing machine, in which cloth is placed in a sulphuric bath, then squeezed between heavy rollers and run through three baking chambers, one at 180 degrees, the next at 200 degrees, and the last at 260 degrees Fahrenheit. All remaining vegetable matter is here carbonized to black ash, then removed in a further operation. (*Courtesy of The Wool Bureau, Inc.*)

FUNCTIONAL FABRIC FINISHES

Finishes are classed as permanent or non-permanent. It is customary to class as permanent a finish which withstands the exposure for which it is intended, whether or not another type of service may damage or destroy it. **Functional** or special-use finishes should be reasonably permanent or readily renewable. Among these finishes for functional effects are the following:

TABLE 9-1 / FABRIC FINISH DATA SUMMARIZED FROM DAILY NEWS RECORD 1956 TEXTILE FINISHING SURVEY LISTING 347 FINISHES IN USE

	Fiber Name	Finishes,* Number of Making Claim	Finishes, % of Total Making Claim
Fibers to which finish may be applied	Cotton	259	74.6
	Wool	121	34.8
	Silk	101	29.0
	Linen	143	41.2
	Rayon (Viscose)	240	69.1
	Rayon (Cupra)	168	48.4
	Acetate	181	52.1
	Nylon	179	52.0
	Acrylic Yarns & Fibers	148	42.6
	Zein	78	22.4
	Vinyl-Acrylics	99	28.5
	Polyesters	144	41.5
Fabric properties affected or improved by treatment	Abrasion Resistance	104	30.0
	Absorbency	20	5.7
	Antiseptic Quality	11	3.1
	Antistatic Quality	76	21.2
	Color Fastness	91	26.2
	Crease Resistance	106	3.0
	Crispness	90	26.0
	Drapeability	145	41.5
	Dry-Cleanability	168	48.4
	Dullness	18	5.1
	Durability	184	53.0
	Flame Resistance	24	6.9
	Gas Fading Inhibited	44	12.6
	Ironing (Minimum)	58	14.0
	Light Fastness	76	22.2
	Lintless Properties	35	10.0
	Luster	32	9.1
	Mildew Resistance	53	12.3
	Moth Resistance	26	7.5
	Perspiration Resistance	92	26.1
	Renewability	22	6.3
	Scroopiness	14	4.0
	Shrinkage Resistance	122	35.1
	Slip Resistance	69	19.8
	Softness	107	30.8
	Stain Resistance	68	19.6
	Stretch and Sag Resistance	94	26.3
	Wash Fastness	135	38.6
	Water Repellency	79	22.7
	Wilt Reduction	77	22.0

* 44 finishes claimed useful for *all* fibers.

Table 9-1 summarizes claims made for 347 textile finishes in use according to the 1956 Daily News Record, Annual Textile Finishing Survey. The summary was prepared for the information of department store sales people. It simply points out the vast number of textile finishes available to converters for the processing of fabrics of all kinds and for many different specific purposes, some having to do with the esthetics and others with the usefulness of the fabric in service. Forty-four of these finishes named claimed to be useful for all fibers; most were specific and limited their claims to a class of fibers, such as cellulose base, protein base, acrylics, etc. One hundred and eighty-four, slightly over half of the total number, claimed that they improved the durability of the fabric.

It must be remembered that permanence is a relative term in spite of its sound of finality. White silks and woolens may turn yellow because of mishandling, whereas bleached linens rarely darken. An incompletely- or surface-mercerized cotton broadcloth may lose its luster in laundering long before a well-mercerized fabric will even begin to become dull. The dyed surface or printed pattern of a fabric may fade from sun exposure, washing, or the effect of perspiration. The glaze of a chintz may be lost after a single washing because the sizing which gave body to the cloth was removed in the soap suds. The napped surface of a woolen may be worn away by friction during wear.

Glazing of an otherwise washable cotton chintz is a non-permanent finish if the glaze is lost during washing. The sun-fading of the dye in a delicate fabric intended for indoor wear likewise shows a non-permanent finish as far as service is concerned. The moiré figure on a silk is not resistant to water-spotting and washing, but that on an acetate fabric can be made permanent. Sizing, filling, flocking, embossing, and crepeing are common non-permanent finishes.

Among the more important permanent functional processes are those of pre-shrinking and making fabrics water-repellent, fire-retardant, insect-resistant, mildew-resistant, and capable of retaining a crease while resisting mussing or wrinkling (wash-and-wear).

sanforizing

The **Sanforizing** process is an intricate mechanical method of reducing to a minimum the residual or service shrinkage, including both natural and relaxation shrinkage, of cotton and linen fabrics. It may also be applied to special cloths containing yarns of cotton or linen fibers mixed with rayon filaments. The Sanforizing process was the first method capable of producing a fabric having low-shrinkage guarantee: a one per cent residual shrinkage under the Federal Trade Commission ruling of 1938 for "Shrinkage of Woven Cotton Yard Goods and Articles Made Therefrom." This method will produce a fabric which can be guaranteed to have a residual shrinkage not to exceed one per cent in either warp or filling when washed according to a standard method recommended by the United States Bureau of Standards (CS-59-44). Cotton and other fibers have a natural shrinkage on washing. The mechanical operations of making and finishing the cloth or manufacturing an article of clothing from it may introduce enough strain and stretching to cause the garment to have a length or width shrinkage in excess of the guaranteed maximum. This is generally termed **relaxation** shrinkage. Therefore, even garments made from "Sanforized" cloths must be tested for shrinkage if they are to be labeled as having been processed to reduce the residual shrinkage. A partial protection is afforded fabrics by **stabilization,** or yarn anchorage by means of synthetic resins so as to prevent yarn shifting and slipping. Fabrics which have been pre-shrunk simply by dipping in water and then drying may still have a residual shrinkage of 5 to 15 per cent.

A brief description of the Sanforizing process is as follows: The fabric is washed by standard procedures under CS-59-44 to determine the shrinkage of that piece of goods. The fabric roll then passes over smooth cylinders to remove wrinkles before entering the Sanforizing or compressive shrinkage machine. As the fabric passes through, it is **tentered,** that is, pulled taut along both sides to stretch the filling yarns and to cause the warp to shrink to the extent of the washing shrinkage value. This is made possible by water spray and steam, which swell the fibers and make the yarns more pliable. This procedure is sometimes referred to as **rippling.** When the fabric emerges from the final bath in a relaxed condition, the warp yarns are still in the shrunken stage, and the fillings are relaxed by passing the fabric through a belt shrinker. The wet cloth sticks to the woolen recovery belt, the surface of which contracts when the direction of curvature is reversed. This tends to push the filling yarns lengthwise, and the fabric is dried in this contracted shape.

Rigmel finish, trademarked by the Bradford Dyeing Association, can also produce pre-shrunk cotton fabric which will not have a residual shrinkage in excess of one per cent. This, too, is a mechanical method, by which a tautly held fabric is steamed and worked into the pre-determined normal wash shrinkage limits.

The F.T.C. regulation does not apply to any woven cotton fabric or garment unless there is a claim made for pre-shrinkage or any reference to a shrinkage limit or tolerance.

There is no economy for any customer to buy cotton garments of which fit is a desired factor unless they have been pre-shrunk and by a good, dependable process. Some wash-and-wear articles of cotton may suddenly begin to shrink when the all-purpose resin has leached or dissolved out. See Wash-and-Wear, page 113.

An added advantage given by a satisfactory pre-shrinking process is that the strength of the fabric has been increased. This increase is due to the fact that after shrinking, the fabric has more yarns per square inch. The fabric has an improved handle, luster, and softness due to the action of the rollers and the steaming. It is well worth the two to eight cents increase in price over a non-Sanforized cloth.

Wool can be made non-shrinkable by the **Harriset** process, a halogenation method: by the **"Drisol"** process, depending on the action of chlorine gas from sulfurylchloride; and by a few others. Woolen and worsted cloths are also pre-shrunk by steaming or by the cold-water method (London Shrunk) to produce a residual shrinkage of less than five per cent, which is usually considered satisfactory for suitings and coatings.

Rayons may be made shrink-proof or shrinkage resistant by means of impregnation with resins or by chemical treatments, including cross-linking within the cellulose molecule. Some of the trade names associated with rayon pre-shrinkage are: **Avcoset** (American Viscose Corporation), **Sanforset** (Cluett-Peabody Company), and **Everglaze** (Joseph Bancroft and Sons Company).

water-repellent finishing

A **water-proof** fabric may be a cotton or rayon cloth which has been coated with rubber or plastic or a silk which has been filled with oil until it will permit neither water nor air to pass through it. Any less complete finish must be classed as water-repellent. Table 9-1 (page 104) shows 79 finishes, all trademarked products, available to converters to make fabrics not waterproof but water-repellent. These methods are varied and may use gums, resins, oils, waxes, metallic soaps, and other chemicals. These processes produce a fabric which will not water-spot and which will shed water if the garment is worn in a light shower. For the most part, these finishes are **non-permanent** or are classed as **renewable,** in that they are removed by washing or dry cleaning the fabric but may be re-applied by the cleaner. Children's snow suits, coats, and hats; men's coatings, suitings, and ski togs; and women's coats, hats, sportswear, and hosiery are all articles of wearing apparel which are frequently given a water-repellent finish. Common renewable process names are: **Cravenette, Neva-Wet, Aridex,** and **Impregnole.**

The permanent finish generally involves impregnation of the fabric with a thermoplastic material, sometimes by actually polymerizing the resin in the fiber by having one of the chemical constituents absorbed by the fiber and then subjecting it to the second monomer at a sufficiently high temperature to develop the resin. Under these conditions, the interstices of the cloth are not affected, and the fabric has the ability to stay comfortable, even in a warm rain. Anyone who has worn one of the impermeable fabrics or a plastic raincoat will recognize the fact that in warm weather the inside of the coat rapidly becomes almost as wet as the outside, due to condensation of body moisture on the inner surface of the impermeable sheath. Among the permanent finishes are **Zelan, Unisec, Cravenette-Superlong Life, Norane,** and **Duraset.** Many of these are both dry-cleanable and washable. However, in both the durable and the non-durable, or renewable types, one should pay particular attention to the label. If the garment is marked "washable" or "wash only," it means that the water-repellent finish was impregnated into the goods from a solvent; therefore, a dry-cleaning solvent might dissolve some of it out, thus making the fabric less water-repellent; on the other hand, washing would not remove any of the chemical. If the article is marked "dry clean only," it would indicate that the chemical treatment had been applied in a water solution; therefore, the article could not be washed without leaching out some of the material. No matter how such garments are cleaned, it is absolutely necessary that every trace of soap be removed, because the presence of soap causes the fabric to wet instantly, and it will leak badly wherever any soap particles are left.

Within recent years the silicones have come into a position of importance in water-repellent garments. One of these successful silicone processes is **Hydropruf.** Another is a **Norane** repellent further identified from its trademarked brother fiber in the durable class as **Norane Four Star** SWR.

SYL-MER   The **Syl-mer** water-repellent finish developed by the Dow-Corning Corporation is described by that company as a durable water-repellent finish for a wide variety of textile materials and textures. This indicates that there is probably a rather wide variety of **resin** and **silicone** compositions, each developed for certain kinds of textile fibers or textile effects, that is, whether the fabric is to be water-repellent and soft or water-repellent and stiff. The versatility of this finish is demonstrated by the laboratory results, which show the following features:[1]

1   Excellent washability with maintenance of water-repellent effect through numerous washings and dry cleanings.

2   Comfort is assured by the ability of the finish to leave the pores of the cloth open for free motion of air. In other words, the fabric can still breathe.

3   Spot-resistance. More specifically perfected for resistance to water-carried spots and stains, Syl-mer has some properties preventing the deep penetration of oil and grease stains as well. These stains are more easily removed with household drycleaning materials without loss of the Syl-mer finish.

4   The presence of the resin aids in the protection of the material against wrinkling in service during wearing. Thus, the need of pressing is reduced.

5   In some fabric textures, at least, this finish imparts a greater wear resistance to the material, so that its service life is extended.

6   Softness of hand is a subjective reaction to the comparison of treated versus untreated fabrics. The presence of this finish makes the fabric seem softer and more luxurious.

7   Needle cutting of the cloth is reduced, because the Syl-mer resin treatment seems to lubricate the needle as it passes through the fabric, thus reducing friction.

Special virtues seem to be associated with this finish when it is applied to fabrics having one of the modern foam laminate liners attached to it. (For details on laminated structures, see Chapter 22, page 346.) The polyurethane

---

[1] Dow-Corning Corp., *Retail Executive Guide to Fibers, Fabrics, and Finishes.*

foam laminates seem to have a slight drag on the needle during sewing. The Syl-mer finish lubrication effect counteracts this drag, thus permitting a more rapid and more even sewing without the material showing a tendency to creep or bunch together. Syl-mer finish also avoids the rapid soaking up of water by the laminate layer.

fire-retardant finishes

It is common practice to **fireproof,** or more properly make **fire-retardant,** the fabrics used in stage settings and costumes. All the fabrics used in decorating most of the new luxury steamships, hotels, and the more recent World's Fairs were made resistant to fire. The method used is to saturate the fabric with a chemical, usually an ammonium salt, which will cause the fabric to burn slowly and only while the flame remains in contact. The fabric will not support combustion, and the cloth will no longer burn when the match or torch is removed. The chemicals used should not affect the handle or draping quality of the cloth. These finishes are removed when the fabric is washed.

The Flammable Fabrics Act of 1953 (Public Law 88), is administered by the Federal Trade Commission and applies specifically to wearing apparel and fabrics intended to be worn which are so flammable as to be hazardous. These materials are not to be introduced into inter-state commerce nor moved between states. This Act applies particularly to cellulose fibers, which in napped or raised surface fabrics and in extreme sheers, such as nets, contains sufficient air to provide a fast burning when they become ignited. Fabrics of this nature and some of the more flammable synthetic fibers intended for wearing apparel must be given a satisfactorily permanent fire-retardant finish so that when tested by the standard procedure under the AATCC test methods, the speed of burning will be reduced to a safer level. The principal offending fabric at the time of passage of this Act was brushed rayon in sweaters and children's wear. Cotton chenille and cotton flannel likewise were somewhat hazardous under certain conditions. It must be noted that these same fibers in decorative fabrics and in carpets and rugs need not be given a fire-retardant finish under this Act.

anti-bacterial finishes

Sanitizing is a relatively old hygienic process making fabrics sterile and **bacteria-static,** that is, it inhibits the growth of bacteria on the fabric. The cloth is saturated with an odorless chemical which does not affect the texture of the fabric in any way. This treatment is readily removed by washing or by the action of plain water, but it is said to be relatively permanent to dry cleaning. It is applied to hotel linens, mattress covers, women's wearing apparel, shoe linings, luggage fabrics, and underwear.

Cyana-finish, perfected by the American Cyanamid Company, may be applied to textiles to reduce the possibility of odor-forming bacteria growing on the fabric. Much of the early research was carried out in Army field hospitals for the purpose of preventing the development of odor from perspiration and from fluid matter exuding from wounds. The chemical formula has been reported as having five major attributes: 1) it is effective against bacteria associated with perspiration; 2) the finish is durable and is removed by washing or dry cleaning only with extreme difficulty; 3) it is inexpensive not only in cost but in application; 4) the finish does not affect the appearance or hand of the fabric; and 5) it is not irritating to the skin. Laboratory washing tests (50 in number) have not removed this finish from cottons and rayons. The producers claim it to be durable for the life of the fabric.

warmth or comfort retention

Wide use has been made of finely dispersed aluminum powder in a resin base as a reflective surface to help maintain body comfort in both cold and hot ambient conditions. This resin base is deposited on a lining fabric, often rayon or acetate, with the metal face toward the body so as to reflect back the body's own heat rays, thus keeping the wearer warm longer. In practice, these methods, such as **Milium, Temp-resisto,** and others, fall short of full theory because the reflectant layer is very close to the body. Another problem has been that of some finishers using a cheap, open lining fabric and depending on the impermeable resin layer to serve as a wind-breaker and thus retain warmth. We have seen garments in which an inferior or low-count lining material was used, the resin layer being depended upon to hold the more sleazy, open weave together. The resin has, at times, proved to be readily dissolved and partly removed by dry cleaning, and the light metallic surface has darkened so as to defeat the entire objective of the product.

spot- and stain-resistant finishes

The synthetic fibers are sensitive to staining by oils and greases. The claim made for them that they are spot- and stain-resistant applies only to water-borne materials. It is important, therefore, that special finishes be developed to protect carpets and rugs, as well as upholstery fabrics of nylon, Acrilan, Orlon, Dacron, and other synthetics, against oily spots. **Scotchgard** is one such finish which is applicable to synthetics and to wool for all kinds of stain resistance.

mildew-resistant finishes

The natural fibers, particularly cellulose, will, if left to the effects of nature, eventually decompose or become consumed by vegetable organisms. This deterioration resulting from bacteria and mildew is more rapid in hot, moist climates than in more temperate or colder areas of the world. In order to preserve these materials under the deteriorating atmosphere, it is necessary to protect them against these organic bodies. This is generally done by means of toxic compounds which destroy the mildew or bacteria but which are not harmful to humans. Metal salts and soaps and various sizing materials may be used. Generally, these protected cellulosic fabrics become somewhat stiff and harsh in texture and may be discolored, particularly if copper soaps are used. However, most of these fabrics are protected for military or industrial use rather than for the average consumer; thus, these changes in physical appearance are not objectionable.

mothproof finishes

Wool is the only common fiber subject to damage from the larvae of clothes moths or of carpet bettles. These larvae may eat other fibers, but generally it is to get at a source of wool or other protein fiber such as hair, fur, feathers, etc. Chapter 12 on Wool deals more fully with this topic. It might be mentioned here that chemicals such as silico-fluorides are used. A number of these methods and chemicals can now be used which will make wool resistant to insects for the life of the garment. **Mitin, Dieldrin,** and **Boconize** are permanent mothproof methods for wool. One of the principal safeguards for the home is to see that wool articles when stored for a season are clean before being packed away and that no soiled garments are left in contact with them or in the same container, because moth eggs might have been laid on the soiled garments.

starchless finish

Because the traditional use of starch and other filling agents may be accompanied by a dusting of the stiffening material when rubbed or a loss of this material upon washing, a number of chemical finishing methods have been developed for the purpose of giving a crisp, starchy appearance without loss or change in texture during repeated washings. This is usually done on cottons either by acid or resin treatment. Often it is tied in with wash-and-wear if a stiffened fabric is desired. It is used mostly on sheer cottons, such as lawns, voiles, and organdies, and to a considerable extent on cotton and rayon marquisette curtain materials. A permanent finish helps hold the individual fibers close together in the yarn. Among these finishes are **Bellmanized,** the Bellman Brook Bleachery Company; **Heberlein,** the Swiss process; **Defiance;** and **Salerized.**

wash-and-wear finishes

Wash-and-wear is one of the most important textile programs of many years, and unless it is deliberately traded down by some of the more unethical producers or those with somewhat less than the usual regard for the welfare of the consumer, the promotion should be a permanent one. Actually, the terminology should be **"minimum care fabrics,"** and articles for **"wash-and-wear"** taken literally would imply that absolutely no iron touch-up was required in order to retain the smoothness of the garment and to make it completely presentable. A wash-and-wear or minimum care garment, therefore, is one which resists the wrinkles and mussiness imposed during wearing, retains creases, pleats, and other ironed-in formations, and, after washing, shows a minimum evidence of wash wrinkling to the extent that it can almost be worn immediately after drying without pressing. Generally, however, collars, cuffs, and front plackets, indeed, most double thickness areas benefit from a touch-up from the iron, but it is not necessary to iron the entire garment, thus saving considerable time and energy on the part of the housewife. The public tends to forget that equally significant is the fact that these garments stay fresh-looking longer and for many more hours wear than do the average articles of wearing apparel. Thus, it is the wearability more than the washability which should be normally stressed.

A garment may achieve this characteristic by one of two ways. It may be a quality or property of the fiber itself, as in the case of most of our thermoplastic synthetic fibers. On the other hand, it may be a property added to the fabric by means of blending or by chemical treatment.

Wash-and-wear as we know it today came out of an economic battle between fibers. When the synthetics came on the market and began to appear in men's suits, women's blouses and dresses, and children's clothing, it was immediately noted that these fabrics, due to their fiber properties, retained creases and pleats. They resisted the wrinkling of wear. Thus, they possessed the various attributes which we now associate with wash-and-wear but which, at that time, were generally advertised as being "all-day freshness," "wrinkle-resistant," "require no ironing," and "all-day without mussing." These and similar claims were made for articles made of nylons, acrylics, and polyesters. They appealed to the traveler who could now make a long trip with a very small wardrobe, two or three shirts replacing eight or ten. Similarly, one or two dresses would perhaps replace an entire suitcase full on a long vacation trip, and two blouses would be sufficient for a wardrobe of most college girls as a bare minimum instead of eight or ten. Furthermore, a dress or blouse worn to work in the morning was still fresh enough to be worn in the evening, so that the working girl or college girl did not have to return to her room or home in order to change before an evening party. Cotton, the principal fiber previously used in these articles, began to suffer, and immediately, of course, the idea of blending cotton with these other fibers was developed. Today we have numerous blends, especially of Dacron and cotton, which possess these same properties, notably the 65 per cent Dacron, 35 per cent cotton which is so widely used in shirtings and fabrics for dresses. The next step, of course, was to apply resins to cottons in order to achieve the same result, and cottons with somewhere between 12 and 18 per cent resin have comparable resistance to wrinkling and ease of washing and ironing as do the synthetic fibers. The washing operation of the synthetic fiber "all-day fresh" articles was to wash them out by hand in a wash basin and hang them to drip dry. Cotton fabrics or blends, after treatment, can likewise be washed and drip-dried, but they possess the other advantages also of being capable of undergoing normal washing operations and of going through a dryer without damage. Space for drip drying became somewhat of a problem in some households as the result of these various articles being bought for all members of the family. Then, it was necessary for the manufacturers of the synthetic fibers to prove that their fabrics likewise could be put through the normal washing operation and the household dryer, that is, that they did not require the hand operation, even though it was a most convenient way of washing, particularly when one is on a journey. But for wear at home, it is better if all articles can be washed, more or less, at the same time and under the same conditions. It is fortunate, therefore, that all wash-and-wear articles, whether all-synthetic, blend, or treated cotton, should best be washed under somewhat moderate conditions. Normal wash temperatures and detergents can be used, but bleaches, especially the chlorine type, should be avoided at all costs, because a chlorine bleach will discolor some of the synthetic fibers and will combine with most of the resin types used in the chemically-treated cottons to the eventual deterioration of the cotton. Furthermore, wrinkles induced by washing are often more serious than those resulting from wear because, being applied to the fabric under a relatively high temperature, there is some danger of their being sealed into the fabric, especially with the synthetics. A light wash load, possibly half the normal washing capacity, and not more than half a dryer load can safely be tolerated by these fabrics.

One of the perils faced by wash-and-wear, which is not peculiar to this promotion in that other good programs have been ruined in the past, is illustrated by a conversation with a friend of the author who endeavored to buy a wash-and-wear dress in a store in New York which had advertised such garments for $2.89. When asked about it, the salesgirl assured the customer that this was a wash-and-wear garment, even though it was not so-labeled, and that all one had to do was wash it and iron it and then wear it.

We cannot have all these various properties associated with wash-and-wear without some sacrifice. One such sacrifice is that the resins required to make cottons crease-recoverable and wrinkle-resistant tend to make the fibers somewhat brittle, with the result that a cotton fabric treated with wash-and-wear resin will lose about one-third of its strength or wear resistance. It is, therefore, poor economy to buy a wash-and-wear item if one is going to treat the garment as one would any garment without such treatment, that is, they should not be treated as ordinary fabrics. The more they are washed like regular garments with heavy loads in the washer and in the dryer, the more wrinkles will be induced and the more ironing will be necessary.

The resin used to provide this crease retention and wrinkle resistance has other factors also. It helps stabilize the fabric, that is, it keeps the fabric from shrinking and from stretching. Indeed, this is sometimes the only stabilization process given to cotton fabrics. The resin also helps hold the dyestuff in the fabric, and, of course, it adds a certain degree of body or weight to the material. Thus, if this finish is not permanent and is gradually removed by repeated washings, there may come a time when the fabric, almost overnight, will appear to be sleazy, faded, shrunken, and wrinkled.

trademark processes for wash-and-wear

Among the more prominent producers of wash-and-wear fabrics, certain trademark names stand out in the memory of the average customer. These are the names most frequently appearing in advertisements in the newspapers and magazines and on labels on goods in the better stores. Many of these names are featured in the catalogues of the mail-order houses.

BELLMANIZED   The Bellman Brook Bleachery name for a durable, crisp, starchless finish particularly useful for dress and curtain fabrics.

"EVERGLAZE"   This trademark designates fabrics finished and tested according to the process standards of the Joseph Bancroft and Sons Company, Inc. It is applicable to patterned and embossed surface effects; it gives fabrics durable wrinkle resistance and shrinkage control. The use of this trademark as an identification of yarns, fabrics, and garments is set forth as the "Everglaze" trademark tag.

FACILITY   The Reeves Bros., Inc., trademarked this name for a wrinkle- and shrinkage-resistant finish, useful also for perspiration and acid resistance.

FRESH-TEX   This is the wash-and-wear trademark of the Cranston Print Works Company. It is also said to control shrinkage and damage from perspiration and mildew.

PERMEL-PLUS   This is the American Cyanamid Company trademark for a washable, water-repellent finish. It is claimed also to add to the strength of the goods.

REDMANIZED   This is the trademark of the F. R. Redman Company for woolen and cotton knit goods to control relaxation shrinkage. It is identified within the processor's quality control plan and applies more to shrinkage control than to wash-and-wear, although it has some attributes in that field as well.

RESLOOM   Monsanto Chemical Company resin finish for cotton, wool, and rayon for wrinkle resistance and shrinkage control.

SANCO 400   The trade-name of the Sanco Peat Dye Works, Inc., primarily for wash-and-wear rayons.

UNIDURE   The United Piece Dye Works' trademark for a permanent wash-and-wear finish.

WRINKL-SHED   The Dan River Mills' trademarked process for permanent crease resistance, shrinkage control, and mildew resistance.

ZESET   The trademark of E. I. du Pont de Nemours & Co., Inc., for crease resistance and shrinkage resistance for fabrics made of cellulosic fibers.

wash-and-wear—consumer reaction

Studies of consumers' reactions to textiles are always interesting and, generally, informative not only to the distributor but to the manufacturer of the garment and buyer as well. A marketing research project of the United States Department of Agriculture (Marketing Research Report No. 493) dealt rather briefly with consumers' reactions to wash-and-wear. This group consisted of 2310 respondents during May and June, 1959.[3] The two basic questions were:

1 "What materials do you think of as being wash-and-wear?"

2 "What material do you think is *best* for women's wash-and-wear clothes?"

Material	Thought of as Wash-and-Wear Per Cent	Thought of as Best for Wash-and-Wear Per Cent
Fiber		
Nylon	68	17
Cotton-polyester	50	24
Acrylic	47	5
Polyester	46	10
Cotton	32	14
No Choice		24*

* Miscellaneous single selections —6.

The position of cotton in the minds of consumers is somewhat surprising, because, as we have shown, cotton by nature of its physical properties is not a wrinkle-resistant or crease-retentive material in fabric form. Presumably, therefore, the cottons to which these consumers referred were cottons which had been given a wrinkle-resistant finish or a wash-and-wear finish. This demonstrates again the extreme importance of textile finishing as it affects performance and use, and the fact that nearly one-third of the respondents thought of cotton as wash-and-wear and almost half of these (14 per cent) thought it best of the wash-and-wear fabrics, is significant.

CONCLUSIONS

Finishing processes are mechanical or chemical in nature. Most of the mechanical processes are permanent; the chemical processes are less permanent and, under certain conditions, have no permanence at all.

The consumer should bear in mind the type of service for which the fabric is to be used. It is an extravagance to purchase a fabric with a special finish if it is

[3] "Women's Attitudes Toward Cotton and Other Fibers in Clothing," *Marketing Research Report No. 493*, Statistical Reporting Service, U.S. Department of Agriculture, July, 1961.

not going to be properly cleaned, if the service conditions are going to be too severe, or, even more wasteful, if the finish is not needed.

QUESTIONS

1   What is meant by an esthetic finish?

2   What is a functional finish?

3   Discuss the relative permanence of each type as applied to cotton, rayon, silk, wool, and synthetics.

4   What is meant by wash-and-wear?

5   To what types of fabric end-use are flammability requirements applicable?

6   What is the difference between waterproof and water-repellent?

7   What do we mean by a durable finish?

8   What is meant by a non-durable or renewable type of finish?

9   What is the difference between the two in effectiveness—let us say, for water repellence?

10   What is meant by bacteriastic?

11   Why is it necessary to protect some fabrics against bacteria, mildew, mold, etc?

12   What special treatments are required by wool in order to give prolonged service?

13   Why are so many finishes seemingly necessary for cotton fabrics?

14   Why should wash-and-wear articles never be exposed to chlorine bleach?

15   What is the effect of chlorine bleach on the three principal types of wash-and-wear articles?

16   What are these three types? How does each achieve its performance rating?

17   What do consumers think of wash-and-wear?

cotton

INTRODUCTION

The seed pod of the cotton plant is called the *boll*. When it opens at maturity, it reveals a treasure-house of products. First, of course, is the cotton fiber which, even today with all our man-made textile fibers, accounts for almost 65 per cent of all the textile products used in the United States and a higher percentage of those used in other countries. Although we are concerned with the textile fiber, the boll also yields cottonseed, of which the United States produces annually almost 6,000,000 tons of which only 500,000 tons are used each year for planting; the rest of the seed goes into oil, cottonseed cake, and cottonseed meal. Another fiber, **cotton linters,** accounts for an industry of its own. Refined cottonseed oil is used mostly in the making of margarine, but it also appears on our tables as salad oils and cooking oils, or it may be hydrogenated and sold as a vegetable shortening for use in cooking. A **cake** is the compressed solid residue after the oil has been pressed from the seed. It is widely used for feeding cattle, sheep, and hogs. Some is ground and made into meal, some is used as fertilizer, some also is utilized for the feeding of poultry. Whole cottonseeds containing the oil are ground and sold as a flour for making bread and other products for use in hospitals and other institutions for persons who may not eat starches or sugar. Even the cottonseed hulls find use as roughage in stock feeding and as a source of chemical compounds for the plastics industry. Some are used as a ground-up filler for plastics and some as a plant mulch.

TABLE 10-1 / COTTON, WOOL, AND MAN-MADE
FIBERS: CONSUMPTION AS A PERCENTAGE
OF TOTAL FIBER CONSUMPTION IN U.S.,
SPECIFIED YEARS, 1925–59
(Per Cent)

| | | | MAN-MADE FIBERS | | |
| | | | Rayon and | | |
Year	Cotton	Wool	Acetate	Other	Total
1925	88.3	10.0	1.7	—	1.7
1927	88.8	8.7	2.5	—	2.5
1929	87.2	9.4	3.4	—	3.4
1931	85.0	9.9	5.1	—	5.1
1933	85.1	8.8	6.1	—	6.1
1935	80.3	12.2	7.5	—	7.5
1937	84.2	8.8	7.0	—	7.0
1939	80.9	8.9	10.2	—	10.2
1941	80.6	10.0	9.2	0.2	9.4
1943	79.9	9.6	10.0	0.5	10.5
1945	75.5	10.8	12.9	0.8	13.7
1946	74.3	11.4	13.5	0.8	14.3
1947	72.9	10.9	15.4	0.8	16.2
1948	70.0	10.9	18.0	1.1	19.1
1949	70.8	9.2	18.3	1.7	20.0
1950	68.8	9.3	19.8	2.1	21.9
1951	71.3	7.1	18.7	2.9	21.6
1952	69.8	7.3	19.0	3.9	22.9
1953	69.0	7.7	19.0	4.3	23.3
1954	68.8	6.4	19.3	5.5	24.8
1955	66.0	6.2	21.3	6.5	27.8
1956	67.3	6.8	18.5	7.4	25.9
1957	65.8	6.0	19.1	9.1	28.2
1958	65.5	5.9	18.8	9.8	28.6
1959	64.0	6.5	18.6	10.9	29.5

From *Inventories in the Textile Cycle* (Washington: U.S. Dept. of Commerce, Business and Defense Services Administration, 1961), p. 14.

Very short fibers clinging to the cotton seed are known as a cotton lint or **linters** and find use in filling materials and as a source of rayon and acetate textile filaments, as we shall see when we study the chapters on those two man-made fibers. Some of the cotton linters are a source of cellulose used in the manufacture of film or in explosives.

The versatility of the cotton fiber itself rivals that of the boll from which it came. No textile fiber can do so many things so well. We shall see that cotton is not resting on its past achievements. Because some new fibers are superior to cotton in some end-uses, it is inevitable that cotton must either be improved through chemical treatment or new ways of using cotton must be developed to hold these markets. Cotton grows in almost every country in the world, but for many years the United States produced more cotton than all other countries in the world combined (see Table 10-2 for World Cotton Production).

TABLE 10-2 / WORLD COTTON PRODUCTION
PRINCIPAL COTTON PRODUCERS*
BY CONTINENTS[1]
1958-59

(in Bales)

North America			Asia and Oceania	
El Salvador	225,000		India	4,300,000
Mexico	2,340,000		Iran	320,000
Nicaragua	225,000		Pakistan	1,300,000
United States	11,500,000		Syria	430,000
Miscellaneous	97,000		Turkey	735,000
Total	14,387,000		Miscellaneous	311,000
			Total	7,396,000
South America			Africa	
Argentina	650,000		Belgian Congo	250,000
Brazil	1,250,000		Egypt	2,039,000
Paraguay	500,000		Sudan	615,000
Miscellaneous	255,000		Uganda	343,000
Total	2,655,000		Miscellaneous	754,000
			Total	4,001,000
Europe			Communist Areas	
Greece	290,000		USSR	7,000,000
Spain	195,000		China & Manchuria	10,000,000
Miscellaneous	37,000		Miscellaneous	135,000
Total	522,000		Total	17,135,000
			WORLD TOTAL	46,096,000

* Producing in excess of 200,000 bales per year (100 million pounds).
[1] Excerpt from Editors of *American Fabrics, Encyclopedia of Textiles* (Englewood Cliffs, N.J.: Prentice-Hall, 1960), p. 75. Reprinted by permission.

growing region in the united states

In the United States, practically all the cotton is grown in a broad belt south of the line between Virginia and North Carolina. If this line is continued due west to Monterey Bay in California, it will have passed north of practically all the cotton grown in the United States. The pattern of growth is not absolutely uniform, there being three major concentrations and three which are slightly smaller. One of these large patches extends down through eastern Arkansas and western Tennessee into Louisiana. The next large area is at the base of the Texas Panhandle, and the third is the southern half of the Imperial Valley in California. The minor concentrations are in the extreme southern tip of Texas, the south-central part of Arizona, and southern New Mexico where the Rio Grande River flows through a part of that state.

The Southern states of the United States still have essentially a one-crop agricultural economy. It was to plant, cultivate, pick, and harvest this crop that the hordes of slaves were brought from Africa to the Western hemisphere around the beginning of the 19th century. Within 50 years the issue of slavery was almost to split the Union in the War Between the States.

history

The origin of cotton is lost in legend, for it is older than any recorded history. Probably this fiber originated in India, for it is mentioned in the historic "Rig Veda" written 3400 years ago.[1] Ruins of cities in the Indus Valley of India show that cotton was grown and used there as early as 3000 B.C. Recorded history tells us that cotton was being woven into cloth as early as 1500 B.C. The spread of the production of cotton and its manufacture into cloth is unrecorded, but probably the cloth and the art of its weaving found their way into Persia, Egypt, and other markets in very early times. Mummies wrapped in fine cotton cloth have been found in Peru in ruins which pre-date the Inca civilization. Although cotton was grown in Asia Minor early in the Christian Era, it was not grown in Europe until its introduction into Spain by the Moors in the tenth century; the name cotton[2] is derived from an early Arab word "Quttan" or "Kutu" meaning "a plant found in conquered lands." The other European countries continued to import cotton from Asia until the Mohammedan conquest of Constantinople closed the trade routes between Europe and the East. Cotton was one of the causes for the growth of the great market cities of the Middle Ages, such as Venice and Genoa. It was to open new roads to India that Columbus sailed westward and Vasco da Gama sailed eastward. Both men strongly influenced history. Columbus found a new world; da Gama reached Calcutta and opened a new trade route which enriched the ports of England and the other Western countries.

To show how great are some of the changes made by time in the economic history of nations, two facts seem most striking. Although Columbus found cotton growing in the Bahama Islands in 1492, there is no evidence that cotton was grown or manufactured along the Atlantic seaboard of North America before the arrival of the English colonists; yet the United States now leads the world in the production and consumption of cotton. England once imported so much cotton from India through the British East India Company (1599) that a parliamentary law was passed in 1700 restricting the sale of that fiber in England in order to protect the British wool industry. One could be fined for wearing a cotton garment. Now England's best customer for woven cotton goods is India.

INVENTIVE GENIUSES   The term "miracle fiber" has been given the synthetics by sales departments and publicity experts seeking always the dramatic presentation of something new. We shall find that of all textile fibers in use, cotton, in addition to being the most important economically, is the shortest; the

[1] W. D. Darby, *Cotton, The Universal Fiber* (New York: Dry Goods Economist, 1924).
[2] National Cotton Council, *Cotton from Field to Fabric* (Memphis, Tenn., 1951).

most deformed as far as any regular appearance is concerned; the most variable in size within the structure of a single fiber; the most uneven in maturity and uniformity; the most demanding in terms of the various handling and processing techniques between fiber and finished fabric; as well as being one of the most versatile of all fibers in its end-use applications after the fabric is fashioned. Literally thousands of men have devoted their knowledge, imagination, and labor to the perfection of cotton textiles from those old fabric remnants and earliest references in history down to the present time. Today, no cotton fabrics are made which are as fine as the muslins described by ancient Arabic writers speaking of the wonderful fabrics woven in Mosel, from which the term "muslin" was derived. These writers have described such fabrics as being so sheer that when laid on the ground and exposed to the dew, the fabrics became invisible; in the poetic Arabic tongue, it was further said that these were "webs of woven wind."[3] These were luxury fabrics and, as in all ancient fabrics, were of hand-loom production.

THE INDUSTRIAL REVOLUTION   The real growth of cotton came with the introduction of machinery which so lowered the cost of cotton goods processing that not only the economics but the politics of great nations were affected by the condition of their cotton trade with other nations in comparison with that of their competitors. The names of seven inventors, six Englishmen and one American, stand out among the many inventive geniuses who contributed to this industrial revolution through the mechanization of the processing of cotton and other fibers.

These men and their inventions are as follows:

John Kay was trained in textiles by his father, a woolen manufacturer. It was his *flying shuttle,* invented in 1730, which enabled English weavers to make cotton as wide as the fabrics from India. Mechanization was to the hand workers of his day, when cotton was practically outlawed in England, much more of a threat than automation is today to our mechanized workers. The first bobbin machine was destroyed by mobs.

James Hargreaves, a cottage weaver, made in 1764, the first practical spinning frame, which was called the *Spinning Jenny.* It could manipulate eight spindles at one time. He finally developed one which could operate 100 spindles.

Richard Arkwright, a barber, conceived the *roller-spinning* method in 1771. Within two years, the first cotton mill was to use his roller-spinning method. The first power to be used was actually horsepower, the movement of a treadmill being used. This spinning frame successfully drew raw stock into a finished spun yarn. Water power as a source of energy was soon used in England by Arkwright's machines.

[3] J. M. Matthews and H. R. Mauersberger, *Textile Fibers,* 5th ed. (New York: Wiley, 1947), p. 149.

A young Englishman by the name of *Samuel Slater* worked as a machinist in an Arkwright mill before coming to America. Though not himself an inventor of the stature of these other men, he brought in his memory a complete working plan for the Arkwright power *spinner* and became, himself, one of the largest builders of cotton processing machinery in the United States at about the beginning of the 19th century. He is one of America's industrial pioneers.

Samuel Crompton was described as a musician and mechanic as well as a dreamer; in 1779, his *spinning mule* perfected the art of spinning fine cotton yarns, and, indeed, it is the principle on which much of today's textile spinning depends. He personally realized less from his invention than did any of his compatriot geniuses. Vast fortunes in cotton fabric were made by others.

Edmund Cartwright was educated to be a clergyman but became an inventor. In 1785, he gave to the textile world its first *automatic powered loom*. Like the other inventions, his depended a good deal upon the work of his predecessors; but there is a vast difference between inventive ideas which do not work and that one which is persistently improved until it does perform efficiently.

Eli Whitney, a young Yale graduate visiting in the South, found that the easy life of his well-to-do Southern friends appealed to him. His inventive ability was challenged by the complaints of his friends of the time, labor, and expense involved in removing the cotton fibers from the seed. In 1792, Whitney's cotton engine, or *gin,* was completed, operated by means of a hand crank; a mass of raw cotton was plucked at and torn apart by small sawteeth, which carried away the lint and allowed the seeds to drop.

So great was the impact of the cotton gin on the cotton economy of the United States that, whereas in 1791, the year before Whitney's invention, America shipped 400 bales of cotton to Europe, in 1800 the shipments rose to 30,000 bales and in 1810 to 180,000 bales. Cotton surely became "King of the South," and in order to plant, cultivate, pick, and process cotton fibers, more and more slave labor became necessary to the economy of the Southern states. Cotton became "King of the North" as well, because in the Northern states where there was an abundance of water power, textile mills grew rapidly in number. The spread of textile mills in Southern states has been somewhat slower, but the combination of the need for changing the economy from primarily agricultural to industrial during the period of two World Wars; somewhat lower pay scales in the South; an abundance of electric power for mills; and the chemical control of the softness and purity of water all helped bring the South to such a position that today about 80 per cent of our textile industry is south of the Mason-Dixon Line.

PRINCIPAL SPECIES OF COTTON

Cotton is the white or yellow-white fiber covering the seeds of a species of plant of the botanical classification **gossypium**. This plant is related to the holly-

TABLE 10-3 / RAW COTTON PRODUCTION BY THE PRINCIPAL PRODUCING COUNTRIES [a]

(Thousands of Bales & Per Cent)

Season Ending July 31	WORLD TOTAL Bales	%	U.S.A. Bales	%	CHINA Bales	%	U.S.S.R. Bales	%	INDIA Bales	%	MEXICO Bales	%	EGYPT Bales	%	BRAZIL Bales	%	PAKISTAN Bales	%	ALL OTHERS Bales	%
1935–1939 [a]	30,415	100	12,389	40.7	3,127	10.3	3,082	10.1	5,320	17.5	302	1.0	1,846	6.1	1,793	5.9	[b]		2,556	8.4
1940–1944	28,222	100	11,550	40.9	2,069	7.3	2,761	9.8	5,088	18.0	382	1.4	1,411	5.0	2,272	8.1	[b]		2,689	9.5
1945–1949 [b]	24,516	100	11,132	45.4	1,923	7.9	2,400	9.8	3,419	13.9	450	1.8	1,292	5.3	1,423	5.8	[b]		2,477	10.1
1950–1954 [c]	36,762	100	14,521	39.5	3,980	10.8	5,220	14.2	3,034	8.2	1,161	3.2	1,753	4.8	1,606	4.4	1,276	3.5	4,211	11.4
1955–1959	42,698	100	12,760	29.9	6,460	15.1	6,754	15.8	4,227	9.9	2,079	4.9	1,714	4.0	1,480	3.5	1,349	3.2	5,875	13.7
1955	41,036	100	13,630	33.2	4,500	11.0	6,720	16.4	4,425	10.8	1,810	4.4	1,605	3.9	1,650	4.0	1,309	3.2	5,387	13.1
1956	43,819	100	14,680	33.5	6,300	14.4	6,300	14.4	3,880	8.8	2,242	5.1	1,541	3.5	1,700	3.9	1,450	3.3	5,726	13.1
1957	42,166	100	13,027	30.9	6,000	14.2	7,000	16.6	4,180	9.9	1,877	4.5	1,498	3.6	1,300	3.1	1,323	3.1	5,961	14.1
1958	41,672	100	10,960	26.3	6,800	16.3	6,850	16.4	4,430	10.6	2,106	5.1	1,870	4.5	1,350	3.2	1,392	3.4	5,914	14.2
1959	44,796	100	11,504	25.7	8,700	19.4	6,900	15.4	4,220	9.4	2,359	5.3	2,057	4.6	1,400	3.1	1,270	2.8	6,386	14.3
1960	47,131	100	14,555	30.9	8,500	18.0	7,300	15.5	3,350	7.1	1,660	3.5	2,109	4.5	1,700	3.6	1,300	2.8	6,657	14.1
1961 [d]	47,353	100	14,300	30.2	7,500	15.8	6,800	14.4	4,480	9.5	2,100	4.4	2,205	4.7	1,800	3.8	1,325	2.8	6,843	14.4

SOURCE: International Cotton Advisory Committee.

[a] Five year averages.

[b] Pakistan included with India through 1940.

[c] 1954 total revised to 41,649 and All Others to 5,061.

[d] Preliminary.

Reprinted by permission of *Textile Organon*, Oct. 1961.

hock, mallow, and okra, and may be from two to twenty feet in height, depending upon the variety. The higher plants are of the variety known as **tree cotton.**

SEA ISLAND   The fibers of this species are about 1.6 inches in length and may be as long as two inches if the soil is good and the cultivation has been carefully maintained. This cotton is raised on the islands off the coast of the Carolinas and along the coast of the Southern states. At present, its production in the United States is small because of inroads of the boll weavil in the areas favorable to the growth of this cotton. Because of the fineness of the fibers and their length and uniformity, this species is highly prized for laces and fine weaving yarns from 120's to 200's count.[4] It was once used for automobile tires but has been replaced by rayon and nylon. To fulfill the ever-present demand for **Sea Island** cotton, it is being cultivated in other parts of the world and is used in producing hybrid varieties.

EGYPTIAN   This species is next to the Sea Island in fineness and fiber length. The average length is 1.4 inches. It is grown along the delta of the River Nile. These fibers are brownish in color and must be bleached. Egyptian cotton is widely used in knitted underwear, tire cord, sewing thread, and fine *mercerized* fabrics. The mercerizing finishing process gives these cottons the luster and appearance of silk.

PERUVIAN   The Peruvian species of cotton is found in Central and South America and the West Indies. Some types are moderately smooth. The characteristic fiber is rough and wiry and approximately 1.25 inches in length. The rough Peruvian fiber is a tree cotton producing two crops a year. Peruvian cotton is principally used in cotton-wool mixtures (merino yarns). These yarns are widely used in the underwear trade because they are cheaper than pure wool, and the fabric is less irritating to some people than is all wool. Another extensive use is in hosiery.

AMERICAN   The bulk of the domestic United States cotton produced for world consumption is of the genus **Hirsutum.** There are three main types of American cotton, classified geographically into Gulf, Texas, and Upland cotton. The cotton belt extends from the Atlantic to the Pacific and from southern Virginia to the Gulf of Mexico; it is natural that within such a large area, distinct types should have developed. **Gulf** cotton is the product of the states bordering the Gulf of Mexico. It is generally regarded as one of the better of the American types. The color is almost pure white, and the fiber length is about one inch. The Gulf cotton is characterized by local names, examples of which are **Peelers** and **Benders.** Peelers refer to cotton grown on the Mississippi Delta and Benders to the cotton grown along the Arkansas, Mississippi, and White Rivers. Oklahoma- and Texas-grown cotton is classified as **Texas.** The fibers are slightly shorter than the Gulf type, and they are harsher. To a large extent **Pima** cotton

---

[4] See page 139, Cotton Counting.

Fig. 10-1 Combed Cotton Fibers: These cottons shown one-half natural size, represent important grades grown in the United States. (*Courtesy of United States Department of Agriculture.*)

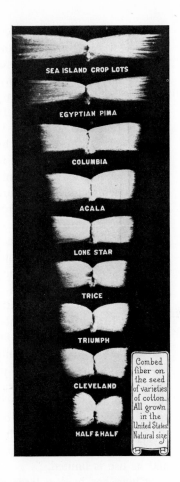

SEA ISLAND CROP LOTS

EGYPTIAN PIMA

COLUMBIA

ACALA

LONE STAR

TRICE

TRIUMPH

CLEVELAND

HALF & HALF

Combed fiber on the seed of varieties of cotton. All grown in the United States. Natural size.

has replaced the shorter fiber Texas type. **Upland** cotton, the major cotton fiber grown in the United States, is produced on the plantations of Georgia, Alabama, Tennessee, Virginia, and the Carolinas. Some varieties grown in Arkansas, Mississippi, and Louisiana are classified as Upland cotton. This type has an average fiber length of $^{15}\!/_{16}$ of an inch. The American cottons are used for all types of fabrics.

new domestic cotton

Pima cotton, developed by the United States Department of Agriculture, is the finest long-staple cotton of commercial importance in the United States. It is grown under irrigation conditions in the southwestern part of the United States, Arizona, the Texas Panhandle, New Mexico, and California. The fiber length of generally about one inch to 1.25 inches.

An interesting example of the rewards resulting from plant breeding and quality control of the product is afforded by the California cotton growers, who produce a type of Pima cotton from a single variety of **Acala** seed (Acala 4-42). The State Legislature in 1925 passed a law forbidding the planting, harvesting, or ginning of any other type of cotton in the State of California. Improvements in this strain by the United States Department of Agriculture increased the yield per acre from 226 pounds of lint per acre in 1921 to 1,050 pounds per acre in 1960. Each year the representatives of the Experiment Station select 50 pounds of hand-pollinated seed for reproduction by the cotton growers; it takes four years for these 50 pounds to develop into the 20,000 to 25,000 tons needed for a single year's planting. The first year's planting is done on a rather secluded and carefully observed, controlled, and irrigated five-acre block. The seed obtained from this crop is planted the second year on about 300 acres; the third year the seed produced is planted over 4,000 acres; the final crop is planted on 70,000 acres. The seed from this planting is then the basis for the entire California crop for the following year, and each year a new 50-pound, hand-pollinated parent seed stock is selected. The results, in addition to increased yield, have been an earlier maturity, a stronger fiber, increased resistance to disease, and better picking, ginning, and tolerance to stress, that is, recovery from stress. The fiber length is 1.06 to 1.18 inches and has between 10 and 20 per cent greater fiber strength than the American-type cotton grown across the Southern states rain belt. In these Western states, abundance of water for irrigation has taken the place of the rainfall characteristic of the Southern states. The total surface area of the leaves in a field of cotton is so vast that the evaporation of moisture through the plants and from the leaf surface may reach 50 tons of water per day per acre.[5]

OTHER VARIETIES   The cotton grown in India has fibers of only eight-tenths to nine-tenths of an inch. This fiber is so short that it is difficult to spin and its use is limited.

China has been a large producer of cotton but of short and coarse fiber. One native cotton called **Million Dollar** was selectively bred and demanded a 20 per cent premium in the market in competition with other Chinese cottons.

THE CULTIVATION OF COTTON

Cotton is the largest of America's agricultural crops. From fiber to finished garment, it provides employment for some 13 million people and represents a capital investment of some 15 billion dollars.[6]

The production of cotton is expressed in bales of 500 pounds weight. The world production in 1959 was 44,796,000 bales, of which the United States produced 11,500,000; China and Manchuria next at 10,000,000; the USSR,

---

[5] J. A. Hildabrand, "Cotton: Foremost Fiber of the World," *National Geographic Magazine* (February 1941), p. 140.

[6] Editors of *American Fabrics, Encyclopedia of Textiles* (Englewood Cliffs, N.J.: Prentice-Hall, 1960), p. 75.

6,900,000; India, 4,220,000; Mexico, 2,360,000; and Egypt, 2,057,000. In consumption, the United States again leads with 7,999,000; China, 7,000,000; USSR, 5,600,000; India, 4,360,000; and Japan, 2,453,000 bales. The discrepancy between the United States' production and consumption emphasizes that some complex problems in distribution exist. Several points will be brought out in the chapter dealing with Textile Production, Chapter 29.

The cultivation of cotton is influenced by many factors. The size of the farm or extent of the acreage, the topography, the usual growing season climate and moisture, the type of soil, and the amount of available labor—all play a part in these variations of practice. Regardless of these factors, however, there are certain basic steps involved in all cottons. The preparation of the land, the planting methods employed, the cultivation, and the harvesting are the essentials. In addition to these, frequent irrigation may be necessary, as in the Western states. Sometimes it is necessary to fertilize, to spray the cotton plants for the control of insects, to defoliate, or remove the leaves from the plants in order to make mechanical harvesting more efficient, and plough under the residue stalks to serve as a mulch for future crops.[7]

preparation of the land

Either in the fall or early spring, residues from the stalks of the cotton plants of the previous season or of corn or other crops which may have been raised on the plot may be broken into small sections by means of a disc harrow; the rotating sharp-edged discs chop the residual cellulosic material into small pieces and mix these with the soil. The cleared land is then ploughed and harrowed to break up large lumps and remove ridges. The separation is usually carried out on small farms by means of mule-drawn equipment. On the large farms located in major growing areas, large mechanical appliances are used.

planting

Small furrows are opened by means of a mule-drawn plough or a number of furrows opened simultaneously with a large mechanically-drawn gang-plough, and, at the same time, the seeds are dropped in one at a time, generally with fertilizer being put in the furrow at the same time. The amount of seed planted depends upon the cotton allotment set for the season by the Department of Agriculture, since cotton is one of the surplus crops (see Chapter 29 on Production and Marketing of Textiles). Generally, cotton is planted in February in the more southerly regions, but it may be as late as June in the northernmost sections of the cotton belt, particularly in the foothills of the Ozarks.

[7] Material condensed from *Cotton from Field to Fabric,* National Cotton Council, 1953, Memphis, Tennessee, pp. 6–10, permission of National Cotton Council.

cultivating

When the plants have grown to a height of 5 to 7 inches, they are generally thinned out so that there are no more than two or three plants per hill, or so that the plants are about nine to fourteen inches apart in rows. This is usually done by hand, although there are a few mechanical cultivators available for large acreages. Weeds must be kept from between the plants and from between the rows. This has traditionally been a hand operation and is still so in small farm plantings. Large mechanical cultivators, designed to fit between the furrows of the mechanical planting devices, accomplish a good job of cleaning out between the rows. On some farms in the West, the farmer raises another crop at the same time that he is raising cotton, this crop being a flock of geese which feed on the grass and weed material but will not touch the cotton plant. Geese are used in a similar manner to keep the weeds out of orchards. One type of weed control is by use of a flame cultivator, the flame being played along the rows between the plantings. The thin-stemmed weeds and grasses wither and die, but the cotton plant, with its woody stalk, is not damaged. The mechanical devices used in various cotton-growing areas are many and varied, and their usefulness depends upon the texture of the soil, the topography, the area to be cultivated, the frequency of cultivation, and whether or not the plants are to be irrigated. Much research has been conducted on this kind of operation.

The chemicals used in chemical control of weeds generally do not affect the hard-shelled cottonseed; however, they do kill the seeds of grasses and common weeds. Therefore, a brand of chemical may be sprayed or spread along the row at the time of planting or shortly before the seedlings emerge. After the seedlings have appeared, any subsequent chemical treatment must be done in such a way as to avoid contact of the chemical with the foliage or stems of the cotton plant. The chemicals, however, may have a profound effect on the life cycle of insects, birds, and other wildlife.

INSECT CONTROL   Within a few weeks after the plant has emerged, the first buds or "squares" appear. These squares consist of three triangular-shaped leaflets, or bracts, and the flower bud. It is at this stage, when the plant is about to bear its blossom and seed, that it is most susceptible to insect damage. The principal enemy to cotton is the boll weevil, though there are numerous other insects which contribute to the annual loss of approximately one out of every eight bales grown in the Southern belt. It is estimated that in 1950 almost $600,000,000 were lost to insects. Other pests are aphids, worms, spider mites, and a number of other small insects. The chemicals for insect control are applied either in liquid as a spray or in the form of dusts. The simplest operation is for a man to walk between the rows carrying a pressurized tank of insecticide on his back and carefully spraying each plant as he passes. In large acreages, it is much more economical to dust from the air, using a low-flying airplane which can cover as many as 1500 acres a day. Other dusters and sprayers are carried by tractors and can spray as many as eight rows on each trip back and forth across the field. Dusting from the air has caused considerable agitation among conservationists, for all insects, harmless and harmful, are killed, and the loss of birdlife is very great. Ranchers raising crops requiring bees or other insects for fertilization of their crops find that their yields are greatly reduced by the killing off of the bees by insecticide sprayings which were spread too far because of wind conditions or spraying at too great a height. These applications of insecticides must be made frequently during the growing season, especially in sections of the country where rain is rather frequent. The boll weevil damages the cotton by laying its eggs inside the buds, and when the eggs hatch, the minute insects feed on the fluids in the maturing boll.

maturing of the boll

About 21 days after the buds are first seen, the cotton blossom appears. This is at first a creamy white to a deep yellow color. Later it becomes pink and eventually dark red. It lasts about three days, after which the petals fall off and the ovary ripens to form a pod which we know as the cotton boll. Next, fibers push out from the coating of the seed, causing the boll to expand until it is nearly one inch in diameter and half again as long. Different varieties of cotton mature at different rates; usually it takes between 45 and 65 days from the blossom to the open boll. The growing season, fertilizer, degree of cultivation, and amount of moisture—all these factors may affect the maturing of cotton crops. Sea Island cotton is slower in maturing, as are most of the other finer and longer-fibered cottons. Thus, they are prey to the boll weevil, the young of which hatch about the same time the Sea Island cotton is reaching its maturity. One advantage of the Upland cotton is that it matures more rapidly and generally before the boll weevil hatches out.

harvesting

With the first frost, the cotton plant normally sheds its leaves, but the bolls have matured and are opened often several weeks before the first frost. When this happens, artificial defoliation can be carried out by treatment with chemicals. This is absolutely necessary if the crop is to be harvested mechanically. Even at best, mechanically harvested cotton contains large quantities of fragments of stem and of the brittle shell of the boll. When the cotton crop is defoliated, all the bolls are more readily exposed to the sun, and the maturity is much more uniform, so that one picking is usually all that is necessary. It once was that cotton was picked two or more times, with just the mature bolls being taken. With defoliation, there is less tendency of those bolls concealed behind leaves to rot in wet weather; it also takes away a source of food for insects.

HAND PICKING   The plant having been defoliated, the heat of the sun causes the cotton fibers to grow more rapidly; finally the pressure is so great that the boll splits open, exposing the white cotton which is now ready to be picked. This is done by hand in the greater part of the cotton belt, where individual acreages are small and plantings are on hillsides. In the Texas, Oklahoma, Arizona, and California area, the bolls may be snapped off by machines. Some machines can cover two rows at a time and will harvest nearly a bale (500 pounds) of cotton an hour and from 10 to 15 acres per day. The machine covering but one row will harvest about as much cotton as 26 laborers hand-snapping or hand-picking the bolls. In hand picking, it is customary to pick a field at least three times; first for the mature bolls near the top of the plant; later those down the side of the plant; and finally those which have been shaded from the direct sun.

processing of cotton

The bolls are carried by truck or wagon to the cotton gin. The modern gins are greatly refined from Whitney's first invention but depend basically upon the same operation as is shown in Figure 10-2.

The gin consists essentially of a series of circular saws mounted on a horizontal shaft. These saws project through a set of steel ribs or bars, and as the seed cotton drops down onto the ribs, the saws catch the lint, snatching it from the seed and pulling it through between the ribs or bars on either side, where a blast of air blows it from the saw teeth onto a belt as lint cotton. In the meantime, as the seed cotton falls and is beaten by a revolving beater (No. 2 in the figure), stem fragments and other organic trash drop into a separate bin. As the cotton fiber or lint is snatched away from the seed, the latter loses its buoyancy and drops into a separate bin. The lint passes on the conveyor belt to a baling press, where it is compressed and packaged into the standard bale of 500 pounds in weight. These bales, commonly wrapped in burlap and strapped with heavy steel bands, are now sometimes wrapped in a plastic bag but compressed to as small a volume as possible for transportation.

The bale of 500 pounds of cotton has produced 850 pounds of seed and approximately 75 to 90 pounds of linters. These cotton linters are such short fibers that they cannot be used in textile applications. They find their principal use in felts, absorbent cotton, stuffings, and as a source of fine cellulose in the rayon and acetate industries. These filaments stick to the cottonseed through the ginning operation and can be removed only by a delinting process which somewhat resembles the original ginning operation, but the sawteeth are much closer so that these very short fibers can be pulled away from the seed.

CLASSIFICATION OF COTTON

The cotton bales must then be sampled before marketing for the purpose of **classifying** them and **grading** them. More and more science and technology

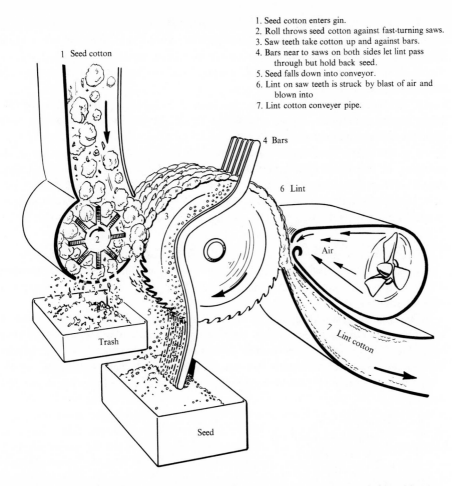

1. Seed cotton enters gin.
2. Roll throws seed cotton against fast-turning saws.
3. Saw teeth take cotton up and against bars.
4. Bars near to saws on both sides let lint pass through but hold back seed.
5. Seed falls down into conveyor.
6. Lint on saw teeth is struck by blast of air and blown into
7. Lint cotton conveyer pipe.

1 Seed cotton

4 Bars

6 Lint

Air

2

3

5

Trash

7 Lint cotton

Seed

Fig. 10-2 Diagram showing operation of the cotton gin. (*Courtesy of the Bibb Manufacturing Company.*)

are being called upon to give a more precise grading to cotton, as to staple length, *grade,* and *character.* Much of it is still classed by experts on the basis of experience and ability quickly to determine the general character of the contents of each bale from the samples submitted.

Though each variety of cotton produces fibers of very similar staple length, there may be a rather wide variation in fiber lengths within the bale, but the bale is classed as being of the predominant staple length as measured or judged. The significance of staple length in spinning cannot be over-emphasized, because the quality of the yarn produced will be greatly reduced if a shorter fiber than customary is used. The longer and finer the staple, the finer the yarn which can be spun from it. A practical grading according to staple length is as follows:

1 Very short cotton—not over ¾-inch staple length. Usually coarse in texture and too short for easy spinning. Therefore, it is used largely in bags and wadding and in heavy, coarse yarns for cheap goods.

2 Short staple—between $^{13}\!/_{16}$ and $^{15}\!/_{16}$ of an inch. This is used in very cheap cotton fabrics.

3 Medium staple—between $^{15}\!/_{16}$ and 1-⅛ inches. This length includes most of the American cotton and is the usual American Upland staple. It is used at home and exported abroad.

4 Ordinary long staple—between 1-⅛ to 1-⅜ inches long. This is the category of the Pima cotton and is consumed in large quantities in the United States in the finer cotton fabrics.

5 Extra-long staple—from 1-⅜ to 2-½ inches long. The lustrous cottons from Egypt and our limited supply of Sea Island cottons belong to this group.

According to the Cotton Council, the first two groups are considered as short-staple cotton and the last three as long-staple. The long staple accounts for only 6 per cent of our domestic crop. About 10 per cent of our output is shorter than ⅞ inch.

The *quality* grade of cotton is affected by color and brightness, the amount of immature cotton fibers which may be in the bale, the amount of foreign material, and, in general, the quality of the ginning operation. For these grades, the United States Government has set the standards. These grades are as follows, with the highest grade being given first and the others in descending order:

1 Middling—fair
2 Strict good—middling
3 Good middling
4 Strict middling
5 Middling
6 Strict low middling
7 Low middling
8 Strict good ordinary
9 Good ordinary
10 Ordinary.

Since these are white cottons, the degree of whiteness also enters into the rating in a sub-classification. These are extra-white, white, spotted, tinged, yellow, stained, and grey.

The last term, *character,* refers to the strength, maturity, uniformity, and smoothness of the fibers, and to other qualities which are not covered by staple length and grade. Regardless of the grade, uniformity is a prime requisite if the best use is to be made of the cotton from the shipment and if it is to go into the most appropriate end-uses.

COTTON MARKETING

Cotton is customarily marketed after classification and baling. Generally, a producer will sell his ginned and baled cotton to a local cotton merchant at a price agreed upon in the light of *current cotton prices* and the cost of *cotton futures*. The current prices are those at which cotton is selling in all the principal cotton markets at that time. It is determined by a daily survey reported to the Department of Agriculture at the end of the day at the commodity exchanges. These are the prices for *spot* cotton, meaning cotton baled and ready for sale. The price is generally given for middling cotton with a staple length of $^{15}\!/_{16}$ of an inch, available for immediate delivery as reported by the spot exchanges. Prices for other grades vary up and down from this middling grade. Cotton *futures* are world markets, such as New York, New Orleans, Chicago, São Paulo (Brazil), Bombay (India), and Alexandria (Egypt). These exchanges consider the world-wide condition of the cotton crop at the time and in the light of cotton in warehouses throughout the world. One may buy cotton for future delivery. Or, one may sell cotton at what appears to be a very favorable price, gambling that when the cotton crop is ready the spot price will be lower; thus, when called upon to fill the order, it can be obtained in the market at a lower price than that which the sale was contracted for months before. These dealings in futures help to stablize the cotton market price, and all futures contracts are legal agreements.

If a producer decides not to sell his cotton to a local merchant or to one of his regular mill customers immediately, he may store it in a warehouse; if need be, he can borrow money on this crop, for it is non-perishable and can be stored for many years without damage. This is, in effect, like having stocks, or bonds, or cash in a bank, against which loans can be made. The future date of sale would depend somewhat upon the spot market as it may change or the futures market prices may vary.

Excess cotton may be purchased by the government at a price somewhat above the world price of cotton as a means of covering over-production (see Chapter 29.

COTTON SPINNING

The twisting process by which fibers are formed into a yarn is referred to as **spinning.** Indeed, the formation of a yarn of man-made fibers is little more than that single operation in some cases. In the cotton textile industry, however, spinning includes all the processes required to prepare and clean the fibers, from the opening of the bale to the twisting of the yarn in its preparation for the textile loom. As the mass of cotton fiber is successively cleaned and formed into ever narrower and more compact configurations, it is identified by different terms. Thus, the term *lap* refers to the broad loose mass of cotton fibers as laid down after the cleaning and picking operation. *Sliver* refers to the somewhat narrower layer of cotton into which the fibers have been combed and lie more parallel. *Roving* is a thinner strand formed by loosely twisting the paralleled cotton fibers into a rope-form. *Yarn* is the fine, more tightly twisted strand produced by further drawing and twisting of the roving until the proper size and tightness have been reached for use in the weaving operation.

It is amazing that as fine a fiber as cotton, usually an inch or less in length, can pass through all the heavy, high-speed equipment by which this raw fiber is transformed from a mass in a tightly tied bale to a yarn strong enough for the most delicate of textile fabrics.

spinning process

OPENING AND PICKING   In order to produce as uniform a product, batch after batch over successive months or even years, it is customary that the cotton fibers from numerous bales be *blended,* or thoroughly mixed together, and from this composite will be produced the final yarns. Ten or more bales of the same grade, but representing cottons from several different areas and often of two or more different years of growth, will be blended. Some cotton of the

Fig. 10-3   Diagram of the operation of the blending feeder (*Courtesy of the Bibb Manufacturing Company.*)

1. Cotton from bales is thrown on apron in hopper.
2. Apron moves cotton to blending apron.
3. Blending apron has sharp spikes which raise cotton until part is knocked off by roll (4). Some of the cotton stays on apron.
4. The cotton knocked back by roll No. 4 continues to churn and blend until picked up again by apron.
5. Roll strips off cotton which was not knocked back by roll No. 4.
6. Cotton falls on conveyor belt which carries it to next process.

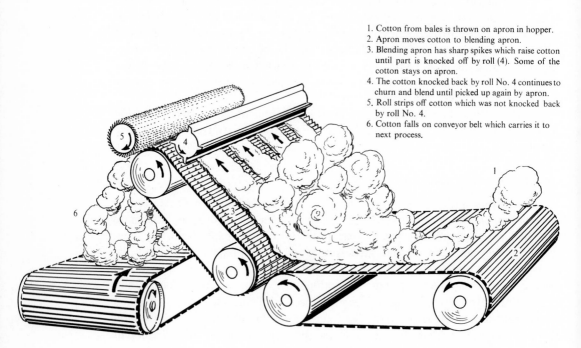

new crop and some of the preceding year or even cottons from two or more years earlier may be used in such blends. The masses of cotton from these numerous bales will be fed into a machine called a **blending feeder.** As these masses of fiber are loosened and thoroughly mixed, some remaining heavy impurities, such as dirt, remnants of seeds, leaves, or stems, are removed by a line of machines known respectively as **pickers, breakers, intermediates,** and **finishers,** each in succession being a somewhat more refined cleaner of the raw cotton. From these machines, the cotton emerges as a **lap,** a loose, formless roll of cotton resembling the absorbent cotton sold in drug stores for bandaging purposes, but being about 45 inches wide (see Figure 10-4).

CARDING   This **picker lap** is formed into a loose roll about 18 inches in diameter, and the lap is unrolled and drawn onto a revolving cylinder covered with fine hooks or wire bristles (see Figure 10-5). These wire bristles pull the fibers in one direction, separate those which are individually tangled together, and form them into a thin film. This process is known as *carding*. The thin

Fig. 10-4 The operation of the opener and picker. (*Courtesy of the Bibb Manufacturing Company.*)

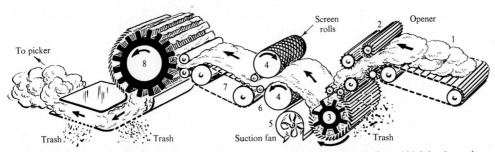

Lint cotton (1) falls on apron and passes between feeder rolls (2) to beater cylinder (3). The rapidly whirling beater blades each take off small tufts of cotton, knocking out trash and loosening up the mass. The two screen rolls (4) are made of screen material, and air is sucked out of them by the fan (5). This draws the cotton from the beater and condenses it on the surface of the screen rolls, from which it is taken and passed on by the small rolls (6). The air suction through the cotton takes out dirt and trash. The conveyor belt (7) passes the cotton to another type of beater. (Many types of beaters are used. Those shown are typical.) From the beater (8) the cotton passes to a conveyor which takes it to the next machine, which is the picker (see below).

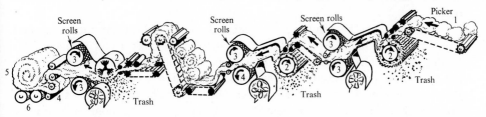

Cotton in a loose mass (1) from the opener enters the picker, which is a series of beaters (2) (2) (2) and screen rolls (3) (3) (3) similar to those described under opening, but gradually more refined. At the final output of the beater and screen system (4) the cotton has again been formed into a sheet or "lap." At this point the "evener" operates to feed more or less cotton as may be required to make the lap perfectly uniform as it wound up into a "lap roll" (5) on the winding rolls (6). From this point the lap roll is taken to the carding process.

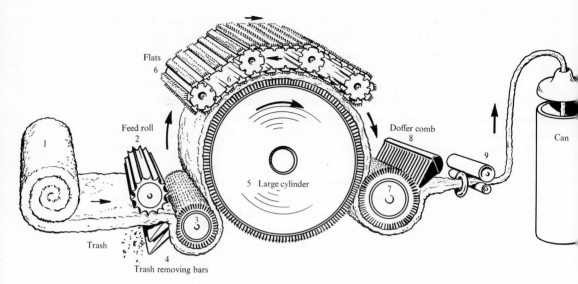

As the lap from the picker (1) unrolls, the feed roll (2) passes the cotton to the "lickerin" roll, which is covered with sawtooth-like wire (3). The lickerin roll passes the fiber against the cleaner bars (4) and gives it up to the large cylinder (5) which passes it between the thousands of fine wires on the surface of the cylinder and on the flats (6). The cotton follows the large cylinder to the doffer cylinder (7), which removes the lint from the large cylinder. The doffer comb (8) vibrates against the doffer cylinder and takes the lint off in a filmy web, which passes through the condenser rolls (9), the coiler head (10), and into the can.

Fig. 10-5 Diagram of the cotton carding operation. (*Courtesy of the Bibb Manufacturing Company.*)

film is drawn into a funnel-shaped opening which molds it into a round rope-like strand approximately an inch in diameter; this is called the *sliver*. The coarser-textured and cheaper cotton fabrics are formed from yarns which have gone through the carding operation, but for finer fabrics and finer and more delicate yarns, the added refinement of combing is almost invariably carried out.

COMBING   The comber is a refining device by which the paralleling and straightening of the individual fibers is carried to a more exact degree. Fine-toothed combs further straighten the cotton, and the shorter fibers still present fall out. These are referred to as the **noils,** and even in accurately graded cotton, they may amount to as much as 15 per cent of the fiber content, but they are just too short and leave too many loose, fuzzy ends to be used in extremely fine cotton fabrics. They may be collected and used for coarser textile materials. The remaining longer fibers are again formed into a sliver, known as the *comb sliver*.

DRAWING   In the drawing operation, further blending is accomplished by working together several slivers and drawing or pulling them out in the drawing frame (Figure 10-6) without twisting but reducing the several slivers to a single one about the same diameter as each of the components.

ROVING   The combined or condensed combed sliver is taken to the slubber, the first of a series of machines called **roving frames** (Figure 10-7). Here the cotton is given a slight twist which, combined with further drawing, causes the strand to become longer, finer, and firmer. A coarser yarn would require only one slubber. Very fine yarns would require three slubbers, and these finer strands are referred to as **roving**.

SPINNING   **Spinning** is a continuation of the roving, and on the spinning frame many spools containing the roving pass through the ring-spinning mechanism which further draws and twists the cotton into a yarn of the re-

Fig. 10-6   Diagram of the drawing operation to form a more uniform sliver. (Courtesy of the Bibb Manufacturing Company.)

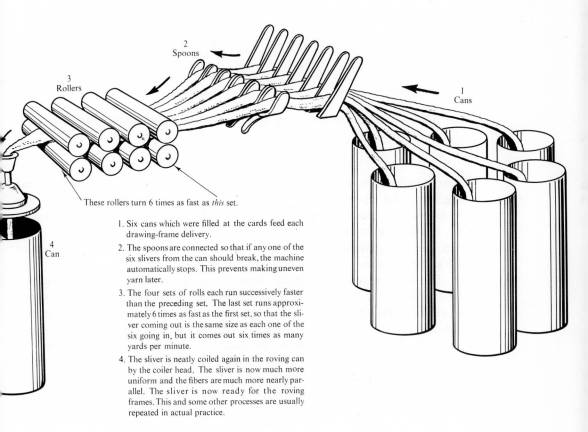

These rollers turn 6 times as fast as *this* set.

1. Six cans which were filled at the cards feed each drawing-frame delivery.

2. The spoons are connected so that if any one of the six slivers from the can should break, the machine automatically stops. This prevents making uneven yarn later.

3. The four sets of rolls each run successively faster than the preceding set. The last set runs approximately 6 times as fast as the first set, so that the sliver coming out is the same size as each one of the six going in, but it comes out six times as many yards per minute.

4. The sliver is neatly coiled again in the roving can by the coiler head. The sliver is now much more uniform and the fibers are much more nearly parallel. The sliver is now ready for the roving frames. This and some other processes are usually repeated in actual practice.

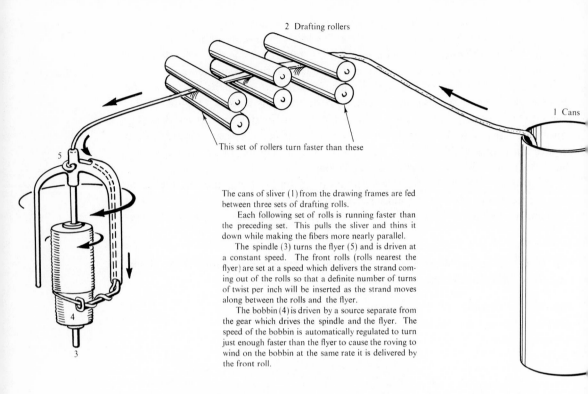

2 Drafting rollers

1 Cans

This set of rollers turn faster than these

The cans of sliver (1) from the drawing frames are fed between three sets of drafting rolls.

Each following set of rolls is running faster than the preceding set. This pulls the sliver and thins it down while making the fibers more nearly parallel.

The spindle (3) turns the flyer (5) and is driven at a constant speed. The front rolls (rolls nearest the flyer) are set at a speed which delivers the strand coming out of the rolls so that a definite number of turns of twist per inch will be inserted as the strand moves along between the rolls and the flyer.

The bobbin (4) is driven by a source separate from the gear which drives the spindle and the flyer. The speed of the bobbin is automatically regulated to turn just enough faster than the flyer to cause the roving to wind on the bobbin at the same rate it is delivered by the front roll.

Fig. 10-7　Diagram of the roving operation. (*Courtesy of the Bibb Manufacturing Company.*)

quired size and twist and winds it on bobbins preparatory to the weaving operation. We have noted in Chapter 7 on Yarns that generally the warp, or lengthwise yarns, are the more tightly twisted for extra strength, since in the weaving operation the greater stress is on them. The crosswise filling, or weft yarns, are usually slightly weaker and have less twist. The operation of the spinning frame is shown in Figure 10-8.

The spinning mill will usually supply yarns of almost any size or geometrical combinations, that is, they may be single yarns, or they may be ply yarns, or cabled yarns, the ply being yarns of two or more singles twisted together. Figure 7-5 on page 74 in Chapter 7 shows the difference between single yarns, ply yarns, and cable yarns, the latter two being combinations of two or more of the preceding class or type of yarn, that is, two, three, or four single yarns twisted together will make respectively two-ply, three-ply, and four-ply yarns, and two or more plied yarns may be twisted together to form a cable.

YARN CLASSIFICATION

The **classification** of yarns is based upon thickness; another way of expressing it would be in terms of the relative fineness. By this method, numbers are assigned to express the fineness of the yarn, the number being the number of hanks or strands of cotton, 840 yards long, required to weigh one pound; thus, if we have a hank of yarn 840 yards of which weigh one pound, we would call this a number 1 or a 1's cotton. Five's cotton would be 1/5 the diameter or thickness of 1's, because it would take five of these hanks, or a total of 4200 yards, to weigh one pound. One of the most widely used grades or classes of cotton yarns is the 30's, which indicate 25,200 yards to the pound. If these are single yarns, the designations for 5's, 10's, or 30's are respectively 5/1, 10/1, and 30/1. If these are two-ply yarns of the same size, the number of the ply would appear below the slanting line as follows: 5/2, 20/2, 30/2. In the case of ply yarns, however, the size or classification depends upon the number of plies as well as the fineness of the individual yarns making up the

Fig. 10-8 Diagram of the principle of spinning a cotton yarn from two or more rovings. (*Courtesy of the Bibb Manufacturing Company.*)

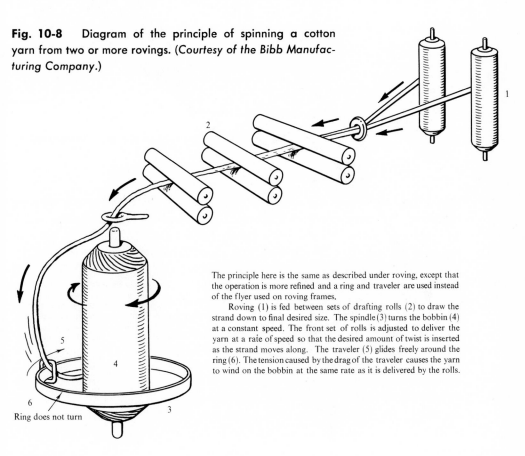

The principle here is the same as described under roving, except that the operation is more refined and a ring and traveler are used instead of the flyer used on roving frames.

Roving (1) is fed between sets of drafting rolls (2) to draw the strand down to final desired size. The spindle (3) turns the bobbin (4) at a constant speed. The front set of rolls is adjusted to deliver the yarn at a rate of speed so that the desired amount of twist is inserted as the strand moves along. The traveler (5) glides freely around the ring (6). The tension caused by the drag of the traveler causes the yarn to wind on the bobbin at the same rate as it is delivered by the rolls.

Ring does not turn

Fig. 10-9 Diagram showing principle of applying twist to a cotton yarn. (*Courtesy of the Bibb Manufacturing Company.*)

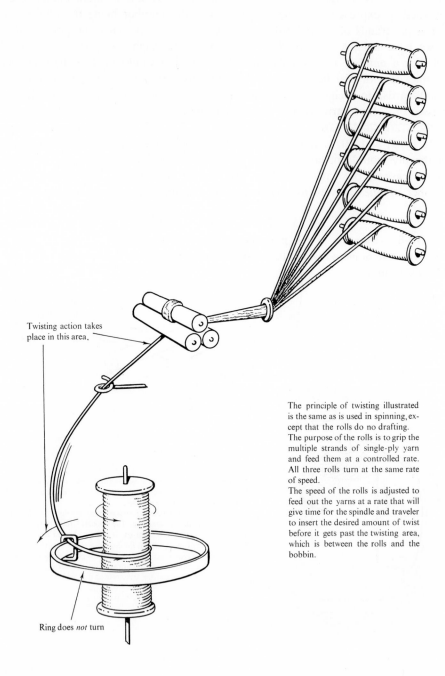

Twisting action takes place in this area.

Ring does *not* turn

The principle of twisting illustrated is the same as is used in spinning, except that the rolls do no drafting. The purpose of the rolls is to grip the multiple strands of single-ply yarn and feed them at a controlled rate. All three rolls turn at the same rate of speed.

The speed of the rolls is adjusted to feed out the yarns at a rate that will give time for the spindle and traveler to insert the desired amount of twist before it gets past the twisting area, which is between the rolls and the bobbin.

ply. For example, if two 10's single yarns are twisted to form a two-ply yarn, it would be described as 10/2; however, in total diameter it would be equivalent in size to a 5/1 yarn, because each of the 10's single would weigh one pound for 10 hanks, and combining these would double the weight of the yarn to the equivalent size of a single 5's, or 5/1.

CHARACTERISTICS OF THE FIBER

The cotton fiber is in reality a long cell composed of countless cellulose molecules. There is considerable conjecture as to the actual construction of the cellulose molecule. One concept is shown in Figure 10-10. The individual tiny fibers have a minute coating of wax. It is to this coating that cotton owes its ease of spinning and other mechanical handling during processing. Without it, the fibers have been found to cling to the finishing frames, causing a waste of fibers.

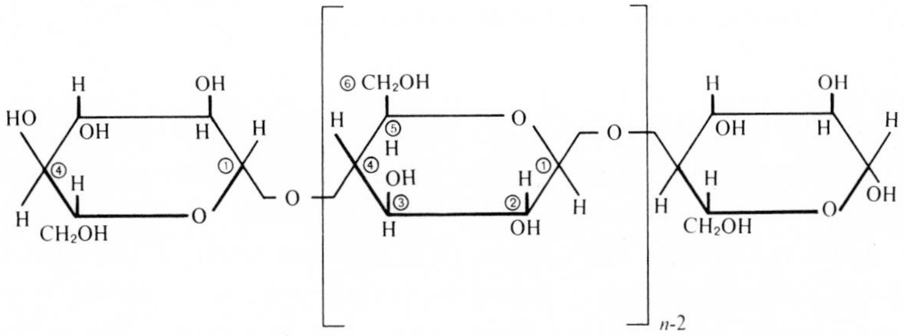

Fig. 10-10 The cellulose chain in glucose units: The heavy lines in the rings represent linkages and portions of the glucose units projecting toward the observer. Light lines recede. This shows the spiral nature of the molecular structure. The six carbons in each glucose molecule are numbered so as to show how and where each substituent (i.e., hydroxyl [OH]; alcohol [CH₂OH]; and glucosidic linkage) is located. (Remember: in the ring structure the corner carbons are usually not shown.) (Courtesy of E. Ott and H. Spurlin [eds.], Cellulose and Cellulose Derivatives [New York: Interscience, 1954], p. 64.)

microscopic appearance

When examined under the microscope, cotton fibers from the boll or from unmercerized fabrics resemble flat, twisted ribbons (Figure 10-11b). The unripe fiber in the boll is a rod-like structure of round cross-section (Figure 10-11a), having a hollow center canal, or lumen, within which the growth fluids are carried. In the mature fiber, this center collapses and may be almost invisible in some fibers even under the microscope (Figure 10-11b). When cotton

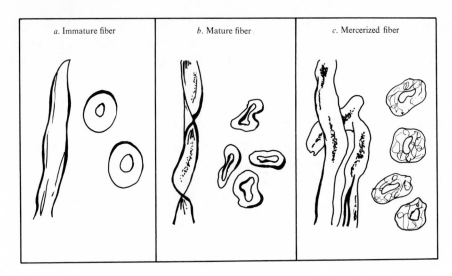

| a. Immature fiber | b. Mature fiber | c. Mercerized fiber |

Fig. 10-11   Sketches of the cotton fiber in three stages.

is Mercerized by treatment with caustic soda, the fibers are somewhat straightened and swollen; the lumen then becomes more readily visible under the microscope. The electron microscope is a research tool used to disclose structures invisible under the optical microscope. The cellulose walls of the cotton fiber are disclosed as a series of concentric growth rings somewhat similar in appearance to the growth rings in a tree stump. Within the rings minute fibrous deposits called *fibrils* have been laid down in a lattice formation. It is due to the physical variations of the lengths of the individual fibrils, particularly those near the surface or cortex of the cotton fiber, that some of the important chemical and physical properties of cotton occur. Many of the advanced researches on modifications in cotton fibers are encouraging the interaction of linkage between adjacent molecules, and higher strength rayons and cottons are being developed for special end-uses.

diameter of fiber

The fiber diameter ranges from .0005 inch to .0009 inch.[8] Sea Island and Egyptian are the finest and Indian the coarsest of commercial cottons.

luster of fiber

The untreated fiber has no pronounced luster. This quality, so generally desired in certain fabrics, is readily imparted to cotton fabrics by means of the

[8] Fiber Chart of the National Association of Dyers and Cleaners.

Fig. 10-12   Idealized cotton fiber
structure.

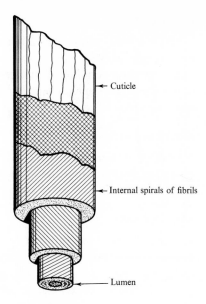

— Cuticle

— Internal spirals of fibrils

— Lumen

Mercerization finishing process. Mercerized cotton fabrics are almost as glossy as silk.

strength of fiber

A single cotton fiber has a low tensile strength. It will support a dead weight of from 2 to 8 grams. The finished cloth can be made strong and durable by using tightly twisted yarns compactly woven together. Mercerized fabrics are made stronger as well as more lustrous. Greater strength in cotton fibers is constantly being sought by plant geneticists as well as by chemists.

elasticity

The elasticity of cotton is largely due to the physical form of the fiber. We have seen that the maturing of the cotton causes the fibers to flatten and twist. This twisted and bent structure of the fibers gives them a small amount of elasticity.

heat conductivity

The property of conducting heat and moisture away from the body causes the body to seem cooler. The various textile fibers vary slightly from one another in this respect, and cotton is ranked as cooler than wool or silk, but not as cool as linen. The fabric structure plays a more important part in the warmth or coolness of fabrics than does the conductivity of the constituent fibers. (See Comfort in Chapter 7 on Textile Finishing, page 110.)

moisture regain

Raw cotton is said by authorities to contain from five to eight per cent of hygroscopic moisture; other scientists place the figure at seven to ten per cent under standard conditions. This moisture is held in the pores and on the surface of the fibers and depends largely on the atmospheric humidity. Cotton is stronger when wet than when dry.

composition of fiber

Cotton is composed of 87 to 90 per cent cellulose and five to eight per cent of water; natural impurities such as proteins, pectic substances, ash, waxes, and sugars are among the other components making up about six per cent.

effect of alkalies

Alkalies have no injurious action on cotton. Concentrated alkalies in the absence of air will Mercerize cotton (see Mercerization, page 95) if it is kept under tension; otherwise, it will cause the fabric to shrink. The fact that even boiling cotton in weak alkaline solutions causes no injury to the fibers but leads to easy sterilization constitutes its claim as being the most hygienic. Boiling cotton with weak alkalies may cause it to become slightly yellow unless the fabric is kept under the surface of the water.

action of acids

Concentrated mineral acids such as hydrochloric, nitric, sulfuric, and hydro fluoric will destroy cotton fibers. Dilute solutions of these acids and of non-volatile acids will greatly weaken cotton, especially if they are permitted to dry on the fabric or if their application is accompanied by heat. The damage is due to the action of acids in forming the readily powdered, structureless *hydro-cellulose*.

action of other chemical solutions

Bleaching agents, oxidizing agents, and reducing agents do not injure cotton if their application is controlled and if no heat is used. Cotton has less affinity for dyestuffs than have the animal fibers.

action of light

Like all cellulose fibers, cotton is weakened by the ultra-violet rays of sunlight. The tendering action is due to the formation of *oxycellulose*.

action of mildew

Pure cotton is not attacked by mildew or bacteria, except under damp or hot and humid conditions. The action is accelerated by the presence of starches, gums, and other sizing or treating agents. The fabric is stained and weakened. If the fabric is intended for out-of-door uses, such as tents, awnings, furniture covers, and boat fabrics, it may be given a protective chemical finish with some sacrifice of texture and color.

action of heat

Cotton is quite resistant to damage by heat. It can be pressed with a hot iron ("cotton" setting) without scorching. At 475° F., it turns brown and burns.

THE VERSATILITY OF COTTON

The cotton fibers can be spun into firm, tightly twisted yarns or soft, fluffy ones capable of being napped. The fabrics woven from cotton, therefore, will range from crisp sheer organdies or fine broadcloth shirtings to heavy ducks and flannels. It may be knitted into sweaters and socks, made into laces and curtains, and laid down in non-woven textile materials as thin as paper or as heavy as felt. Cotton is peculiarly adaptable to these many uses because of ready washability, coolness, water absorption or repellency (depending on its weave and finishing), good color permanency, resistance to yarn shifting, and strength. Cotton fabrics can be made to resemble silk, rayon, or wool. The fibers can be mixed with other textile fibers either in the fiber stage, in the yarn stage, or

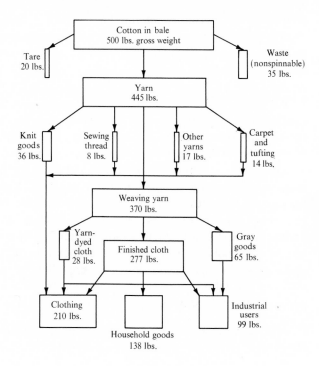

Fig. 10-13 Approximate distribution of a typical bale (500 lbs.) of cotton, 1954. (*From: Inventories in The Textile Cycle* [*Washington: U. S. Department of Commerce, Business and Defense Services Administration, 1961*], p. 21.)

during weaving. Other important factors are its widespread availability and low price. Figure 10-12 shows the many final textile classifications into which a typical 500-pound bale may go.

WHY CONSUMERS LIKE COTTON FABRICS

There is no questioning the fact that consumers do like cotton. According to the figures of the National Cotton Council of America,[9] the preliminary figures for 1961 in terms of (a) thousands of 500-pound bales of cotton consumed, and (b) cotton's percentage share of the total market, was as follows:

Apparel Use, Total	(a) 4,243	(b) 61%
Men's, Youths', and Boys'	(a) 2,470.5	(b) 73%
Women's, Misses', and Juniors'	(a) 1,088.3	(b) 41%
Girls', Children's, and Infants'	(a) 684.2	(b) 77%
Household Uses, Total	(a) 2,289.0	(b) 47%
Industrial Uses, Total	(a) 1,413.6	(b) 23%
Grand Total—All Uses	(a) 7,945.6	(b) 44%

Consumer preference studies conducted by the Marketing Research Department of the Department of Agriculture indicate time and again the reasons for consumer preference of cotton over other fibers for many wearing apparel items. Predominant among their reasons for purchasing cotton are: launderability, absorbency, comfort, color fastness, strength, and cost. Rarely is mention made of the extreme versatility of this fiber, which is found ranging from the most sheer to the most heavy; in fine yarns and in dense heavy yarns; in loose weaves and tight weaves—all depending upon the end-use item and what the consumer expects.

advantages of cotton

Cotton fabrics are generally recognized as being long-wearing, due to good abrasion resistance. There are other fibers which will out-wear cotton, but the combination of long wear and comfort is a significant advantage.

COMFORT   Comfort can be that either of coolness or warmth. Cotton is more outstanding for coolness than for warmth. Cotton is cool in the summer because of its porosity in the lightweight summer fabrics, combined with its absorbency of moisture, its capacity for holding moisture, and its speed of drying. All these contribute to a rapid withdrawal of body moisture from the skin and to the cooling effect from the evaporation of this moisture vapor. The garment is also lightweight and does not cling to the body. Warmth, or the ability of the fabric to prevent transmission of body heat to the cold surrounding or ambient conditions of winter, depends largely upon the construction of

[9] *Cotton Counts Its Customers* (Memphis, Tenn. National Cotton Council of America, July 1962).

the fabric, the amount of dead air which can be held in the fabric structure and its resistance to draft or air flow through the structure. A thick fabric will be warmer than a thin one with the same degree of napping. Wool and the textured yarns of some synthetic fibers are superior to cotton in their ability to retain this loftiness and high nap over long periods of wear and washing. However, numerous research experiments conducted by the Quartermaster Corps discovered the **layer principle** for greater warmth and comfort for troops in the field in extremely cold weather. Here, cotton as the outer layer must be closely woven to prevent wind entry. It acts as a protective shell beneath which the lofty and fluffy under-garments can be worn. The two-layer principle is both lighter in weight than a heavy wool overcoating and will give greater warmth.

Cotton is losing ground in sweaters, jerseys, pull-overs, hosiery, rugs and carpets, blanketings, bedspreads, and laundry and dry-cleaning equipment cloths. In many of these, resiliency of the fiber and fabric is a very important factor; resiliency and warmth go together to the extent that the more resilient fiber will retain its loft for a longer period of time during laundering, as previously mentioned. In 1957, something less than one million pounds of stretch and bulk yarns of nylon were produced. In 1961, 40 million pounds of nylon went into these stretch yarns (see Stretch and Textured Yarns, Chapter 7).

ABSORBENCY   It has been noted that cotton fabrics are comfortable under extreme heat and humidity because of the **rate or speed of perspiration absorbency** and evaporation. In numerous household fabrics, rapid absorbency and total moisture capacity, combined with a good drying, are of importance to the consumer. Most other textile fibers fall down in one or more of those three essentials.

SHRINKAGE   Cotton has a natural shrinkage of approximately five per cent. Of the natural fibers, all shrink more. Even this figure, however, is too high for satisfactory service in wearing apparel if a close fit is desired. Fortunately, cotton can be given a special finish, **Sanforizing,** by which the shrinkage can be controlled within one per cent. Only a very careless consumer would buy wearing apparel which had not been Sanforized-Shrunk or shrunk by some other guaranteed process and clearly labeled as such (see page 105).

COLOR FASTNESS   Color fastness to sunlight, washing, perspiration, crocking, and other conditions depends, of course, more upon the nature and permanence of the dyestuff than upon the identity of the fiber. However, cotton will take readily the most color-fast of all dyestuffs and in greater variety of colors. Manufacturers who are extremely cost-conscious may use cheaper dyes which will give inferior performance in use.

FLEXIBILITY   By flexibility is meant the ease of bending. It is the property of textiles which makes a garment so comfortable, especially when the wearer is in motion. Stiff fabrics make clothing confining. On the other hand, very limp fibers have a tendency to cling to the body and obstruct freedom of movement in that way. Table 3 (page 544) shows cotton to be about at the intermediate point between the most stiff fibers, such as glass, hemp and jute, but being firmer and more self-supporting than nylon, rayon, and wool. Cotton is also classed as a tough fiber and is one of the best in durability. The very flexible cotton fabrics would be diaper fabrics, flannels, blankets, handkerchiefs, and voiles. Among the more rigid or firm fabrics of cotton would be denims, whipcords, coverts, ducks, and chinos. It will be noted that the tough, durable family group goes primarily into men's and boys' work clothing and into shelter fabrics such as cotton duck for awnings.

AIR PERMEABILITY   This feature again is one which demonstrates the versatility of cotton. On one hand, it can be made into tight, almost air-passage resistant fabrics, such as Byrd cloth and other lightweight, closely-woven materials for protection against the passage of wind or air in cold-weather garment assemblies. Loosely-woven, lightweight cotton fabrics help keep the body cool in the summertime by permitting ready passage of air through the material; even in somewhat heavy fabrics, if they are woven of porous construction, air movement is assured. Referring to the moisture absorbency in cotton, the point was made that regardless of the density of the fabric construction, cotton offers little obstruction to the rapid removal of moisture vapor. Thus, perspiration and the almost imperceptible skin moisture can be removed by cotton fabrics, thus avoiding winter chill and summer humidities within the garment or between the garment and the skin of the wearer.

HEAT RESISTANCE   When one reads any of the U.S. Department of Agriculture Marketing Service Reports on Consumer Attitudes toward Cotton and Other Fibers in clothing, cotton is preferred because of comfort, weight, and the combination factor of ease of washing and ironing. Reference has already been made to the fact that cotton can be washed at higher temperatures than other textile fabrics, and the cotton setting on the electric iron of about 400°F. is higher than the ironing temperature of any other textile fiber except linen. One of the claims made for today's vastly improved rayon fabrics is that they can be washed like cottons, but one must remember that rayons are weaker when wet than when dry; therefore, washing like cottons refers to the temperature and not to the severe stresses imposed upon the fabrics when a heavy wash load is used.

modifications in finishes

Chapter 9 on Fabric Finishes gives in more detail a number of the functional finishes which can be applied to cotton fabrics to improve them. Thus, **flammability** of cotton in loosely woven or napped cotton fabrics can be controlled by means of flame retardants. Cotton fabrics for outer wear use can be made fairly **water-repellent** with new finishes, some of which may be permanent, while others are of the renewable types. **Minimum care** and **wash-and-wear** fabrics of 100 per cent cotton can rival in **wrinkle resistance** and **crease retention** the garments made of synthetic fibers but with some sacrifice in durability and comfort. If, on the other hand, some of these minimum-care effects can be achieved by manipulating the cotton molecule without introducing resins, the adverse strength effect and loss of absorbency would no longer be true. It is partly for this reason that researchers in some of the cotton laboratories are endeavoring to make fundamental changes in the molecule of cellulose through cross-linkages within a single molecule or between adjacent molecules lying almost parallel in the card or yarn. Some of these same researches have indicated an increase in the tensile strength of cotton; whether this can be raised by 25 or 50 per cent without injuring other desirable properties is still unknown, but such an increase would result in lighter-weight and much less bulky wearing apparel.

TABLE 10-4 / CHARACTERISTICS OF COTTON FIBERS [10]

1. Microscopic Appearance	Flat tube, spiral twists
2. Length of Fiber	¾ to 1½ inches
3. Diameter	0.0005 to 0.0009 inches
4. Color	Yellowish or cream; may be clean white
5. Luster	Not pronounced
6. Strength	Single fiber, 2 to 8 grams
7. Elasticity	Lower than silk or wool; spiral structure makes it better than linen
8. Conductivity to Heat	Fair
9. Hygroscopic Moisture	7 to 10 per cent
10. Capillarity and Penetrability	Has capillarity
11. Composition	87–90 per cent cellulose; 4–6 per cent gums, proteins, etc.; 5–8 per cent water
12. Preparation of Fiber	Ginning

Chemical Properties

13. Effect of Light	Weakens
14. Mildew	Readily attacked
15. Heat	Withstands well; can be heated to 300° F. with no damage; scorches at 475° F. and burns.
16. Water	Even boiling water has no action.
17. Mineral Acids	Concentrated acids destroy. Cold dilute acids do not injure if washed out or neutralized. Dilute solutions (3 per cent or less) of these acids, if allowed to dry, make tender and destroy.
Sulphuric	
Hydrochloric	
Nitric	
Hydrofluoric	
18. Volatile Organic Acids	No detrimental action.
Formic	
Acetic	
19. Non-Volatile Organic Acids	Will tender slightly if not removed, especially if heat is applied.
Oxalic	
Tartaric	
Citric	
20. Strong Alkalies	No injury, even if concentrated and even if

[10] Courtesy of National Institute of Dry Cleaning.

Chemical Properties (cont'd)

Caustic Soda Soda Ash	heat is applied when air is excluded. Concentrated solution will mercerize if cotton is under tension; otherwise cotton will shrink.
21. Weak Alkalies Ammonia Boraxo Phosphate of Soda Silicate of Soda Soap	No injury.
22. Oxidizing Agents Like Potassium Permanganate	Destroys if not controlled.
23. Metallic Salts	Has practically no affinity for metallic salts.
24. Affinity for Dyestuffs	Less than that of silk and wool.
25. Classes of Dyestuffs Met with in Common Use	Direct Sulfur Basic with mordant Coloring matter developed on fiber Vat colors
26. Bleaching Agents Chlorine Bleach or Hypochlorites	Cold dilute not detrimental to fiber. (Must be removed, as heat and concentrated solutions destroy.)
27. Other Oxidation Bleaches Hydrogen Peroxide Sodium Perborate Potassium Permanganate plus Bisulphite of Soda	No injury if properly controlled.
28. Reduction Bleaches Sulphurous Acid (sulphur dioxide plus water) Hydrosulphite	No injury if controlled.

INDUSTRIAL USES OF COTTON TEXTILES

Approximately 30 per cent of all the fibers used in the United States go into industrial textiles, the end-uses of which vary from liners in doll carriages to casket linings, from sewing thread to tow rope, from typewriter ribbons to conveyor belts. In recent years, cotton has taken roughly one-third of this industrial fabrics market. Tire cords, once a very important outlet for cotton fabric, have now gone almost 100 per cent to man-made fibers, either high-tenacity rayons or nylon. It is predicted that cotton ducks will, within the next few years, be replaced with synthetics having a greater resistance to abrasion and being un-attacked by bacteria or mildew and more resistant to sun rotting.[11] Important cotton outlets are as follows:

[11] Edward A. McMaster, "Fabrics in Industry," Papers of the American Association for textile Technology, *Modern Textiles Magazine*, 12 No. 3 (September, 1957), pp. 76–79.

1   Laundry Textiles. These are the covers for the flatwork ironer rolls or press covers, including dry-cleaning press covers, all of which must be heat-resistant to ironing to a minimum of 350°F. and must have good flex life and abrasion resistance. Another requirement is a smooth surface. All these are advantages possessed by cotton. Some of these uses blend the cotton with asbestos and have been used for the flatwork ironing covers and in some press covers, particularly for dry-cleaning plants. Blends of nylon, asbestos, and cotton have been used in addition to all-cotton fabrics.

2   Filter Fabrics. A wide variety of fibers may be used in filter fabrics, depending upon the chemical or other kind of exposure involved in service. Cotton has been used widely when the chemicals are non-acidic; here the synthetics are superior.

3   Laminating Fabrics. Cotton has been used for a long time in this application. However, the hydrophobic or non-moisture-absorbing fibers may be preferred to be more sure that there is no particle of moisture in or adhering to the fabric being used as a core in some molded plastic articles. Cotton is usually good in compatibility with most of the resins, and, of course, it is also resistant to higher temperatures than are most of the man-made fibers.

4   Hose Fabric. Heavy cotton yarn is braided to make an outer or inner lining for rubber hose. Some hose, especially heavy-duty fire department hoses, and indeed most fire hose, is 100 per cent textile. Cotton has long been used because of its high wet strength and toughness. Some hose is made of heavy cotton duck, and some is of linen. Of the synthetics, Dacron seems to be giving cotton the greatest amount of competition. The percentage of the market held by cotton has decreased from 86 per cent in 1939 to 54 per cent in 1956. However, the total number of bales of cotton going into hose has increased from 35,900 bales in 1939 to 52,900 in 1956.

5   Beltings and Conveyors. The carrying of merchandise in store warehouses and delivery departments and the transportation of finished goods in factories; the carrying of coal and ore from mine outlets to loading platforms, sometimes several miles away; the transportation of grain from unloading platforms to the tops of huge storage elevators; and many other industrial uses require many thousand of miles of conveyor belts. High-strength nylon and other synthetics are being used, but cotton is still a very important fiber for this service. A special yarn marketed by the United States Rubber Company under the name of **Ustex** is specially chemically-treated cotton with reduced elongation and with possibly a 50 per cent increase in breaking strength. In 1939, 57,700 bales of cotton accounted for 78 per cent of the textile fibers used for this purpose. In 1956, the consumption was 94,700 bales, and this was 72 per cent of the market.

6   Automobile Fabrics. The principal applications of fabrics for automobiles is in the seat covers, linings, and upholstery, tire cords, and tops for convertibles. There are also some special trimmings and some sound-deadening materials, a portion of which may be fabric; the rest may be foam rubber or solid foams. Luxury cars generally use wool or a synthetic fiber upholstery material. Less expensive cars generally have cotton-backed vinyl-surfaced materials of at least 90-pounds warp breaking strength and 70-pounds filling strength with sufficient stretch during installation to give a smooth fit and with a maximum of five per cent shrinkage when soaked with water or steamed. Color fastness to light and to crocking must be of a very high order so as to avoid discoloration in service. One advantage of the modern upholstery materials is that they generally shed liquids which may be spilled on them. Thus, they are much less likely to be stained by accidental exposure to rain and the effect of rain water on some color-bleeding material which may have been on the car seat and became wet. In 1939, seat covers accounted for 45,100 bales of cotton, or 49 per cent of the textiles used for that purpose in automobiles In 1956, the percentage had decreased to 13 per cent in the race with synthetics, but the automobile industry had increased so that the bale count was not very different, 26,700. In linings and upholstery, the consumption had actually increased materially, from 43,500 bales, or 27 per cent, in 1939 to 108,000, or 39 per cent, in 1956. In tire cords, there has been a great reversal in the face of rayon and more lately nylon. In 1939, 602,700 bales accounted for 96 per cent of the tire cord business. In 1956,, the number of bales had decreased to 120,000, accounting for only 7 per cent of the tires in automobiles, trucks, buses, and aircraft.

In bags and sacks, the total quantities of cotton used—498,100 bales in 1939; 169,400 in 1956. These include feed and flour bags and a great miscellany of small bags. All textiles are yielding to transparent plastic bags in the merchandise wrapping industry.

COTTON IN NON-WOVEN FABRICS

Non-woven fabrics are discussed in detail in Chapter 5, however, some special mention of the qualities brought by cotton to this kind of fabric may appropriately be listed at this point. Whenever paper is the competitor, the non-woven fabrics have certain points of superiority:

1   A more cloth-like appearance.
2   Better absorbency.
3   Superior wet strength.
4   Superior draping characteristics.
5   Less tendency to lint.
6   A smoother or softer surface.
7   They are not dispersible in water.

The last-named property may sometimes be a liability to the non-woven fabric, especially in a disposable item such as diapers, facial tissue, etc. These are sometimes disposed of through the plumbing system. In the case of paper, the article would be dispersed in water and would break up into small fragments. This is not true in the case of the non-woven cotton. There is thus danger of blocking up the plumbing system.

Compared with woven fabrics, on the other hand, we find that the non-wovens are somewhere between paper and the woven fabrics. The woven have the following advantages:

1   Better launderability.
2   Superior resistance to abrasion.
3   Greater strength.
4   Better uniformity.
5   Better appearance.
6   Superior draping characteristics.

1. SOFTNESS   To the non-wovens, cotton brings its softness to the skin, making it one of the most comfortable of materials in the non-woven field.

2. ADHESIVE QUALITIES   The laminators report that the adhesive qualities of cotton are superior to those of most other materials.

3. ABSORBENCY   Cotton just holds more liquids than any of the other materials used in the non-woven fabrics, and this is of great importance in aprons, towels, napkins, table pads, and diapers.

4. DURABILITY   The very fine cotton fiber and its normal position of being a flattened ribbon-like structure assure the fabric of greater compactness, and the material holds together better during abrasion than in the case of fibers which do not cling together nor twist together as intimately as does cotton.

5. LINT AND FUZZ   One wishes a facial tissue to be free of lint and fuzz. It is also important in napkins and tablecloths that the small loose particles or fibers do not come off on the clothes, and manufacturers of tea bags wish to have a compact, uniform surface without any loose fiber.

6. WHITENESS   Cotton waste is whiter than waste of other fibers going into the non-wovens, and it is the most easily bleached. This quality makes it very desirable in napkins, table wear, towels, and wiping cloths in general.

merchandising problems

The first merchandising problem is the resemblance of non-wovens to paper. Although the appearance is often similar, it is easy to distinguish between them because moistening a paper tissue causes it to disintegrate readily with very little tension, whereas a wetted non-woven fabric of cotton still has considerable wet strength. It also absorbs much more moisture than will the paper product. Paper is invariably very much weaker in one direction than in the other; whereas in the non-wovens, especially those which are laminated, the strength in the two directions is comparable. In marketing, the choice between the two must be on the basis of quality.

limited use life

Many consumers regard a woven or knitted fabric as having almost an unlimited service-life expectancy as long as it is washed and cared for properly. Therefore, the use of a disposable or semi-disposable non-woven material seems to be a gross extravagance. Admittedly, however, there may be times when convenience will prevail, such as in the case of non-woven fabrics for diapers, napkins, table wear, tablecloths, perhaps for bedsheets, aprons and bibs when traveling, when, on occasion, these articles can be discarded when badly soiled. Often persons are unable to distinguish between non-woven fabrics and paper, with the result that the non-wovens are usually classed as being markedly inferior. Therefore, they must find their place in the market on the basis of cost compared with woven or knitted fabrics.

The National Cotton Council, in surveying the field of non-woven fabrics, states:

> There are wide differences of opinion among non-woven manufacturers as to cotton's position from the standpoint of price in relation to the cost of other materials. Manufacturers whose operations provide a supply of cotton waste find cotton considerably cheaper than competing materials. At the time of the survey, these companies indicated that the cost of about 17 cents a pound for good grades of cotton waste compared to a price of from 23 to 24 cents a pound for rayon waste. Manufacturers who purchase their raw material on the open market reported that they paid from 18 to 25 cents per pound for cotton waste, the price depending on the type and grade of waste. Additional cost for cleaning and for processing were reported to make cotton waste more expensive than rayon, even when the cotton was purchased at prices slightly under the rayon cost. On the basis of this information and at price relations existing at the time of the survey, it appears that companies with their own supply of wastes will use cotton as the cheapest raw material, while companies purchasing raw material on the open market use rayon waste as the cheapest raw material available to them.[12]

COTTON STRETCH AND BULK YARNS

We generally consider that stretch and bulky yarns are identified with the synthetic fibers (Chapter 6, pp. 76–79) which can be heat-treated to give them various types of crimp and loops and jumbled texture which, when knitted or woven into fabrics, can produce a stretchy or a soft and lofty fabric structure. Chemical research on cotton has enabled the industry to produce some degree of both bulkiness and stretch in a cotton yarn. The so-called stabilized knit

[12] Frank A. McCord and Raymond Steibach, Jr., "Cotton in Non-woven Fabrics" (Memphis, Tenn.: National Cotton Council of America, May, 1949).

cotton garments are made of stretch fabrics by mixing synthetic bulk or stretch yarns with cotton. Generally, these have cotton warps and a textured continuous filament filling, usually of nylon. A woven all-cotton fabric has been produced which has a stretch of around 10 per cent, considerably less than that of the synthetic fiber stretch fabrics; but this stretch is completely foreign to the ordinary properties of cotton and has been achieved to some extent by three different processes: (1) cross-linked cotton in which the cross-links hold the crimped yarn; (2) mercerizing cotton in a slack or relaxed state[13] and (3) chemical modification by means of resin-treating a highly-twisted yarn, drying it, curing it at a relatively high temperature, then washing and back twisting. When in the relaxed state, it tries to return to the twisted position, forming small coils.

According to Fisher,[14] all-cotton, stretch, and bulk-yarn fabrics present wonderful opportunities for cotton in the wash-and-wear field.

USE OF LINTERS

cotton linters

Cotton linters, very short fibers adhering to the seed, are removed from the seed by a ginning operation resembling that used to separate cotton fiber or lint. These fibers, about ¼ inch in length, are packed in bales of approximately 600 pounds and classified by grades, of which there are seven, established by the Cotton Standard Act of 1926 and based upon the amount of long and short fibers, as well as on color, foreign matter content, and the area of production. Grades of "one" through "four" are preferred by manufacturers of battings and paddings, because the predominance of long soft fibers assures a more permanent and durable matting action. These are usually produced in the first cut, or first process step by which the closely-set saw edges separate these fibers from the seed. Grades "five" through "seven" are generally used in the chemical industry, because the cellulose is more easily removed from the shorter fibers. These are generally second-cut linters, produced on the second run through the ginning operation. If a mill uses only one step in separating these fibers, they are termed a "mill-run."

If these linters are to be used for batting, several processes must be carried out. First, the bale is broken, and the fibers are loosened, cleaned, and mixed. The mass of fibers is then passed through rollers set with fine teeth which pull the fibers into a thin, uniform web. The batt is built up of successive layers of web, with the thickness of the batt depending on the number of webs used. Sometimes

[13] C. F. Goldthwait and A. L. Murphy, *Textile Research Journal*, No. 25 (1955), pp. 47–57.

[14] C. H. Fisher, "All Cotton, Stretch, and Bulk Yarns and Fabrics," *Textile Research Journal*, No. 32 (1962), pp. 313–320.

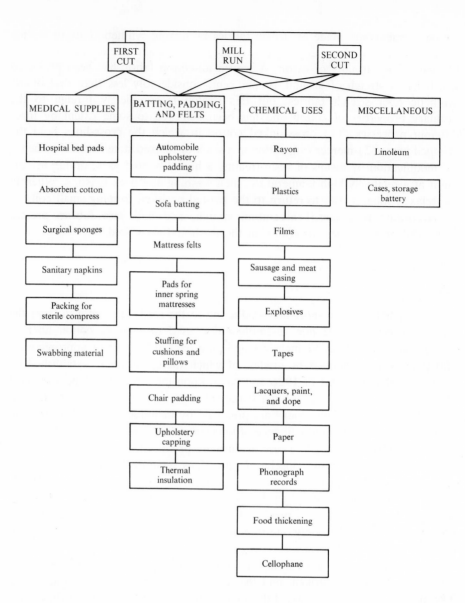

Fig. 10-14 Chart on uses of cotton linters. (*Courtesy of The National Cotton Council [Memphis, Tennessee].*)

cotton waste or lint cotton is blended in small percentages in order to provide extra softness and better cohesion. Production of absorbent cotton involves many of these same operations, but, in addition, absorbent cotton must be bleached, sterilized, and packed in sanitary containers conforming to the requirements of the Federal Food, Drug and Cosmetic Law.

Figure 10-4 shows the products into which cotton linters flow.[1]

production and competition

Production depends upon the size of the cotton crop and upon the grade. It has been noted, for example, that the Acala Cotton strands, of which Pima is the example, produce very few linters adhering to the seed, whereas the typical American Upland cotton produces a considerable quantity of linters. Production for the years 1947 through 1950 is given in Table 10-5 in terms of thousands of bales of 600 pounds. The chemical industry provides the principal market for linters, consuming approximately 60 per cent of all linters used in the United States. The competition here lies in the use of wood in the rayon and acetate industries. Table 10-6 shows the estimated domestic consumption of linters by major use of the chemical industry of the crop years 1947 to 1950 in thousands of bales of grades 5, 6 and 7.

TABLE 10-5 / ESTIMATED PRODUCTION
OF LINTERS BY GRADE, 1947–1950[1]

(000 Running Bales)

Year Begin-ning Aug. 1	LARGELY FELTING				Total Felting	LARGELY CHEMICAL			Total Chemical	Total
	1	2	3	4		5	6	7		
1947	34	164	142	58	398	79	312	499	890	1,288
1948	38	155	153	116	462	339	516	329	1,184	1,646
1949	36	159	220	176	591	439	487	188	1,114	1,705
1950	27	115	158	126	425	314	349	135	798	1,223

[1] Includes production from all sources.
SOURCE: *Weekly Cotton Linters Review,* United States Department of Agriculture, 1947–1951.

TABLE 10-6 / ESTIMATED DOMESTIC
CONSUMPTION OF LINTERS BY MAJOR
USE IN CHEMICAL INDUSTRY,
CROP YEAR, 1947–1950[1]

(000 Running Bales)

	1947	1948	1949	1950
TOTAL, All Rayon	*338*	*443*	*498*	*488*
Viscose + Cupra	209	246	302	263
Acetate	129	197	196	225
Plastics, including cellulose acetate and butyrate	*85*	*88*	*114*	*90*
Nitro-cellulose products, including explosives and film	*68*	*70*	*90*	*75*

[1] Frank A. McCord and Neil J. Dikeman, Jr., "Cotton Linters—Utilization of Research Division of National Cotton Council of America, January 1952, p. 4.

	1947	1948	1949	1950
Paper	34	40	49	38
Sausage Casings	22	14	24	22
Cellulose Ethers	17	27	42	38
TOTAL, Domestic Consumption	564	682	817	751
Exports of Refined Pulp[2]	72	159	151	58
TOTAL, CONSUMPTION	636	841	968	809

[1] Trade estimates.

SOURCE *Weekly Cotton Linters Review*, United States Department of Agriculture, 1947–1951.

COMPETITION IN THE PADDING AND FELTING INDUSTRY   The principal competitors for cotton linters in comforters, mattresses, box springs, box spring pads, automobile seat liners, and upholstered furniture arms and backs are cotton waste, foam rubber, sisal, jute waste, rubberized hair, shredded wood pulp, and now, one of the most serious competitors, the solid foams.

QUESTIONS

1   List the last five articles you purchased which were made of cotton.

A. In your own words, write about the reason cotton was selected instead of some other fiber.

B. What special features, if any, were considered by you in making your purchase?

2   Which countries produce the greatest amount of cotton?

3   Name the cottons having the longest and finest fiber. From what country or countries do these come?

4   Name the inventor and describe the purpose of each of the five machines which contributed most to industrial development of cotton products.

5   Which invention brought cotton to the United States as a major industry?

6   List the grades of domestic (United States) Upland cotton.

7   Define the Pima cotton.

8   How is the quality of cotton determined?

9   Define roving, mercerization, moisture regain, carding, count of yarn, ply yarn, spinning, cellulose, and linters.

10   Discuss the launderability of cotton, as compared with a) rayon, b) wool, c) synthetic fibers.

11   What is the effect of each of the following on cotton: a) sunlight, b) strong mineral acids, c) weak acids, d) strong alkalies, e) chlorine bleach, f) mildew, g) heat.

12   What is the weight of the average cotton bale?

13   Beginning with the unopened bale, what are the steps involved in producing the cotton yarn? Describe each step.

14   List the applications of cotton in the automotive industry.

15   Define versatility as exemplified in the properties of cotton.

16   Explain the count of cotton yarns for both single and two-ply.

17   In what woven constructions are cotton fabrics made? Name at least three important fabrics illustrating each construction.

18   Distinguish between regular finishes and functional finishes as applied to cotton.

List and describe the purpose of at least eight in each category: a) How does each of these finishes affect the consumer use of the product? b) Why and in what way does the Federal Government endeavor to control the production and price of cotton? c) What properties of cotton contribute to 1) comfort in warm weather; 2) ease of washing; 3) color fastness of dyes; 4) durability in use; 5) style in cotton fabrics?

19 What are cotton linters? Describe their use in the chemical industry.

20 What are some of the competitive products to the use of linters as a filling or stuffing material in a) quilts, b) comforters, c) furniture, d) automobile seats?

linen

HISTORY

Fragments of linen cloth, fabrics spun from flax or lin, pre-date the existing records of the earliest prehistoric ages. Some of these fragments of nets and clothing made from flax have been found in the villages of the Lake Dwellers, a Neolithic people who dwelt in Switzerland.[1]

Linen cloths were used as burial shrouds and wrappings of the Egyptian Pharaohs. Today's archeologists find the linen wrappings in the old burial tombs still intact after many centuries. Linen is frequently mentioned in the Bible, and cloths woven from flax were used by the Hebrew, Egyptian, Greek, and Roman priests. During the Middle Ages, fine linens were the regal and highly fashionable cloths. Flax was introduced into Northern Europe by the Finns and the Gauls. According to some authorities, the name linen comes from the Celtic **Llin** or possibly the Anglo-Saxon **Lin.** Flax itself is a name derived from the Anglo-Saxon **Fleax.**

PRODUCTS

Flax is commonly raised for one of two purposes, either for fibers or for seed. The flax plants raised for fiber do not produce good seed, and the plants raised for seed produce a mediocre fiber. The flax plant is difficult to raise.

[1] H. G. Wells, *The Outline of History* (New York: Macmillan, 1921).

fiber flax

Linen is a vegetable stem or **bast** fiber and is found inside the woody stalk of the flax plant, of which **Linum usitatissimum**[2] is the most important commercial type. Fiber flax is raised principally in Europe, with Russia producing the greatest amount and Belgium the finest grade. Other important flax-producing countries are Poland, France, Germany, Holland, Ireland, Italy, Latvia, Lithuania, and Egypt.

seed flax

The greater part of the United States flax production is for seed. This seed flax is grown in the northwestern states, chiefly in Michigan, the Dakotas, Minnesota, and Oregon. Smaller quantities of flax seed are produced in Argentina, Canada, French Morocco, India, Latvia, and Lithuania. In the raising of flax for seed, the plant is permitted to ripen fully. After the seed has been harvested, it is sold to manufacturers of linseed oil. This oil is used in making paints and varnishes and in linoleum floor coverings. The seed cake from which the oil has been pressed out is used as fodder for cattle and other livestock. Only the best portions of the straw can be used for rug backing, upholstery tow, or twine and rope. The rest of the straw is simply waste.

PRODUCTION

The culture of flax demands a moist and mild climate. In the northern countries, where the greatest amount of flax is produced, the flax is sown in the spring, as is done with the grain crops. The plant, two to four feet high, has a growing period of about three months. The flax crop is harvested in late July or August, when the stalks begin to turn yellow at the back and the seeds begin to turn brown. The plant is commonly pulled up by the roots to give a long, unbroken fiber. The world production in recent years has been close to three billion pounds.

rippling

The seeds and bolls are stripped from the pulled stalks by **rippling.** The stalks are spread out fanwise and are pulled through the teeth of an iron comb, or rippler. Mechanical de-seeders have largely replaced hand rippling.

retting

The stalks are dried and then tied in bundles of uniform length preparatory to **retting.** This process loosens the outer woody stalk and the intercellular

[2] J. M. Matthews and H. R. Mauersberger, *Textile Fibers,* 5th ed. (New York: John Wiley & Sons, 1947), p. 307.

gummy substance holding the fibers together and permits the removal of the flax fibers. There are several methods for carrying out this retting process:

1. Pool retting. In Ireland and Belgium, natural outdoor pools are still used. The bundles are placed stem end up in pools of clean, soft water. The bundles are covered with straw and weighted down with stones or earth. The water and bacteria usually hydrolyze the gum from the woody stalk in about two weeks, and the bundles are then removed from the pool.

2. Dew retting. This most primitive method is still used in some areas. The loose stalks are spread out on grassy fields. The retting takes place slowly through the action of rain, sunlight, and dew.

3. Stream retting. The flax bundles are anchored in the running water of a stream. This process is used in Belgium, where the fine quality, strong, clean fiber is retted out in the River Lys. Even here, however, the more carefully controlled vat methods are taking control.

4. Vat retting. This is a more rapid process than the natural elements can provide. The flax is steeped in clear, warm water (75–90°F.) in wooden vats. The softened stalks are then passed between rollers by the methods known as Pownall's Process.[3] The continuous flow of clean water over the stems removes any gums or other extraneous matter.

5. Chemical retting. The quickest retting process is to boil the stalks in dilute sulfuric acid or to steam them. These accelerated processes give a weaker fiber. Hodge and Cross[4] report that retted flax contains the following:

1	Pure cellulose	65–70 per cent
2	Pectin substance	20–25 per cent
3	Woody and cuticular tissue	4–5 per cent
4	Ash	1 per cent

scutching

The retted flax is throughly dried and is then run through a machine which shakes down and crushes the brittle woody stalk, or **shives.** The fibers are cleaned or **scutched** free from the woody fragments by means of a machine having a series of fluted rollers which beat the fibers free from the stalks.

hackling

This is a straightening operation which corresponds to the carding and combing of cottons. The purpose is to lay the fibers parallel so that they can be spun into a yarn. This process is best done by hand by skilled operators. The scutched fibers are pulled through a series of iron combs of increasing fineness. Some short fibers adhere to each comb or fall out of the cluster as the fibers are

[3] Isàbel Wingate, *Textile Fabrics* (New York: Prentice-Hall, 1935), p. 179.
[4] National Institute of Drycleaning, Inc., Chart on Characteristics of Linen Fibers, p. 253.

pulled through the coarse comb and the successively finer ones. These shorter fibers are called **tow** and are used in the irregular or vari-sized yarns of cheaper linens and towels. Such fabrics are commonly called **tow linens.** The long, even fibers which have been laid parallel by the hackling combs are called **line.** These line fibers are used in fine table damasks, handkerchiefs, and sheer linen fabrics. The cleaned fibers are tied in bales weighing between 200 and 224 pounds.

CHARACTERISTICS OF THE LINEN FIBER

microscopic appearance

The microscope shows the linen fiber to be somewhat bamboo-like in appearance. The round, transparent fibers have cross-markings or nodes resembling the joints on bamboo stalks. The **lumen** or central canal is so small as to be almost invisible.

Fig. 11-1 Sketch of the flax stem under magnification: Based on a photomicrograph. (*Courtesy of Glendenning, McLeish and Company.*)

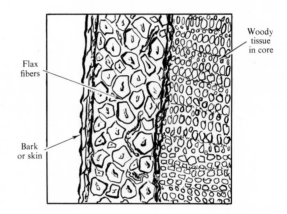

Flax fibers

Bark or skin

Woody tissue in core

length of fiber

Linen fibers may be from six to forty inches but average approximately eighteen inches in length. It is, therefore, not so necessary to spin the fibers tightly to hold the ends in. The rounded, irregular structure of linen makes it harder to spin than cotton.

diameter of fiber

Linen fibers range from 0.0047 to 0.0098 of an inch. Cotton has a wider range of diameters, and though the finest cotton fibers are finer than the finest linen fibers, the coarsest of each are about the same in diameter.

color of fiber

Linen ranges from a pale yellowish-white to a light tan. Some linens are a steel gray. Dew-retted flax is the darkest. Bleached flax of good grade is pure

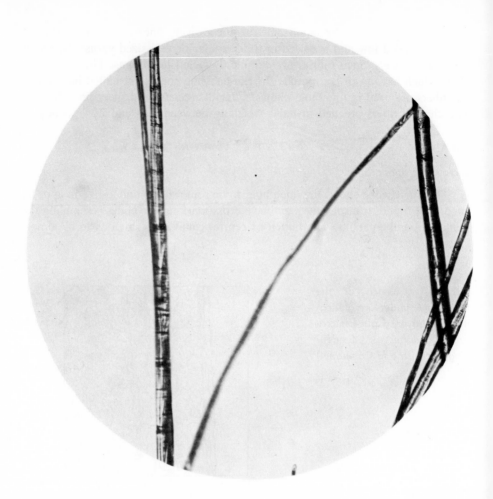

Fig. 11-2 Flax fibers: Individual flax fibers photomicrographed to a magnification of 175 diameters. Note structure similar to that of bamboo pole. Each fiber is also hollow like a tube. (*Courtesy of Glendenning, McLeish & Co., Inc.*)

white, but bleaching slightly weakens linen by separating it into its individual filaments.

luster

Linen fibers have a silky luster which is more pronounced than that of any untreated cottons. Linens are not mercerized, but the natural luster is increased by pounding the fabric after it has been woven.

Fig. 11-3 Photomicrograph of cross-section of linen cloth magnified to 175 diameters: Note the flattening down of the individual circular tubes of the fibres, due to pressure in cutting. (*Courtesy of Glendenning, McLeish & Co., Inc.*)

strength

Linen is two to three times stronger than cotton, and its tensile strength increases when it is wet. Over-retting and bleaching weaken the fibers.

elasticity

Linen feels harder and smoother than cotton because of its poorer elasticity. This lack of elasticity is the cause of the creasing and wrinkling of linen. Resins and other substances are introduced into linens to make the fibers more resilient and hence less easily mussed.

heat conductivity

Linen feels cooler than cotton because it has better heat conductivity. The linen fibers carry the body heat away.

hygroscopic moisture

Linen has about the same moisture regain as cotton—between 10 and 12 per cent. Linen fabrics absorb moisture rapidly. The moisture seems to pass through the fibers. It can, therefore, evaporate much more rapidly from linen than from cotton, and linens are useful for drying purposes. An old test to distinguish between linen and cotton was the water drop test. It is not so reliable today with resin finishes on fabrics. A drop of water on cotton gives a round wet spot. On linen, the water passes along the yarns in both directions to give a cross.

composition of fiber

The linen fiber is composed chiefly of cellulose, but it contains about 25 per cent of pectin substance and wax.

hygienic quality

Linen fibers are smooth, and dirt and bacteria do not collect on the fabric easily. The fabrics do not shed lint, and the absence of loose fiber ends makes linen a hygienic textile material.

Linen launders easily, comparing favorably with cotton. The linen fibers are more readily weakened by alkalies and bleaching agents than are the cotton fibers. Boiling will weaken linen. Weak alkalies such as soap, borax, ammonia, trisodium phosphate, and other detergents do not injure linen.

action of strong acids

Linens, like cottons, are destroyed by strong acids such as hydrochloric, sulfuric, hydrofluoric, and nitric acids. Dilute acids slightly weaken both these cellulose fibers, but, unless the acid is allowed to dry on the fabric, they will not destroy either linen or cotton.

action of light

Ultraviolet light rays lower the strength of linen but to a lesser degree than that of cotton.

action of mildew

Linen, like cotton, is readily attacked by mildew.

affinity for dyestuffs

Linen takes and holds dyes less readily than cotton. This is due to the lack of penetrability of the linen fiber. Only severe bleaching and strong alkali can break down the intercellular structure by removing the pectin and gum. A dyed linen yarn will often, when untwisted, show the core to be lighter dyed than the outer surface. Table 11-1, taken from the Fiber Chart of the National Institute of Dry Cleaners, shows the properties of linen.

TABLE 11-1 / CHARACTERISTICS OF LINEN FIBERS
Physical Characteristics

1. Microscopical Appearance	Number of small fibers cemented together. Has cross-markings at intervals. Resembles bamboo pole.
2. Length of Fiber	Averages 18″ to 20″ long.
3. Diameter of Fiber	0.0047″ to 0.0098″.
4. Color of Fiber	A yellowish buff to gray.
5. Luster	Greater luster than cotton. Characteristic silky luster.
6. Strength	Stronger than cotton. Strength increases when wet.
7. Elasticity	Not elastic.
8. Conductivity to Heat	Better conductor of heat than cotton.
9. Hygroscopic Moisture	10 to 12 per cent.
10. Capillarity and Penetrability	Has no capillarity or penetrability. Therefore more difficult to dye than cotton.
11. Composition of Fiber	Chiefly cellulose. Less than cotton. Has 15 to 30 per cent natural impurities.
12. Method of Preparation	By retting flax (separating stalk from the fiber).
13. Effect of Light on	More resistant than cotton.
14. Mildew	Attacked.
15. Heat	About the same as cotton.
16. Water	As amount of moisture increases, the strength of linen increases.
17. Mineral Acids Sulphuric Hydrochloric Nitric Hydrofluoric	Same as cotton.
18. Volatile Organic Acids Formic Acetic	No detrimental action.
19. Non-Volatile Organic Acids Oxalic Tartaric Citric	Same as cotton (page 149).
20. Strong Alkalies Caustic Acid, Soda Ash	Same as cotton (page 149).
21. Weak Alkalies Ammonia	Same as cotton (page 149).

Physical Characteristics

Borax
Phosphate of Soda
Silicate of Soda
Soap

22. Oxidizing Agents	Same as cotton (page 150).
Like Potassium Permanganate	
23. Metallic Salts	Same as cotton (page 150).
24. Affinity for Dyestuffs	Less than cotton (page 150).
25. Classes of Dyestuffs Met with in Common Use	Same as cotton (page 150).
26. Bleaching Agents	Same as cotton but more difficult to bleach due to presence of natural impurities.
Chlorine Bleach	
or	
Hypochlorites	
27. Other Oxidation Bleaches	Same as cotton (page 150).
Hydrogen Peroxide;	
Sodium Perborate;	
Potassium Permanganate	
plus	
Bisulphite of Soda	
28. Reduction Bleaches	Same as cotton (page 150).
Sulphurous Acid	
(sulphur dioxide plus water)	
Hydrosulphite	

THE LINEN YARN

The hackled fibers have been laid parallel in a thin sheet, or sliver. The sliver is made longer and more narrow by means of the drawing frame. From this machine, the fine strand or **roving** is taken to the spinning frame. Coarse yarns can be spun dry, but the fine yarns must be spun wet because of the fact that the dry linen fiber is weaker than the wet fiber.

The fine even yarns spun from **line,** when they are untwisted, show fibers of approximately the same length and of about the same fineness lying parallel. The yarn spun from **tow** discloses fibers of varying length and diameter, and the untwisted filaments stick out in all directions.

The more loosely twisted linen yarn can often be distinguished from cotton by the parallel arrangement of the glossy filaments, whereas cotton yarns show numbers of filaments in each turn of the yarn.

Ply yarns are rarely used in linen fabrics because the greater strength of the fiber as compared with cotton makes it unnecessary. The natural hardness of the linen fiber would make a ply yarn round and hard and unsuitable for many of the uses for which linen is so desirable.

count of yarn

In England and America, the weight and fineness of a yarn is expressed by numbers, called **counts.** Linen yarns use as the base a **lea** of 300 yards. The count is the number of leas required to weigh one pound. Thus, if 3000 yards of a yarn weigh one pound, the count would be 3000 divided by 300, or 10. The lower the count, the coarser the yarn. Handspun thread for laces may be as high as 400's.

mixed yarns

Many fabrics may have a linen yarn warp and a filling of cotton yarns. Linen yarns may be used as backing or the ground structure of wool-pile rugs or of cotton, rayon, or silk velour upholstery fabrics. Linen and Dacron blends make excellent wash-and-wear fabrics for dresses and sportswear.

LINEN FABRICS

Most linen fabrics are woven. Fabrics, such as sheeting, canvas, crash, and duck, are woven with a plain weave. Drillings are constructed with a twill weave; towels have either a twill or a figure weave, usually the huck or diaper design. The satin weave is used for all linen damasks. These table covers are woven on the Jacquard loom. Rayon is now a strong competitor of linen for table linen. The composition of the fabric must now be labeled in conformance with the Fiber Identification Act of 1958.

Fine laces were formerly made by hand, using the finest linen. Most of the present-day lace is machine-made, using fine cotton yarns and cleverly copying the old designs.

serviceability of linen

A good quality linen becomes more glossy and white during service. The ultimate service a linen will give depends on the strength of the individual fibers. An over-ripe plant yields a brittle fiber, over-retting gives a weaker fiber, and excessive bleaching to give snowy whiteness also tenders the fibers. Linen requires a great deal of care and skilled hand-working throughout its processing in order to produce the finest fibers and the greatest quantity of such fibers. It is stated[5] that 7770 pounds of dried flax plants produce 702 pounds of finished fiber. These factors made linens expensive fabrics as compared with cottons.

USES OF LINEN

wearing apparel

Traditionally a linen dress has been regarded by many consumers as the most comfortable from the standpoint of coolness in summer wear. As has been mentioned, the lack of resiliency of the linen fiber makes it highly susceptible to wrinkling, and linen, therefore, was one of the first of the natural fibers to which

---

[5] J. M. Matthews and H. R. Mauersberger, *Textile Fibers,* 5th ed. (New York: John Wiley & Sons, 1947), p. 322.

synthetic resins were applied for additional wrinkle resistance and crease retention. Some sacrifice was made, however, in comfort, because the introduction of
resins reduced the water absorbency of the fabric. Dress linens may be of various
grades and degrees of fineness. Usually, 25's linens are the most widely accepted
weights, but there are coarser linens down to 20's which are used at times in
looser weaves. Linen suits and slacks for men, generally of a somewhat lower
count than women's wear, were at one time popular but have been largely
supplanted in recent years by tropical worsteds and by blends of synthetic fibers
with wool. Nevertheless, in many parts of the world, particularly in the Orient,
the linen suit is the most highly regarded summer apparel item for men.

The linen shirt and linen underwear are distinctly prestige items and would
be made of finer yarns.

household fabrics

Rather coarse linen yarns in 16's size are used in dish towels and many
other applications where great moisture absorbency and rapid drying are
requisites. Finer towels in degrees of fineness down to 70's are used for finger
towels and doilies. The finest handkerchiefs are of line flax and require light
yarns as fine as 200's. Similarly, fine Cambrics require this approximate fineness
in lightweight fabrics for slips, nightgowns, and similar delicate-looking materials.

Linen is one of the most widely used fibers in table coverings. A survey of
homemakers' preferences as to fibers used in several types of household furnishings[6] reported that in 1958, among the respondents to the questionnaire, about
60 per cent of all table coverings were of cotton; 25 per cent, linen; and 7 per
cent, plastic. In the full-size cloths, linen accounted for 29 per cent; luncheon
cloths, 23 per cent; sets of place mats, only 15 per cent. In general, the linen
articles were found in the metropolitan areas and principally among the more
well-to-do families. When one visits a store, a wide variety of qualities of linen
cloths are immediately available, some being rather loosely woven and of a
coarse or heavy yarn. These, generally, are of tow fibers. The highest quality
linen cloths for tablewear are the damasks, which are of line fiber. The damasks
are generally of approximately 120's yarns and are in the satin weave, usually
woven on Jacquard looms (see Chapter 3 on Weaving of Fabrics). Table
damasks described as single damask and double damask is somewhat misleading terminology, because the yarns in both cases are singles. The difference lies
in the number of shafts used originally in the hand looms for the binding weave.
The single damask has a five-shaft harness to form the satin figure. In the
double damask, eight shafts are used. In forming the binding weave with the hand
loom, a skip of one shaft was necessary on each succeeding pick for the five-leaf

---

[6] Daniel B. LeVine, "Homemakers Appraise Cotton, Wool and Other Fibers in Household Furnishings," Marketing Research Report No. 279, Agricultural Marketing Service.
U.S. Department of Agriculture, pp. 34–35.

satin (single damask), whereas two shafts were missed in selecting the next pick for the eight-leaf satin (double damask). A further control in quality in damasks is in the **count.** Most single damasks are approximately a square or even weave. In some, there are fewer weft or filling yarns than warp. These are said to be under-wefted. If the number of filling yarns exceeds the warp, they are said to be over-wefted, some of these by as much as 10 to 15 per cent, and these are the higher quality of single damasks. In the double damasks, a finer and richer fabric is produced and one having greater luster, because there are seven floats for each warp instead of four in the single, or five-leaf, construction. The double damask contains 180 threads per square inch and is usually over-wefted by about 50 per cent. This is true of the real double damask. It is possible to cheapen this construction by using a lower count per square inch and with somewhat coarser yarns. Under these circumstances, the honest square weave of the single damask would be the superior fabric.

The damasks have for years been regarded as the ultimate in table napery, especially in formal settings. The well-cared-for table damask will last for many years and is generally regarded by the bride as a potential heirloom gift. Pressed with a hot iron when wet and on both sides, linen takes on an ever-increasing luster and beauty. The wear of table linens, not only damasks but some of the cheaper as well, is often reduced by the housewife meticulously ironing the cover along the same fold time after time in order to have it in perfect balance when spread on the table. The center fold should be varied from side to side on different washings and ironings, so as not always to impose the strain along exactly the same yarns the full length of the cloth, because the center fold or inner fold does take a great deal of strain during the time it is folded. Another frequent cause of damage to table fabrics of all kinds is the careless handling of table utensils by children and by inattentive adults. Pressing the edge of a knife or spoon against the fabric or careless writing on table covers—in addition to the fact that it violates codes of etiquette—both cause snagging and catching of the floats in fine damask and, in fact, will weaken and abrade the yarns even in the coarser square-weave fabrics.

Lacy-type linen table napery is frequently found in tea cloths and in individual place settings. These are of extremely fine fiber or yarn and naturally have a resistance to wrinkling. Their durability will be greatly increased by light ironing, depending on their natural crispness, and never starching them, for starching increases the brittleness or the tendency of the yarns to break under bending pressure.

FLAX PAPERS

Flax is used in fine papers. It imparts great flexibility and tear resistance to fine papers for currency and writing bond. Another extensive use which annually consumes about four million dollars worth of paper in the United States alone is in cigarette papers. Flax papers burn without odor.

QUESTIONS

1   What is flax?

2   Where and under what conditions is it grown?

3   Describe the flax fiber.

4   What is a bast fiber?

5   Define the following terms and indicate those which correspond to certain processes common to cotton fiber.

    a. Scutching   d. Rippling

    b. Retting   e. Beetling

    c. Hackling   f. Line fiber

6   How do cotton and linen counts differ?

7   How long is the flax fiber? How does this affect the properties of the yarn?

8   Define and describe single and double damasks.

9   Is flax a durable fiber?

10   How should it be cared for?

wool

It is possible that wool fibers were the first textile materials to be woven into clothing as early man began to discard pelts and skins. Probably felted wool was an intermediate clothing material. The wool or underhair of prehistoric sheep was coarser than that of the types of sheep raised today, and the animal was covered with a coarse, straight, inelastic outer hair. Even today, we find similar hairs in the wool of sheep which have gone wild or of very old animals; this is a throwback or reversion to the original stock.

The best wool is found on sheep which have been specially and consistently bred for yielding wool. (Animals bred for the quality of their flesh give inferior grades of wool.) The Romans are said to have improved the wool type of their stock as early as 200 B.C. by cross-breeding with African rams, and the Roman Empire spread sheep-raising and wool-fabric handicraft throughout Europe.

Wool-like hair is found on such animals as the alpaca, angora goat, camel, cashmere goat, llama, and vicuna. The minor differences in these fibers and the special uses to which the hairs are put will be discussed in Chapter 13.

the influence of the merino strain

The merino sheep developed in Spain is a famous wool-bearing strain known as early as the year 500 A.D. Spain was actively engaged in cross-breeding sheep for wool improvement as early as the fourteenth century, and the merino is the forebear of the present flocks in the United States, Canada, France, Germany,

Australia, New Zealand, Austria, South America, and South Africa. Von Bergen[1] refers to merino sheep husbandry as the saga of sheep breeding. In each of these countries, there have developed differences in the physical characteristics of the wool produced. Cross-breeding, climatic differences, variations in the food, and other factors have produced such distinct strains as our own fine merino "Ohio Delaine," England's long-fibered "Lincolnshire" and "Leicestershire"; France's silky "Rambouillet"; Germany's "Saxony"; and Australia's fine "Cross-bred" product. The colonists in Virginia and New England began to spin and weave wool from their own flocks soon after landing in America. The merino strain was introduced into the United States from Spain early in the nineteenth century and greatly improved the strain of the Atlantic seaboard flocks into which the imported merino rams were introduced. American sheep breeding now extends from coast to coast.

types of united states wool

The United States produces three main classes of wool. These classifications are regional, that is, each of three sheep-growing regions produces its own typical wool. There are many grades of wool within each region.

1   Domestic wools—mostly merino wools from Eastern and Midwestern states.

2   Territory wools—from the Rocky Mountain Plateau states.

3   South Western wools—from Arizona, California, Nevada, New Mexico, and Texas.

The wools from the latter two regions are the coarser fibers characteristic of sheep bred for meat as well as for wool. The two differ from one another in that it is customary to shear the sheep twice a year in the Southwestern region and but once a year in the Rocky Mountain region.

Statistics often tell an interesting story. In Table 12-1 are given the 1960 wool-production data. All the important wool-producing countries are shown. As important as the United States is in producing wool, it does not produce enough for its own consumption and must import vast amounts, especially from Australia, where the climatic conditions favor the production of some of the world's finest wool. Part of the deficit is made up by using re-worked wool and other fibers admixed with wool. Blending of wool fiber with synthetics in suitings and coatings still further stretches the supply of this fiber.

In the year 1959–1960, in which the United States produced 292 million pounds of wool, we imported the following quantities from principal producers.

Australia	51,000,000
Argentina	71,000,000

[1] Werner von Bergen, Chap. XII, in J. M. Matthews and H. R. Mauersberger, *Textile Fibers,* 5th ed. (New York: John Wiley, 1947), p. 451.

Union of So. Africa	36,000,000
Uruguay	18,000,000
New Zealand	69,000,000
Total	245,000,000

WOOL PRODUCTION

shearing

The majority of sheep are sheared in the spring. All clipping was formerly done by means of hand shears, but now machine-powered shears are used almost exclusively, and a skilled shearer can clip as many as 200 sheep a day. These shearers transport their equipment from place to place, beginning in the southern part of the United States early in the spring and gradually working north. This makes machine shearing possible to many growers who could not otherwise afford it. The fleece is clipped off in one piece and, although the variation is great (6 to 18 pounds), the fleece weight averages about 8 pounds to each animal, from which is produced about 3 pounds of scoured wool. In Australia, recognition is made at the time of shearing that the quality of wool varies on different parts of the animal, and often the superior wool from the sides and shoulders of the sheep is treated as one fleece and a second fleece is made up of the wool from the head, belly, legs, and breech. The order of preference is shown in Figure 12-2.

quality of raw wool

The quality of the fleece is affected by the climatic conditions, the health of the animal, and the nature of the grazing land. A season of heavy rains may remove much of the wool grease or **yolk** exuded from the skin and always found in the fleece of healthy sheep. When this grease is removed, the fleece mats,

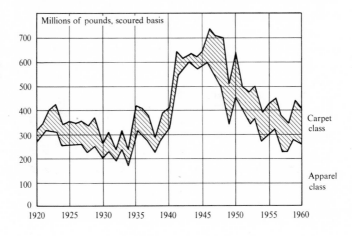

Fig. 12-1 United States wool consumption 1920–1960. (Courtesy of Textile Organon, Dec., 1960, p. 203.)

TABLE 12-1A / ESTIMATED WORLD PRODUCTION OF RAW WOOL, 1959-60 TO 1963-64

Country and Type	1959-60 Mil. lb.	1960-61 Mil. lb.	1961-62 Mil. lb.	1962-63 Mil. lb.	1963-64[1] Mil. lb.
Australia	1,680	1,625	1,699	1,663	1,738
New Zealand	577	588	587	620	630
United Kingdom	124	121	131	131	127
Argentina	423	413	413	408	415
South Africa	319	317	337	321	335
United States	319	323	320	299	290
Uruguay	159	181	185	190	190
Other	911	897	897	905	900
Total Free World	4,512	4,483	4,569	4,537	4,625
Soviet Bloc	1,113	1,120	1,144	1,147	1,165
World total	5,625	5,603	5,713	5,684	5,790

Courtesy U.S. Dept. of Agriculture, *Wool Situation* (Washington), Oct. 1963, p. 29.

TABLE 12-1B / ESTIMATED CONSUMPTION OF WOOL IN THE 10 CHIEF WOOL MANUFACTURING COUNTRIES, CLEAN BASIS, ANNUAL 1960-62, BY QUARTERS, JAN.-MAR. 1962 TO DATE

Country	Year 1960 Mil. lb.	Year 1961 Mil. lb.	Year 1962 Mil. lb.	1962 Jan.–Mar. Mil. lb.	1962 Apr.–June Mil. lb.	1962 July–Sept. Mil. lb.	1962 Oct.–Dec. Mil. lb.	1953 Jan.–Mar. Mil. lb.	1953 Apr.–June Mil. lb.	Percentage Change Apr.–June 1963 to Jan.–Mar. 1963 Pct.	Percentage Change Apr.–June 1963 to Apr.–June 1962 Pct.
United States[1]	411	412	429	108.9	110.2	103.6	106.4	112.6	109.5	−2.8	−0.6
United Kingdom	481	472	448	121.5	113.2	97.4	116.3	121.6	118.7	−2.4	+4.9
France	301	301	291	79.2	75.0	58.1	78.4	78.4	76.9	−1.9	+2.5
Japan	302	350	320	83.0	88.0	76.0	72.8	74.4	79.3	+6.6	−9.9
Italy	198	187	205	48.8	51.2	48.5	56.5	51.4	52.1	+1.4	+1.8
West Germany	151	150	148	38.8	37.0	34.9	37.3	37.7	37.8	+.3	+2.2
Belgium	86	82	100	25.6	22.9	21.2	30.1	25.9	26.5	+2.3	+15.7
Australia	74	65	73	17.4	18.6	18.3	18.4	17.8	19.4	+9.0	+4.3
Netherlands	22	21	22	5.8	5.7	5.1	5.4	5.9	6.3	+6.8	+10.5
Sweden	12	11	10	3.0	2.4	2.0	2.8	2.9	2.4	−17.3	—
Total	2,038	2,051	2,046	532.0	524.2	465.1	524.4	528.6	528.9	+.1	+.9

[1] Consumption on woolen and worsted system only.

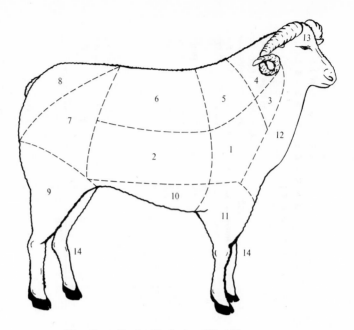

Sheep Fleece, Showing Distribution of Wool Fibers
as Classified by the Sorter.

1. Shoulder wool is usually the best fiber and often
referred to as *prime*.
2. Sides produce next grade, or *super*.
4-5-6. Back produces *choice* wool.

Fig. 12-2 Sketch showing variations in wool fiber quality in a single fleece when judged by a skilled grader.

due to the fibers twisting around each other, producing a **cotted** fleece. Such a fleece cannot be combed without breaking the fibers or tearing them apart. Our western fleeces, in particular, are often ragged and dirty and full of burrs and other foreign materials caught in the fibers. This is due to the method of grazing the flocks, herding them from place to place as the seasons change, and allowing them to roam at large. In Australia, the sheep are grazed in large enclosures called paddocks, which are kept as clean and as free from burrs as possible.

pulled wool

Approximately 8 per cent of the virgin (new) wool used in the manufacture of cloth is **pulled** wool. Pulled wool is that obtained from the pelt of dead sheep. Animals shipped to market to be killed are not clipped before shipment, because the wool gives the sheep protection against bruises and cuts which would affect the grading of the mutton or lamb flesh. Pulled wool has the closed end of the root of the fiber. This interferes with the dye absorption; also, the fiber is less elastic and lustrous than fleece wool.

In pulling wool, the skin of the sheep is softened by one of several processes. Lime paste [Ca(OH)$_2$] may be used to soften the soft gelatinous part of the skin. In another process, sodium sulfide is applied to the under side of the skin and allowed to react for a sufficient time to dissolve the fiber roots, so that the wool fibers can be pulled out readily. Bacterial action destroying the connective tissue constitutes the sweating process for loosening the fibers. The sulfide method is widely used in the United States because it damages the hair and skin to a lesser degree than do the others. The lime method affects the dyeing property of the wool because of the deposition of lime in the medulla or core of the fiber.

Kemp is a straight, weak, coarse, and inelastic fiber which is commonly found in varying amounts in merino wool. These kemp fibers do not react to dyes as do wool filaments, therefore, show up as flecks in the finished cloth.

the grading of wool

Wool fleeces are graded according to what the skilled inspectors, called **wool classers,** judge the majority of the fibers in the bale may be. The fiber classification is based on the diameter and is broken down into fine, medium, coarse, and carpet. There are 13 grades of wool as defined by the U.S. Department of Agriculture. Twelve were enacted into law on June 18, 1926, and the thirteenth (62's) was added in 1940, because it was a grade used by some mills. These figure grades and the American "blood" equivalents are shown in Table 12-2. The numbers are based on the English system and are recognized internationally.

TABLE 12-2 / STANDARD WOOL GRADES USED IN THE UNITED STATES

British System	United States System
80's 70's 64's	Fine
62's 60's 58's	Half-blood
56's	Three-eighths-blood
50's 48's	Quarter-blood
46's	Low-quarter-blood
44's	Common
40's 36's	Braid

Full-blood is 100 per cent Merino.

A second classification is based on fiber length. This is judged by the **sorter** working for a mill. The longer fibers, **tops,** are classed as **combing** wools for use in worsted yarns. The shorter-fibered wools and the short fibers or **noils** removed during combing are used in woolens. These woolen fibers are usually less than two inches long. The terms used are: **strictly combing** for fibers over 2.5 inches long, **French combing** for fibers 1.5 to 2.5 inches, and **clothing** for less than 1.5-inch-long fibers. Extremely long coarse wools, mainly from South Africa, are classed as **carpet wools.**

The English classification system for **worsted** yarns is widely used. The wool is given the number showing the number of hanks of 560 yards which can be spun from it to weigh one pound. Thus, if one 560-yard hank can be spun, the wool is a No. 1, but if 40 such hanks, or 22,400 yards, weigh one pound, the wool is a No. 40. Yarns below 40's are classed as coarse. According to the **run count** system used in New England mills, a No. 1 **woolen** yarn means that 100 yards of yarn weigh one ounce, or that 1600 yards weigh one pound. A No. 10 woolen yarn by this system is so fine that 1000 yards weigh one ounce.

re-worked wool

A large amount of re-worked wool is used in combination with virgin wool fibers. The average person does not realize that there are many grades of re-worked wool, and the indiscriminate use of the term **shoddy** unfairly implies a product of inferior value. The term shoddy originally referred to fibers which had been shod or shed, but now it is applied to waste fibers. Now generally termed **reprocessed wool,** it is commonly obtained from the waste from worsted mills, knit-goods mills, clothing manufacturers, etc. Shoddy consists of reclaimed worsted or knitted fibers which have been reduced to fiber form. The best grades of shoddy have an average fiber length of about one inch and are superior to some lower grades of virgin wool.

Mungo or **re-used wool,** is an inferior grade of re-worked wool obtained from woolen or felted rags. The reclamation or **garneting** process tears and breaks the felted fibers and yields a shorter and poorer fiber.

Extract is obtained from rags which contain cotton, rayon, synthetics, or silk admixed with wool. The process involves sorting, cleaning, and carbonizing the rags. Dilute sulfuric acid solution or hydrochloric acid gas is used to carbonize the cotton and rayon fibers. The concentration and temperature are so regulated that the cotton is attacked by the acid but the wool is not injured. After neutralization with a solution of soda ash, the rags are dried and the cotton is dusted out in the form of brittle hydrocellulose. It might be mentioned that a similar carbonization process is often used to remove vegetable matter, such as burrs, straw, etc., from fleece wool.

Noils are not really recovered waste but the short fibers removed in combing fleece wool. They are spun into woolen yarns. Short-staple noils are usually classified as re-worked wool. The short waste fibers from fulling, scouring, brushing, and shearing woolen and worsted fabrics are classified as **flocks.**

A re-processed yarn made from unfelted knit goods is superior in durability to a virgin wool yarn made up of flocks mixed with longer staple wool fibers. It is difficult to distinguish a fabric made of re-worked wool from one composed of virgin wool. Microscopic examination might show broken or flattened scales on the fibers if mungo were used, but even an expert cannot always find conclusive differences between virgin wool and a good shoddy yarn, such as that from Botany wool. If there is a great difference in the length of individual fibers, and if there are fibers of many colors in the cloth, it may be assumed that some re-worked wool has been used in the fabric.

wool products labeling act

Because of this confusion and the prevalence of introducing re-worked wool into fabrics and selling them as new or virgin wool, the Federal Wool Products Labeling Act of 1939 was passed by the Congress and became effective July 14, 1941. It is administered by the Federal Trade Commission, which issued 35 rules and regulations to guide business as to the correct manner in which to label and promote wool products. Some of the old terms describing wool were discontinued, and since that date, fabrics and garments containing wool must be labeled as to fiber content. A few products were specifically exempted from the law: carpets, rugs, mats, and upholstery fabrics.

Under this law, wool is classified in three ways as follows:

1   Wool. Means new wool which has never before been woven, knitted, or felted.

2   Reprocessed Wool. Means wool fibers which have been woven, knitted, or felted and which have never been used by the consumer before being reduced back to the fiber state and again made into a consumer product.

3   Re-used Wool. Means wool fibers which have been used in consumer products, after which they have been reduced back to the fiber state and again formed into a consumer product.

Only the new wool can be called **wool** in labeling, advertising, or by word of mouth at the time of sale. Thus, a blend of 50 per cent Wool, 30 per cent Re-processed Wool, and 20 per cent Re-used Wool is only 50 per cent Wool. The other fibers are not legally termed "wool." If, in place of the re-worked wools, the fiber blend contains other wool-like fibers, such as camel hair, cashmere or mohair, the exact composition in the order of the predominance of each fiber, must be disclosed. Similar label requirements exist for addition of rayon, cotton, synthetics, etc.

Because of this Act of 1939, wool products are not included in the Fiber Identification Act of 1960. It is interesting to note that neither act covers the disclosure of the fiber compositions of upholstery fabrics, although slipcover materials not containing wool are included in the new law.

These names for the re-worked wools are more exact in disclosure of the past history of the fiber and of the possible alteration or damage suffered through

Fig. 12-3 Wool blending: Workers blending various types of scoured wool in batches on a combination scale which indicated by the markers on the dial the amount of each type of wool to be used in the blend. (*Courtesy of The Wool Bureau, Inc.*)

extra processing than were the more picturesque terms. It should be noted, however, that virgin wool from the weaker wool fiber areas of the fleece are not as good as certain grades of re-processed wool.

manufacture of worsted yarns

Wool fibers may be woven into worsted cloths or woolen cloths. These have been referred to briefly in discussing re-worked wool.

Worsted cloths are made from long-staple wool fibers, usually from 2 to 8 inches in length. The fibers are first scoured to remove the wool grease, dirt, and perspiration, or **suint.** Wool grease is purified to yield **lanolin,** a product widely used in ointments and cosmetic creams. The alkaline solution used to remove the grease, and the soap and water to remove the dirt and perspiration, result in a considerable amount of weight loss or **shrinkage.** In the United States, this loss is estimated to average nearly 60 per cent. If all the burrs and other vegetable matter are not removed in the scouring operation, it may be necessary to carbonize the fleece. Another method sometimes used is to freeze the fleece at a very low temperature to harden the grease and to make the burrs brittle enough to be brushed or shaken out.

The wool fibers are then carded in much the same way as is cotton. The card consists of several cylinders equipped with fine wire teeth which lay the fibers in a soft sheet or sliver, much as a rake lays grass stems roughly parallel.

In worsted cloths the fibers are then combed out as nearly parallel as possible. The pattern of the woven cloth is clearly shown, and it is necessary that the short fibers shall be combed out; these combinings are the noils. The slivers are drawn out narrower than they were in the carding machine and are slightly twisted. The individual fibers are all of about the same length after combing. The dyeing operation commonly follows the combing. Yarn-dyed cloths have a more uniform color due to the pressure-dyeing process, and the fastness of the color to service conditions is better than if the cloth is dyed after weaving. In the latter case, the color is not always uniform throughout the yarn, and different shades of color may show up during wear.

Spinning puts the desired twist in the yarn. The speed and tension of winding the slivers is regulated to give the yarn the desired twist as it progresses from one spool to another. Worsted yarns are usually given a greater twist and are firmer than are woolens. The count or size of worsted yarns has already been defined in terms of the number of hanks required to weigh one pound. Weavers purchase the yarn on the spool or in hanks. Worsted yarns may be single-ply, two-ply, three-ply, or four-ply. Multi-ply yarns are graded according to the number of plies and the size of the individual ply strands making up the twisted yarn.

manufacture of woolen yarns

The shorter wool filaments are used for woolen yarns. The merino wool fibers are specially suited for this use. Woolen cloths are characterized by softness of handle and texture, indistinctness of pattern, and often a slight napping of the surface. The properties of blankets, typical woolen cloths, are discussed in Chapter 27.

Woolens may be made up entirely of virgin wool fibers or in combination with re-processed or re-used wools or other textile fibers such as cotton, rayon, or synthetics. In low-grade woolens, the fiber content may be nearly all reclaimed fibers, or other textile fibers may constitute a high percentage. The napping of woolens, the indistinct pattern, and the slight felting in the finish make possible the use of fibers of varying lengths and render it difficult to distinguish the identity of the fiber types which have been spun into the yarn.

Wool fibers, whether new or re-worked, are customarily scoured and gar-

Fig. 12-4 Carded wool looks almost web-like: A web of carded wool as it comes from the first card, having just passed through the peralta rollers. These metal rollers exert tremendous pressure on the web of wool and tend to reduce to dust seed and other foreign vegetable matter which may still be in the wool. (*Courtesy of The Wool Bureau, Inc.*)

Fig. 12-5 A Warping creel or frame: An inside view of a warping creel. On this large frame, the operator mounts the bobbin of yarn and the strands are then drawn through reeds as seen in the photograph and wound at high speed upon large loom beams. Extra bobbins lie between the two banks of warps. (*Courtesy of The Wool Bureau, Inc.*)

Fig. 12-6   Scouring wool: Photograph shows one of a series of four bowls used in the scouring process. Wool is seen dropping from the feed mechanism at the right into the first tank. The raised spikes move slowly toward the rear of the tank, drop, and then move forward to force the wool through the solution. This action is constantly repeated. The first tank through which the wool passes in the scouring process contains soap and soda in solution, and the strength of this solution usually is maintained by hourly additions of these ingredients. As the wool passes from bowl to bowl, the alkalinity of the solution is reduced, and it is not an uncommon practice to give the wool a clear-water rinse in the last bowl. (*Courtesy of The Wool Bureau, Inc.*)

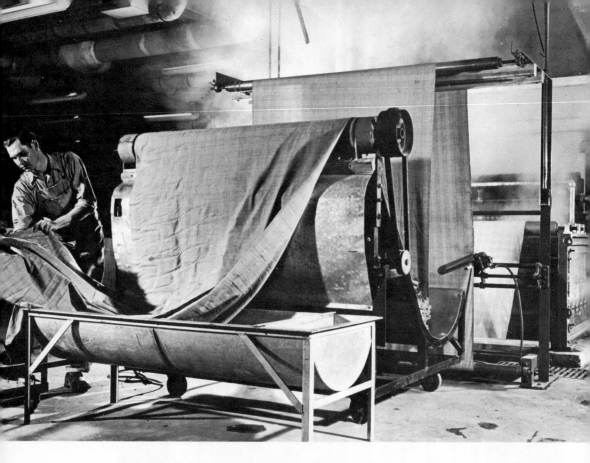

Fig. 12-7 Crabbing machine for evening the alignment of yarns: Crabbing machine, where woven patterned goods and other cloths are run through hot water over a series of small rolls to fix the warp and filling threads permanently, so there will be no uneven shrinkage in later stages of finishing. (*Courtesy of The Wool Bureau, Inc.*)

neted before they are used. The carding operation on yarns for woolens is designed to leave the individual fibers in a tangled mass. Woolen yarns are, therefore, not combed. The final yarn is fuzzy, is less tightly twisted than the worsted yarn, and can be easily napped after weaving. The fuzzy structure retains or traps air, and thus woolens are warmer than worsteds. These yarns may be carded several times. They are usually dyed before weaving and are described as **stock-dyed** if at the sliver stage, **yarn-dyed** if at that step, or **piece-dyed** if colored after the cloth has been woven.

varieties of cloths made of wool

In general, worsteds are characterized by distinctness of weave, compactness, resistance to wear and to soiling, and perhaps lightness in weight. Woolens are indistinct in pattern and weave, soft, warm, and generally fulled or napped. Loosely woven woolens are often napped or felted until they appear to be

Fig. 12-8 Pressing the woven cloth: Pressing machine in a woolen mill. Every piece of cloth passes between the steam-heated cylinder and pressure plate. (*Courtesy of The Wool Bureau, Inc.*)

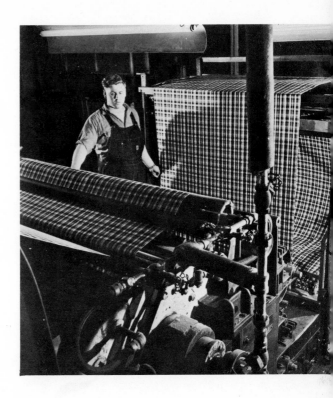

compact. Some lightweight broadcloths and flannels are woven with a worsted warp and a woolen filling which is then slightly napped.

As in other fabrics, the appearance of wool goods must have both an initial and a long-lived appeal. Two of the essential steps with fabrics made of wool fiber are evening of the grain and selvage (Figure 12-8) and properly smoothing the surface by pressing (Figure 12-9).

PHYSICAL CHARACTERISTICS OF WOOL

microscopic appearance

Wool is a hair and originates in the skin. There are as many as 40,000 to 50,000 per square inch of surface. Under the microscope, it appears as a solid rod covered with horny scales. These scales resemble those of fish. The luster[2] of the coarse wool fibers is due to the reflecting surface of the tightly-fitting large scales typical of those fibers. Finer cross-bred wool fibers have scales which project out from the fiber and are smaller in proportion to the fiber diameter and do not reflect as much light.

[2] Fiber Chart of the National Association of Dyers and Cleaners, p. 192–193.

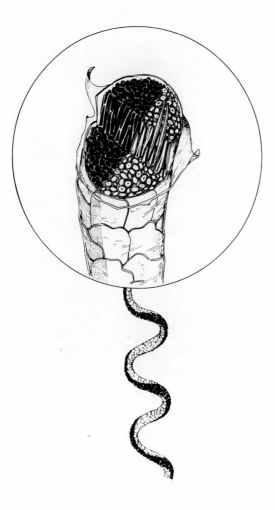

Fig. 12-9 The wool fiber greatly enlarged: Lower portion shows crimped and spiraled configuration of the wool fiber. Upper portion (further magnified) shows the scaly exterior and the cellular interval structure as theorized by many research worker on wool. Cortex spindle-like cells smaller than those in medulla.

The fiber consists of three portions:

1   The epidermal **scale,** or horny portion.
2   The **cortex,** or cellular portion underlying the scales.
3   The **medulla,** or central portion containing the pigment coloring matter of the fiber.

The cortex is the main constituent of the fiber and is built up of numerous small, spindle-shaped cells which vary from 0.0014 to 0.0025 inches in length. The cells in the medulla (which may be compared with the marrow of a bone) are larger than those of the cortex. This central portion may be continuous or broken up into isolated segments. Wool fibers do not always show this medulla clearly.

length of fiber[3]

The wool fiber ranges from 1 to 8.5 inches in length, depending on the type of sheep and other factors. The fibers for worsteds commonly average from 3 to 8 inches, those for woolens, 1 to 3 inches.

diameter of fiber[4]

Wool fibers vary from 0.0005 to 0.0015 inches in diameter. Thus, they are coarser than silk, rayon, cotton, or linen fibers, and woolen fabrics are generally heavier and more bulky than those made from other textile fibers.

color of fiber[5]

The natural color of wool ranges from yellowish to brown and sometimes black. The pigment is in the cells of the medulla.

luster of fiber[6]

This characteristic has been explained as being due to the reflection from the fiber scales. When wool garments have been worn, the yarns and scales tend to become flattened out and to reflect more light. Worsteds, especially those made from coarse, naturally shiny wool fibers, tend to develop a shine more readily than do the fuzzy-surfaced, tangled yarn woolens.

strength and elasticity of fiber[7]

The theory is that the strength and elasticity characteristics of the wool fiber depend on the structure of the cortex and on the movement of the cells when subjected to tension. Wool is the most elastic natural fiber and can be stretched from 25 to 30 per cent of its length before breaking. This is a valuable characteristic of wool. The strength of wool for equal diameters is less than that of silk, cotton, or linen. Wool is weaker when wet than when dry; conversely, the strength of cotton and linen is greater when wet. On the basis of equal fiber diameter, the very fine Saxony merino fibers are stronger than the coarser wools. Another characteristic believed to depend on the cortical layer is the curl of the fiber. If the cells are uneven in growth or arrangement, the fiber will be wavy. Fine staple fibers are naturally more curly than the coarser ones. The springiness of wool fabrics is due to this curl and to the elasticity of the fiber. The intertwining of these curly fibers is believed to contribute to the felting property of wool.

[3] *Ibid.,* p. 192.
[4] *Ibid.,* p. 192.
[5] *Ibid.,* p. 192.
[6] *Ibid.,* p. 192.
[7] *Ibid.,* p. 192.

heat conductivity[8]

Wool, like silk, is a poor conductor of heat and, therefore, will not conduct the body heat away in cold weather. However, of greater importance to the warmth of a fabric is its enmeshed air retention.

hygroscopic moisture[9]

Wool normally carries from 10 to 15 per cent of moisture; the amount may be greater or less, depending on the temperature and humidity of the air. The hydroscopic property of wool makes it important that the testing of wool fabrics and the purchase of raw wool and of finished fabrics be done under known conditions. The standard condition for testing room is 70°F. and 65 per cent relative humidity. In purchasing wool, it is rather generally accepted practice to add to the bone-dry weight an allowable **regain** or moisture weight of 11 per cent. It is easy to determine the moisture content of a wool fabric by laboratory test, but very difficult for a customer to judge by the feel or apparent weight of a fabric how much water it contains. Wool can contain as much as 30 per cent of moisture without feeling damp. The fibers absorb moisture and dry out again slowly. A bather who is wearing a wool bathing suit is less chilled while the suit is drying out than is one who is wearing a cotton suit.

capillarity and porosity[10]

These physical properties affect the readiness with which wool is dyed or bleached for they control the moisture penetrability of a fiber. Since **porosity** is the measure of the volume of voids or openings in a volume of fiber or other solid, the more irregular the outer surface of a fiber, such as wool, the greater the porosity and the greater the surface area. Both factors in wool serve to make it easier to dye and finish. If voids connect with one another, or if the void is a central canal, such as the lumen in cotton, the passage of water and other solutions is promoted by **capillarity.** Mention has been made that shorn wool is more easily dyed than pulled wool because the medulla of massed fibrils in the fiber is open at both ends and available for capillary transmission of water. In wool, however, the scaly structure makes porosity the more significant factor in moisture penetration.

composition of fiber[11]

The hairs are the only textile fibers which contain sulfur and which consist largely of the protein known as **keratin.** This protein is composed of:

[8] *Ibid.*, p. 150.
[9] *Ibid.*, p. 150.
[10] *Ibid.*, p. 150.
[11] J. M. Matthews and H. R. Mauersberger, *Textile Fibers,* 5th ed. (New York: Wiley, 1947), p. 566.

Carbon   . . . . . . 50 per cent
Nitrogen . . . . . . 16 to 17 per cent
Hydrogen . . . . . . 7 per cent
Sulfur   . . . . . . 3 to 4 per cent
Oxygen (by difference between 100 per cent
        and the total of the other elements)
               22–24 per cent

The chemical formula is essentially $(C_{42}H_{57}O_{15}N_5S)_n$.

effect of light

Sunlight affects the strength of all textile fibers. Some investigators ascribe the effect to the ultraviolet rays. Others believe that ozone is developed, which, with the presence of moisture, affects the fibers. Experience has shown that, whatever the actual mechanism, wet woolen fabrics exposed to ultraviolet light are more severely faded and weakened than are dry fabrics.

mildew

Wool is attacked by mildew only after being damp for some time.

effect of heat

When heated to between 212° and 220°F., moist wool becomes bone dry and harsh to the feel. The original softness is not fully restored, even after the hydroscopic water is regained by exposure to the air. If heated to 212°F. in a moist atmosphere, wool becomes plastic and can be shaped and creased and will retain the new shape after it has cooled. Wool begins to decompose at 275°F. dry heat.

action of water

Wool is slightly weaker when wet than when dry, but it is not normally soluable in cold or hot water. Prolonged boiling, however, has been found to dissolve or decompose small amounts of the fiber. Boiling water also reduces the luster and promotes the felting of wool fabrics. Wool can hold about 35 per cent of its own weight of water without feeling wet. Much of wool garment comfort and protection in cold, damp weather are due to this rapid moisture regain and the heat of absorption.

action of acids

Dilute mineral acids, even if boiled, do not injure wool. Wool fibers are treated with acids to remove burrs from the fleece or similarly to carbonize cotton from re-worked wool. Concentrated mineral acids destroy wool if the fabric is soaked in them for more than a few minutes or if the acid dries on the fabric. Formic and acetic acids are not detrimental to wool. Oxalic, citric, and tartaric acids are not injurious if the acid is washed or sponged off the fabric.

action of alkalies

Wool is very susceptible to damage by alkalies. Weak alkalies, such as soap, sodium phosphate, ammonia, borax, sodium silicate, etc., will not damage wool if the temperature is kept below 68°F. Wool must be washed with soaps containing no free alkali. Wool is dissolved in a few minutes when boiled in a 5 per cent solution of soda ash. Concentrated alkalies below 68°F. impart an increased luster and strength to wool, probably by fusing the scales together. This is called **mercerized** wool.

effect of bleaches

Chlorine and hypochlorite solution (Javelle water) are harmful to wool. Chlorine and other halogens in various forms are used to make **chlored** or **unshrinkable** wool. When viewed under the microscope, it is shown that the scales have been more or less destroyed. This wool is weaker and less elastic than untreated wool and has no felting properties. Its dye affinity is greater. In Italy chlored wool was mixed with **lanital,** a synthetic wool protein fiber, for more even dyeing than was possible with untreated wool-lanital mixtures. Reducing agents do not harm wool, but their bleaching action on the coloring matter in wool is not permanent. Under normal conditions, oxidizing agents will not tender wool. Widely used bleaches are potassium permanganate, sodium peroxide, and hydrogen peroxide.

affinity for dyestuffs

Wool has great affinity for dyestuffs. Chlored wool is still more readily dyed. The most important types of dyestuffs for wool are the acid, chrome, and vat types.

Functional finishes modify wool in many ways (see Chapter 9).

TABLE 12-3 / CHARACTERISTICS OF WOOL FIBERS *

Physical Characteristics

1. Microscopic Appearance	Solid rod with its surface covered with horny scales resembling scales of fish.
2. Length of Fiber	Woolen averages 1" to 3". Worsted averages 3" to 8".
3. Diameter of Fiber	0.005" to 0.0015".
4. Color of Fiber	Yellowish to brown, sometimes black.
5. Luster	High in coarse grades. Low in good grades.
6. Strength	Average per single fiber, 15 to 30 grams.
7. Elasticity	Most elastic. Average wool stretches 25 to 35 per cent of its length before breaking.
8. Conductivity to Heat	Poor.
9. Hygroscopic Moisture	10 to 15 per cent.
10. Capillarity and Penetrability	Has both.

11. Composition of Fiber	Keratin: A mixture of nitrogen, sulphur, amino-acid compounds.
12. Method of Preparation	Mainly scouring to remove natural impurities such as wool perspiration and wool grease.

Chemical Characteristics

13. Effect of Light on	Changes chemical structure, making its action towards dyestuff different (usually has greater affinity).
14. Mildew	Attacked if left in damp condition for a period of time.
15. Heat	At 275° F. dry heat, begins to decompose. If heated to 212° F. in moist atmosphere, becomes plastic and can be shaped and retains new shape if cooled.
16. Water	Boiling reduces luster and strength.

17. Mineral Acids
   Sulphuric
   Hydrochloric
   Nitric
   Hydrofluoric
	Dilute acids do not injure, even at a boil. Concentrated acids destroy.

18. Volatile Organic Acids
   Formic
   Acetic
	No detrimental action.

19. Non-volatile Organic Acids
   Oxalic
   Tartaric
   Citric
	Not injurious if removed.

20. Strong Alkalies
   Caustic Soda
   Soda Ash
	Strong solutions injurious. Dilute cold solutions not injurious if removed or neutralized. Dilute solutions of soda ash can be used lukewarm but must be removed.

21. Weak Alkalies
   Ammonia
   Borax
   Silicate of Soda
   Phosphate of Soda
   Soap
	Weak alkalies not injurious if action is controlled.

22. Oxidizing Agents Like Potassium Permanganate	Same as cotton.
23. Metallic Salts	Has affinity for metallic salts.
24. Affinity for Dyestuffs	Good.
25. Classes of Dyestuffs met with in Common Use	Acid colors Chrome Some basic Direct

26. Bleaching Agents
   Chlorine Bleach
      or
   Hypochlorites
	Ordinarily harmful. Under some conditions may produce chlorinated wool, which has high luster and is unshrinkable.

27. Other Oxidation Bleaches
   Hydrogen Peroxide;
   Sodium Perborate;
   Potassium permanganate
	Same as cotton.

                        plus
              Bisulphite of Soda
28. Reduction Bleaches   Same as cotton.
        Sulphurous Acid
           (sulphur dioxide plus water)
        Hydrosulphite
  * Fiber Chart of the National Association of Dyers and Cleaners.

THE PERFORMANCE CHARACTERISTICS OF WOOL

Among the words of highest praise which producers of synthetic fibers can give their products is the brief descriptive phrase, "This fiber produces a wool-like fabric." The fibers can be spun into compact, tough, strong yarns or into loose, fluffy, soft yarns. Thus, the fabric is suitable for heavy-duty work clothes or dress garments, for soft-textured knitted sweaters or blankets, and for such durable materials as upholstered fabrics and carpeting. The fiber possesses a natural crimp, lending itself to easy spinning into yarns and providing fabrics with a built-in ability to absorb shock, such as sudden stresses. Then the crimped fibers straighten out and the interlocking surface scales release their grip between adjacent fibers and, finally, the natural resiliency of the fibers takes over. Wool fabrics are not brittle and they will not break under sudden stress.

Low wet strength is a disadvantage, but it can be compensated for in this stretchability of the yarns.

comfort

It has previously been said that wool stands head and shoulders above all other textile fibers and serves as an actual source of heat for the protection of

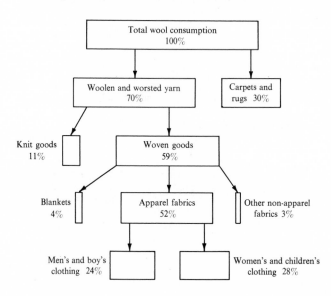

Fig. 12-10   Wool consumption: approximate distribution according to end use, 1954. (Courtesy of Inventories in the Textile Cycle, [Washington: U.S. Dept. of Commerce, Business and Defense Services Administration, 1961], p. 480.)

the body when one moves from a heated, indoor, dry atmosphere on a winter day to a cold, damp exterior. The process of rapid moisture absorption by wool actually produces heat through the heat of moisture absorption. When a solid substance absorbs moisture, heat is produced. Little wonder that it is a wool blanket Linus carries for comfort in the *Peanuts* comic strip. Under these same conditions, the wearer of any other natural fiber or any synthetics of comparable weight would be chilled to the bone within a matter of a few minutes. Similarly, there is no chilling of the body when one wears a bathing suit of wool and comes out of the water to stand in a breezy, shaded area. Wool can hold about a third of its own weight of water without feeling wet to the touch. Under these same conditions, other textile materials would be clammy and cold and cling to the body. This same property of wool—moisture absorbency—combined with the ability of the fiber to be manipulated when subjected to steam, enables the tailor to produce a more perfect garment structure as far as fit is concerned than can be obtained with any other textile material.

The shrinking characteristics of wool are generally recognized and usually do not constitute a problem to the housewife who knows how to wash wool blankets, sweaters, and similar articles, but she would not dare experiment with a woven suiting, although these washable fabrics are figuratively just around the corner. Washable wools and even permanently moth-proofed wools are available as the result of special finishes developed by science to widen the application of this fiber and to avoid the two principal complaints voiced by consumers. Rarely have complaints been voiced about the loss of color in wool garments during service.

Even this fiber benefits from technological advances. In addition to the finishing improvements mentioned above, modern concepts of protective wearing apparel for wet, cold exposures benefit wool. A lightweight, wind-breaker shell of closely-woven cotton replaces a thicker, heavier wool fabric and permits the use of the much lighter-weight wool shirt or other under-garment combination to help keep in body heat during extremely cold weather. It is the modern technologists approach to the eskimo dress which in winter has the vapor-barrier skin surface outside the heavy winter garment and the hair side or insulator toward the wearer's body.

CONCLUSIONS

The service qualities of wool have long been taken for granted, with very little attempt on the part of scientists to probe the mysteries of this fiber to find out just why it behaves as it does, for example, why it makes such a comfortable fabric when one goes from the warm interior of a home to a rather chill and damp outer atmosphere or vice versa. If we view textile production statistics simply in terms of the percentage of the various fibers used in the United States in wearing apparel or for other uses, one sees wool hovering around 7 or 8 per cent compared with approximately 60 per cent for cotton and 25 per cent for rayon and acetate, and its significance is lost. Thus, we overlook the facts of the real growth in wool consumption in terms of total poundage to take care of the needs of the present 180 million persons in the United States, as well as wool users elsewhere in the world. During the 1930's, approximately 2 billion pounds of wool were produced throughout the world; in 1960, the figure has risen to almost 3 billion pounds. It is estimated, furthermore, that there is approximately one sheep in the world for every two persons. Wool possesses a great ability to carry over many of its natural properties into blends containing significant qualities of synthetic fibers. Thus, suitings of wool blended with Dacron, Orlon, Acrilan, and other synthetic fibers possess some of the tailoring qualities of all-wool; likewise, this hydrophilic fiber makes such blends more comfortable than those made entirely of synthetic fiber and somewhat less prone to storage of static electricity. There is no synthetic fiber on the immediate horizon to challenge wool's prestige as a coating and a suiting fiber.

QUESTIONS

1   Describe the wool fiber.

2   What is the importance of the merino strain?

3   What is fleece wool?

4   What is pulled wool?

5   Define the wool count. What is meant by 64's wool?

6   How many wool grades are commonly used?

7   List these grades.

8   Define re-processed wool. What is its origin?

9   Define re-used wool. From whence is it obtained?

10   How is wool affected by
a. Moisture c. Heat   e. Dilute acids
b. Sunlight d. Flame   f. Strong acids?

11   What is meant by worsteds? Describe them.

12   What is a woolen? Describe a woolen cloth.

13   What was the purpose of the Wool Products Labeling Act?

14   Why is wool not included in the new labeling law?

15   Distinguish between two types of shrinkage of wool.

specialty hair fibers

There are many special fibers which are commercially valuable because of their wool-like characteristics or because in combination with wool they produce fabrics with interesting properties. The following chart (Chart 13-1) shows the various animals yielding these special fibers:

CHART   13-1   /   SPECIALTY   HAIR   FIBERS[1]

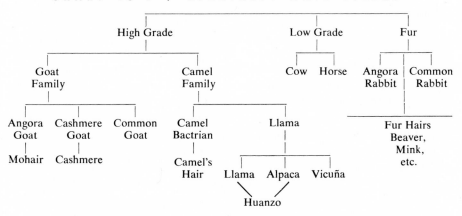

[1] W. von Bergen, *Wool Handbook* (New York: Interscience Publisher, 3rd Ed., enlarged, 1963) Vol. 1, p. 315.

197

MOHAIR

history

The raising of mohair goats was long limited to Turkey, but in the nineteenth century, the demand for mohair became so great that the Turks were unable to supply sufficient fiber. Attempts to breed these goats in other European countries were unsuccessful, but the goats were successfully introduced into South Africa. Nine Angora goats were imported into the United States in 1849, and small herds were developing rapidly in the South and Southwest at the time of the Civil War. Texas proved to be the best region for this animal and produced the greatest clip of mohair. Other states, such as Arizona, California, New Mexico, Oregon, and Utah, are prominent in the Angora goat industry. The United States is now the largest producer of mohair and produced 24.2 million pounds in 1959.

Table 13-1 shows the production in the principal producing countries.

TABLE 13-1 / WORLD MOHAIR PRODUCTION, EXPORTS AND AVAILABLE

(Millions of Pounds)

	1957			1958			1959		
	Prod.	Export	Avail.	Prod.	Export	Avail.	Prod.	Export	Avail.
Turkey	21.3	7.2	14.1	21.3	7.4	13.9	22.6	18.6	4.0
United States	19.1	10.0	9.1	20.9	13.2	7.7	24.2	18.6	5.6
Union So. Africa	5.4	5.4	0	6.0	6.6	−0.6	6.0	7.3	1.3
Basutoland	1.1	1.1	0	0.8	0.8	0	1.2	1.2	0

The United Kingdom alone imported 27.9 million pounds in 1957–58, or 54 per cent of the available fiber in those two years.

production

The use of imported bucks and cross-breeding with common does has resulted in an improved registered stock. Scientific breeding has greatly reduced the amount of kemp[2] in Angora fleeces. The average yield of mohair from a range stock animal is 3.5 to 4.5 pounds per year and is commonly taken in two clips each year. Pure-bred Angora goats may produce twice as much. A compact, well-ringleted fleece is preferred, because a fluffy type of fleece would be broken and matted by the brush through which the animals range for food.

The goats are sheared in the same general way as sheep, usually in the spring. In the Southwest the animals are sheared twice a year. Soiled and stained wool is packed separately, and it is common for the fleeces to be separated according to grade. Kids' fleeces are segregated from the others and are prized for their extra fineness.

[2] *Textile Organon,* Vol. 31, No. 12 (Dec., 1960), p. 204.

physical characteristics of mohair

MICROSCOPIC APPEARANCE   The mohair fiber is very similar to wool, but some structural differences aid in its identification. The epidermal scales are only faintly visible, scarcely overlap, and fit so closely to the fiber that it appears to be a shiny, smooth, planar surface. Mohair is, therefore, a lustrous fiber.

The cortex layer, or the spindle-shaped cells underlying the scales, is clearly visible and appears under the microscope as striations in the fiber. The medulla is rarely visible in mohair. When visible, it appears very like the medulla in wool fiber. The mohair fiber is nearly circular in cross-section.

LENGTH OF FIBER   The mohair fiber ranges in length from four to six inches for a half year's growth and from six to twelve inches for a full year's growth.

DIAMETER OF FIBER   The diameter of mohair fibers varies widely. The range is from 0.0008 to 0.0020 inches. There is no universally recognized standard of fineness.

COLOR OF FIBER   The best grades of mohair fiber after scouring show a clear white color and have a silky luster. The raw fleece is yellowish or grayish in appearance because of the presence of 15 to 25 per cent of foreign matter, such as sand, dust, and grease. The grease content is about 4 per cent. The luster is caused by light reflection from the scales, which, as already explained, are flat and present a plane surface.

STRENGTH AND ELASTICITY OF FIBER   The mohair fiber has a strength equivalent to wool of the same diameter. The fiber is not as elastic as wool and is naturally slippery because of the flat scale structure. These qualities make mohair extremely resistant to wear and abrasion and peculiarly well-suited for use in automobile and railroad-car upholstery and for lightweight suits for men.

PHYSICAL AND CHEMICAL PROPERTIES OF THE FIBER   The mohair fiber is almost identical with wool in its moisture regain, heat conductivity, dye penetrability, and other physical properties. The chemical properties are the same as those of wool.

uses of mohair

Mohair is extensively used for upholstery fabrics, lightweight suits, suit linings, coating fabrics, draperies, and theatrical wigs.

CASHMERE

Cashmere hair is obtained from the cashmere goat. This animal is native to Tibet, northern India, Iran, Iraq, and southwestern China. The word cashmere is familiar through history as the name of the beautiful shawls made from this fiber in the Indian province of Kashmir.

production

This goat is kept as a domestic animal and is sometimes known as the shawl goat. The cashmere fiber is the fine, soft undercoat or down underlying the heavy, coarse, long outer hairs. Instead of shearing the animals, it is customary to pluck the hair by hand at the time of the annual molting or shedding season, which begins in June and lasts several weeks. The under hair and the smaller amount of outer hair caught on brush and shrubs as the animals rub against them are collected also. The "Pashm Wool" bought from the natives is a mass of fine hair, coarse outer hair, dust, and twigs. The yield from each animal is only about 8 ounces, of which only 3 to 5 ounces are the valued cashmere fibers. The annual consumption of this fiber in the United States is between 100,000 and 200,000 pounds. Most of the hair which is not used in the province of Kashmir for making pashmina shawls is marketed in London. It is shipped in iron-bound, 220-pound (100 kg.) bales and is made up of about 80 per cent clean fiber and 20 per cent sand, dust, and vegetable matter.

characteristics of the fiber

The true cashmere fleece contains coarse waves. The fibers are soft and have a silky gloss or luster. These fibers are usually white, gray, or brown. The range of fiber length is from 1¼ to 3½ inches. The stiff, coarse outer fibers, or **Beard hair,** are from 1½ to 5 inches in length.

The cashmere wool hair when examined under the microscope shows the typical scale structure, and the cortical cells are distinctly seen. The pigment of the dark-colored hairs is in small granules on the surface. There are fewer scales per unit of fiber length than are found in ordinary wool. The fibers are very fine (15 μ in diameter) and are almost circular in cross-section. (Only by the higher percentage of very fine fibers can cashmere be distinguished from fine wools.)

The Beard hair shows all three layers when observed under the microscope. The medulla, or core, is by far the largest part of the hair but disappears toward the tip and the root of the fiber. The hair is about four times as coarse as the wool.

Cashmere is chemically identical with wool and mohair. It is much more readily acted upon by chemicals, however. This greater susceptibility to alkali damage and tendering during processing is due to the extra fineness of the fibers and to the **wetting-out** properties. It has been observed that a mass of cashmere wool when immersed in water will become saturated and sink in a few seconds. Wool, however, must be worked by hand for about half a minute or longer before it will lose the enmeshed air and sink.

uses of cashmere

Cashmere is distinctly a luxury fabric. Its softness, luster, and lightness make it a symbol of the highest quality, but it is a costly fiber because only one overcoat requires the hair of more than 30 goats. Cashmere is used in the highest quality fabrics for women's coats, dress goods, silk-warp velours, and, occasionally, men's coatings. Another extensive use is for knit goods, such as for infants' wear and fine sweaters.

COMMON GOAT HAIR

This hair is rarely used in woolen or worsted fabrics. It is principally made up of Beard hairs, and because it is a shed hair, it has the roots attached. The down and Beard hairs are of about the same average fineness as the corresponding cashmere hairs, but the range is greater. Goat hair is used to some extent in place of **kemp** in novelty weaves for ladies' sportswear.

CAMEL HAIR

Camel hair is a very widely used member of the special hairs group. The greater part of this hair used in the wool industry of the United States comes from Mongolia, Chinese Turkestan, and the northwestern provinces of China proper. The camel bred in these districts is the two-hump or **Bactrian** type, as distinguished from the one-hump **Dromedary** type common in Arabia.

history

Neither of the types of domestic camel now exists in the wild state. Wild camels are said to have existed in Arabia at the beginning of the Christian era but were apparently unknown to the Egyptians. This suggests that both types might have originated in Asia.

An English army officer stationed in India is believed to have been the first person to study the hair of the Bactrian camel as a possible source of a textile fiber. This officer, Captain Thomas Hutton, found that the Dromedary throve in heat but could not withstand cold weather. The pure Bactrian camel strain was incapable of withstanding heat but was a splendid beast of burden in colder regions. The cross-bred hybrids of the two types had for thousands of years been known to possess shaggy coats capable of resisting both heat and cold. The natives of the Bokhara region owned great herds of these cross-breed animals, known variously as *Bokhara, Goghdi,* or *Boghdi* camels. This hybrid is the Bactrian camel of today. It is as invaluable a beast of burden on the almost barren mountain plateaus of Central Asia as is the Arabian camel on the hot sand deserts of Arabia and northern Africa.

Two attempts were made to introduce the camel into the United States. It was hoped that camels introduced in 1856 and again in 1866 might prove to be useful beasts of burden in Arizona, Nevada, New Mexico, and Texas. The animals did not thrive, and the remnants of the herd owned by the Federal Government were turned loose.[3]

[3] The author lived in Nevada as a boy and saw a small herd of these wild animals in 1912.

production of camel hair

In the spring, when the weather becomes warmer, the camel begins to shed. The hair begins to form matted strands which hang from the animal and fall off. Camels are neither sheared nor plucked; the loose clumps of hair are picked up and sold to traveling merchants. This hair is collected from the ground where the traveling caravan has rested. As the caravan travels, the loose hair from the animals is gathered and placed in baskets mounted on the last camel in the string by a man acting as the *trailer*. Although the greater amount of hair is collected in the spring, camels rub off or shed some hair the year round. Eventually the hair sold to the merchants in the small towns is brought to some shipping point, such as Tientsin, where it is sorted, graded, and baled for export.

It is estimated that the regions of Central Asia have more than one million Bactrian camels and from each animal is obtained an annual yield of 8 pounds of hair. Great Britain has dominated the market, and most of the hair is shipped to London. It is shipped as loose hair or in a semi-manufactured stage, such as camel-hair tops and camel-hair noils.

The camel fleece is a mixture similar to that of the cashmere goat. The valued fiber is the very fine wool or undercoat. The long, coarse outer Beard hair is separated in the combing machine and makes up the camel-hair tops; the fine wool constitutes the camel-hair noils. The grade is based on the amount of long hair remaining in the wool.

properties

MICROSCOPIC APPEARANCE   The epidermal scales are less visible than in wool and mohair. The cortex is distinct and is filled with granules of pigment. The medulla is interrupted, as in certain types of wool. The Beard hair contains a wide, fairly continuous medulla. Both the medulla and cortex contain pigment granules.

FINENESS OF THE FIBER   The finer grades of camel hair wool are finer than cashmere, but the fineness varies widely, ranging from 0.0005 to 0.0030 of an inch (5 to 30 μ). The Beard hair is more than three times as coarse.

COMPOSITION   The raw camel hair contains between 75 and 85 per cent fiber, the rest consisting of sand and dust and about 4 to 5 per cent fat. The chemical composition of camel hair is practically the same as that of the other hair fibers, and the chemical reactions are, therefore, the same. Camel hair, like mohair, is easily charged with static electricity during spinning, and the moisture content must be carefully controlled and must be kept above 12 per cent. The smoothness of the fiber causes some difficulty in the fulling process. This hair cannot be bleached white but can be dyed a dark color. The greatest volume of sale is in fabrics of the natural color.

uses for camel hair

The finest grade cloth commanding the highest price is made from 100 per cent camel-hair noils. However, the hair is commonly blended with wool or other hair fibers to produce fabrics with different color effects and textures. Cheaper blends may contain as little as 20 per cent camel hair. Probably no fabric is as widely misrepresented to the consumer as is camel hair. This is especially true in ladies' sport coats and men's topcoats; many of these selling at low prices contain no camel hair whatever. The presence of camel hair in a blended fabric can only be determined by an expert using microscopical analysis of the fabric. It is virtually impossible to determine the exact fiber composition of a camel-hair blended fabric. The most extensive use of this fiber is in fine coatings for men. It is highly prized by Arctic explorers and hunters because of its great warmth. The extreme fineness of this wool fiber enables it to entrap more air and to retain the body heat for a longer time than wool.

THE LLAMA FAMILY

The mountainous region of western South America is the habitat of several species of llamas, animals which produce wool-like fleeces. These are known as the **camelidae** and are distinctly different from the camels of the Old World. Fossil remains of the true camel have been found in several parts of North and South America, and it is possible these two distinct families may have come from the same parent stock.

The **llama** and **alpaca** are the only two natural species which are completely domesticated. The **guanaco** or **huanaca** and the **vicuña** are wild members. The guanaco has also been domesticated by the Indians. There are also two hybrid strains which have been developed for certain fleece characteristics.

distribution of the llama

The llama and alpaca have been domesticated by the Indians of the Andean region for probably 1200 years. The domesticated animals differ in physical characteristics from the wild specimens of the same species. The Spanish conquistadores, who conquered the land for Spain, found these animals serving as beasts of burden and as sources of clothing fabric. It is believed that the alpaca and llama are both descendants of the guanaco and that the vicuña is a distinct species.

The llama, alpaca, and vicuña are found in the high Andean regions of southern Ecuador, Peru, Bolivia, and northwestern Argentina. The map of South America shows this "llama land" to be a large, almost uninhabitable plateau, known as the Puna, lying between the two high mountain ranges forming the Andean system. The members of the camelidae family live on the mosses and the Ychu grass found on this plateau. The guanaco once ranged over this entire area and the pampas regions, but it is now found principally in Patagonia and in the rocky islands south of the continent of South America.

the llama

The llama is the largest of the camelidae, weighing about 250 pounds and being about one-third the size of the true camel. It stands between four and five feet in height. The coat, which is thick and coarse, consists of a soft fleece and a coarser, straight outer hair. In general, the colors tend to be various shades of brown, though some are white. The belly hair is usually white. The llama is the Indian's beast of burden, and it is estimated that there are about two million of these animals in Bolivia, about one million in Peru, and perhaps a hundred thousand in the other mountain countries.

the alpaca

The alpaca is of more importance to the textile industry because of its superior fleece. It was important to the livelihood of the Incas, and even today, despite the increase in the number of sheep on the lower mountain slopes, the alpaca is still of great value to its Indian owners as a fleece-bearer. The alpaca is smaller than the llama, standing about three-and-a-half feet high. It is more bulky in body, and its hair hangs from its body in long, tangled strands which measure from eight to sixteen inches. The alpaca varies in color from white to black, but as with the llama, the brown shades predominate.

The fleece fiber is silky, fine, and strong. Unlike the llama, the alpaca fleece contains no coarse hairs or kemp. There are two types of alpaca. The smaller, the **Suri,** produces the silkier, finer fleece, and the clip, taken every two years, averages six-and-a-half pounds. The larger, the **Unacaya,** produces about a pound less.

The alpaca is found principally at elevations of 13,000 to 16,000 feet. Its range is restricted to the Andean plateau, because only there is its chief food substance, the Ychu grass, to be found. Attempts to raise the animal in other parts of the world have met with failure, and the Peruvian government has made further experimentation impossible by prohibiting the exportation of the alpaca. Hybrids (Huarizo and Misti) have been developed for wool production. The **huarizo** is an animal having a llama father and an alpaca mother. The **misti** has an alpaca father and a llama mother. The fleeces of these hybrids are neither as heavy nor as fine in quality as that of the alpaca.

production

All these animals produce fleece, but the alpaca is by far the most important, amounting to about 93 per cent of the four million pounds of fine fleece produced in 1936. The shearing is done by hand in November or December, just after the rainy season. The fleeces are shipped in hanks to a sorting station, where they are sorted as to grade and color. The alpaca is sorted separately. The fleeces are shipped in 220-pound (100 kg.) bales.

vicuña

The vicuña is the smallest of the llama family and exists in the wild state in the high mountains of Peru. It weighs only about 100 pounds and bears a remarkably soft chestnut or fawn-colored fleece. It is one of the wildest and most wary animals known and cannot be domesticated. The animals must be killed to obtain the fleece. The vicuña is protected by the Peruvian government, and only about 15,000 pounds of fleece is obtained per year. A vicuña fiber topcoat costs $350 or more and requires the fleeces of 40 animals.

properties of llama fleeces

The fleeces of the llama and alpaca have been developed through centuries of breeding, much as has that of the angora goat, until the under hair has practically disappeared and the whole fleece is quite uniform in fineness. In terms of wool fineness, the llama, alpaca, and huarizo range from 56's to 60's; the vicuña from 120's to 130's.

The chemical constitution is practically the same as that of wool, and the physical structure is like that of mohair and camel hair.

OTHER SPECIAL FIBERS

Cow hair is sometimes mixed with wool in very low-grade carpet yarns, blankets, and felts. Horse hair is used exclusively as a filler or stuffer. It is forecast that the hair of the Musk Ox may one day be an important special fiber, if the animal is successfully domesticated and introduced into Alaska. Various fur fibers are becoming popular for special effects in women's woolen dress fabrics and in knitting yarns. The most common of these is the fur of the angora rabbit. This fiber may be present in from 2 to 70 per cent and is one of the softest of all fibers, so soft and fine that it is not used alone except as a narrow trim. These rabbits may be clipped four times a year. Fragments of ostrich feathers or the down of geese and ducks may similarly be used to give novel texture or color effect in fine specialty woolens.

FUR FIBER FABRICS

Waste clippings from the fur-coat or the fur-trimming industry producing collars, cuffs, and fur-pelt linings for winter garments provide fur fibers which are blended with wool to produce extra softness and novel visual effects. Among these fur fibers are beaver, mink, skunk, muskrat, and similar "precious" fibers.

Men's winter coats in 1962 featured fur inner linings and collars and cuffs. Most of these are made of waste pelts of the "fur bearing" animals, though others have utilized fur fibers blended with wool or synthetics in a woven fabric or knitted fabric inner layer for greater warmth.

QUESTIONS

1 Why are these wool-like hairs used?

2 How do they differ from wool?

3 How are the following fibers obtained and from what part of the world?
a. Camel hair   b. Cashmere
c. Mohair   d. Alpaca
e. Vicuña

4 How would one analyze a 50-50 mixture of wool and cashmere?

5 Which of the specialty fibers is the most costly? Why?

silk

HISTORY

The origin and development of silk as a textile fiber is so lost in antiquity as to be the subject of many fascinating and romantic legends. There is the story of the Chinese princess who accidentally dropped a cocoon which she had found in the garden into a cup of hot tea and found that the hot liquid had softened the filaments so that it was possible to unwind the strong fibers. There is also the legend ascribing to the young Empress Si-Ling-Chi the origin of the silk industry: The Emperor Huang-Ti is said to have told her to study the rearing of silkworms and the preparation of the fibers, so she lovingly tended the worms and from the fibers wove a silken robe for her husband. This discovery, said to have been made about 2700 B.C., has caused her to be venerated by the Chinese people as "The Goddess of the Silkworms."

Whether these stories be fact or fiction, we know that silk was produced in China a very long time ago. For about 3000 years the cultivation of this fiber remained a jealously guarded secret. The Japanese learned about it from the Koreans sometime during the third century, when some of the silkworm eggs were smuggled into Japan in hollow staffs or canes carried by travelers. A similar legend describes the advent of the silk industry into India. Silk cloths were an important part of the loads carried by caravans to Persia and Asia Minor. Alexander the Great is said to have brought the knowledge of silk to Europe in the fourth century B.C. Pompey returned from his campaign in Asia in 91 B.C.

with a gorgeous silk robe. During the time of Julius Caesar, purple-dyed silk was in demand by the nobility and commanded a price of $1,800 a pound.

The Chinese domesticated silk-producing moths at an early date. Several types were utilized, but the mulberry silkworm, **Bombyx Mori,** is the species universally bred and used by sericulturists wherever silk fiber is produced. Through these thousands of years of development, the female moths have become egg-laying machines which move only a few inches during their few days of life.

PRODUCTION OF SILK

the life of the bombyx mori

In the houses of peasants in China and Japan, silk culture is still carried out as it has been for thousands of years despite the modernization of methods in many producing centers. **Sericulture,** the production of the worms, their development, and the spinning of the cocoon, is largely a home industry. In the modern scientific industry the tiny eggs or **seeds** are deposited by the carefully bred female moth on cards or strips of cloth. The cards are stored in racks in a cool, dry place until the incubation of a new crop of silkworms is desired. The cards are distributed to the peasants, and the eggs are incubated by mild warmth: the eggs may be covered with a blanket, or the cards may be worn under the clothing and the tiny **ants** or **silkworms** are hatched. These ants are a day-and-night care. The young ants are provided with shredded, fresh, tender mulberry leaves **(Morus alba).** The leaves to which the worms cling are lifted to the feeding trays. The weak worms are discarded. The worms are kept in a room at a uniform temperature, they are fed five or six times a day, and the trays are kept clean. The care of these worms is given to the women and children in these home plants. In model sericultural establishments the worms are nursed in rooms like hospital wards under controlled temperature and humidity.

The ants are initially about three millimeters long. During its growth the worm sheds its skin four times at about 5-day intervals, and after the fourth shedding it develops for about ten days more. The fully grown worm is 8 to 9 centimeters in length and has increased its weight by a thousand-fold to five grams.

The fully developed worm has a total life period of approximately a month. It first learns to eat and begins to seek something on which to spin its cocoon. This worm is then transferred to a wooden frame containing twigs or straw, on which the cocoon is spun. To spin this cocoon the worm spins a net and then forms a shell around his body. The worm swings its head in a figure-eight formation and expels fluid from two sacs in its body. The two strands are excreted from minute openings, or **spinnerets,** close together in the lower jaw. The fluid solidifies when in contact with the air. The two filaments, known as **fibroin,** are cemented together by a glue known as **sericin.** The sericin is excreted from

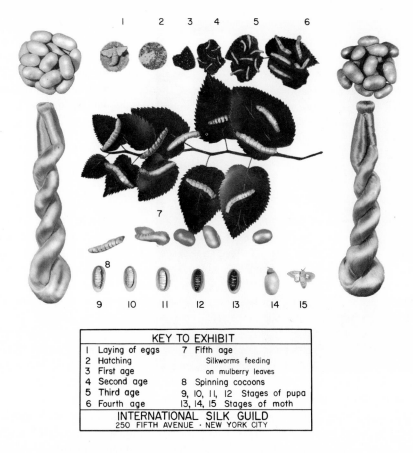

KEY TO EXHIBIT	
1 Laying of eggs	7 Fifth age
2 Hatching	Silkworms feeding
3 First age	on mulberry leaves
4 Second age	8 Spinning cocoons
5 Third age	9, 10, 11, 12 Stages of pupa
6 Fourth age	13, 14, 15 Stages of moth
INTERNATIONAL SILK GUILD	
250 FIFTH AVENUE · NEW YORK CITY	

Fig. 14-1 An Exhibit of the life cycle of the silkworm: Stages of the life history of the silkworm. Photograph of an exhibit with replicas of silkworms. (*Courtesy of The International Silk Guild, Inc.*)

two glands. The worm makes more than one movement of its head each second and can be heard at work even after the cocoon has become so thick that the worm cannot be seen. It takes two or three days to complete a cocoon. The worm then changes into the **pupa** or **chrysalis.**

In about two weeks the moth will develop if the chrysalis is permitted to live. The moth escapes through the bottom of the cocoon and breaks the silk strands in the several layers in making its escape. An alkaline solution secreted by the moth allows it to break the strands more easily. It is customary to permit the development of only enough moths for breeding and egg-laying, because the broken cocoons are of less value than those having long, unbroken filaments. In order to produce unpierced cocoons the chrysalis is killed by heat in dry air,

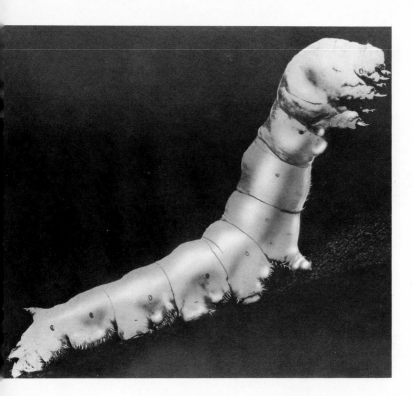

Fig. 14-2 Silkworm: Microphotograph of the full-grown silkworm ready to spin its cocoon. (Courtesy of The International Silk Guild, Inc.)

more rarely by hot water or steam. The cocoons are weighed; the female moths, being heavier, can thus be selected and allowed to escape. The moths live only a few days, during which they mate, and the eggs, about 700 from each female, are laid on the cards or sheets. Thus the cycle begins once more.

It is interesting to note[1] that 30,000 to 40,000 eggs weigh one ounce. An ounce of eggs will produce about 140 pounds of cocoons and 12 pounds of raw silk. It is estimated that nearly 3000 cocoons are required to make a yard of silk fabric. The worms consume about 300 pounds of mulberry leaves to a pound of raw silk; a mature tree of 20 years of age will produce slightly more than 200 pounds of leaves.

Silkworms are subject to many diseases. The most important of these, **pébrine,** is hereditary; the germ of this disease was discovered by Pasteur and can be identified in the body of the moth by microscopic examination. All moths are examined in the modern sericulture establishments, and the eggs from diseased or weak stock are destroyed. The worms are damaged by changes in room temperature and by moisture in their food. These factors influence the quality of silk produced. In Japan especially has scientific sericulture been

[1] W. D. Darby, *Silk, the Queen of Fabrics* (New York: Dry Goods Economist, 1924), p. 23.

Fig. 14-3 Feeding silk worms: One girl is weighing out mulberry. (*Courtesy of The International Silk Guild, Inc.*)

highly developed under government control, and only the best eggs are stored under refrigeration until wanted and are then distributed to the hatcheries.

Wild silk is that produced from other types of moths, which have not lent themselves to domestication. These cocoons must be sought in the trees, and many of them have already been pierced when found. Wild silk is less uniform but is coarser and somewhat stronger than the cultivated variety. The most common wild silk is that from the **tussah** or **tussar** silkworm of Asia. This worm feeds on mulberry, oak, and other trees. The term is generally applied to all wild silks, but strictly speaking, the tussah is an Indian silkworm.

the making of raw silk

The unpierced cocoons are sorted according to color and texture before the **reeling** or unwinding operation. The reeling is still done much the same as the Chinese peasants have done for centuries. Even in the modern **filature,** the reeling depends upon the sight, touch, and skill of the reeling girl.

Several cocoons are soaked in a basin of water at about 140° F. in order

Fig. 14-4 Moths laying eggs: The masses of eggs may be seen on the hatching tray. (*Courtesy of The International Silk Guild, Inc.*)

to soften the gum or sericin. The outer filaments are coarse and tangled and make up **waste** silk. The filaments of four or more cocoons are drawn together to form a single strand of uniform diameter. Six ends commonly are used to make the 1-1 **denier** size yarn widely used in the United States. The ends are drawn through a small glass or porcelain orifice to form a thread as nearly smooth and uniform as possible. Because the filament of each cocoon is not uniform, the reeler must cast on or take off ends to produce a strand with as few thin spots, knots, or loose filaments as possible. The cocoons, being unwound, bob up and down in the basin as the figure-eight cast filaments are pulled and are held down only by the water absorbed. Each cocoon contains between 300 and 1,000 yards of fiber which can be reeled. The inner portion is too weak to be reeled, and this portion and the outer portion brushed off by beaters are known as **frisons** and constitute waste silk. The reeled thread is wound onto

Fig. 14-5 Cocoons: Photomicrograph of cocoons, showing how filament is spun in the form of a figure 8. (*Courtesy of The International Silk Guild, Inc.*)

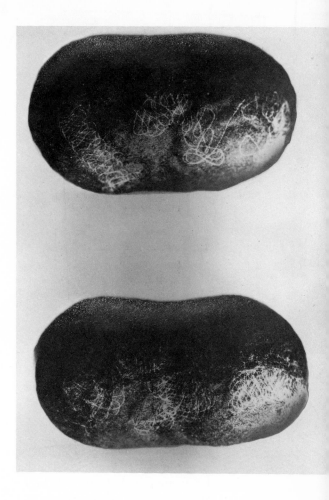

a reel operated by hand or foot power in homes or filatures and by steam power in large filatures or factories having several hundred basins. The price of the raw silk thread depends to a considerable degree upon the quality of the cocoon and the manual skill of the reel girl. No device has yet been perfected[2] which will consistently produce a quality as good as the girls can make, at as low a price.

The reeled silk, twisted to form a strong thread, the waste silk from the discarded portions of the cocoons (about half the filament length), and fibers from the pierced cocoons make up the silk of commerce. Skeins of reeled silk weighing 50 to 100 grams each are wrapped in bundles called **books,** which weigh from 5 to 10 pounds each. These books of Japan and China silk are

[2] D. D. Leonard, "The Story of Silk," *Natural History* (March, 1935), pp. 221–236.

Fig. 14-6 Sorting out the cocoon crop: Harvesting the cocoons. The collection of the crop begins three or four days after the worms begin to make the cocoons. (*Courtesy of The International Silk Guild, Inc.*)

packed in **picul bales** weighing one picul (133⅓ pounds). Italian silk bales weigh about 200 pounds. The bales of silk from the Orient are covered with tea matting and shipped all over the world. Before World War II, the United States imported approximately 85 per cent of Japan's raw silk. The classification of raw silk grades is a loose one, and there is no generally accepted standard. Silks are graded for uniformity by visual examination by commercial laboratory technicians.

silk yarn

The raw silk strands are transformed into a yarn by **throwing.** This consists of increasing the twist or of adding more strands and twisting them together. This thrown silk is wound on spools or twisted into skeins and is then ready for the weavers. **Singles** are strands consisting of from 3 to 8 or more double filaments twisted together to form a yarn suitable for either warp or filling yarns or for knitting. **Tram silk** consists of two or more strands of singles slightly

Fig. 14-7   Showing the various steps between the reeling of silk and its final market form: This photograph shows the steps in preparing silk for shipping after it has been reeled. From right to left, the silk is shown on drums, from which it is wound onto six-armed reels, then laced, twisted, tied in bundles, packed into cotton bags, and protected by straw matting. (*Courtesy of The International Silk Guild, Inc.*)

twisted together. **Organzine** is formed by twisting together two or more singles strands in the opposite direction to the twist of the singles. This is the usual warp yarn and is commonly made from the best fibers.

The skeins are usually soaked in a soap solution before throwing in order to remove the sericin gum still contained in the raw silk to an amount of approximately 25 per cent. The different grades are tinted in different shades during soaking so that they can be more readily identified in future handling.

The count and size of reeled thrown silk is based on the denier system. A denier is a legal coin weighing 0.05 gram. The size is expressed as the weight in deniers (International Denier of 450 meters of the silk). Note in Chapters 19 to 22 on man-made fibers a multiple of 20 is used in expressing denier. Thus denier is the weight in grams of 9000 meters of yarn or filament. The weight is subject to a correction of 25 per cent to allow for the sericin removed in the degumming bath.

The American silk industry grades silk on the clean basis. Silk from fifty bobbins is wound around a black frame. These individual skeins are graded as to uniform size, evenness, and freedom from defects.

spun silk yarn

The waste silk is made into spun silk yarn by the same process as the yarns from other short fibers are fashioned. The pierced cocoons, wild cocoons, and the frisons or waste compose the raw materials for spun silk. The silk is degummed by boiling off in soap suds. It is then dried and cut into 9-inch lengths. The cut fibers are combed in order to straighten them, and they are then rolled several times in the drawing frame. The yarns are twisted on a spinning frame, which gives them a tighter twist than is needed for the long-filament thrown silk yarn. The spun silk yarn is less lustrous than thrown silk because of the tighter twist, and it is less elastic and strong and has a harsher feel or handle. It is less expensive and is suitable for filling yarns in woven cloth. Spun silk sizes are computed by two methods, the English and the French. The English method sets 840 yards equal to 1 pound (as for cotton). A pound size of 20-2 would have 840 yards of two-ply yarn times 20, or 16,800 yards. The French system base is the number of 1000-meter skeins weighing 1 kilogram.

silk weighting

Silk is purchased in the raw state on a weight basis, and the 20 to 30 per cent of gum it contains is charged for as if the yarn were all silk. It is customary to replace with metallic salts some of this gum which has been boiled off before the yarn can be dyed. Silk has a great affinity for the salts of tin and iron and for tannin. An insoluble tin phospho-silicate is the usual weighting material. A **pure silk** or **pure dye silk** is one which is defined by the FTC (Trade Practice Conference, April 21, 1932) as containing no more than 10 per cent of weighting, except in black silk, which can have 15 per cent. This amount is not injurious to the serviceability of the silk, and the usual bead test and characteristic odor are given when the burning test is used. It is possible to *load* or dynamite silks to the extent of approximately three times the weight of the raw silk (before degumming). Weighted silks purchased by the consumer commonly contain between 40 and 60 per cent weighting calculated on the basis of the finished cloth.

In the trade, amounts of weighting are expressed as the number of ounces of boiled-off, weighted, and dyed cloth to be returned by the dyer for every pound of silk delivered to him for processing. Thus, 16-ounce weighting means that for every pound of raw silk sent to the processor, the owner of the silk expects 16 ounces of finished silk to be returned to him and refers to it as **par** value. This means that approximately 30 per cent of weighting has been added, an amount equal to the gum that has been boiled off. Twenty-two-ounce weighting means that for each pound of raw silk sent the dyer, 22 ounces are to be returned. If a gum content of 25 per cent (4 ounces) had been boiled off, a total of 10 ounces of weighting, or 83 per cent of the 12-ounce degummed silk weight, has been added. The trade, however does not base the calculation on the actual fibroin content. The calculation is based on the raw silk weight (16 ounces) and is reported as 37½ per cent.

Heavily weighted silks containing in excess of 40 per cent are not serviceable. The tensile strength is low, the fibers are inelastic, sunlight and perspiration rapidly deteriorate the fibers, and the fabric is difficult to wash and dry clean.

CHARACTERISTICS OF SILK

Raw silk, when examined under the microscope, has the rough appearance of a piece of wood. Often two filaments are held together with lumps of sericin. After the gum is boiled off, the fibers have the structureless appearance of hollow glass rods. Wild silk is coarser and more irregular. The microscopic appearance of the wild silk fiber resembles a flat, wavy ribbon having characteristic shadowy markings running obliquely along the fiber.

length of fiber

The usable length of the fibers for thrown silk varies from 1200 to 4000 feet. This great length permits the reel operator to combine a number of filaments together with little twist to produce the uniform, lustrous strand.

diameter of fiber

Silk has the finest diameter of any natural fiber and is rivaled only by one type of rayon and by the finest of the glass filaments. It is estimated that the diameter of silk fiber ranges from .00059 to .00118 of an inch.[3]

color of fiber

Cultivated silks in the gum are usually yellow or cream in color. The Chinese and Japanese silks are cream-colored, and the Italian are more yellow. The color is in the gum. Wild silks are usually brown, and the color is in the fiber itself and is not completely removed.

luster of fiber

The lusterless raw silk is given a soft, rich luster after the gum is removed. The beauty of many silk fabrics depends on the rich luster imparted by the floating yarns or the soft nap giving silk fabrics an unbroken sheen.

[3] Fiber Chart of The National Institute of Dry Cleaning.

Fig. 14-8   Reeling silk. (*Courtesy of The International Silk Guild, Inc.*)

strength of fiber

The silk fiber is stronger than any other natural fiber, based on equal diameters. Silk will sustain from 5 to 28 grams before breaking.[4] The silk fiber is weaker when wet than when dry, but it recovers its strength when dry.

elasticity of fiber

Silk is very elastic, and the fiber can be stretched from $\frac{1}{7}$ to $\frac{1}{5}$ of its length before breaking. The resiliency of the silk fiber enables silk fabrics to keep their shape and makes them resistant to wrinkling.

[4] *Ibid.*

heat conductivity

Even very fine silk is a poor conductor of heat. Garments made from silk are warmer than those of rayon, cotton, or linen. Weighted silks containing metallic salts permit the conductivity of heat and are therefore less warm.

electrical conductivity

Silk is also a poor conductor of electricity and is thus well-suited for the insulation of wires in electrical apparatus and wires. It is electrified by friction in the manufacturing operations, and the difficulty is lessened by maintaining standard conditions of 65 per cent relative humidity and 70° F.

hygroscopic moisture

The silk fiber is capable of absorbing from 10 to 30 per cent of moisture. Like wool, it still feels comparatively dry in spite of the moisture it has absorbed. The **regain** of silk is 11 per cent. Perspiration and oil from the skin are readily absorbed also, but silk is readily cleaned. The absence of short fibers causes silk to shed dust and dirt readily even if absorbed with the skin oils.

composition of silk fiber

Raw silk consists of fibroin and sericin or glue. The cultivated silk also contains small quantities of fats and waxes, which are removed with the sericin in the degumming boil-off. Raw silk is described by Richardson[5] as containing the following constituents:

Fats and waxes	3.02 per cent
Sericin	22.28
Fibroin	73.59
Ash or mineral matter	1.11

The fibroin or actual silk fiber is a proteid substance made up of the following elements:

Carbon	48.3 per cent
Hydrogen	6.5
Nitrogen	19.2
Oxygen	26.0

effect of light

Silk is more sensitive to weakening by ultraviolet light than any of the other fibers. Weighted silk is especially susceptible to this deterioration. Raw silk has been found to lose 50 per cent of its strength after six hours' exposure to an

[5] In J. M. Matthews and H. R. Mauersberger, *Textile Fibers,* 5th ed. (New York: John Wiley, 1947), p. 713.

ultraviolet lamp, scoured silk after two to two-and-one-half hours, and weighted silk after one-and-one-half to two hours.

effect of mildew

Silk is rarely attacked by mildew.

effect of heat

If white silk is heated in an oven at 231° F. for 15 minutes, it begins to turn yellow. The use of too hot an iron in pressing will similarly yellow silk. Above 330° F. silk disintegrates.

effect of acids

Concentrated mineral acids, such as sulfuric, hydrochloric, and nitric, will dissolve silk completely. The application of heat causes the silk to dissolve more rapidly. Cold dilute acids, except hydrochloric, will not injure silks.

Formic and acetic acids have no injurious effect on silk unless heated. Oxalic, citric, and tartaric acids do not injure silk if they are removed promptly. Perspiration greatly tenders silk, especially if weighted.

effect of alkalies

Cold concentrated solutions of alkali, such as caustic soda or caustic potash, have slight action on silk. Heated solutions completely dissolve silk. Weak alkalies, such as built-up soap, ammonia, sodium phosphate, and borax (all common detergents), attack silk more readily than they do cotton and linen. Free alkali must therefore be avoided in washing silk garments.

action of bleaches

Chlorine and hypochlorites (Javelle water) yellow silk and tender it. Hydrogen peroxide, potassium permanganate, and sulfurous acid may be used on silk if a suitable reducing agent is used as an after-treatment and followed by thorough rinsing.

action of metallic salts

Silk has a great affinity for metallic salts. This characteristic is the basis for the process of silk weighting.

action of dye stuffs

Silk has a greater affinity for dye than has any other textile fiber. It absorbs dyes at a low temperature, and, being a protein, it possesses both an acid and a basic property and can therefore be dyed with basic or acid dyes.

The following table from the Fiber Chart of the National Institute of Drycleaning summarizes the physical properties of silk:

1	Microscopic appearance	Double fiber; thin places
2	Length of fiber	Up to 4,000 feet
3	Diameter	0.00059 to 0.00118 in.
4	Color	Yellow
5	Luster	Dull with gum; bright when removed
6	Strength	5 to 28 grams/denier
7	Elongation	Stretches about ⅟₇ to ⅕ its length before breaking
8	Heat conductivity	Low
9	Hygroscopic moisture	About 11 per cent
10	Capillarity and penetrability	No capillarity
11	Composition	Sericin gum and fibroin
12	Method of preparation	Boil off in soap to degum
13	Effect of light	Seriously weakened
14	Effect of mildew	Rare and slight

CARE OF SILK

Light-colored silks, the color fastness of which has been found to be good, can be washed by hand in the same way as rayon. Lukewarm water and a neutral soap should be used. A thorough rinsing must be used to remove all traces of soap; this is especially important for weighted silks. If there is any doubt about the fastness of the color, the garment should be dry cleaned. Silks should be ironed while slightly damp with a warm iron; iron on the wrong side or with a pressing cloth.

U.S. SILK CONSUMPTION

Figure 14-9 shows how silk consumption was at a peak in the United States in 1929–30, then plunged to virtually zero in 1941 with the outbreak of World War II. It is now (1960) about 38 million pounds, half the 1938 figure.

Before World War II, 85 per cent of silk imported into the United States went into hosiery for women. Now, the percentage is less than one, but silk consumption has risen from virtually zero to 59,000 bales in 1956. There are three types of women who wear silk stockings: the older ladies who still prefer it; young girls who are allergic to nylon; and those who desire warmth not afforded by nylon.

Imports of Japanese silks to the United States in 1959 were: silk fabrics. 43 million dollars; raw silk, 41.5 million dollars; scarfs, 17 million dollars; silk yarn, 2.5 million dollars; a total of $104 million. Fabric imports show the following:

Habutai silk	35%	Pongee silk	4
Organdy	25	Chiffon	4
Fuji	12	Georgette silk	2
Shantung	9	Miscellaneous	9

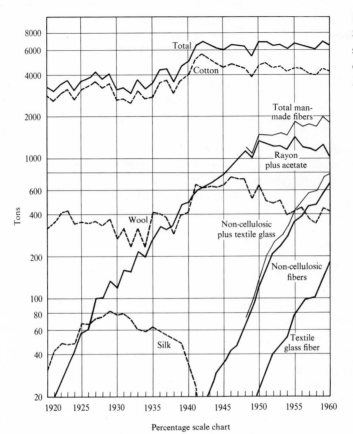

Fig. 14-9 United States fiber consumption. (*Courtesy of Textile Organon, March.*)

Percentage scale chart

QUESTIONS

1 Outline the life cycle of the silk moth.

2 What is the purpose of degumming silk, and how is it accomplished?

3 a) Distinguish between pure silk and weighted silk? b) Why is silk weighting carried out? c) What effect does weighting have on the price, performance, comfort, launderability, and durability of silk fabrics?

4 What is the difference between filament silk and spun silk? Into what end-use products does each go?

5 How are the sizes of silk yarns determined?

6 a) What are the chief characteristics of wild silk? b) From what countries is it principally obtained? c) What are the main uses?

7 Are there FTC regulations applying to the silk fabric industry?

8 Define the following terms:
  a) Spun silk   f) Resiliency
  b) Weighted silk g) Fibroin
  c) Tussah   h) Sericin
  d) Chrysalis   i) Raw silk
  e) Boil off   j) Pupa

inorganic fibers: glass, mineral, and metallic

GLASS FIBER FABRICS

On one occasion a very unhappy young mother telephoned our laboratory about a lost glass fiber ironing board cover. Through carelessness, the cover had been placed in the washer along with soiled clothing instead of washing the glass fiber article alone. Upon completion of the wash cycle, all that was visible of the heavy glass fabric was the cotton tape around the edge and for ties. The filaments of glass had permeated all the clothing, and the woman said, "My small son is crying his eyes out because of the itching. What shall I do?" At the time, we had no suggestion other than trying to wash out the glass by multiple washings and rinsings, then, if not successful, burning the articles lest they contaminate others in fabric wash loads. Later, we learned that glass fibers can be beaten out of clothing, hung on an outdoor line on a windy day, if one stands on the windward side and beats the fabric with an old-fashioned carpet beater or a tennis racket.

Although experimentation on the formation of fibers from glass had proceeded for many years, the first truly successful method of spinning glass into fiber form was developed in 1931 by the Owens-Illinois Glass Company and the Corning Glass Works. In 1938, the firms combined as the Owens-Corning Fiberglas Corporation. The growth of textile glass fiber has been phenomenal, rising from 7,600,000 pounds in 1949 to 147,400,000 in 1959. According to *Textile Organon,* the 1960 production was 239,000,000 pounds, an increase of 36 per cent.

production

[Glass is a completely inorganic material.] The common ingredients are silica sand and limestone. However, other constituents, such as metal oxides and hydroxides and borax, may be added for special glasses, depending upon the serviceability required. The making of glass filaments does not differ greatly from the formation of glass for any other purpose, because silica sand and limestone with one or more of the other constituents must be melted at about 3000° F. in a furnace. The molten glass may then be formed into a flat surface for window glass; it may be molded or blown into bottles or other containers; or, in the case of filaments, it may be spun through a very fine spinneret while still in the molten and fluid state. Glass is regarded by the scientist as a solid solution or a super-cooled liquid, one so thick that it will not flow perceptibly at room temperature. There are no definite chemical compounds and no evidences of crystallization in glass filaments.

Although sand, limestone, soda ash, and similar inorganic materials are generally regarded as the raw materials from which glass fiber is formed, the preparation of continuous filaments actually begins with an intermediate product.] The glass formed in the furnace is allowed to fall in the molten state from a high tower. As it falls, it forms a perfect sphere, and when cool, this **cullet** of uniform glass marbles of about five-eighths of an inch in diameter constitutes the raw material for the fibers. These marbles are carefully inspected for air bubbles, discoloration, or the presence of any undissolved particles or ingredients. The inspected marbles are then re-melted to 2500° F. in an electric furnace, and the molten mass is allowed to flow down into a spinneret having about 100 orifices. These filaments are drawn together, given a slight oil lubrication, and wound into a strand. One marble, weighing about one-third of an ounce, will produce a hundred miles of filament.

CONTINUOUS PRODUCTION   Newer glass-fiber-producing plants bypass the marble step. They thus avoid one heating of the mass. Fibers for staple sliver yarns or for batting are prepared in a similar manner. Generally, the composition may be altered, depending upon the chemical nature of the material against which this particular pad is to be resistant. Again, the molten glass comes through fine openings in the bottom of the furnace, but in this case, a very strong jet of steam blows against the filaments, tearing them into varying short lengths. Bats, or loose masses, of other inorganic fibers, such as rock wool, slag wool, etc., are formed in a similar manner and used for heat insulation in homes, freezers, ovens, and air-conditioning units. Four or five plants are under construction for the direct production of glass fibers from the original melt. This type of product is *not* included in data referring to textile glass fiber. By definition, "textile glass fiber" is produced in two forms, namely, continuous strand (filament) and staple sliver.

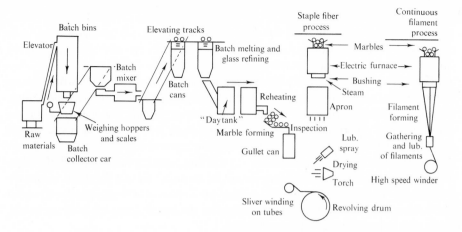

Fig. 15-1   Flow chart of glass fiber. (*From Leonard Mauer and Harry Wechsler,* Man-made Fibers *[New York: Rayon Publishing Corp., 1953], p. 28.)*

properties

Glass fiber is completely non-flammable. Furthermore, it has high strength, shows good resistance to heat, and is not attacked by insects, mildew, or bacteria. It also is resistant to many chemicals, although the degree of resistance will depend some upon the composition of the glass. The filaments have no stretch or resiliency; however, they are usually very pliable. Continuous filament fiberglas is heavy, having a specific gravity close to that of aluminum—2.5. The staple glass wool which is blown aside contains large quantities of air and has a specific gravity of approximately 0.025. Glass absorbs no moisture; therefore, it is extremely difficult to dye. Generally, the coloring material in the form of inorganic pigment is introduced into the melt bath, and the extruded filaments are thus colored throughout. This method is not too popular with manufacturers because it does involve a considerable stockpiling program, and if colors of certain hues do not sell as expected, then a tremendous amount of stock may be left on hand. Furthermore, it is an arduous task to clean out the melt furnace and the various lines between consecutive runs if different colors are to be produced.

The fiberglas curtains and draperies of the early 1940's were rather stiff and did not hang in graceful folds. The **Coronizing Process** widened the application of fiberglas as a truly decorative material, for this heat treatment reduced the weight, improved the handle and dimensional stability, and held the colors. It is reported that the Coronizing Process consists of coating the fiberglas filaments with colloidal silica, such as **Syton,** after which it is heat-set. The fabric is passed through a hot oven and the fiber given a slight crimp. The heat-treating is sufficient to destroy the finish, and the silica seems to be actually fused onto the surface. The fabric is then passed into a bath containing pigments for coloration or for printing purposes.

Glass fiber draperies are often screen-printed by methods somewhat similar to the Coronizing. There has been some objection to screen-printed glass fiber fabrics because of the color rubbing off after a rather prolonged period of abrasion. Such fabrics, whether printed or unprinted, cannot be expected to stand up indefinitely against rubbing. Abrasion against a window sill or between that of the back of a chair or sofa, or rubbing against Venetian blinds, contributes to rather rapid deterioration of the fabric. Glass fiber fabrics can be washed; generally, they should be washed one or two at a time in order to avoid wet rubbing which can cause the filaments to disappear completely in the wash, due to the low resistance to wet rubbing.

TABLE 15-1 / TYPICAL PROPERTIES OF CONTINUOUS FILAMENT GLASS FIBERS[a,b]

Tenacity, g./den.	6.3–6.9
Wet	5.4–5.8
Loop	2.0–4.0
Knot	2.0–4.0
Elongation, %	3–4
Wet	2.5–3.5
Elastic recovery, %	100
Tensile stress, p.s.i.	204,000–220,000
Initial stiffness, g./den.	307
Specific gravity	2.54
Water absorbency	Up to 0.3% (surface)
Effect of heat	Will not burn; strength begins to decrease at 600° F. and continues to decline to limiting temperature of about 1000–1500° F.; softens at 1500° F.
Effect of sunlight	None
Effect of acids	Attacked by hydrofluoric and hot phosphoric only.
Effect of alkalies	Attacked by hot solutions of weak alkalies and cold solutions of strong alkalies.
Effect of organic solvents	Insoluble
Dyes used	Resin-bonded pigments. Also suitable dyes for special coatings.

[a] At standard conditions unless otherwise mentioned.
[b] From Textile World, 105, No. 9 (September 1955).
From J. J. Press (ed.), *Man-made Textile Encyclopedia* (New York: John Wiley and Sons, 1959), p. 135, Table 1. Reprinted by permission.

uses

Glass fiber is not successful for wearing apparel, the main reason being that of the broken fiber ends, which, though finer than cobwebs, do have sharp points, and the skin of sensitive persons may develop a dermatitis after prolonged rubbing. This has been noted in such articles as ironing board covers. Some persons cannot rub their hands across one of these glass fiber board covers without suffering a sensation of intense itching. Immediately after World War II, there was a definite shortage of lining materials of rayon and acetate in the United States, and one enterprising manufacturer of coats for small girls obtained some surplus glass drapery materials which he made into coat linings. The results, of course, were that all the children itched badly around the neck and the wrists where the glass fibers were in contact with the skin. A new ultra-fine fiber, half the diameter of the finest known and called **Beta fiberglas,** is said to be so fine and supple that it can be worn.

As important as this material is in the decor of today's home, as a drapery, a curtain, or a table cover, many of its uses are industrial. Fiberglas and other glass fibers are widely utilized in braids, in tapes, in battings for heat insulation, for fire blankets, for mail bags carrying important documents to be protected from fire, and in heavy fabrics impregnated in plastic for boat hulls, bathtubs, fishing rods, and countless other molded articles, including the controversial vaulting pole with which the height of 16 feet was first attained in 1961.

TABLE 15-2A / GLASS FIBER BRAND NAMES

Fiberglas	Owens-Corning Fiberglas Corporation
Fiberfrax	Carborundum Company
Unifab Uniformat Unirove	Ferro Corporation
Modiglass	Modiglass Fiber, Incorporated
Pittsburgh PPG	Pittsburgh Plate Glass Company
Garan Vitron	Libby-Owens-Ford Glass Fibers Company

TABLE 15-2B / MANUFACTURERS OF GLASS

	FIBER		TYPE AVAILABLE			
Company	Generic Name	Trade Name	F	S	T	M
Gustin-Bacon Mfg. Company	Glass	Ultrastrand	X			
Johns-Manville Fiber Glass, Inc.	Glass	Vitron	X			
Modiglass Fibers, Inc.	Glass	Modiglass	X			
Owens-Corning Fiberglas Corp., Textile Division	Glass	Fiberglas	X	X		
Pittsburgh Plate Glass Company	Glass	PPG	X			

F—Filament
S—Staple
T—Tow
M—Monofilament

MINERAL FIBERS

We are accustomed to regard textiles as intended primarily for wearing apparel or for household decorative purposes. The textile fibers of nature are growing things which live and develop until man takes these fibers, processes them, and eventually converts them into cloth. One important fiber is obtained from a stone in which the ground waters have dissolved portions of the original rock and changed it to a mineral called **Serpentine,** a magnesia-silica-water ($3MgO \cdot 2SiO_2 \cdot 2H_2O$) mineral. This is deposited in a stringy form and, according to legend, was once termed "cotton stone." We now know it as **asbestos,** a completely non-flammable fiber. It is possible that wicks of asbestos were used in the lamps of the temples to the vestal virgins of ancient Greece because, though these lamps were kept ever-burning and were once a year supplied with oil, the wick, made of **Carpasian linen,** was not consumed by fire. This so-called Carpasian linen is supposed to have been made of asbestos mined in Cyprus. The Chinese are said to have used overcuffs made of asbestos which they put over the sleeves of their regular clothing when they wished to warm their hands over an open fire at night. According to Rossiter,[1] a well-known story of the early use of asbestos as a textile is that of Charlemagne's tablecloth, which was made of asbestos. Often he mystified his guests after the meal was over by throwing the tablecloth into the fire and drawing it out cleansed. At one time war was averted by this tablecloth. Charlemagne's country was threatened with invasion by the savage hordes of Harun-al-Raschid, Emperor of the East. Charlemagne called a peace conference to hear the demands of Harun-al-Raschid's chief ambassador and during the course of the conference tossed the tablecloth into the fire and drew it out unharmed. The ambassadors were convinced that they were dealing with a great magician and subsequently advised Harun-al-Raschid not to attempt the invasion of Charlemagne's country.

origin of the fiber

Asbestos is still somewhat of a mystery—or at least a subject of considerable debate among mineralogists—as to the exact manner in which it was deposited in the great green-stone region of Canada. The mineral is composed of iron, magnesia, and silica. Possibly hot ground waters under pressure dissolved some of the magnesia and silica which was then re-deposited in fissures and cracks, as mentioned before, in a stringy form. Asbestos is found in other parts of the world in somewhat different physical form, but no deposit compares with the Canadian. There is some in South Africa, Russia, Arizona, California, Cyprus, and Vermont; the principal deposits of the **chrysotile asbestos** in Canada are in Quebec and Ontario. These deposits are said to have been discovered in 1877, when a forest fire burned all the timber and even bared the rock beneath, disclosing the striations or veins of fiber. It was possible, however, that the Indians discovered the use of asbestos long before this, because one of the treasures in the British Museum at Bloomsbury near London is a small purse of Indian handcraft which Benjamin Franklin sold to an English collector of

---

[1] In J. M. Matthews and H. R. Mauersberger, *Textile Fibers,* 5th ed. (New York: Wiley, 1947), p. 916.

curios in 1724. This plaited bag would not burn and proved to be of asbestos fiber.[2]

the mining operation

Because the initial discoveries were all near the surface, the original method, and one still in use in many of the so-called mines, is a quarry or open pit operation. Some of these are very large; one quarry is said to be about 3,000 feet across and to contain 12 miles of railroad track. At greater depth, conventional mining operations are carried out, usually following an outcropping and pursuing the vein back through tunnels. Curiously, in all phases of asbestos mining and milling, it is absolutely necessary to keep wood out of the mine or plant. Asbestos ore is milled dry; thus, if any small pieces of wood were mixed in with the ore, they would splinter and break into small particles. These would be carried with the fiber through the various suction devices used to transport it, and the wood would severely damage the machinery and equipment. All beams and ties in the mines, even the ore chutes, are of all-steel construction; tamping sticks used for tamping the dynamite in the hole after drilling are not of wood but of copper tubing. The dynamite received at the mine in wooden boxes is transferred to cotton sacks. Even matches are forbidden, lest a match stick cause damage to the expensive equipment.

A long fiber brought out of the mine contains some quantities of rock adhering to the fibers. These particles are removed by **cobbing.** This consists of striking the fiber, flattening it out, and knocking loose rock particles; at best, even this crude fiber still contains some 5 to 20 per cent of rock dust and short fiber which is of too short a length to be spun successfully. These are removed when the fiber is opened at the factory.

preparation for spinning

In 1943, the asbestos producers of the Province of Quebec adopted a classification[3] which is regarded as standard in other asbestos-producing countries. There are three groups of spinnable textile fiber; lower groups are used for fireproof shingles, asbestos paper waste, stucco or plaster material, and a general refuse of very short fibers with which little can be done. Group I (¾-inch fiber and longer) and Group II (⅜-inch to ¾-inch) are the principal spinning fibers, although crude run-of-mine Group III is used in some woven asbestos fabrics. These various grades may be mixed with each other or blended with cotton in various proportions to give a spinnable fiber. This blending is a carefully concealed art, according to authorities.

The blended mixture of asbestos and cotton is taken to the card room

[2] *Ibid.,* p. 923.
[3] *Ibid.,* p. 930.

by suction or by air pressure, and the conventional carding operation removes the remaining short fibers, together with sand and rock dust. It also parallels the fibers and completes the card roving. It is spun into single-ply yarns which, in turn, are transferred to twister machines and twisted into two- or three-ply yarns, which are then placed on spools for the braiding or weaving operation.

prices

At the time of World War I, it must be remembered that the only non-flammable fiber we knew was asbestos; therefore, the price rise was meteoric, rising from a low of $275.00 per ton for crude No. 1 in 1913 to $3,000.00 a ton at the end of 1918. Since then, the price has stayed relatively stable, being $450.00 a ton for No. I and $200.00 a ton for No. II in 1932, from which it rose slowly to $700.00 and $300.00 in 1943. Since then, of course, the man-made fireproof fiber, glass fiber, has been developed. Except for industrial uses, little asbestos has ever been used in the woven textile industry, most of it going into papers, boards, and asbestos cement products for building, brake linings for automobiles, and railroad wheels where heat and fire must be combated. However, large quantities go into conveyor belts, insulating tape, pressing covers for the laundry and dry-cleaning industry, fireproof draperies, fire-resistant blankets, and safety clothing and safety mitts for bakeries, barbecue cooks, and others. A method was developed by textile engineers of the United States Rubber Company to spin shorter-length asbestos into satisfactory yarns. This process, patented in 1937, led to the special asbestos product called **Asbeston.**

Statistics on the production of asbestos are rather scarce in areas other than Quebec. Canada accounts for approximately 65 per cent of the world's production; the Quebec area yields close to 500,000 tons of fibers per year.

properties of asbestos fiber

Asbestos can be heated to a temperature of about 750° F. without appreciable damage. It can be heated to over 1700° F. without catching fire.

SPECIFIC GRAVITY   The fiber is quite heavy, its specific gravity being 2.2.

ACID DAMAGE   Strong acids cause approximately 50 per cent loss of weight at room temperature. Damage proceeds more rapidly at the boil.

SPINNABILITY   Spinning quality is improved by the addition of small quantities of cotton. A good type of cotton for this use is the rough-textured somewhat dark-colored Peruvian cotton.

COLOR   The Canadian type is generally slightly green-colored. Other asbestos may be found which is yellow, and in certain grades, especially from South Africa, the fibers have a bluish tint. There is very little need to dye asbestos, but alkali-type dyes can be used; some manufacturers use a color-cord system to distinguish by color their different kinds and weights of insulated electrical wire. The traditional asbestos curtain at the front of the stage of theaters is generally painted or printed, and the side curtains on stages are similarly colored.

STRENGTH   The tensile strength test cannot be run satisfactorily on asbestos yarns nor on fabrics because of the slipperiness of the fibers. They shift and slide over one another with such ease that no true strength can be determined.

METALLIC YARNS

Metallic yarns have been known for hundreds of years and were, in fact, the first of the man-made threads. Civilizations known for literally thousands of years engaged in hand weaving, and some patterns of silver and gold threads are still lovely today. These metallic threads were of extremely thin ribbons and often twisted around a strand of linen or cotton for strength. Only gold was capable of resisting tarnishing and corrosion. The other fibers would become dull upon prolonged exposure to the air, or they might tarnish from the action of water or perspiration. They were generally somewhat sharp and tended to cut the adjacent yarns in the fabric and might even abrade the skin of the wearer. Gold is the most ductile metal and can be beaten into thin gold leaf.

The metallic yarns of today are longer lasting, less abrasive, and fully as beautiful as the finest of those hammered out so painstakingly by the artisans of Persia, India, and other countries of the East. Modern metallic yarns are generally of colored aluminum ribbons sandwiched between two layers of transparent plastic. The most commonly used plastic is now du Pont's **Mylar,** which is chemically the same as Dacron. It has excellent clarity and is extremely strong.

The aluminum foil most commonly used is 0.00045 inches in thickness and about 20 inches wide. If this is to be colored, a thermoplastic resin containing the coloring material is attached to each face of the aluminum foil. It is then heated to about 190° F., which fixes the color on the aluminum, after which it is laminated between two thicknesses of Mylar or other transparent sheeting material. These metal threads are found in many articles of wearing apparel as a decorative effect. They are found in nylon, Dacron, and wool sweaters. They are widely used in upholstery materials and even find their way into decorative Turkish towelings. These materials are thoroughly washable and can be ironed at a temperature up to 300° F. The colors are fast to light, have good elasticity, and are not as subject to cutting and abrading as were the other metallic yarns. Sometimes the color is applied by dyeing the Mylar sandwich film.

The principal manufacturer in the United States is the Dobeckmun Company. Their products are **Lurex MF** and **Lurex MM.** The Metlon Corporation manufactures **Metlon;** the Reynolds Metal Company, **Reynolds** aluminum yarns; The Standard Yarns Mills manufacture **Lamé.** The special properties of the better-known metal yarns are given in Table 15-3.

TABLE 15-3 / FACTS ON LEADING METALLIC YARNS FOR USE BY WEAVERS AND DESIGNERS

Registered Name	Uses	Characteristics	Effects of Heat, Light, Chemicals	Construction
Chromeflex-MM	To be styled with cottons, synthetics, woolens, silks, straw, and non-wovens for apparel and decorating fabrics; domestics; commercial novelties; and industrial applications.	Soft hand, non-tarnishing, may be washed or dry cleaned, ironed at moderate dry temperatures or steam ironed.	Melting point of Mylar is 450° F. Softening temperature approximately 302° F. Excellent light fastness. Light fastness tested for all special color orders. Resists mildew, alcohol, odor, perspiration. Is non-hydroscopic and hydrophobic.	Metallized Mylar* laminated to clear Mylar. Color added to adhesive.
Chromeflex-MF Chromeflex-NL (above by Metal Film Company)	Same as above A special-purpose yarn designed for fine knit and woven goods where soft hand and flexibility are desired.	Same as above Thinnest and softest metallic yarn made—highest yield. Non-tarnishing, may be washed, dry cleaned, dry- or steam-ironed at temperatures under 150° F.	Same as above Same as above, except do not submit to heat over 150° F.	Foil laminated to Mylar. Mylar—not laminated.
Fairtex	Automotive fabrics, upholstery and drapery materials, dress fabrics, and novelty fabrics.	Highest quality in strength, luster, yield, and pliability.	Will withstand temperatures up to 160° F. with experimental dyeing of sample recommended. Light fastness over 100 hours.	Yarn produced by laminating aluminum foil between two films of cellulose acetate butyrate. Also available in supported form, staple form, and "wink."

Trade name	Uses	Characteristics	Care	Composition
Fairtex with Mylar (Metallized Tape)	Mattress ticking, automotive fabrics, upholstery and drapery materials, hosiery, rugs, towels, bedspreads, and other novelty fabrics.	Exceptional strength and brilliance, softness, and pliability. High yield.	Light fastness over 100 hours. Can be carbonized, mercerized, easily handled in normal finishing processes.	Produced by laminating one or more plies of Mylar polyester film to the metallized film. Also available in supported form, staple form, and "wink."
Fairtex with Mylar (Foil Tape) (above by Fairtex Corp.)	Same as above. Of particular application in towels and other fabrics to be laundered.	Same as above	Same as above	Produced by laminating Mylar polyester film to aluminum foil. Also available in supported form, staple form, and "wink."
Lamé	Draperies, upholstery, knit goods, blouses, lingerie, shoe material, dresses, braids, ribbons, hats, handbags, automobile upholstery, etc.	Non-tarnishing, non-irritating, soft, and pliable. Perspiration proof.	Unaffected by No. 4 wash test (laundering at 180° F.); dry cleanable. 100 hours minimum in Fadeometer.	Bright aluminum foil laminated between two plastic films. Available in special strengths, construction, and supports for easy and practical running.
Lamé with Mylar (Foil)	Most particularly cotton dress goods, bedspreads, corduroys, and products which require caustics or mercerization.	Similar to Lamé.	May be dyed at a boil, washed at a boil. Dry cleanable. Resistant to caustics. May be ironed at 300° F. Resists most chemicals and has excellent abrasion characteristics. Accepts mercerization.	Bright aluminum foil laminated between two films of Mylar.

TABLE 15-3 / FACTS ON LEADING METALLIC YARNS FOR USE BY WEAVERS AND DESIGNERS (continued)

Registered Name	Uses	Characteristics	Effects of Heat, Light, Chemicals	Construction
Lamé with Mylar (Metallized)	Draperies, upholstery, knit goods, lingerie, tricot.	Non-tarnish, non-irritating, soft, and pliable. Perspiration proof and mothproof.	Same as above, except for the caustic and mercerization.	Consists of laminating Mylar to metallized Mylar film on either one or both sides.
Lamé with Mylar (Non-laminated)	Circular knit, upholstery, drapery.	The same as the other Lamé yarns.	May be dry cleaned, washed at 160° F., non-resistant to caustics.	One layer of metallized Mylar non-laminated.
Lurex Metallic Yarn (Butyrate Lurex)	Fashion, furniture, and automotive fabrics. Linens and domestics, curtain and drapery fabrics. Men's wear. Knitwear. Narrow woven fabrics. Decorating plastics. Floor coverings. Knitting and crochet yarns.	Soft, pliable, cannot flake off. Unaffected by moths, mildew, perspiration, chlorinated or sea water. Non-tarnishing. Odorless. No sensitizing effect on skin.	Can be laundered, dry cleaned. Excellent light fastness. Moderate heat resistance. Resistant to selected acids, alkalies, and organic solvents. Resistant to bleaches, reducing agents, and salts.	Aluminum foil base bonded between two layers of cellulose acetate butyrate film. Available in plain or supported form. Special warp yarns available.
Lurex-MM (Made with polyester film, Mylar)	Extremely well adapted to raschel tricot and circular knitting machines. Schiffli embroidery. Nottingham and Lever lace machines.	Exceptional abrasion resistance and flex life. Exceptional tensile properties. Completely launderable and dry-cleanable. High yield. Minimum electrical conductivity.	Excellent light fastness. Resists common wet processing temperatures. Generally acid-resistant. Resistant to bleaches, reducing agents, salts, and selected organic solvents.	Metallized Mylar base bonded between two layers of clear Mylar film, or one layer of clear Mylar bonded to one layer of metallized Mylar.

Lurex-MF (Made with polyester film and bright aluminum foil)	Two layers of clean polyester film with a layer of aluminum foil bonded between.	Excellent light fastness. Alkali-resistant under controlled conditions. Resists common wet processing temperatures. Generally acid-resistant. Resistant to bleaches, reducing agents, salts, and selected organic solvents.	Good abrasion resistance and flex life. Exceptional tensile properties. Completely launderable and dry-cleanable.	Especially well-suited to a full range of textile wet processing.
50-C Metallic Yarn	Metallized polyester base protected on both sides by a plastic coating.	Excellent light fastness; resists common wet processing and dyeing temperatures; dry-cleanable.	As in Lurex MM, but with increased thinness and yield, giving yarn outstanding softness. For drapable fabrics.	Especially adapted to circular knitting.
Malora	Aluminum foil laminated between two films of acetate butyrate. Available unsupported or supported with various fibers.	Dry-cleanable; can be laundered and dyed.	Non-tarnishing, pliable, and non-irritating.	Upholstery, drapery, shoe, automotive, dress, and ecclesiastical fabrics, knitted goods, narrow woven fabrics, novelty fabrics, braids.
Malora with Mylar (Metallized)	Made by laminating clear Mylar film to metallized Mylar film. Available unsupported or supported with various fibers.	Can be mercerized, carbonized, withstands high temperatures, dry-cleanable and washable, high resistance to abrasion.	Non-tarnishing, brilliant luster, softness, high yield, exceptional strength and pliability.	Knitted fabrics made on circular or raschel machinery. Narrow, woven fabrics, trimmings, drapery, upholstery, automotive, and shoe fabrics.
Malora with Mylar (Foil)	Made by laminating clear Mylar film to aluminum foil. Available unsupported or supported with various fibers.	Withstands high temperatures, wet and dry processing, dry-cleanable.	Non-tarnishing, pliable, strong, economical, lustrous.	Linens, toweling, upholstery, suiting and shirting materials. Automotive fabrics, dress fabrics.

TABLE 15-3 / FACTS ON LEADING METALLIC YARNS FOR USE BY WEAVERS AND DESIGNERS (continued)

Registered Name	Uses	Characteristics	Effects of Heat, Light, Chemicals	Construction
Metallic Cellophane	Various types of braids, disposable ribbons, certain upholstery fabrics, display and theatrical materials, wrapping cords.	Non-tarnishing, most economical, good luster, high yield.	Not washable or launderable.	Made by laminating a clear viscose cellophane film to aluminum foil. Available unsupported or supported with various fibers.
Metlon Metallic Yarn	Belts, bags, trimmings, braids, drapery, upholstery materials, table linens, rugs, bedspreads; men's wear, suitings, blouses, dresses, lingerie, knitted materials, bathing suits. Shoe materials, ribbons, laces, automobile upholstery; industrial material for Army and Navy.	Pliable, non-tarnishable. Unaffected by salt water, chlorinated pools, climatic conditions. Mothproof. Unaffected by rubber, chemicals, perspiration.	Launders at temperatures not exceeding 160° F. Ironing temperature same as used for any acetate fabric. Dry cleans. Dyeable at temperatures not exceeding 160° F., with experimental dyeing of sample recommended.	Flat yarn produced by laminating extremely bright aluminum foil between two plies of specially formulated plastic film. Yarns may be supported with some other fibers.
Metlon with Mylar	Same as above and towels, sheets, tufted rugs, and bedspreads.	Same as above	Completely launderable. Approved by the American Institute of Laundering. Iron as for fabric in which used. Dry-cleanable. Dyeable at the boil with experimental dyeing advised. Launders at temperatures up to boil.	Mylar-F: (Foil) Flat yarn made by laminating extremely bright aluminum foil between two plies of Mylar polyester film. Mylar-V: (Vacuum) Flat yarn made by laminating a clear Mylar film to a Mylar film upon which there has been a vacuum deposition of aluminum. Both yarns may be used without supporting.

Metlon H.T. Mylar	Wherever great tensile strength is required, such as sewing, knitting, stitching, embroidery, or in weaving where extreme strength is needed.	Same as above, except that strength is approximately double.	Exactly as above	Flat yarn, exactly as Metlon with Mylar, except specially processed from high tenacity, high strength raw materials.
Ultravat Metlon with Mylar	Primarily for automotive upholstery and outdoor furniture fabrics, where extreme resistance to Fadeometer is required.	Same as above, except that in addition, yarn will exceed all automotive requirements for Fadeometer resistance.	Same as above	Same as Metlon with Mylar. Available in high tenacity quality.
Reymet	In all decorative applications. Particularly adaptable to automotive and home upholstery, draperies, curtains, tablecloths, crochet yarns, apparel, novelties, and other home furnishings.	Soft, pliable filament yarns easily handled on conventional types of textile equipment. Excellent dimensional stability. Non-tarnishing and non-toxic. Staple fiber can be blended and spun with most fibers on most systems.	All Reynolds yarns offer a minimum of 100-hour fade resistance on Weather-o-meter test. All yarns can be laundered and dry cleaned using conventionally approved methods. Can withstand scouring, bleaching, dyeing, finishing by nearly all standard textile wet processing techniques.	Made of strong, clear plastic films laminated to pure aluminum foil or to another film which has been metallized. Various films used, including du Pont's Mylar polyester film. All products available as continuous filaments or staple fibers. Filament yarns may be supported with wide range of natural and synthetic yarns for variety of effects.

SOURCE:
Excerpt from *America's Textile Reporter* (July 21, 1960), pp. 20–27.
* du Pont's polyester film.

QUESTIONS

1 What is meant by an inorganic fiber?

2 a) What three distinct types of inorganic fibers have been discussed in this chapter? b) What properties do they have in common, if any? c) How is asbestos fiber produced?

3 For what special purposes is asbestos intended?

4 Describe the production of glass fiber filaments.

5 What is the distinguishing feature between filament glass fibers and staple?

6 What is glass fiber batting, how is it prepared, and for what purpose is it intended?

7 Outline the physical properties of glass fabrics of greatest importance to the consumer, listing both good and bad features.

8 Why is glass unlikely to become a popular fiber for wearing apparel?

9 Is there any evidence that glass fibers may eventually get into the field of wearing apparel?

10 How are metallic yarns produced today and how do they compare in appearance, durability, and satisfactory service with the original or traditional metallic yarns?

11 Give the names of at least six manufacturers of metallic yarns and the brand names of each. What advantages or disadvantages do each of these products have over other competition?

rayon and acetate: the man-made cellulosic fibers

RAYON   A generic term for man-made fibers, monofilaments, and continuous filament yarns composed of regenerated cellulose with or without lesser amounts of non-fiber-forming materials. (Note: regenerated cellulose fibers made by the complete saponification of cellulose esters are rayons.)

ACETATE   A specific term used for man-made fibers, monofilaments, and continuous filament yarns composed of acetylated cellulose with or without lesser amounts of non-fiber-forming material.

These are the official definitions of rayon and acetate according to the American Society of Testing Materials, Committee D-13 on Textile Materials.[1] The key to this difference of the chemical nature of the fibers is the word **regenerated** in the case of rayons, and the word **acetylated,** which connotes the idea of an "ester" or "organic salt." By whatever process rayon fibers and filaments are made, the fiber is made of cellulose, and is chemically the same as that with which the process started, whether in the form of cotton linters or pulp from spruce and other woods. In the case of acetate, however, the resultant fiber is a salt, that is to say, an ester, of cellulose with acetic acid, and its chemical and physical properties in use are sufficiently different to require the identification of these fibers by law for the benefit of consumers.

[1] *ASTM Standards on Textile Materials,* American Society for Testing Materials, 32nd Edition, October, 1961.

RAYON

Rayon is an outstanding example of man's ingenuity in perfecting a textile fiber to rival and to compete with silk, wool, and even cotton. Originally a substitute or artificial silk, this group of cellulose fibers was given the generic name **Rayon** in 1923. Now these vastly improved fibers are so versatile that there are some 200 different rayons on the market; the cellulose-derived fibers totalled over 8,000 million pounds in 1962 and were produced in more than 40 countries.

TABLE 16-1 / 1962 WORLD-WIDE PRODUCTION CAPACITY OF MAN-MADE FIBERS
(in Millions of Pounds)

Country	Total Plants	Non-cellulosic	Rayon and Acetate	Glass
United States	102	1183	1431	363
Argentina	11	21.2	63.6	—
Australia	7	12.8	16.5	3
Austria	2	—	117.8	—
Belgium	9	15.9	83.8	—
Brazil	21	24	107.3	—
Canada	12	58.4	107.0	4.8
Chile	4	—	12.9	—
China (N)	2	—	18.3	—
China (R)	7	9	147	—
Columbia	3	1.2	29.3	—
Cuba	2	—	31.0	—
Czechoslovakia	10	10	175	—
Denmark	1	0.3	—	—
Finland	2	—	43	—
France	26	187.5	355	33
Germany (E)	20	30	340	—
Germany (W)	40	237.1	614	15
Greece	1	—	3.6	—
Hungary	2	3.5	10	—
India	17	13	174.7	—
Israel	4	3.6	—	—
Italy	43	176	513.7	16.5
Japan	70	542	1578	27.2
Korea (N)	—	—	40(?)	
Korea (S)	2	3.6	—	—
Mexico	10	10.2	75.1	2
Netherlands	14	45.9	120	11.6
Norway	4	0.3	408	—
Peru	3	0.5	4.8	—
Poland	11	20	161.1	—
Portugal	3	—	16.7	—
Romania	6	—	15	—
Spain	12	39.1	156	—
Sweden	5	0.4	4.4	2.4
Switzerland	8	17	54	—
Turkey	1	—	2.8	—
U.A.R. {Egypt / Syria}	3	1.6	31.2	—
U.S.S.R.	?	100	350	?

United Kingdom	37	243	575	?
Uruguay	2	1.1	2.0	—
Venezuela	3	7.1	9.7	—
Yugoslavia	2	8	65	—
TOTAL	544	3026.3	8094.3	478.5

The early historical background begins with the writings of European scientists who appreciated the value of a silk substitute or a silk-like fiber if one could be made. The first experiments to bring significant progress in the synthesis of a textile fiber were performed in England and France.[2] An Englishman in 1840 invented a method for producing wood pulp; a Frenchman in 1855 took out a patent for producing a fine thread from nitrocellulose. By many, Sir Joseph W. Swan[3] is considered to be the inventor of artificial silk, because he made fibers and exhibited fabrics prepared from collodion, a **nitrocellulose,** in 1885. Count Hillaire de Chardonnet is considered to be the father of the rayon industry, because his researches culminated in the patented workable process which bears his name.

Chardonnet was a pupil of Pasteur, who, in 1878, was studying the silkworm diseases which threatened to ruin the silk production of Europe. The pupil was more interested in creating a fiber through chemistry than in the protection of the natural fiber or the health of its insect creators. In 1889 he exhibited in Paris the yarns and fabrics made by his nitrocellulose process. It took about two years of experimentation to place the process into production on a commercial scale and to reduce the flammability hazard of the fabrics by removing nitrate from the filaments. These first fabrics, though of vegetable and not of animal origin, resembled silk and for years were identified as artificial silk or "silk made by art."

The development of other and safer processes for the manufacture of rayon has been a gradual one. The cuprammonium process first attained commercial proportions in 1890 and marked man's first success in spinning filaments finer than those of natural silk. A year later the fundamental chemical reactions on which the viscose process depends were discovered. These early fibers were weak and harsh, but this process has outstripped all the others because of low manufacturing cost and the fact that no expensive recovery process is involved. The cellulose-acetate process was originally grouped with the rayon processes, even though the filaments produced differ chemically from the regenerated cellulose of the other three. The chemical cellulose-acetate was known in 1869, but not until the turn of the century was the product put to use to make textile fibers. The acetate was used as a "dope" or varnish to protect the fabric wings of airplanes during World War I. When the war was over, it became necessary to find other outlets for the acetate, and after much research, excellent yarns

[2] E. W. K. Schwartz and H. R. Mauersberger, *Rayon and Synthetic Yarn Handbook,* 2nd ed. (New York: Rayon Publishing Corporation, 1936), p. 1.
[3] *Ibid.,* p. 2.

and fabrics were developed. The acetates will be discussed separately from the regenerated cellulose fibers, the rayons.

the naming of rayon

Although the original chemical research and early development of these processes are the product of many European scientists, the United States has stood out prominently in the engineering and chemical developments which have made this country the leader in the rayon industry. As the industry developed and this man-made fiber became a powerful competitor of natural silk, the matter of a name assumed great importance. The manufacturers, retailers, and consumers all found the complexities of many names and the word "silk" to be confusing. In 1923, the National Retail Dry Goods Association selected the name Rayon to denote all the synthetic fibers formerly known as artificial silk. The Bureau of Standards of the U.S. Department of Commerce defined the term as follows:

> Rayon—the generic name of filaments made from solutions of modified cellulose by pressing or drawing the cellulose solution through an orifice and solidifying it in the form of a filament or filaments by means of some precipitating medium.

The F.T.C. and business adopted this definition, but despite the efforts of the producers and sellers of rayon goods and articles made from rayon to familiarize the public with the nature of rayon fiber, much confusion still remained. Each producer had his own brand names to identify his product. The store salespeople were confused when asked to identify rayon, acetate, cotton, silk, and synthetic fiber fabrics, and consumers had a very hazy idea as to what rayon was and how to care for it.

To separate the confusion in the mind of the consumer as to what was rayon and what was acetate, and with the introduction of countless new physical forms and special rayon fibers with unusual properties, to say nothing of the ever-present problem of the heat sensitivity of acetate compared with rayon, the NRDGA (renamed the National Retail Merchants Association in 1960) pressed for aid and clarification for their buyers and for their customers. As a result of this action and similar requests from industry, a new interpretation of the Federal Trade Commission ruling for labeling and advertising rayon and acetate was promulgated on December 11, 1951. This became effective in February of 1952, the differentiation being essentially that of Committee D-13, the textile committee of the ASTM. Now acetate fibers, yarns, and products, which were formerly grouped with rayon, must be called acetate, and this same separation is emphasized in the new Fiber Identification Labeling Law of 1960 (see Chapter 29). This new ruling on acetate has somewhat softened the severity of the identification of fabrics made from these fibers. Under the 1937 rules, if a fabric such as taffeta, which had long been associated with silk, were made of rayon, the name of the fiber had to be given in conjunction with the name of the fabric;

thus, it was to be referred to as rayon-taffeta to distinguish it from the genuine article, which was of silk fiber. Under the present Federal Trade Commission rulings, however, the fabric name may stand alone in an advertisement or on a label, provided that the advertising states the article is made of acetate or rayon. Partly due to the concealment of the fiber identification in the textile product advertisements, the Federal legislation of 1960 became necessary.

Not only the purchasing but also the performance of rayons and acetates in service led to another type of standard, the L-22 Standard on Rayon and Acetate Fabrics, which became effective in 1951. This was promulgated through the American Standards Association and is discussed together with the extended standard, the new "L-22," now applied to all textile fibers (Chapter 25).

rayon processes

Rayon is made by chemically treating cellulose to produce a viscous solution which has the consistency of molasses. This solution is forced through small spinneret orifices of almost microscopic size, rather like tiny openings in a miniature shower nozzle. This filament is hardened as it emerges from the spinneret. The hardening is done either by evaporation of the chemical solvent or by coagulation in a chemical bath. The technical details involved in each of the processes need not be repeated here. A brief outline of each process will serve

Fig. 16-1 A rayon spinneret. (Reproduced through the courtesy of the American Viscose Corporation.)

Fig. 16-2 Preparation of alkali cellulose for the viscose: Steeping cellulose in alkali during the rayon process; the resulting product is alkali cellulose. *(Courtesy of American Viscose Corporation.)*

to indicate only the order of the several chemical and mechanical steps required to produce the filaments.

CUPRAMMONIUM PROCESS   Schweitzer in 1857 dissolved cellulose in an alkaline copper solution. In 1890, Despeisses developed a method to make a filament. The method was frequently modified until now it is capable of producing the finest diameter of any of the rayons.

1. Cotton linters afford the greatest purity and are the preferred source of cellulose. These fibers are cleansed by cooking in a mild caustic alkali and bleached with chlorine.

2. The purified **alpha-cellulose** is washed, dried, and treated with basic copper sulphate and ammonia.

3. The viscous solution is forced through spinnerets into water, which removes much of the copper and ammonia.

4. The filaments are passed through a mild sulfuric acid bath to coagulate them and to remove the copper.

5. The skeins are washed and rinsed.

6. The yarns are sorted according to denier.

Fig. 16-3 Shredding the alkali cellulose: After steeping, the alkali cellulose sheets are crumbled by the revolving blades of shredding machines. (*Courtesy of American Viscose Corporation.*)

This yarn is capable of withstanding a hot iron and claims the greatest wet strength per denier and whiteness permanence of any of the ordinary rayons, that is, excluding special-tenacity fibers.

VISCOSE PROCESS   The English chemists Cross and Bevan prepared the alkali-cellulose Xanthate and patented the process in 1895. The first viscose yarn was exhibited in 1900. This yarn was weak.

1. Cellulose from a mixture of sheets of spruce wood with or without cotton linters is the preferred source of the **alpha-cellulose** used in this process. Other woods may be used also.

2. The sheets are steeped in caustic soda to produce **alkali-cellulose,** which is shredded into crumbs.

3. The crumbs are aged.

4. The alkali-cellulose crumbs are changed into **cellulose Xanthate** by treatment with carbon disulfide.

5. The Xanthate is dissolved in dilute caustic alkali to produce **viscose.**

6. The viscose is filtered and aged until it is the right consistency for spinning.

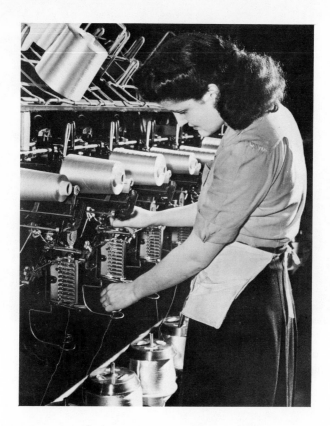

Fig. 16-4 Winding rayon filament yarns: Continuous filament yarn comes from the spinning machines in the form of cylindrical cakes (visible at the bottom of the photograph) which, after chemical processing and drying, are wound onto cones (above). (*Courtesy of American Viscose Corporation.*)

7. The viscose is forced through the spinneret into dilute sulfuric acid solution. This wet spinning process **coagulates** the filaments, which are simultaneously regenerated into pure cellulose, and the mass of filaments is in the form of cakes.

8. The filaments are wound onto a skein, and the sulfur is removed by means of an alkaline sulfide bath.

9. The washed filaments are bleached and graded.

purification of cellulose raw material

Because most producers of rayon and of acetate begin their processing with a purified cellulose, one might be tempted to believe that the production of the fiber and the flow sheets for cuprammonium viscose and acetate, respectively, begins with a mixture of cotton and tree trunks. Some clarification should be made. As a matter of fact, the key to a fine rayon fiber lies in the purification of the cellulose raw material and the uniformity of this product. Although German scientists, as early as 1918, were using spruce wood as a source of cellulose for their rayon industry, the producers in the United States

Fig. 16-5 Chemical reaction in viscose rayon.

$$(C_6H_{10}O_5)_n + n\,NaOH \longrightarrow (C_6H_9O_4ONa)_n + n\,H_2O$$

cellulose   caustic soda   soda cellulose

$$(C_6H_9O_4ONa)_n + n\,CS_2 \longrightarrow [SC \overset{SNa}{\underset{OC_6H_9O_4}{\diagdown}}]_n$$

soda cellulose   carbon disulfide   sodium cellulose Xanthate

The reaction has taken place on No. 2 carbon. Thus, the conversion of Xanthate to viscose on a structural basis might be considered to be

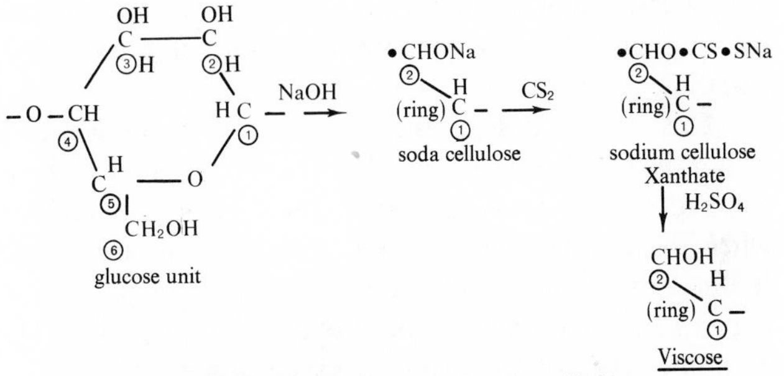

glucose unit   soda cellulose   sodium cellulose Xanthate   Viscose

Viscose is chemically identical to the purified cellulose, but each molecule of cellulose contains fewer glucose molecules. Thus, n is about 9,000 in cotton, somewhat less in wood pulp, and 350–500 in viscose.

were slower to turn to wood as the primary source of cellulose, but World War I, with the strategic priority assigned to cotton linters, making them unavailable for the textile industry, caused the change. Greater abundance at lower prices and improved technical knowledge as to processing have combined to keep spruce wood at the head of the materials selected for this textile industry. Other woods are now being used, but generally they require different chemical cooking methods.

Logs are transported to the pulp mills by truck or floated in great rafts along river or lake waterways. The water method is much cheaper, and for that reason many pulp mills are located on the banks of rivers or the shores of inland lakes adjacent to large forest areas. The logs are cut into lengths of about 20 feet, and the bark is stripped off by means of hydraulic pressure jets. The skinned trunks are then taken to a chipper, a large machine with revolving blades against which the conveyor holds the logs. This cuts the wood into small chips about one inch square and approximately a quarter of an inch in thickness. These chips are transformed into a pulp by treatment with strong alkali and sodium sulfide and a pre-treatment with a sulfate. This method produces a very pure white cellulose which is free of pigment and contains about 90 per cent of **alpha-cellulose.** This pulp commonly is bleached to make it perfectly white. This is a purer grade of cellulose than that produced by the sulfite process for newsprint. The alpha-cellulose predominant in the cellulose pulp for the textile industry is generally referred to as **chemical cellulose.** See Figure 10-10, page 141, for the structure of cellulose.

The chemical reaction given above is a simplification of the viscose process. It is interesting to note that the value for "n," the number of glucose molecules in a molecule of cellulose, is important to the fiber performance in use. The higher the number, the stronger and more stretchy the rayon, especially when wet.

The secret to good rayon production is the production of cellulose with as long a molecular chain as possible; the further treatments to put cellulose into solution and ready for spinning should not too greatly reduce the molecular length.

This watery pulp is then laid down on screens in the form of a large sheet rather closely resembling white blotting paper, which is wound on rolls and shipped to the fiber-producing plant. For the maintenance of quality control when these large rolls are used, two or more are shredded at the same time and fed into the vat in which the cellulose is to begin its transformation from blotting paper to luxury fiber. Some alpha-cellulose pulp is shipped in tank cars to the manufacturers of rayon or of tissue grade papers.

comparison of the rayon processes

The fundamental processes have been briefly described in the preceding pages, and some account should be given of the advantages and disadvantages

Fig. 16-6 Flow chart of regular viscose rayon. (*Courtesy of Modern Textiles Magazine.*)

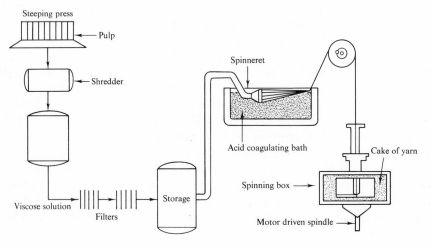

of each. The nitrocellulose process can be omitted from the discussion, because it is no longer in production in the United States.

The filaments produced by the cuprammonium process are the finest in diameter. The yarns spun from them are also very fine and find wide use in lingerie and knit garments.

Table 16-2 shows sketched outlines of typical cross-sections of several of the commercial rayons on the market, together with their physical characteristics, affecting properties of interest to the consumer in her care of garments and other textile items made of rayon. (One should remember that rayons are the second most important textile family, being exceeded only by cotton in its world-wide volume and importance.) Rayon fibers may be continuous **filaments** of infinite length, or they may be made into cut or **staple** yarns; practically all blends of rayon with other fibers are, of course, of staple yarn, with the fibers cut to approximately the same length as the natural fiber or other man-made fiber or fibers with which the rayon is blended. Wide ranges of fiber size and strength are available; therefore, there is no simple rayon performance classification and to assign a set of test values to this fiber would be a grave mistake. Rayon can, in fact, be tailored to almost any kind of application. This table indicates a clear difference, however, between what technologists consider to be typical viscose or typical cuprammonium rayon of moderate strength, and the so-called high-tenacity or high-strength rayons. In this category, another important rayon, **Fortisan,** must be recognized as one of the most important of the rayon fibers for household decorative use. This rayon is prepared through the acetate process; but before spinning, the cellulose acetate is completely saponified, that is, changed back to pure cellulose with the characteristic alcohol or hydroxyl groups and acetic acid, which may be treated to a re-usable concentration for another batch.

cold stretching

All the high-tenacity rayons, including Fortisan, are **cold stretched** in order to give them additional strength through better orientation of the individual molecules. (For greater detail on cold stretching and the concept of crystallinity of fibers resulting therefrom, see Chapter 19, "Nylon," page 290.) Figure 16-7, showing the elongation under stress of typical rayons, demonstrates the wide differences between Fortisan, a relatively firm and very low-yield fiber, and the usual textile rayon. In most of these rayons, and indeed in most textile fibers, there is a range in which, when a stress or load is applied, the fiber tends to behave as an elastic solid, that is, the original dimension is regained when the stress is removed. However, if the load is increased, a point is reached where recovery no longer takes place, and eventually a third region is reached in which there is a very rapid stretching or extension of the fiber. Only Fortisan fails to show this typical stress-strain curve among the six rayons portrayed. The high-strength or high-tenacity tow yarn of slightly over four grams per denier just begins to show the second region where recovery is incomplete and then breaks. The other rayons all pass through this hump region and then progress with rapid

TABLE 16-2 / IMPORTANT USE CRITERIA FOR RAYONS

	VISCOSE			AVRIL	ZANTREL	CORVAL	CUPRAMMONIUM	FORTISAN
Microscopic Cross-Section (500x)								
TENACITY	**Filament and Staple**			**High Wet Modulus**	**High Wet Modulus**	**Cross-linked**	**Filament**	**Filament**
	Regular	Medium	High					
Tenacity (gpd) Dry	1.5–2.6	2.4–3.2	3.0–5.1	5.0	3.4	2.1–2.4	1.7–2.3	6–7
Tenacity (gpd) Wet	0.7–1.8	1.2–1.9	1.9–3.9	3.5	2.7	1.2–1.3	0.95–1.35	5.1–6.0
Elongation at break (%) Dry	15–30	15–20	9–26	18	10	12–15	10–17	6
Elongation at break (%) Wet	20–40	17–30	14–34	21	12	12–17	17–33	6
Specific Gravity	1.50–1.53			1.5	1.51	1.53	1.52–1.54	1.5
Water Absorbency Std. (%)	13 (11 is commercial standard)			13	11.5	13	12.5	9.6–10.7
Effect of Heat	300° F.—loses strength; 350–464° F.—decomposes			Similar	Decomposes about 300° F.	Similar	Decomposes about 300° F.	Scorch at 68° *above* other rayons
Effect of Acids and Alkalies	Most rayons damaged as is cotton. Swells and weakens in alkali.			Similar	Similar	Resistant to Alkali	Similar	Similar
Resistance to Mildew, Sun, and Aging	Attacked by mildew. May yellow and weaken under prolonged sun exposure and age.			Resists sun damage and aging.	Similar	50% more resistant than cotton	Similar	Similar
Effect of Bleach	Attacked by strong oxidizing agents. Peroxide and chlorine bleach satisfactory.			Similar	Avoid Peroxide	Similar	Similar	Similar

Materials obtained by courtesy of *Textile World.* Copyright © McGraw-Hill Publishing Company, Inc., 1962.

extension until the breaking point is reached. Note that most of the rayons used for wearing apparel have a stress of only about two grams per denier at the break but have the ability to yield and thus absorb some of the applied stress.

rayon and consumer

Were rayon not a satisfactory textile for wearing apparel, it would never have reached the production volume it has, nor would it be the man-made fiber produced in more countries than any other of our man-made textiles. Viscose rayon is cheaper than cotton, and like that cellulosic material, it can be dyed and finished by the best of processes and materials or by the most inferior. Let us view some of the more important properties of apparel rayon and, for the time being, disregard special rayons such as the high-tenacity rayons, the cross-linked cellulosics, and certain others.

STRENGTH   As we have seen, ordinary rayon, viscose or cuprammonium, has a dry breaking strength of approximately two grams per denier (2 gpd).

Consumers know from past experience that rayons lose somewhere between

Fig. 16-7 Stress-strain curves for commercial rayons and acetate. (*From J. J. Press* [ed.], *Man-made Textile Encyclopedia* [*New York: John Wiley and Sons, Inc. 1959*], *p. 97.*)

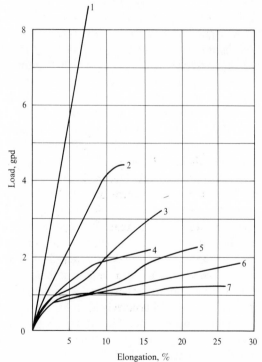

1. Fortisan
2. High-tenacity tire cord
3. High-tenacity apparel yarn
4. Cuprammonium yarn (continuous spinning)
5. Regular-tenacity textile yarn
6. Cuprammonium yarn (reel spinning)
7. Acetate multifilament

30 and 60 per cent of their strength when wet, the weaker members of the family losing the higher percentage. It is important, therefore, that if wet strength in a fabric is of significant importance to the consumer, then a somewhat higher-strength rayon should be selected. Numerous authorities have demonstrated in experimental and research work that the shorter the cellulose molecular length in rayon, the weaker it is. To some extent, this weakness can be corrected by stretch spinning, the theory being that when the molecules are made more parallel by pulling, then there is more opportunity for cross-linking, and we have more of a "crystallinity" entering sections of the molecular structure. The un-stretched rayon, on the other hand, is generally regarded as being rather amorphous in character, with the individual molecules being every which way within the fiber. Water tends to gain entry into the fiber more readily in this amorphous structure. By reducing the friction of molecule against molecule and perhaps helping to break the chain of cross-linked bonds between adjacent molecules, there results a more ready breakdown when the rayon fiber is wet.

MOISTURE   The moisture absorbency of viscose rayon is so rapid that this fiber is not appropriate for certain end-uses, one of which is draperies with a viscose warp. Water absorbency is not serious if viscose is in the filling direction, but a drapery with a viscose warp will on a humid day tend to stretch as much as eight to ten inches, while on a very dry day, it may shrink so that the bottom hem may be four to eight inches off the floor. These were average figures found on some rayon draperies which Kaufmann's had tested by its Fellowship at Mellon Institute some years ago. The customer is not so conscious of any tendency of the drapes to stretch or shrink in width. These fabrics were not made of high-tenacity rayons now available.

REGAIN   The average regain for apparel rayons is 11 per cent under constant temperature-humidity conditions. The total moisture holding capacity or imbibition is about 100 per cent, that is, rayon will hold its own weight or a trifle more of water. This feature is an advantage in towels and wearing apparel if one desires rapid moisture and perspiration absorbency.

THERMAL PROPERTIES   Rayon behaves like all cellulose materials when subjected to flame or to heat. It burns with the characteristic odor of burning paper. Rayon will begin to char or scorch if ironed at a temperature above 350°F. and loses some breaking strength if held at a temperature of over 300°. Viscose fabrics tend to turn yellow if held at a high temperature over a long period of time and will, therefore, require some bleaching.

COLOR   The characteristic color of rayons is slightly off-white, usually on the cream-colored side. The whiteness can be improved by the use of Titanox (TiO_2), which, at the same time, gives rayon the attractive "dullness" or "opacity" rather than the high luster characteristic of this fiber. Generally though, one must admit that white rayons do not stay white indefinitely.

LIGHT EXPOSURE   When exposed to direct sunlight, rayon loses strength, just as do other cellulose fibers. The amount of strength loss varies depending upon the humidity, the room temperature, and the time of exposure to intense sunlight per day. To some extent, it would be dependent also upon the degree of luster or dullness (the dull viscose rayons seem to lose somewhat more strength than do the bright) and upon the kind of finish applied to the goods. Mildew and bacteria will react upon the cellulose, but generally, insects will not attack rayon.

RAYON YARNS

preparation of rayon yarn

The filaments emerging from the spinneret into the acid bath for **saponification** or **coagulation** may be modified as to texture by means of chemicals in the bath. If, for example, the bath contains small quantities of zinc sulfate, the rayon filament will have a somewhat thicker skin. Similarly, the bath composition can produce the normal **serrated** cross-section rayon filament or one which is more nearly round. One interesting method of producing a **crimp** or wavy type of rayon filament is by means of extruding from two closely adjacent spinnerets a fresh and a somewhat older Xanthate solution. When these two strands meet at the mouths of the spinnerets, they immediately coalesce to form a larger filament in which the older Xanthate produces a thicker skin. Thus, we have a condition in which half of the filament has a thick skin, the other half, a thinner. This fiber can be formed into a wavy helix as it is extruded. This is known as **chemical crimp,** as distinguished from crimp artifically put into the fibers for special applications, such as rugs and carpets (see Chapter 27). The filaments from the various orifices in the spinneret may be twisted together and collected on bobbins by a direct spinning method. This is very commonly used for viscose and cupra rayon. Viscose rayon is sometimes made into a yarn by the pot spinning method, in which the filaments are extruded into a revolving pot or box. The centrifugal force gives a slight twist and throws the yarn to the side of the container; thus, when they are removed, the yarns are in the form of a cake.

rayon waste and staple yarns

Production of rayon yarns would naturally result in a considerable amount of waste from the spinning operations and also from bobbins, knitting machines, and other equipment in the plant which uses textile yarns. It has been estimated that some four to five million pounds of this by-product waste is produced annually. This is **garnetted,** that is, separated and broken into staple lengths usable in the woolen or worsted industries. Much of this once went into low-priced clothing for men and boys, often without distinguishing or identifying labels, prior to the Federal Trade Commission rules. At one time, the Kaufmann Fellowship analyzed the fabric content of 15 different samples of boys' suiting fabrics. All were mixtures of rayon and wool, and the rayon content varied between 60 and 30 per cent by weight. Today, of course, such blends would have to be identified by percentage on the label. The ready acceptance of this waste, however, led to the commercial production of rayon staple of controlled fiber length. The rayon staple and tow currently account for almost half the total rayon production of the world. The viscose staple is produced in many deniers and staple lengths for spun yarns. Generally, fibers from one to three inches in length are used on the cotton system, either alone or in combination with cotton fibers, two to three inches for the woolen system, three to seven for the worsted system, and three to seven inches for the spun silk system. The denier of the staple, too, is generally chosen to match the fineness of the natural fiber or of the blending fibers in order to produce a more uniform yarn and not one which shows soft, fine spots and coarser ones in the same yarn and fabric.

The viscose process is by far the largest producer of rayon both for yarn and for staple. The viscose fiber is cheaper than the others because it can be made from wood pulp alone or mixed with linters. The prejudices of the early 20's against the poor durability of this fabric, its shine, and its hardness are now unjustified. Viscose yarns still have a tendency to ravel if seam edges are not protected. Acetate yarns are more resistant to raveling and shifting than are the viscose fibers.

sizes of rayon yarns

There are several sizes or counts of rayon yarns identified as to fineness by **denier.** In the United States, the denier of a yarn is computed from the weight of 450 meters (492.12 yards) of yarn. The legal or International denier is a skein of yarn 450 meters long which weighs 5 centigrams, or 0.05 of a gram. This corresponds to the ASTM definition: "The denierage of a yarn is the weight in grams of a length of 9000 meters of a yarn." If 450 meters of a yarn weigh $\frac{1}{20}$ of a gram, 20 times as much, or 9000 meters, is required to weigh one gram. Thus, a 2-denier yarn is calculated in the following terms:

450 meters of yarn weigh 0.1 gram
492.12 yards of yarn weigh 0.1 gram
9000 meters of yarn weigh 2 grams

The average size of rayon apparel yarns is between 100 and 200 denier. The finest is 15 denier, made from cupra-rayon.

manufacture of staple

Production methods for viscose rayon staple and tow are the same as those for continuous filament yarns as far as the coagulating bath step. Instead of being wound on bobbins or formed into cakes, the mass of filaments emerging from the coagulating bath may be cut to any desired length to provide staple yarns. Ingenious modern machines providing tow-to-top or direct spinning permit the spinning of yarn in the form of a rope made up of the gathered filaments from the 2000 to 3000 holes in the large spinneret used for staple or for tow filament spinning. The purchaser then breaks this rope into whatever lengths he desires for his own purpose.

Fig. 16-8 Slashing rayon yarns: Slashing and beaming of rayon tire cord at American Viscose Corporation's Lewistown, Pennsylvania, plant. (*Courtesy of American Viscose Corporation.*)

Although many plants producing viscose filament and fiber still operate on the step or individual batch basis, all three types of viscose, filament, staple, and tow, usually are produced by the continuous process. This process requires extremely accurate controls. As the mass of filaments converges from the coagulating bath, it is caught on a series of reels over which the rope passes through a route by which it is given a series of finishing sprays and treatments and is dried. When under proper control, this rope is thoroughly dried as it passes the last reel, and it is ready for spinning, twisting, and winding or can be given any kind of stretch. The continuous method is said to give a more uniform filament or staple yarn than the batch method, and if the reels are in proper adjustment, the cold stretching operation for obtaining high-tenacity rayon fibers and yarns is said to be comparable to that produced by a bobbin or cake.

FORTISAN

Mention has been made that although Fortisan is manufactured by means of the acetate process, it is properly called a rayon, since the fiber is pure cellulose. The acetic acid has been removed by saponification from the cellulose acetate and has been replaced with the hydroxyl, the OH group. The fibers born 20 years ago were made in United States by Celanese Corporation of America. In World War II and then again during the Korean conflict, Fortisan was of great value to the military due to its high tenacity, its lightness in weight, and resistance to climatic conditions. Thus, parachutes, shrouds, cordage, and many types of protective fabrics utilized this fiber. Its initial use for consumer goods while still scarce was for window curtains; generally, since it received much publicity at the time, it was mixed with other fibers. The Fortisan yarns were in the warp direction, and the filling might be silk, cotton, acetate, rayon, nylon, or almost any other fiber. At the time, labeling was somewhat lax, and usually these curtains were sold as Fortisan with no mention of the other yarns. Thus, many disappointing experiences were had by consumers who expected miracles of this high-strength fiber and then found upon exposure to sunlight that the fabric was no better than the weakest link, which, if sensitive to sunlight, rapidly deteriorated in use. There has been some difficulty in washing Fortisan due to shrinkage. Thus, many consumers possessing Fortisan curtains have preferred to have them dry cleaned.

processing

Fortisan owes its great strength and fineness to a very high degree of orientation due to special stretch-spinning procedures carried out on the acetate fiber. The acetate yarn passes through a chamber of compressed air at high pressure, as much as 32.5 pounds per square inch. The yarn proceeds on a series of rollers into a steam chamber, at the end of which the yarn is passed onto high-speed rollers turning at ten times the speed of the original carriers. This serves to stretch the filament to ten times its original length with a corresponding loss in diameter. The resultant yarns have a very high order of orientation. The saponification is carried out by placing the bobbins or other holders of the stretched yarn into a solution of sodium hydroxide with an excess of sodium acetate. The solution is pumped through the filaments from the outside to the inside of the bobbins and back until the saponification has been completed, after which the yarn is sized and dried and rewound onto skeins for use. It may be used in the filament form or as staple. Extra high-strength Fortisan is produced by a slightly different method.

Shortly after the introduction of Fortisan into the consumer market, the writer had a telephone call in the laboratory from a woman who wanted to know about this wonderful new fiber CORTIZONE of which she had been reading. When asked for more detail, she went on to explain that this new fiber was used in curtains; whereupon she was told that the fiber in question was called FORTISAN, and she was given the information for which she had asked.

Fortisan loses less strength when wet than do other rayons, and it has a very low elasticity and a low elongation, or break, of 6 per cent. These two features are, of course, what one would expect of a highly oriented fiber. Its excellent resistance to ultraviolet light and to weather degradation make it ideal for curtains and other uses where light is a problem. Its chemical properties are the same as any other cellulose. It is an expensive fiber: first, because of the chemical and engineering steps required in its manufacture, and also because of the very high weight loss, 38 per cent, sustained during the saponification operation. The competitive position of Fortisan, in the curtain field particularly, would be an interesting study in terms of consumer needs, wants, and price (see Chapter 29). In the meantime, the limited production and difficulty in finding 100 per cent Fortisan curtains mean that the bulk of this fiber, for the present, at least, will go into special uses, into industry, and into the military, where serviceability is of far greater concern than cost.

OTHER SPECIAL RAYONS

The story about the lady's confusion with the name Fortisan substantiates the wisdom of fiber producers in their custom of introducing new fibers under code numbers, letters, or other means of identification, rather than immediately investing in the cost of establishing and advertising a new name at the time when the fiber itself is more or less on trial. If consumer reaction is not satisfactory, the fiber may never become economically feasible and may be quietly withdrawn from the market.

Four companies have recently introduced new rayons with somewhat unusual properties. Comparatively little is known about some of these, but preliminary literature of fiber properties throws some light on possible consumer use in the textile or fabric form. These fibers are **Avril** (formerly Fiber 40), produced by the American Viscose Corporation; **Corval** and **Topel,** Courtaulds of Alabama; and **Zantrel** (formerly Fiber 500), American Enka Corporation, (Hartford Fibres Company, Division). Their production is still rather secret, with no great amount of publicity being given.

Zantrel seems to be somewhat different from the others, insofar as its cross-section is concerned, and it has been given the trademark description of **polynosic** fiber.

All these fibers, alone or in combination, should have great popular appeal. They seem to give additional softness and richness of texture to regular viscose and to cotton fabrics. Dimensional stability, especially freedom from shrinkage, is one of the strong points claimed for these new fibers, and their wet strength is higher than that of the usual apparel rayons. Thus, they seem to behave more like cottons. The manufacturing process has apparently resulted in less shortening of the cellulose molecule, so that the degree of polymerization of these fibers is closer to that of cotton than it is to the more greatly shortened cellulose chains of the rayons ordinarily produced.

cotron

The American Viscose Corporation has embarked upon a blending program involving cotton and rayon. They term this blend **Cotron.** Fabrics of various weights in these blends must meet appropriate performance standards for articles commonly using these constructions. They are aimed at the L-22 American Standard in this regard, and the company has long been a strong supporter of this Standard. From the cotton, this blend obtains its strength, launderability, and durability; from the viscose rayon is obtained the luster, clarity of color, fabric evenness, and luxury of hand and drape. Minimum care finishes can be applied and help to give the blended fabrics greater strength after repeated launderings. Some of the features which have been noted in such standard fabrics as a traditional 80-square print cloth, after being laundered a number of times, are a tendency to lose crispness, colors to lose their intensity, and tensile strength to begin to diminish. In the same weave, however, a 70 per cent cotton, 30 per cent rayon after five washings becomes silkier, the colors remain bright, the tensile strength gains slightly, and the savings in the yarn costs due to less expensive rayon enable the producer to use a better finishing agent.

TABLE 16-3 / AVRON IN WASH-AND-WEAR *

	LAWNS		COMBED BROADCLOTH		CARDED BROADCLOTH	
	Required	Avron	Required	Avron	Required	Avron
Filling Tensile Strength	18 lbs.	34 lbs.	25 lbs.	44 lbs.	25 lbs.	40 lbs.
Filling Tear Strength	350 grams	1000 grams	450 grams	1600 grams	450 grams	1600 grams
Wrinkle Recovery	220°	250°	220°	250°	220°	250°
Wash-and-Wear Rating	3.0–5.0	3.0–5.0	3.0–5.0	3.0–5.0	3.0–5.0	3.0–5.0

* Required data suggested by National Association of Shirt, Pajama and Sport Shirt Manufacturers as minimum performances for satisfactory wash-and-wear fabrics.

Carrying this concept further, high-strength rayon viscose staple XL may be blended with other fibers, not only cotton but also a number of synthetics in the Avron program in wash-and-wear. Table 16-3 shows the comparative performances of several satisfactory all-cotton fabrics compared with Avron blends of the same construction and relative weight. The values were suggested by the National Association of Shirt, Pajama and Sport Shirt Manufacturers as minimum performances for satisfactory wash-and-wear fabrics.

cross-linked cellulosic fibers

The cross-linkage of groups within the cellulose molecule produces unusually soft-textured but highly-absorbent fibers suitable for blending or mixing with other fibers for luxury or special-purpose textile materials. In Chapter 10, page 148, the cross-linking of cotton cellulose fibers was discussed briefly. The same general operation can be carried out with cellulose of rayon types. Two of these fibers, **Corval** and **Topel,** are both trademarked by Courtaulds of Alabama. Though their chemical and physical properties differ from those of the ordinary cellulosic fiber, they must still be designated as rayons according to the Fiber Identification Law. Manufacturers and other producers interested in this type of product are endeavoring to get a special designation or generic name for these unusual materials. The fibers in staple form are generally described as "wool-like" and give a very lightweight, high-bulk, soft-textured fabric which is readily dyed and easily resin-treated for special performance characteristics; it has good dimensional stability and the typical rayon behavior of somewhat lower wet strength than dry. Men's summer shirtings and certain lightweight dress fabrics seemed to be the uses arousing most consumer interest in these two fibers in 1962.

zantrel

First commercial production of **Zantrel polynosic** fiber began in the fall of 1960 at Hartford Fibres Company. This registered trademark name is a coined word describing the modified cellulosic fiber—**poly,** meaning many, and **nosi,** meaning fibrils. Extremely fine and lustrous, this cellulosic fiber of unusual physical structure was originally developed by a Japanese scientist, Dr. Schozo Tachikawa, in 1938. The process was later acquired by a group of European textile interests, from whom Hartford Fibres Company obtained the license to produce the fiber in the United States. The claim is made for this particular cellulosic structure that it is not tendered as is ordinary cellulose when subjected to resin treatment for minimum-care and wash-and-wear fabrics.

THE FUTURE OF RAYON

Since the end of World War II, we have had a constant string of new and glamorous synthetic fibers. Referring to the history of nylon, we will note that although this fiber was in commercial production in 1940, it was available to consumers in the United States for only a little over a year before the outbreak of World War II. Thus, nylon "went to war for the duration," and only at the end of the war did this, the first of the synthetics, become useful in more than one consumer end-use item, that is, women's full-fashioned hosiery. Particularly since 1950, the pace of synthetics has been accelerated constantly.

Rayon and acetate grew with these fibers, and, in spite of the disparity in advertising and promotion, rayon and acetate are still the most important fibers in our market, next to cotton.

The production of rayon and acetate rose from 1945 to 1959 and has fallen off slightly during 1960 and 1961. The figures in millions of pounds are as follows:

1945	792.1
1958	1034.9
1959	1166.8
1960	1028.5
1961	1028 (approximate)

A greater part of the loss over the last two years probably has been in the automobile tire industry, where nylon has proven to be superior even to the high-strength rayons in the heavier duty tires. The important sales program of wash-and-wear or minimum-care conditions of use, which are more characteristic of the synthetics, has probably contributed also to some loss of rayon and acetate in certain items of wearing apparel where minimum-care promotion is still being actively carried out, for rayon, like cotton, requires resin treatment if it is to retain creases and resist mussing or wrinkling.

We have seen that there is no one rayon. Therefore, if we are to talk about the future of rayon, it should be the future of rayons, both regular rayons (and acetates) for wearing apparel and those which have been given special performance characteristics as the result of fundamental research. These researches which have been carried out within the last few years, have caused organic chemists interested in polymer chemistry to re-survey the knowledge they had regarding the cellulosic fibers. These, to the textile chemist, have been somewhat "old hat," but the new rayons, such as the high-tenacity grouping, the polynosic, and the cross-linked (a development of the triacetate Arnel fiber), reflect research triumphs of recent years. These have been carried out at almost every level, including studies of molecular structure and the arrangement of individual molecules in the fibrils or sinews giving strength to the fiber itself. In addition to these types of fundamental research, a new look has been taken at many of the technical processes in order to simplify them; to cheapen or to make them more efficient; to make better use of by-products; and to study more carefully the market to which these fibers may be aimed.

The future remains bright for both regular and special rayons in many areas of application.

TABLE 16-4 / MANUFACTURERS OF RAYON

Company	FIBER Generic Name	Trade Name	TYPE AVAILABLE F	S	T	M
American Enka Corporation	Rayon		X	X		
		Zantrel		X		
American Viscose Corporation	Rayon	Avisco	X	X	X	
		Avicolor	X	X	X	
		Avicron	X			
		Avril				
		(Fiber 40)		X		

Company	Fiber	Brand	F	S	T	M
		Avron (Avisco XL)		X		
		Rayflex	X			
		Super Rayflex	X			
		Super L		X		
Beaunit Fibers, Div. of Beaunit Mills, Inc.	Rayon (Cuprammonium)	Bemberg	X			
	Rayon		X	X	X	
Celanese Fibers Company	Rayon		X		X	
Courtaulds (Alabama), Inc.	Rayon	Fibro		X		
		Coloray		X		
		Corval		X		
		Topel		X		
E. I. du Pont de Nemours & Co.	Rayon	Super Cordura	X			
Fairhaven Mills, Inc.	Rayon					X
Industrial Rayon Co., Div. of Midland-Ross Corporation	Rayon		X			
		Strawn (mono-filament only)				X
New Bedford Rayon Div., Mohasco Industries, Inc.	Rayon	Newbray	X			
		New-dull	X			

F—Filament
S—Staple
T—Tow
M—Monofilament

ACETATE

Though derived from cellulose, acetate is the first of our **thermoplastic** fibers. By thermoplastic, we mean a fiber which is softened when exposed to sufficient heat, and in this respect, acetate resembles our synthetic fibers.

Nearly 100 years ago, in 1869, to be exact, a German chemist named Schultzenberger made cellulose acetate, the acetic acid ester or salt of cellulose. This could be dissolved in chloroform and used as a lacquer, but no fiber textile experimentation was carried out. In 1894, Cross and Bevan[4] were working simultaneously with both viscose and acetate as potential sources of textile-fiber-producing polymers. They discovered that certain chemicals, such as mineral acid or zinc chloride, would catalyze or speed up the formation of cellulose acetate sufficiently to make it commercially important as a protective surface applicable to textiles in order to make them more weather-resistant. During World War I, this solution or **dope** was applied to the fabric wings of our airplanes in order to make them more weather- and light-resistant. This necessitated the building of many large plants to produce acetic anhydride, the source

[4] J. M. Matthews and H. R. Mauersberger, *Textile Fibers,* 5th ed. (New York: John Wiley and Sons, 1947), p. 790.

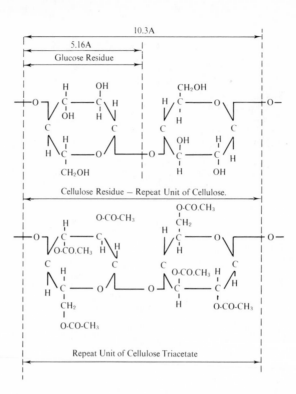

Fig. 16-9 Cellulose tri-acetate. (*Courtesy of Cela-nese Corp. of America.*)

of the acetic acid used in this reaction, and with the end of the war, some new uses had to be found for this material. The shift was also made necessary by the creation, about this same time, of metal fuselages and wings. The Celanese Corporation of America in 1924 perfected a process for the production of a fiber from this dope. The contributing factor to the safety and efficiency of this process was the discovery that if some of the acetate groups were saponified or removed from the cellulose molecule, the resulting acetate was soluble in acetone. This was a great improvement in safety over the use of chloroform as a solvent.

It will be remembered from the chapter on cotton that cellulose consists of an almost endless chain of some 10,000 glucose units attached end to end, and that on each glucose unit there are three OH, or hydroxyl, groups. When acety-lated, that is, treated with acetic acid (usually in the form of acetic anhydride), each of the hydroxyls will be replaced by an acetate radical, as shown in the equation above. This was the triacetate which Cross and Bevan made and which could be formed into a rather inefficient fiber by spinning from chloroform. The process has now been perfected so that triacetate is an important commercial fiber under the name **Arnel** and is made by the Celanese Corporation of America (see page 269). Commercial acetate, however, of which **Celanese** fiber is one of

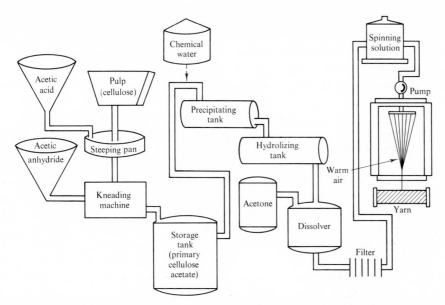

Fig. 16-10 One simplified flow diagram of the acetate process. (*From Leonard Mauer and Harry Wechsler,* Man-made Fibers [*New York: Rayon Publ. Corp., 1953*], *p. 17.*) (*Reprinted by permission.*)

the best known brand names, is partially saponified so that each glucose unit contains, on an average, between two and three acetate radicals or molecules. This is technically referred to as the secondary acetate, which is acetone-soluble.

manufacture

Like rayon, acetate was first made from cotton linters, the purest of the natural cellulose sources for the production of fibers. Today, however, much spruce wood is used as an alternate source. Although the reaction may be written simply as the esterification of one glucose unit and three molecules of acetic acid, or the complete esterification to the triacetate form, the reactant chemical used to supply the acetate is acetic anhydride:

$$\begin{matrix} CH_3CO \\ CH_3CO \end{matrix} \Big> O$$

acetic anhydride

The formula for acetic anhydride suggests the combination of two molecules of acetic acid binding together the anhydride form with the splitting out of one molecule of water.

The various stages of the process are as follows:

1. CELLULOSE PURIFICATION   Cotton linters, purchased in bales, or chemical cellulose in the form of great sheets described under rayon production, are treated with an alkali for several hours, after which they are rinsed, washed, and, if necessary, bleached with sodium hypochlorite, followed by another washing and drying.

2. ACETYLATION   The cellulose is often allowed to soak in glacial acetic acid to make it more reactive and thus shorten the time required for the **acetylation** or **esterification** process. The cellulose is then placed in a closed vessel equipped with a powerful stirrer, and into this vessel are introduced acetic anhydride and an excess of glacial acetic acid, which are thoroughly mixed. A small amount of sulfuric acid dissolved in an excess of glacial acetic is then added. This is the real acetylating agent. Although the sulfuric acid is actually used up in the process, as distinct from the usual catalyst which remains unchanged, the role of the trace of sulfuric acid is primarily that of a catalyst. It is necessary to cool the reactant vessel because of the great amount of heat produced by this exothermic reaction. Too high a temperature would result in too great a chemical reaction upon the cellulose, causing a shortening of the cellulosic chains and thus producing a weaker fiber. The reacting material becomes more viscous, and in about eight hours the cellulose becomes completely acetylated to the primary cellulose acetate and is completely in solution.

3. HYDROLYSIS   The primary acetate is run into water so that the concentration of acetic acid is now 95 per cent, and it is allowed to stand approximately a day at this concentration and at a higher temperature. During this time, acid hydrolysis takes place, and the mixture is poured into an excess of water. The acid is now so dilute that it can no longer hold the cellulose acetate in solution, and the product precipitates out in white flakes. This is a **secondary acetate** (the commercial compound) and is soluble in acetone after filtration from the acetic acid solution which, from the standpoint of economy, must then be extracted from the water by means of an organic solvent and reconcentrated for use in another batch.

4. SOLUTION   Secondary acetate flakes from many different batches are blended in order to produce as uniform a product as possible, and these batches are mixed with about three times their weight of acetone in a closed vessel with very powerful stirring. In some 24 hours of processing, the solution will be complete.

spinning

The dope is a viscous molasses-like textured solution containing somewhere between 25 and 35 per cent cellulose acetate. The fibers or filaments spun from this solution would normally be rather shiny and lustrous. If a dull acetate is to be prepared, the delustrant material, usually titanium dioxide (Titanox), is added. This gives a permanently white yarn and fabric. It is at this stage also that many dyestuffs may be added to acetate in order to produce the so-called **"dope-dyed acetates"** (see Chromespun and Celaperm, page 268). The flow of "dope" from the feed tank is carefully controlled, and the heavy liquid flows through the spinneret which is in the shape of a metal plate in which numerous small orifices have been drilled. The filaments emerge into a heated cabinet which immediately evaporates the acetone solvent, leaving a solid strand. This may be given a light stretching at this point by having the take-up rolls operating at a slightly higher speed than the flow of the solution through the jets or openings in the spinneret. The acetone is recovered and re-used. Note that no receiving solution is involved in the spinning of acetate. This is characteristically a dry-spinning operation, simpler and less costly to carry out, and to a considerable measure this more costly fiber is also aided commercially by the near-complete recovery of the acetic acid and of the acetone as much as by the properties of the cellulose acetate.

properties

Though the properties and other features of cellulose acetate are summarized in Table 16-5, some expansion or further explanation seems called for in evaluating this fiber, if for no other reason than the past confusion regarding its properties and its identification during the period when it was a part of the rayon family under the original Rayon Rules. In a certain sense, it was legitimatized by the revised rules of 1951 (see Chapter 16, page 242), but prejudices often linger in the minds of the public, and the many virtues of this fiber are often overlooked.

TABLE 16-5 / IMPORTANT USE CRITERIA FOR ACETATES

		ACETATE	ARNEL
Microscopic Cross-section (350 X) See Appendix P. 547		Shape very irregular	Shape rather bulbous
Tenacity	Dry	1.4	1.2
(gpd)	Wet	0.9	0.8
Elongation at break	Dry	25	20–28
(%)	Wet	35	35–40
Specific Gravity		1.30–1.35	1.38
Water Absorbency (%) Regain		6.3–6.5	3.5
Effect of Heat		Melts at about 450° F. with	Melts about 580° F. but

	decomposition. Loses strength about 200°, tacky at about 350°, slightly flammable.	sticks slightly about 100° lower; can be heat-set in pleats, etc.
Effect of Acids	Decomposed by strong acids. Dissolved by acetic acid.	Damaged by strong acids; slight effect by dilute.
Effect of Alkalies	Saponified to cellulose. Weak alkali, little effect on short exposure.	Good resistance to dilute alkali.
Resistance to Mildew, Sun and Aging	Not affected by mildew. Weakened by sunlight. Slight strength loss on age.	Like acetate.
Effect of Bleach	Unaffected in cold solution.	Stable to most common bleaches.
Static Electrical Effects	Noticeable under winter conditions.	Like acetate.

From: R. W. Moncrieff, *Man-made Fibers* (New York: John Wiley and Sons, Inc., 1959), pp. 193–97.

TENACITY   Cellulose acetate has a tenacity of about 1.4 gpd when dry and loses less strength when wet than does viscose, partly due to the fact that it does not have the moisture absorbency of viscose because of the absence of the OH groups in the glucose units. It has only a moderate stretch, and its stress-strain curve is shown in Figure 16-7 on page 251 in comparison with other cellulose-derived fibers.

EFFECT OF HEAT   Cellulose acetate was our first heat-sensitive thermoplastic fiber, and it was to protect acetate garments, and garments made of acetate blended with other fibers, that electric irons, many years ago, had a special setting which was wrongly termed "the rayon setting" for cool pressing of these heat-softened materials. The melting point of acetate is generally considered to be about 450° F. However, it exhibits a tendency to soften and stick to the iron sole at temperatures between 350° and 400° F., depending upon the fiber diameter, the texture of the fabric, and other physical factors. Usually a safe ironing temperature to avoid glazing an acetate is regarded as being not in excess of 275° F., because even below the temperature of softening, acetate fabrics may glaze and become shiny if ironed at temperatures in excess of that value. For this reason, it has long been recommended that acetate garments and blends of acetate with rayon should be ironed on the wrong side.

FIRE RESISTANCE   Acetate is usually considered to be a very slow-burning material. However, lightweight fabrics can flame and at the same time melt into a beaded edge. According to Tesi,[5] the flammability characteristics of acetate are such that to date no commercial fabric, either plain-woven or a 100 per cent

[5] A. F. Tesi, "Acetate and Triacetate Chapter," in J. J. Press (ed.), *Man-made Textile Encyclopedia* (New York: John Wiley and Sons, Inc., 1954), p. 104.

acetate pile, has been known to fail to pass the requirements of the Federal Flammability Act, that is, a basic burning rate of not faster than 3.5 seconds per 5 inches by the AATCC Method.

Certain foreign authorities have compared the flammability of acetate with that of cotton and rayon without the protection of fire-retardant finishes.

MOISTURE REGAIN   Moisture regain is 6.5 per cent under standard conditions, and at complete saturation, 18 per cent. Both values are much less than those of rayon.

ELECTRICAL PROPERTIES   With a relatively low regain, cellulose acetate is a good electrical insulator. It was the first of our fibers showing static electrical effects in dry ambient surroundings. This was noted particularly when a slip was worn under a silk or a wool dress in low humidity conditions.

RESISTANCE TO LIGHT   Some tendering takes place when acetate fabrics are exposed to sunlight. The amount varies according to the size of yarn, that is, denier value, color, and fabric construction. The evaluation of strength retention after exposure in the fadeometer or under outdoor conditions shows acetate to be of about the same order of magnitude as rayon and cotton. It has less resistance than the acrylics, but considerably more resistance than nylons and silk. Two hundred hours of fadeometer exposure reduces the strength by about 25 per cent.

CHEMICAL RESISTANCE   Strong acids will deteriorate acetate, but cold dilute acids have no adverse effect. Strong alkalies saponify the fibers, that is, remove the acetate group, giving regenerated cellulose. Thus, acetate should not be washed in strong soaps but at a pH not to exceed 9.5 and a temperature not to exceed 189° F.

FIBER MORPHOLOGY   A microscopic view of acetate fibers in the longitudinal direction appears to be a smooth cylinder; a cross-section, however, shows the fiber to be multi-lobed. The presence of an opaque filler shows as dark spots in the cross sections.

OXIDATION   Chlorine bleach and hydrogen peroxide have no ill effect on acetate if applied in the cold and at relatively low concentrations suitable for household use.

BIOLOGICAL RESISTANCE   Moths, carpet beetles, and in fact most household insect pests do not affect acetate, since there is no nutrient value. However, they will chew their way through acetate in order to get to or from a food source. Acetate will not support the growth of mildew, and it has a clear record with regard to dermatitic effect on the skin of wearers.

dyeing of acetate

Cellulose acetate fibers have been difficult to dye for two reasons: 1) a relatively low hygroscopicity, or moisture absorption, and 2) a serious dearth of reactive groups, due to the esterification of the available OH groups in the cellulose molecule. These two conditions required the preparation of special classes of dyes; the common type is the so-called dispersed-base dyestuff which is formed into a paste with water and a wetting agent. The dyeings are very satisfactory as to wash fastness and, for the most part, have good resistance to sunlight.

GAS FADING   Unfortunately for acetate, none of the light-blue dyestuffs in this category were satisfactorily fast both to sunlight and to what later became known as gas- or fume-fading. When these dyed fabrics are exposed to certain of the oxides of nitrogen from incompletely burned gas, the blue component is destroyed and the fabrics tend to redden; not only light blue itself is affected, but all colors in which there may have been a small amount of light blue compounded with other dyes to produce certain shades: chocolate browns tend to turn red, lavenders and light blues to pink, grays to a muddy shade, greens to yellow. Though the change is usually not quite as marked, exposure to acid substances or to acid vapors in the air of industrial cities can produce similar fadings with some of these colors. Again, it is the light blue which is at fault. Thus, perspiration can affect the color of some acetates.

Wool fabrics are slightly acid, sufficiently so that over a prolonged period of contact, the linings in men's coats, the bands on men's hats, and other acetate fabrics will be found to fade. Similarly, if a light-blue acetate robe is hung in a closet in contact with a wool garment for several months, the acetate garment may show streaks of color change wherever it was in contact with the wool. The presence of rubber latex in the shoulder pads of women's suits has, on certain occasions, caused severe fading of the shoulders of acetate suits, due to the production of hydrochloric acid during the cleaning operation; smoggy acid atmospheres in some industrial cities have been known to change the color of dresses exposed in store windows. This particular difficulty can be partially controlled by means of protective agents and protective finishes, but best of all is the new dyeing technique used to produce the so-called dope-dyed acetates in which the color is introduced into the acetone solution of cellulose acetate prior to spinning. These fibers, of which **Chromspun** (Tennessee Eastman), **Celaperm** (Celanese Corp.), and **Colorspun** (American Viscose Corp.) are examples, have phenomenal color fastness.

SUBLIMATION OF DYESTUFFS   The dispersed dyestuffs used for acetates have a tendency to discolor white or lightly tinted acetates by sublimation of the dye. The dyestuff in the colored garment may vaporize and be absorbed by the uncolored garment where the two are in direct contact.

trubenizing

For many years a fabric of mixed acetate and cotton, usually 2-ends cotton then 2-ends acetate, has been used as a stiffening inner liner in men's semi-soft shirt collars to keep them more firm and shapely. When this collar is fused with a hot iron, the acetate yarns soften and adhere to the cotton fabric on each side. This is the **Trubenized** collar. The structure is not impervious to air, as it would be if the liner were all acetate.

ARNEL — CELLULOSE TRIACETATE FIBER

A pure form of cellulose is used as the raw material, and the initial steps in the manufacture are essentially the same as preparing the regular cellulose acetate, that is, the purified cellulose is treated with acetic anhydride, acetic acid, and sulfuric acid catalyst. When the esterification is complete, all the cellulose will have gone into solution. Whereas at this stage in the preparation of acetates, some of the acetic groups were hydrolyzed off the glucose units, in the case of triacetate, all these acetic groups are left in place. However, a mild hydrolysis of the mixture is made in order to remove any sulfuric ester groups which might have adhered to some of the cellulose molecules. If any sulfuric acid is left in the cellulose, the fiber will be greatly weakened. After hydrolysis, the triacetate is passed into water, where it precipitates as flakes and is washed and dried. The dried flake is dissolved in methylene chloride, in a concentration of about 20 per cent; then the solution either is forced through the spinnerets to produce continuous filament **Arnel,** or the emerging filaments may be crimped and cut and deposited as **tow** or staple fibers. The solvent evaporates rapidly, because its boiling point (107.6° F.) is lower than that of acetone (134.6° F.). Cool condensers at the top of the column cause the vapor to recondense as a liquid which is collected, purified, and re-used. Often an anti-static finish is added to these fibers and filaments because of Arnel's low moisture absorption and its susceptibility to building up static electricity.

properties

When the properties of Arnel and acetate are compared, it becomes apparent that although Arnel is superior to acetate in most respects, it is more like that fiber than any other with which it is in competition. Thus, the Celanese Corporation in its introduction of triacetate is providing more competition for its other fiber, Celanese, than for those produced by its competitors. One might say, then, that Arnel is a super-acetate in its performance. Some of the most important physical properties of Arnel are as follows:

TENACITY   1.2 gpd dry and 0.8 gpd wet, slightly better than acetate.

EXTENSIBILITY   22–28 per cent under standard conditions and approximately 40 per cent wet. Again, quite like acetate.

DENSITY   1.33; essentially the same as acetate.

MELTING POINT   550°–600° F. Approximately 100° F. above that of acetate. Caution should be given, however, to these melting point values, because often fabrics will be glazed and somewhat softened considerably lower than the actual melting point of the polymer.

269

APPEARANCE   The fibers of both acetate and Arnel show lengthwise striations, and the cross-section of the Arnel shows numerous spots, according to photographs available.

FLAMMABILITY   Arnel behaves in a similar fashion to acetate, that is, the fiber tends to pull away from a flame, then shrinks, and melts to a bead as it burns.

MOISTURE REGAIN   About 3.5 per cent, as compared with 6.5 per cent for acetate. [It is a low moisture absorbent or **hydrophobic** fiber.]

CHEMICAL RESISTANCE   Arnel and other triacetates are resistant to boiling water, dilute alkalies, and dilute acids. They are hydrolyzed, however, by hot, strong alkali and by concentrated strong acids. They are resistant to most bleaches used in the home or commercial laundry. It is dry-cleanable with naphtha, carbon tetrachloride, perchlorethylene, and benzene. It is softened by trichlorethylene, which should, therefore, never be used in dry-cleaning this fiber.

COLOR FASTNESS   Color fastness to light is comparable to that of acetate, but Arnel is superior to acetate in color fastness to gas or fume fading and to acid fading. It is possible to "dope-dye" Arnel. Some dyestuffs in Arnel have shown the peculiar tendency to fade from fabrics exposed to the atmosphere in regions of high electrical storm intensity. This is apparently due to the effect of the ozone created by lightning.

Arnel fabrics are usually heat-treated at about 400° F. before or after dyeing. This improves the color fastness, reduces shrinkage when washed, and aids in wrinkle control. It is obvious that all these improvements are of benefit to the consumer.

COLOR   Generally, Arnel is white; however, its luster may be reduced by the use of customary delustrants, such as titanium dioxide.

ELECTRICAL RESISTANCE   Arnel has very high resistance to electricity, due largely to its hydrophobic nature.

uses

Beautiful colors, crisp feel, good draping qualities, and other esthetic features of Arnel have introduced it successfully into wearing apparel, especially for women's and children's wear. Alone and in combination with other fibers, it has been featured in most of the high fashion magazines. The fact that they can so successfully be given permanent pleats has made both woven and knitted fabrics readily accepted for skirts and blouses. Blends have been introduced into outerwear garments, such as suits and coats. Curtains and draperies of Arnel are excellent in performance and in resistance to most destructive elements, bearing in mind that none of the acetates are as resistant to sun rotting as are some of the synthetic fibers, notably the polyesters and the acrylics.

TABLE 16-6

A. MANUFACTURERS OF ACETATE

Company	Generic Name	Trade Name	F	S	T	M
American Viscose Corporation	Acetate	Avicolor	X			
		Avisco	X			
		Fiber 25	X			
Celanese Fibers Company	Acetate	Celanese	X	X		
E. I. du Pont de Nemours & Co.	Acetate	Acele	X			
Eastman Chemical Products, Inc.	Acetate	Estron	X			
		Chromspun	X			
Polyarns, Inc.	Acetate					X

B. MANUFACTURERS OF TRIACETATE

Company	Generic Name	Trade Name	F	S	T	M
Celanese Fibers Company	Triacetate	Arnel	X	X	X	

F—Filament
S—Staple
T—Tow
M—Monofilament

PAPER YARNS — ANOTHER CELLULOSIC

One sometimes hears it said that the day may come when some, at least, of our clothing and household textiles will be made of paper instead of the conventional textile fibers. Probably the first things which come to mind in this connection are the non-woven fabrics (Chapter 5) as sources of semi-disposable garments. Although it is true that much research is being conducted in this field and many textile mills are engaged in the development of sheetings of various weights and thicknesses and using a variety of textile fibers in order to achieve practical protective work clothes and similar garments, we overlook the fact that for many years we have had textile fabrics made of paper yarns. We have had woven paper yarn fabrics of very open construction, such as the brightly-colored, strong net bags in which citrus fruits and garden produce reach the market in many of our large grocery stores. For many years, the so-called **fiber** automobile seat covers have been predominantly made of woven or knitted paper yarns. Other uses of this kind of material are in the replacement of hemp or jute in burlap bagging, or as a back reinforcement for carpets and rugs, or as the protective scrim interliner over the stuffing of upholstered furniture, or as a backing for rubber foam padding in furniture. A rather recent use has been the replacement of glass fiber and nylon as a woven or knitted fabric filler for molded plastic articles, such as cafeteria trays, decorative table tops, and molded articles, such as radio cabinets. Egerton[6] reports that "cafe curtains and draperies made from plain crude knit paper fabrics will soon be available in stores. These curtains will be offered in the full range of sun-fast colors and will collect less dirt in use than curtains made with conventional fabrics comprised of spun or filament yarns."

Sample garments of knitted or woven paper yarns have been worn in style shows and at technical meetings to create interest in such materials. This yarn is already being used extensively in hats, handbags, shopping bags, hat bodies, and numerous industrial applications, including bagging and sacking materials for agricultural raw products, such as fruits and vegetables, and sheets for the collection of leaves for cigar wrapping and of smoking tobacco. Another use is as a cheap covering sheet to help protect against soil erosion.

Briefly, the material is a high-grade paper having lightweight and maximum uniformity of composition. This paper is cut in slices from ⅛ to ½ inches wide, and these narrow ribbons are tightly twisted to form the yarn. The narrower the ribbons of paper, of course, the finer will be the yarn. For most industrial applications, ½-inch ribbons of moderate twist will be satisfactory. For articles to be used in textiles for wearing apparel and for finer fabrics, the ⅛-inch ribbons are utilized. This twisting paper must have a high wet tensile strength. This is achieved by treating the paper with a thermosetting resin of the melamine formaldehyde type, because any fabric made of untreated paper yarn which becomes soggy, such as a wet newspaper, of course is no good. These paper yarn fabrics take dyes readily and generally have good color fastness. Furthermore, they are stable dimensionally. Their softness is largely controlled by the addition of wetting agents. Other chemical finishing agents can be used to soften the yarns and to hold them in place during the cutting and sewing operation. In the summer of 1962, a number of stores featured burlap-like skirts for sports and vacation wear. Many of these were, in fact, made of paper yarns. Others were of genuine burlap from hemp. Very cheap to make, paper yarns cost less than half as much as cotton yarns of the same size. As of now, who can say where yarns of this type may go and at very little cost? It remains for industry and consumer acceptance to show what end-uses currently belonging to other fibers may be taken over in part, at least, by this novelty material.

[6] G. Y. Egerton, "Market and Uses," Part III of three papers on "Paper Yarns and Fabrics" presented at June 6 meeting of New York Chapter of the AATT, *Modern Textiles Magazine,* 43, No. 8 (August, 1962).

QUESTIONS

1 Who perfected the first cellulose fiber?

2 Why is the nitro rayon process no longer used in the United States?

3 Name the two processes in commercial use.

4 What are the essential steps in each?

5 How does regular textile rayon react to:

    a. Tension   d. Strong acids
    b. Sunlight   e. Weak acids
    c. Bleach   f. Strong alkalies

6 How does textile rayon compare with high-tenacity rayons? With "special" rayons?

7 Name four of these modified rayons.

8 What is meant by polynosic fiber?

9 What is the process called?

10 Describe the various steps in the process.

11 How does acetate vary from tri-acetate? Give details.

12 Compare acetate with viscose rayon in strength, elasticity, regain, melting point, specific gravity, wet modulus, dyeability, cost.

13 Who makes acetate?

14 What is the definition of an acetate?

15 What is meant by solution dyeing?

16 Why is it used? Name at least two fibers colored by this method.

17 For what articles of wearing apparel is acetate best suited?

18 How does it perform in household goods?

azlons[1] and alginate fibers (textile delicacies)

That rayon and acetate fibers are man-made rather than chemically created is easy to understand, for, after all, the cellulose molecules were in fibrous form in nature. Chemical processing has simply reconverted them into almost endless filaments. When we view a grain of corn, a soybean, a pan of milk, or a cut of meat, it is difficult to conceive of their yielding textile fibers, except through chemical synthesis. The fact is, of course, that the protein molecules in the vegetable, milk, or meat are still virtually the same chemical compounds in the final fiber. Thus, they have been **modified** or **made** into fibers, rather than having been **created** or **synthesized** into fibers. The two animal fibers—wool and silk—are proteins. It is not surprising, therefore, that other sources of protein were viewed many years ago as probable sources from which a man-made protein fiber might be evolved.

CASEIN FIBERS

Casein, the protein constituent of milk, is readily separated from the other constituents and thus appears to be the logical source first to be attacked by scientists. The first casein fibers were made in 1904 but were so brittle and

[1] Azlon—a manufactured fiber in which the fiber-forming substance is composed of any regenerated, naturally-occurring proteins. Federal Trade Commission Rules and Regulations under the Textile Fiber Products Identification Act—effective May 3, 1960.

had such low wet strength that they proved to be impractical. The first casein fiber of sufficient strength to be both useful and patentable was developed in Italy by a chemist named Ferretti in 1935. The fiber was produced by an Italian rayon company, Snia Viscosa, and given the name **Lanital.** Although casein fibers appeared in several other countries of Europe at about the same time, none were as actively promoted as Lanital, and the soft textured blends of Lanital and rayon came into the United States market in small quantities. This Italian fiber was called **Merinova**, and seven million pounds were produced in 1955. The American fiber called **Aralac** was developed independently of the Italian patents by the Atlantic Research Associates, Inc., and came on the market in 1939; about 5,000 tons were made in 1943. To some extent, this initial success was due to the World War II shortages of wool and to the War Production Board regulations requiring the incorporation of other fibers, including Aralac, in domestic wool fabrics produced during 1942 and 1943. Hats made of wool or rabbit hair felt had to contain a minimum of 15 per cent Aralac or other fiber. The casein fibers were still too weak when wet to be used alone in a fabric; therefore, they were used primarily as blending fibers in order to capitalize on their soft texture and appealing hand. Unfortunately, in humid weather, the casein fibers smelled something like sour milk, and in 1948, Aralac, Inc., transferred their plant and process to the Virginia-Carolina Chemical Corporation to make Vicara fiber from corn protein (see page 277).

The similarity of casein protein and wool protein is shown in Table 17-1.

TABLE 17-1 / COMPOSITION OF CASEIN PROTEIN AND WOOL

Element	Aralac	Wool
Carbon	53.0%	49.2%
Hydrogen	7.5%	7.6%
Oxygen	23.0%	23.7%
Nitrogen	15.0%	15.9%
Sulphur	0.7%	3.6%
Phosphorus	0.8%	—
	100.0%	100.0%

processing

Cream, the most valuable food constituent in milk, is removed by centrifuging or skimming. The skim milk is heated to 100° F., and an acid is added to coagulate the protein. The resulting curd is washed, then dried. One hundred pounds of milk yields three pounds of casein which, in turn, yield three pounds of fiber. The powdered casein is carefully blended at the fiber factory, that is, casein from many different batches is mixed together in order to achieve some equality of product. It is dissolved in a strong solution of alkali and extruded through fine jets into a water bath containing acid, formaldehyde, and sugar. The tow, resembling wool, is hardened with formaldehyde and cut into the staple length corresponding to the wool, rayon, or other fiber with which it is to be combined, and spun into a soft yarn for knitting or weaving.

properties

Casein fiber is warm and extremely soft to handle. It does not felt, because it lacks the characteristic scale structure of wool. Its specific gravity is 1.29, the same as that of wool. The cross-sections are nearly circular. The wet strength is about one-third that of wet wool. Being a protein, it is attacked by the larvae of clothes moths and carpet beetles and is subject to mildew. It is easily dyed with any colors or types suitable for wool.

In addition to Italy's Merinova, England's Fibralane casein fiber has been widely used as a blending material in felts, carpets, and wearing apparel.

SOYBEAN FIBERS

In 1939, the Ford Motor Company carried out research on the protein constituent of the soybean as a potential source of textile fibers. (Henry Ford, Sr., was vitally interested in the land and the science of chemurgy.) At that time, it was envisioned that all the upholstery of the Ford automobiles would eventually be made of this protein fiber. The process was later sold to the Drackett Products Company of Cincinnati, but production was stopped in 1945. The Japanese soybean fiber **Silkool** was dropped also after World War II.

The soybean contains 35 per cent protein compared with 24 to 26 per cent for the peanuts and 10.5 for corn (maize).

VICARA

The Corn Products Refining Company applied for a patent for a protein fiber made from zein, the protein in corn, in 1935. However, research was required to perfect the process to commercial scale. Much of this work was done by the Northern Regional Research Laboratory of the United States Department of Agriculture.

The Virginia-Carolina Chemical Corporation of Richmond, Virginia, after a disappointing experience with Aralac, entered the research efforts on zein and re-designed and re-equipped their plant to produce a fiber. The fiber was called **Vicara,** a name derived from the manufacturing firm's name. This fiber was promoted actively for about 10 years as a luxury fiber additive to fine wools. With extremely soft hand resembling that of cashmere, it proved to be a very desirable blending fiber.

process for vicara

The protein is dissolved in isopropyl alcohol and then dried and ground to a yellow powder. The zein is then redissolved in dilute alkali solution, from which it is spun into an acid bath which hardens the filament. This is essentially the fiber-forming procedure; however, the Vicara process involves certain modifications, particularly with regard to time, which contribute to the uniformity of the product. Blends of zein are prepared, that is, batches of powdered zein extracted from different lots of corn are mixed. When the protein is dissolved in caustic soda to a concentration of 20 per cent, it is extremely viscous and must be filtered, de-aerated, and then allowed to stand in storage for a day or two. It is believed that during this storage period there is a certain amount of uncurling of the molecules and of cross-linking between adjacent molecules. Certainly, the Vicara fiber produced by this method is stronger than if it were extruded immediately. The viscosity or density of the solution increases, indicating that there is some combination of individual protein molecules to form larger molecules made up of 10 to 20 units. The solution is then spun through fine spinnerets into the coagulating acid bath; the filaments are so fine that each spinneret contains about 5,000 holes, and the tow is made up from the product of 50 spinnerets, so that it contains approximately 250,000 filaments. The filaments are further hardened with formaldehyde and other salts, after which the fibers are stretched and, while still under tension, are put in a bath of formaldehyde and sodium chloride. After this treatment, the filaments no longer will shrink when placed in water. They may be less straight or crimped. The tenacity of Vicara is 1.1 to 1.2 grams per denier, but approximately 0.7 when wet. It is a slight yellow color; therefore, it is particularly suitable for dark shades. Its normal moisture regain is 10 per cent under standard atmospheric conditions, but it can hold 40 per cent of its weight of water, at which time the diameter of the fiber increases greatly. It can be dry-cleaned and is one of the protein fibers resistant to insect damage and to mildew and bacteria. It does not felt or shrink, the fibers having a smooth wall and having been dimensionally stabilized due to many molecular cross-linkages brought about by the formaldehyde treatment. Another important advantage of this fiber is that it has no odor when wet. It is easily dyed by conventional dyestuffs used on wool or can be colored with vat dyes.

Late in 1958, the Virginia-Carolina Chemical Company closed down its production of Vicara and endeavored to sell the process. It is possible that with the introduction of some of the newer acrylic fibers having softness and "luxuriousness" somewhat similar to that of Vicara and with better chemical resistance and wet strength, the fate of this fiber was sealed.

It is a problem of ethics more than of science as to whether it is appropriate to create a textile fiber out of good edible food. With food shortages in many parts of the world, it does not seem right that milk, peanuts, corn, or whale meat (the source of a fiber developed in Japan) should be converted into textiles. Admittedly, our distributive system probably could not deliver these foods to places where they are most needed, and, in some cases, the foodstuff is so foreign to the food customs of some of these peoples that they would not even eat it. We can hope that success may finally crown the efforts of some scientists who have for several years been struggling to make a textile fiber out of the protein constituent of a completely inedible source—chicken feathers.

present status

No Azlon fibers are being produced in the United States today.

ALGINATE FIBERS

Everyone who has walked along an ocean beach has seen and probably touched one or more of the seaweeds washed up on the shore at high tide and has marveled at the water-holding ability of the thickened stems and the air-filled nodules which serve to keep the tops of the seaweed near the surface of the water. The extent of these ocean gardens and the length of the seaweed stem have long interested researchers seeking new sources of fibrous material for textile application. One of the chief constituents of all seaweeds is **alginic acid.** This is a linear polymer and is, therefore, a potential source of fibers. On the California coast, the giant kelp is used extensively as a source for iodine. Seaweeds of several kinds have long been used by the Chinese and other Orientals as a source of food. Similarly, Irish moss has been used for gels and jellies.

More attention has been given to these seaweed or alginate fibers in Great Britain than in any other country, with the possible exception of Japan. Indeed, alginic acid was first isolated about 1883 by a British chemist named Stanford. He noted that certain of the brown seaweeds could be dissolved in a water solution of sodium carbonate, and that when this was acidified, there was a precipitate of a jelly-like nature. This precipitated jell was an acid which the investigator named alginic acid. It was further discovered that this product existed in the brown seaweeds but not in the green or red. The investigator appears to have been far ahead of his time and was not able to create any interest in his new fiber source. During World War II, a coarse monofilament was made from alginic acid, this being the chrome salt or chromium alginate. This was used for camouflage purposes and had a natural green color. Subsequently, other investigators at Leeds University developed good multifilament textile fibers of calcium alginate. These fibers were flameproof, and they dissolved when washed in soap and water. Interestingly enough, it is this negative factor from the consumer point of view which has made the alginate fibers particularly useful in Great Britain. Extremely fine wool yarns can be used in combination with durable alginate fibers, calcium alginate, in the construction of extremely lightweight wool fabrics and in very open lace and embroidery background fabrics. When these fabrics are then washed with soap and water, the alginate fibers disappear, leaving a more gauze-like and filmy fabric than one could possibly weave using wool yarn alone. The term **scaffolding** is sometimes applied to this method of wide open fabric production.

properties of alginate fibers

Research is constantly going on in attempts to develop an alginate fiber of some other metal salt of alginic acid having greater stability as far as the washing procedure is concerned. The calcium alginate yarns have a dry strength comparable with that of viscose rayon—approximately 2.2 grams per denier—but under standard testing conditions (65 per cent relative humidity), the tenacity is only 1.14 grams per denier. Some use has been made of calcium alginate in end-uses and under conditions not requiring wetting of the finished fabric. Thus, theater curtains of alginate are used in many English theaters, just as asbestos curtains are required here in the United States.

There are several interesting medical applications of these fibers as dressings, for they have been found to stop bleeding quickly and to accelerate healing. Sometimes they are used by dentists to fill cavities after the extraction of teeth. In this use, they stop the bleeding, and they may be left in place and eventually disappear through the blood stream.

In the case of alginates, the raw material is literally ocean-wide. Whether research can ever conquer the inherent weaknesses of today's fiber is an open challenge to the organic chemist.

QUESTIONS

1   Define Azlon.

2   From what natural proteins have these fibers been produced commercially?

3   Why are Azlons no longer being manufactured in the United States?

4   List the physical and chemical properties of these fibers and note the advantages and disadvantages they contributed as blending fibers with wool, rayon, and other textile products.

5   What is an alginate fiber and from what natural product is it evolved?

6   What are the general properties of alginate fibers and what are some of the special uses to which this fiber is being applied in such countries as Great Britain and Japan?

7   For what reasons should further researches be carried out toward the improvement of the properties of these fibers?

synthetic fibers

MAN-MADE VS. SYNTHETIC

There is an old saying that "cow is a four-legged animal, but all four-legged animals are not cows." Similarly, we might say, "A synthetic fiber is a man-made fiber, but all man-made fibers are not synthetics." The point of this differentiation is that the ever-increasing number of new textile fibers fall mostly within the classification of synthetics; that is to say, they are fibers formed from the combination of many simple chemical units (sometimes several thousand) to form large molecules whose physical properties permit them to be drawn into a fiber or filament. They are different, therefore, from the man-made fibers already studied, which are derived from cellulose such as the rayons and acetates, or of protein origin, the Azlons. In the fibers made by man, the chemical nature of the cellulose or of the protein has been changed but little. The main difference between the man-made fibers and the natural fibrous material from which they have been transformed lies in the physical shape of the fiber and the molecular size of the polymer.

RESEARCH OF SEVERAL TYPES

It may be said that all of us recognize that the introduction of a new textile fiber, finish, dyestuff, or method of manufacture is the result of research. We are, however, hazy in our ideas as to just what this research may have been. To many people, a research discovery is still the result of a so-called "flash of genius," an idea suddenly occurring to the researcher and which, when tried, proved successful. More often research is simply the compilation of knowledge through long, arduous investigative procedures which sometimes result in disappointment and other times reward the investigators with a new discovery of importance to mankind.

According to Miss Irene L. Blunt,[1] the term research is interpreted in different ways.

> The scientist refers to his work in the laboratory as research. The product designer regards as research his seeking of new and improved products, perhaps based on the information that the scientist has gleaned from more basic investigation. The market consultant speaks of research in describing his analysis of present and potential markets. The economist applies the term to his study of business and financial movements. The advertising agency speaks of its research on the effect of promotion material or product. The common characteristic of all these activities is quest for facts.

Thus, we see how many kinds of research are required to make a commercially successful textile material from a new form of polymer fiber. The consuming public must know of the performance and capabilities of this new material before it is to have a wide and rewarding market. Likewise, serious flaws in the fiber or fabric product must be ascertained before the product reaches a wide market, so as to avoid disappointment on the part of the early users and the reflection of such bad experiences on its future acceptance by the public. Generally, these various types of research must be carried out consecutively, and yet there are a few of them which can be more or less simultaneously carried out.

1 The first step is the synthesis of a new textile fiber material. Of course, we have to have this fiber before we make any further investigations. Does the polymer make a good fiber, and what are the physical and chemical properties of this material?

2 Once satisfied that the new fiber has possibilities, researches into product development may be started. One way is to supply mills making fabrics with test samples from the laboratory production line. What kind of fabric does it make? How easy is it to dye? What are the fabric properties? Does there seem to be any serious obstacle to its success in terms of future consumer acceptance? Here, two types of research can be started promptly:

    a. The market research to study the possible place which such a fiber alone or in combination with others might occupy in the market.

    b. Does it have anything unusual to offer not found in other fibers, or

---

[1] Irene L. Blunt, "Basic Research Related to New Uses for Textiles," U.S. Department of Commerce, Business and Defense Services Administration, Textiles and Clothing Division, 1961.

can it be obtained and marketed somewhat more cheaply than its eventual competitors? How much might the consumer be expected to spend for the product in view of competition?

    c. At the same time, reports from various manufacturers of consumer-use articles are being studied. How many of these manufacturers of finished articles are interested in this new material and at what price?

3   Some of the potential markets may have proven to be unsuccessful. Possibly the fiber is not suitable in its properties, or perhaps its cost was out of line with good competitors. But the successful uses, as indicated by the studies of the market consultant and the economist, now require the advertising research application in order to promote the product accurately and actively for what appear to be the most profitable, prominent, and promising consumer-use applications.

Probably no two new fibers have been introduced in exactly the same manner, but it is certain that no fiber has been marketed without the accumulation of all these facts. Even then, researches must be conducted in order to improve the product and to find new uses for it. In view of the constantly increasing competition through improvement of established fibers and through unique properties offered by newer ones, fiber uses shift frequently. As we shall see in several chapters of the book, fibers are continually losing and sometimes regaining markets; sometimes a lost market is never regained because the newer material is so much better than the one formerly used.

Despite all these research endeavors, there may arise obstacles of various kinds. Disinterest in the new product may slow down its acceptance. Sometimes potential customers are distrustful, especially if they have experienced a poor product in a previous experimental trial, or they may have heard of such a failure to give good service. Maybe it just seems not worth while to try the new because what we have is good enough. These elements have been with us throughout history and have affected the introduction of every new product or of every new idea. The rebellion against change in habits may actually pre-date history as portrayed in the following letter composed by a frustrated textile research scientist to represent the suspicions and resistance of Stone-Age Man to a new idea.

AN HISTORICAL NOTE ON CLOTHING [2]

Archaeologists have uncovered a tablet, apparently carved during the Stone Age by an indignant member of the Neanderthal Hide, Skin, and Pelt Clothing Association. The tablet reads in free translation as follows:

"To the Secretary, NHSPCA: Sir—There appears no limit to the foolhardiness

---

[2] Submitted by Dale W. Kaufmann, technical director, International Salt Co., Clarks Summit, Pa., "in a moment of frustration to which all research and development men are subject at times." Courtesy Howes Publishing Company.

and irresponsibility of some members of the human race. I note recent suggestions to displace hides, skins, and pelts now used for clothing. The substitute material is to be made from thin strands or fibers of the plants known as flax or cotton—and even from strands of sheep wool.

"Regardless of the dictates of common sense, it is actually proposed to 'weave' these thin strands into sheets which can be made into clothing. To 'weave' means to interlock the separate strands together in an over-and-under rectangular pattern.

"This is utterly ridiculous. Such a fabric is not tight, but open, loose, and porous, and has innumerable disadvantages. It lets rain and snow through. It lets the winter wind through. It lets the hot sun through. Insects can penetrate it, or bite through it. Much more labor is required to 'weave' it into garments, and the garments are more costly. The fabric soaks up water, and is weak and short-lived. It can not be made into boats, roofing thatch, war shields, or water containers after the user is through with it as clothing. It can not be used for barter. It can not be kept in the family tribe for generations, as a tangible evidence of ancestral frugality and thrift.

"Whom the Gods would destroy they first make mad. It is even proposed to remove the wool from sheep and thereafter 'weave' it into clothing. This is the very nadir of reckless sophistication. The wool is *already* attached to the sheep skin. Why remove it and make a separate 'woven' fabric in a blasphemous attempt to improve on nature? Nature obviously did not intend the wool to be removed from the sheep—otherwise, why was it put on in the first place. Proponents of wool removal are, mentally speaking, wool-gathering. Ha! Ha! (My friends say I have a delicious gift of humor.)

"And aside from all common-sense objections to removing the wool, let us consider the moral and humane aspects. Think on the sufferings of the sheared sheep, subjected to this unnatural and profane practice, and exposed to the heat and biting insects of summer and the icy blasts of winter, shorn of their natural protective covering.

"Let us remember, too, that hides, skins, and pelts are, happily, a co-product of the meat business, and their sale helps keep meat prices down. Use of 'woven' clothing is an economic waste. The hides and skins would have to be thrown away, and the loss of revenue from this source must be offset by a corresponding increase in the price of meat. We want no part of this economics-be-damned philosophy.

"Hides, skins, and pelts have *always* been the preferred, and in fact the only clothing of the personable person. Their advantages are obvious to all who observe and reason. They are in abundant supply, strong, durable, comfortable, cheap, rain-proof, snow-proof, insect-proof, wind-proof, dust-proof, and improvement-proof. They are the sole choice of the well-dressed Neanderthaler.

"When worn with the attached fur, hair or wool either outside or inside, they are ideally warm in winter and cool in summer. The layers of hair, etc., with its entrapped air forms a scientifically correct insulation layer against cold or heat, and an impervious barrier against insects.

"The animals themselves have been blessed with these coverings of fur, hair or wool by a beneficent Nature, as a protection against environmental hazards. Granting that we are a superior type of animal, nevertheless, the Gods obviously intended us to use the lower animals not only for food but for clothing. It was blasphemy to think otherwise.

"I have the reputation of being alert and progressive. I am strongly in favor of research and technical progress. However, this reckless attempt to substitute 'woven' plant and animal fibers in place of our present highly satisfactory hides, skins and pelts is a step backward—not progress, but technology gone mad.

"Let us live up to our responsibilities to ourselves and our fellow men, and kill this irresponsible and impractical new idea of 'woven' clothing before gullible fools waste time, energy, and money on it."

Yours in the name of common sense,
(*Name partly obliterated, but seems to be the following*)
"Status Quo"

PROPERTIES COMMON TO ALL SYNTHETIC FIBERS

The student studying textiles may feel some helplessness when confronted by the vast number of synthetic fibers and fabrics on the market, either used alone or in combination with one another or with the natural fibers. The consumer shopping for textile products in stores faces exactly the same uncertainty. Which shall I buy? For what purpose is the fiber intended? Which is going to be the more washable? The more color fast? More durable? Shall I buy synthetics or fall back on tried-and-true wool for rugs and carpets? Then, when labels are read, one discovers that in addition to the fiber name, very often there will be a family name on the label too: for example, **Lycra, Spandex fiber; Acrilan, Acrylic fiber;** or **Dacron, Polyester fiber.** This labeling is the result of the Textile Fiber Products Identification Act of the United States Congress, and the family or generic name will be of some help to the more informed and skillful consumer and will certainly aid the understanding student.

Of help also is the knowledge that regardless of the fiber type, or name, or family, all synthetics have some properties in common. There will be some differences in the actual test values, but they are similar enough that even a new and untried member of the synthetic fiber family can have some of its serviceability features forecast with fair accuracy. The following points in common are possessed by all today's synthetic fibers.

low moisture absorbency

That is to say, they are all *hydrophobic fibers*. They dislike water. Immediately one should realize this means a dyeing problem; perhaps special dyes or unique dyeing methods will have been developed in order to color these fibers. It means also that they will resist aqueous or water-carried spots and stains. Any water will flow off; a spilled "coke" or lemonade will be brushed away. It should mean also that the article will wash readily and quickly, even in a lukewarm water and suds bath. Having absorbed less wash water, the article should dry rapidly, though some fabric structures are slower to dry than others because of less air circulation through them. It should be rather free from wrinkles both from wearing and from washing, provided that wrinkles are not heat-sealed in the article by drying it in a dryer with too heavy a load. Low moisture absorbency means also that the fabric will not be as comfortable in hot weather as a similar fabric construction with cotton, nor will it be as warm in winter as a wool fabric of the same construction. Hand in hand with low moisture absorbency goes the problem of static electricity, because it is the absence of moisture from the fabric which helps it hold static when rubbed under certain conditions. Static is much more prevalent indoors during the winter time when the relative humidity in the room is low. To some extent, also, pilling or balling-up of fibers is contributed to by static.

thermoplasticity

All synthetic fibers are composed of *thermoplastic polymers,* that is, they are all heat-softened. True, their melting points will vary, but one cannot depend entirely upon melting points as limits of safe ironing temperatures, because some of these synthetics begin to soften, distort, or glaze at temperatures as much as 100 degrees below the actual melting point. This indicates that garments should always be pressed with a relatively cool iron if synthetic fibers are in the dress, suit, or shirt, if glazing is to be avoided. This heat sensitivity is an advantage, too, in these fabrics, because were it not for this thermoplasticity, we would not be able to heat-seal creases or permanent pleats in dresses or suits, nor would we have as good wash-and-wear properties in synthetic fiber garments. We would not have pre-boarded hosiery which never varies in size or shape. It must be admitted, however, that this same property of thermoplasticity is a disadvantage when careless smokers drop live cigarette ashes or lighted matches on carpets or on upholstery materials, for all these fabrics will melt into holes under such flame.

insect, mildew, and bacteria resistance

Synthetic fibers are generally regarded as being completely resistant to damage from bacteria, mildew, and the common textile-destroying insects, such as carpet beetles and clothes moths. Thus, some of the more common storage worries about textiles do not apply to the synthetics.

surface slip

The synthetic fibers themselves, especially the monofilament yarns and those made from highly twisted filaments, tend to be slippery. To some extent this is due to the fact that these fibers are smooth-walled, especially in the lengthwise direction, because the spinning operation extrudes a smooth strand. As a class these fibers are rather firm or hard, that is, the individual fibers in the yarn do not tend to crush or squeeze into a somewhat flattened cross-sectional shape as the result of compression. This feature calls for special care in sewing operations to be sure that all seams are adequate in depth, or that they are reinforced, to prevent raveling out during service.

oil staining

Most synthetic fiber fabrics tend to be sensitive to staining from oil and grease spots left on for too long a time. This sensitivity varies somewhat for the individual members, but it is a good precaution for consumers to be sure that all stains from salad oil, butter, cooking fat, and such materials are removed rather promptly with a dry cleaning solvent or suds of a good detergent. If this is not done, permanent gray spots eventually appear. This is rather noticeable in pastel-shaded carpets of synthetic fibers and in some upholstery materials of these fibers. It should be mentioned that wash-and-wear garments sometimes show permanent stains from foods of a greasy nature spilled on the front, but this is also the case in resin-treated cottons, for these resins likewise have an attraction for oil and grease spots.

Recognizing these points in common and the good and bad features affecting care and serviceability, one is better able to cope with the problem of selection. One need not fear the unknown in a new textile fiber nor worry too much about the serviceability of some strange blend of synthetic with natural fiber, nor should the student despair over the ever-increasing list of new names, for they do not necessarily imply new properties on the part of the new product.

Equally important is the help given by the generic name, because if one knows the properties and behavior in service of, let us say, Orlon acrylic fiber, one can expect somewhat the same general properties and behaviors on the part of new acrylics. There will be differences in degree as to melting point, moisture absorbency, freedom from static, strength, resiliency, and other physical features, but acrylics should be more like one another than like nylons or polyesters, such as Dacron.

QUESTIONS

1 What kinds of research are required in the marketing of a new fiber?

2 In your own words, what is the scope or purpose of each type of research?

3 What properties are common to synthetic fibers?

4 How is the consumer affected by each?

5 What are the main provisions in the Textile Fiber Identification Act?

6 What is a generic name?

7 Of what advantage is such a name?

nylon

NYLON   Forming substance is any long-chain synthetic polyamide having recurring amide groups as an integral part of the polymer chain.[1]

This fiber of such varied use was the first of the synthetic fibers. In many ways, its development was both unique and remarkable, for it demonstrates what may be accomplished by intensive research in pure science conducted by a team of highly trained men without any immediate thought of commercialization. In 1928, Dr. Wallace H. Carothers was placed in charge of a team of research scientists to explore a field of pure or fundamental research devoted to the preparation of large molecules. Dr. Carothers chose to work in the field of polymerization, wherein small molecules are made into very large ones with molecular weights of ten to twenty thousand or more. The results of this research placed the E. I. du Pont de Nemours and Company of Wilmington, Delaware, actively in the field of textiles of synthetic origin. Among the several kinds of polymers being studied by this research team were those made from dibasic acids and dihydric alcohols. These are organic acids and alcohols with a reactive group at each end of the molecule, the reaction being similar to simple **esterification,** or organic salt formation.

SIMPLE ESTERIFICATION

$$C_2H_5OH + CH_3COOH \longrightarrow CH_3COOC_2H_5 + H_2O$$
ethyl alcohol + acetic acid   ethyl acetate

[1] Textile Fiber Products Identification Act, 1958.

POLYMERIZATION BY ESTERIFICATION

$$HO(CH_2)_6OH + HOOC(CH_2)_4COOH \longrightarrow$$
$$HO(CH_2)_6OCO(CH_2)_4COOH + H_2O$$

When enough of these two simple chemicals were added one to another to produce a long, straight chain polymer (much as dominoes are matched end to end), a polyester, or multi-salt, was formed. This research was later modified to use dibasic acids and diamines as the monomers, with the result that a better fiber was produced. Various treatments, new catalysts, and modifications in polymerization changed their physical properties, and finally, after some five years of research, certain combinations and molecular weights were produced which could be drawn out into fine filaments while hot. Further drawing or pulling after the filament cooled made them more transparent, stronger, more flexible, and more elastic. Here were products suitable for the textile industry, but even then years of patient research and development were required before the first nylon stockings were made available simultaneously in stores all over the United States in the summer of 1940. So completely has this fiber taken over the women's hosiery market that many consumers do not order stockings; they simply order "nylons" when they go into a store.

Today's nylon may have a wide variety of uses and properties, depending upon the raw materials and the method of processing. The raw materials commonly used are **dibasic acids** and **diamines.** There are many of each of these kinds of simple chemicals, and the variety of types of nylon are, therefore, almost infinite. However, some types are suitable for molding-plastics, or transparent sheeting, or bristles, or even adhesives; whereas relatively few of them are suitable for the production of fine filaments required for our textile industry.

The name, nylon, is no longer a proprietary one belonging to du Pont, the original manufacturer. Therefore, nylon is properly spelled with a small "n." Du Pont has licensed numerous others to use their nylon patents.

NYLON MANUFACTURE

The popular press at first portrayed nylon as being made from coal, air, and water, as if a magician were able to mix these elements together and, with the help of a few magic words and proper temperature and pressure, miles of filament nylon would be produced. The principal type of nylon in the United States is designated as Nylon 66 and is so described because both the dibasic acid (adipic acid) and the diamine (hexamethylene diamine) contains six carbon atoms. Other nylons are similarly known to industry by the number of C atoms in the monomers.

$$HOOC(CH_2)_4COOH + H_2N(CH_2)_6NH_2 \longrightarrow$$
adipic acid   hexamethylene diamine
$$HOOC(CH_2)_4COHN(CH_2)_6NH_2 + H_2O$$

Then two molecules of the dimer would give:

$$HOOC(CH_2)_4COHN(CH_2)_6NHOC(CH_2)_4OCNH(CH_2)_6NH_2$$

One of the many chemical by-products which can be made from coal is this adipic acid. During the process, ammonia is used, and one of the ways of making ammonia is by a combination of nitrogen of the air and hydrogen which one might consider as being produced from water. Thus, the coal, air, and water concept is a rather general and inexact statement of origin.

The diamine may also be synthesized from corn husks, bran, and other cereal waste.

Figure 19-1, showing the flow chart of the production of nylon, illustrates the production beginning with the two monomers and ending with the cold drawing of the filament. Because Type 66 nylon is the one principally used in the United States, the raw materials depicted as entering the reactor in this reaction picture are adipic acid and hexamethylene diamine. Measured amounts of the two reactants are entered into this stirrer-equipped reactor vessel and thoroughly mixed to form the nylon salt. This salt, with a small amount of water, is fed into the evaporator, in which the solution is concentrated by evaporation of the desired amount of water to give the proper concentration of salt. This is then passed into the jacket autoclave, in which the reaction of polymerization is carried out. This is simply the condensation or adding on of molecules, one to another, until the desired molecular chain length and weight have been attained. This reaction is carried out by increasing the pressure and temperature in the reactant vessel, accompanied by constant stirring. The equation for the chemical combination is given on page 288. This is termed a *condensation polymerization* because, as the two monomers combine, a mole-

Fig. 19-1 Production of nylon: A simplified flow chart. (*From Leonard Mauer and Harry Wechsler, Man-made Fibers [New York: Rayon Publ. Corp., 1953], p. 23.) (Reprinted by permission.*)

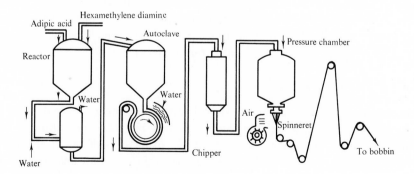

cule of water is condensed and evaporated out of the vessel. In any condensation reaction, a by-product chemical, such as water or ammonia or some other simple compound, is produced. During this reaction, nitrogen is passed through the autoclave in order to prevent contact with air, the action of which would oxidize the polymer. As the molecules reach the desired size, the mass becomes solid, and it is melted in the autoclave and extruded as a thick, whitish ribbon, which is solidified by contact with a spray of cool water. This polymer may be delustered or dyed in the autoclave during the process of polymerization. These ribbons of solid nylon are taken from the casting wheel and transported to the chipper, in which the ribbons are broken into small flakes or chips, and it is these chips from which the nylon fiber is made.

PRODUCTION OF NYLON FILAMENT

In the actual spinning operation, the flakes from several different batches are customarily mixed for the sake of greater uniformity of product. Although these flakes can be dissolved in various solvents and extruded through spinnerets to form filaments, a common process for this synthetic fiber is high-temperature extrusion or melt spinning, during which the molten nylon is forced through the fine openings of a spinneret. A nitrogen atmosphere is maintained, because oxygen would discolor (yellow) the nylon at the high temperature. This filament is generally rather weak because the constituent molecules are in a helter-skelter arrangement in the individual filaments. When this extruded filament is cold, it can be given a *cold stretch,* during which time it is pulled out from two to seven times its original length. The fiber particles become oriented, that is, they tend to lie in a straight line, and the resultant filament is clear, lustrous, strong, and elastic. The long chains in the molecule are lined up side by side, the fiber is more crystaline, and, in effect, molecules reinforce one another so that the tensile strength is more than doubled. Nylon filaments can be spun over a wide range of diameters. The deniers may vary from 0.1 within the fine filament classification up to 10 for the coarse, heavy monofilaments suitable for the toothbrush industry. Wide varieties of types of yarn are used in textile products; even nylon hose, for example, may be monofilaments as fine as 10 to 15 denier or as heavy as 60-denier 20-filament yarns. If staple nylon is desired, the filaments are cut after the cold drawing. The fibers may be given a permanent heat set crimp and then are baled for shipment.

NYLON PROPERTIES

For many end-uses, a dull or less lustrous surface is desired than that produced by the cold-stretch method. This can be done by putting a small quantity of delustrant, such as an inorganic oxide or sulfate, in the molten polymer. Another method is to roughen the surface. Unfortunately, the dull nylon has proven to be somewhat sensitive to ultraviolet light and has a tendency to sun rot, but at a rate less than that of silk. The bright nylon is more sun-resistant. Nylon is stable chemically and resists all the solvents commonly used in dry-cleaning operations. It is not affected seriously by dilute (less than 3%) mineral acids such as hydrochloric and sulfuric; however, it is weakened at an increasing rate as the acid is more concentrated and, if it is boiled for several hours with concentrated hydrochloric acid, the reaction is reversed and the adipic acid and hexamethylene diamine salt are recovered. Strongly acid chemical vapors and fly ash from heating plants using high sulfur coal can, under certain conditions of humidity, cause damage to nylon fabrics on which the ash falls. This accounts for the mysterious popping of nylon hose which has constituted a news story on several occasions. The acid-weakened nylon yarns can no longer bear the strain as the wearer walks. Its resistance to alkali is very great. The more common solvents in which nylon is soluble are formic acid, cresol, and phenol.

An important property making this fiber of great value to the consumer is that it is resistant to mildew and bacteria. Furthermore, it is not eaten by moth larvae, although they and carpet beetles will chew through the fiber to get at other materials or to escape.

The specific gravity of nylon (1.14) is lower than that of other fibers, including cotton and rayon. Thus, fabrics tend to be somewhat lighter in weight. On the other hand, the fact that the filaments are round in cross-section causes them to pack rather densely in the yarn; thus, nylon fabrics tend to have a somewhat transparent appearance. Nylon does not absorb moisture (about 4.2 per cent at 70° F. and 65 per cent relative humidity). This means that the fabric resists water-carried spots and stains and, when laundered, that it dries rapidly. An important property of nylon is that certain articles such as women's hosiery, may be molded into shape. Similarly, it is possible to heat-set pleats with fair success, although other synthetics surpass nylon in this regard. The Chemstrand Corporation[2] advises that if pleats or pre-set creases are to be altered, the conditions of temperature and moisture under which the patterns were set must be exceeded. Although the melting point of nylon is 482° F., it is generally preferable that an iron setting not to exceed 300° F. be used, because sticking begins to develop at about 356° F. When heated in air at a temperature of about 300° F., nylon tends to become yellow, not as rapidly as silk and wool, but more rapidly than the cellulosic fibers. Nylon does not burn if undyed; however, certain dyestuffs may render nylon slightly flammable. In general, however, it melts rather than burns and gives a glassy, globule at the end of the yarn. In common with all synthetics having a low moisture regain, nylon produces a considerable charge of static electricity when rubbed, particularly under ambient or room conditions of low relative humidity.

[2] The Chemstrand Corporation, *Nylon Service Manual,* p. 19.

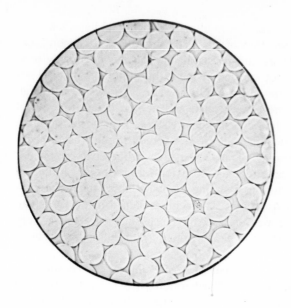

Fig. 19-2 Note almost exact round cross-section of these nylon fibers. (See also No. 28 in Appendix p. 547.)

One outstanding attribute of nylon is its resistance to wear. Indeed, this fiber can wear away most other textile fibers rubbed against it in wearing. Thus the occasional wearing-away on the inside of the hem of a skirt or the gradual disappearance of hem binding is due more to the rubbing action of the nylon stocking than to any flaw in the other textile fabric. In a later discussion (Chapter 25), dealing with blends, the effectiveness of nylon as a strengthening fiber will be more fully demonstrated.

Perlon is the British equivalent of nylon but is generally the nylon 6 or *polycaprolactam* type. Nylon 610, made from hexamethylene diamine and sebasic acid, has a greater resiliency than nylon 66 and is being used in carpets. Except for its very low moisture regain (2.6 per cent), it feels much like wool.

For ready reference, the properties of nylon 66 and nylon 6, the most common apparel types, are given in Table 19-1.

TABLE 19-1 / NYLON PROPERTIES

	Nylon 66	Nylon 6
Strength, g/den.		
Regular tenacity (dry)	4.6–5.8	4.1–5.8
High tenacity	6.1–8.4	7.5–8.3
Extensibility, %		
Regular tenacity (dry)	26–32	23–42.5
High tenacity	19–24	16–19
Specific gravity	1.14	1.14
Melting point (deg. F.)	482	420

a. Oriented

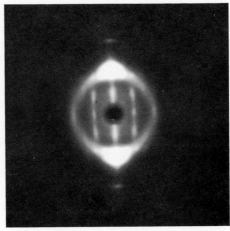

b. Unoriented

Fig. 19-3 X-ray diagrams of nylon16.

Average toughness		
Regular tenacity	1.08	0.67
High tenacity	0.77	0.68
Elastic recovery, % at stretch shown		
Regular tenacity	100 at 2%	100 at 2%
High tenacity	100 at 8%	100 at 8%
Moisture regain at std. cond.	4.5	4–5

Courtesy John Wiley & Sons, Inc.
Man-Made Textile Encyclopedia, p. 112.

DYEING

The hydrophobic nature of nylon, that is, its resistance to moisture absorption, has made the dyeing of this fiber difficult, and the more crystalline the fiber is, as a result of cold stretching, the more resistant it is to the access of water. This is a distinct advantage of the fiber and nylon when it comes to resistance to water staining, that is, discoloring from water solutions of soil, ink, beverages, or other water-carried coloring material; it is also a barrier to the easy entry of dyes. Special procedures have had to be adapted to this fiber, both through special dyestuffs and also the use of higher pressures.

Considering the technical problems of level or uniform dyeing of nylons, it may seem inconsistent that white nylon appears to be so easily discolored in washing. White nylon articles washed with colored garments often have a tendency to pick up any loose dye which may stain the wash water. It seems to act as a scavenger, picking up this loose color, which, although not deeply imbedded in the fibers, is difficult to remove. Of course, this accidental dyeing is objectionable no matter how even or uneven may be the discoloration of the formerly white garment. Thus, white nylons should never be washed with colored fabrics of any type, and nylon trimming on colored garments is a somewhat dubious form of decoration from the standpoint of the consumer.

USES OF NYLON AS AFFECTED BY EARLY DISAPPOINTMENT

More appropriately, one should emphasize the uses of nylons, for we must recognize the several types now being used in textile products with properties varied by the various degrees of cold-stretching orientations to which the yarns have been put, the amount of pre-setting of the yarn or fabric, and whether it is of filament, staple, or stretch yarn nylon. This synthetic fiber fabric is widely used despite several physical disadvantages which limit its application in some end-uses. Sensitivity to sun rotting and low moisture absorbency are its main limitations. Thus, the properties of the nylon fibers and of the yarns and fabrics made from them influence the suitability of any fabric construction for specific end-uses.

The discussion of hosiery, pages 300 to 301, gives in further detail the high degree to which nylon performs in service. At the present time, no other textile fiber seems to threaten nylon's place in women's hosiery. From the time nylon was introduced in women's full-fashioned hosiery in 1940 to the entry of the United States into World War II in December 1941, there was little opportunity for more than experimental batches of this fiber to get into other textile applications, and at that time, the inventor company, du Pont, was the only producer of this fiber; whereas today, there are no fewer than eleven companies engaged in its manufacture. During the years of the war, much was recorded about the strength and durability of this miraculous new yarn and of the service it was giving in military fabrics. Thus, the civilian economy eagerly awaited the time when nylon might be applied to consumer goods of all kinds when the war ended. Unfortunately, two of the first applications were inappropriate for the fiber. For example, in glass curtains for windows, the strength, wear resistance, sheerness, washability, resistance to water spots and stains, and freedom from need of ironing were among the performance features promising excellent satisfaction of this fiber. The sensitivity of this fiber to rotting under sunlight has proved to be disastrous, especially for dulled nylon. It was not uncommon to have lots or batches of curtains which lost up to 40 per cent of their strength in approximately three months' exposure in a sunny window. These curtains rapidly went into holes. Bright nylon is less susceptible to this damage, but it is still among one of our more delicate fibers when it comes to exposure to ultraviolet light. New importance was given to the recommendations made by most curtain manufacturers that curtains be rotated from one window exposure to another in order to equalize the wear from this destructive exposure. Fortunately, other synthetic fibers have taken the place of nylon in this important household fabric.

Another misapplication was in some beautiful woven fabrics in men's sport shirts. Here acute discomfort was the principal obstacle to their use, and part of the observation made even today by men who purchased these shirts in 1950 and 1951 that they never wore out is due as much to the fact that they refuse to wear them except on rare occasions as much as it is to the durability of nylon. In this case, the fabric was rather closely woven in order to minimize the transparency of the fiber, especially in light shades, when the garments became wet with perspiration. The fabrics did not absorb body moisture. The result was that the human body, endeavoring to cool itself, produced more and more perspiration, so that the water-vapor level or humidity between the skin and the fabric became higher and higher. Many of these shirts were discarded after very few wearings; they were simply intolerable in warm weather. When one asks why it is that nylon tricot has become such an important textile fabric for women's undergarments, the solution lies in fabric construction. The tricot knit structure (see Knit Fabrics, Chapter 4) is more open than the woven fabrics. Thus, there is more opportunity for moisture vapor and air to pass through the fabric, and this air and moisture transmission increases with the movement of the body. The elasticity or stretchy nature of knit fabrics serves as a pump, forcing air through the fabric with every movement of the body. The same weight of nylon in woven form would still be an uncomfortable article of wearing apparel in contact with the skin in warm or humid weather. These observations as to comfort are not new; they existed even in the days of the first nylon stockings, when these were made of heavier yarns, 30 to 35 denier. Some women complained that their feet were cold in the winter and hot and moist in the summertime. This is entirely a physiological effect, and the condition was probably noticed more by individuals who perspired more profusely and whose skin surface was more generally moist than that of the average person.

These disappointments point out the fact referred to several places in this book that criticisms of fibers through unfortunate experiences are somewhat unjust. It is usually the result of an *inappropriate fabric of that fiber,* and corrective measures can only be taken by the industry if these faults are called to its attention by consumer complaints (see Consumer Preferences, Chapter 25).

In review of the properties of nylon, the unique suitability of this fiber for many end-use applications, both industrial and household, will be apparent. Doubtless any reader can visualize still other end-use items for which this fiber is or will be useful, either alone or in combination with other fibers in blended fabrics.

PROPERTIES OF NYLON

wear or abrasion resistance

In this respect nylon surpasses any other commonly used textile fiber. Indeed, so great is its resistance to rubbing that it, in turn, will rub or fray away other materials abraded against it in service, and nylon fabrics must be sewn with nylon thread if a permanent structure is to be attained. Industrially and militarily, cordage, tarpaulins, beltings, parachute cordage, and work clothes or uniforms are suitably made of nylon in either filament or staple yarn, depending upon the nature of the fabric. Mention has been made that fabric blends containing 15 to 20 per cent of nylon give greater durability and wear than the fabrics of the other fibers without the addition of nylon. Thus, nylon carpets and upholstery materials, as well as some wearing apparel fabrics intended to give good durability against abrasion, are highly desirable. It must be admitted that some of the peculiarities of nylon enter into these end-use applications, and the somewhat decreased resiliency compared with wool combined with greater sensitivity to oil staining and to melting in contact with lighted cigarette butts and ashes are points of objection to nylon in these applications. It is, however, a matter of compromise between those factors and the increased wear, resistance to water stains, better dimensional stability, and resistance to insects and mildew which are obstacles to the perfect performance of wool in these same end-use items. Slipperiness of the individual fibers makes it necessary for seams to be specially reinforced in upholstered furniture of nylon. The same thing is true of other synthetics for this end-use. Hosiery, luggage, cord wrappings, fish lines, and fish nets also depend upon this fiber for long-lasting service.

tenacity

The high tenacity of nylon combined with its flexibility contribute to its durability in full-fashioned or circular knit hose for women. Military lines, tow lines for aircraft, and sewing threads depend also upon the combination of these two features. Sometimes this flexibility and stretchiness have a slightly detrimental effect to the end- use application. This can be true in sewing thread if the tension is too high. In this case, the nylon thread will be stretched somewhat during the sewing operation, and when it relaxes, the seam will be puckered. Somewhat the same objection is held against nylon for mooring ropes for boats and vessels. If such lines are used, the moored vessel may ease out of its normal position by stretching of the nylon line in bad weather or high seas, but this same stretchiness is desirable when a sharp pull is to be exerted upon the rope, reducing the shock of the sudden jerk. This is also true in the case of climbing ropes for mountaineers and explorers and in tow ropes for picking up gliders.

Stretchiness in nylon can be further enhanced in the stretch yarns (Chapter 7), many of which are made of nylon staple.

heat resistance

Though heat sensitivity makes nylon somewhat a problem in ironing at a high temperature, this feature permits nylon to be pre-set under moderate heat to a desired physical form. Some other synthetics lend themselves better to permanent pleating than does nylon, due to the molecular structure of the fiber, but nylon can be pre-boarded to size for women's hosiery, and these stockings will not curl or crawl when wet but will lie perfectly flat. They may be permanently shaped on leg forms and will not bulge at the knee or ankle. Their fit is permanent with no shrinkage or stretching. The high tenacity and wear resistance of the fiber combined with this pre-boarding have permitted a constant change toward sheerer and sheerer hose. The stockings of pre-World War II were 30 denier; today, stockings worn on the street are as fine as 15 denier, and there have been 10- and even 8-denier hose made for evening wear, the threads of which are finer than those of natural silk. Foundation garments utilize this same feature of "boarding" to shape and retain size and dimension. The secret behind most of the stretch and bulk yarns (Chapter 7) lies in this feature of permanent setting of nylon under heat and pressure. The Chemstrand Corporation states that the unusual (for nylon) pleating and crease pressing by their **Chempleat** process is due to pressing the nylon fabric under taut condition and while damp.

pilling

The consumer recognizes pilling as the balling-up of fibers on the surface of some fabrics, notably in sweaters and other finely knit articles and, to a somewhat lesser extent, in fine-textured coatings and suitings. The first nylon sweaters were particularly bad in this respect, and the pills, or loose balls of fuzz, soon became eye-sores. The fact that they were easily removed by a stiff brush did not minimize their objection in the mind of the consumer. So great was the public's resistance to these sweaters that the manufacturers, upon the recommendation of the du Pont Company, began to use a slightly heavier denier yarn. With this change, the damage diminished rapidly. Other synthetic fiber sweaters have been known to do this, as have blankets. It should not be thought, however, that only synthetics and man-made fibers suffer this disadvantage. Very fine wools, such as cashmeres, do likewise both in knitted and woven fabric structures. The cause of pilling is rather complex. To some extent static electricity causes individual filaments in the yarns to become erect and, therefore, to entrap one another and also attract the dust or lint which may be in the air. These particles trapped by the fabric structure become cores around which fibers gather to form the balls. Abrasion also contributes to it by scuffing loose the fiber ends, and probably the flexibility or waviness of the finer fibers increases their tendency to catch together.

slipperiness

Mention has been made of the slipperiness of nylon and the problems it introduced in the sewing of upholstered furniture covers. This same slipperiness can prove to be an advantage in such uses as laundry bags. Here the individual wash loads fall more freely from the bag, whereas in the case of the cotton bags formerly used, it was often necessary for the operator to peer into the bag and perhaps reach in and pull out a vagrant sock or handkerchief clinging to the side of the bag. This slipperiness, combined with the extra durability and wear resistance of nylon, makes laundry bags of this fiber very useful in spite of the somewhat higher cost. Filter sacks in which clay for the pottery may be pressed free of excessive moisture may use the properties of nylon in a similar fashion. Durability, low moisture absorbency on the part of the sack itself, and easy drop-out of the moist clay cake without sticking to the side of the filter bag are features of nylon bagging. Fishermen use nets of nylon for strength, resistance to sea water, low moisture absorbency, and greater saving of weight when pulled in. These nets are almost invisible to the fish when in the water. Similarly, nylon fishing lines have been widely used by both the salt-water and the fresh-water fisherman.

heat resistance

Although nylon will melt at 482° F., it is not seriously damaged by heat at lower temperatures. This fact, combined with its strength, durability, and degree of stretchiness, makes it exceedingly valuable as a tire cord, especially in heavy-duty truck and airplane tires. Only high-tenacity rayons can rival nylon in this end-use application. The tire industry is one of the largest consumers of nylon in the American market. (See Chapter 29, p. 515, for additional data on tire cord.)

MOLDED NYLON LACES — 1959

The Liberty Fabrics of New York, Inc., makers of lace and elastic fabrics, in cooperation with the Chemstrand Corporation began researches into the manufacturing of a molded nylon lace for brassieres and other support garments. A special nylon thread, knitted into a lace on the Raschel machine, could be molded into a permanent shape. This was called **Libform.** This unique process permits the molding of a cup into permanent form without the need of any stitching or other reinforcements. It is claimed that they are washable and machine-dryable without losing shape or size. In any kind of undergarment, this lace, through minimum stitching, should give better service than the conventional type of garment.

MANUFACTURERS OF NYLON

Among the most important producers are those listed as follows:

TABLE 19-2 / MANUFACTURERS OF NYLON

	FIBER		TYPE AVAILABLE			
Company	Generic Name	Trade Name	F	S	T	M
Allied Chemical Corporation	Nylon (6)	Caprolan	X			X
American Enka Corporation	Nylon (6)		X			X

Company	Nylon Type	Trade Name	F	S	T	M
Beaunit Fibers, Div. of Beaunit Mills, Inc.	Nylon (6)		X			
Chemstrand Company	Nylon (66)		X			X
		Cumuloft	X			
		Cadon	X			
Dawbarn Brothers, Inc.	Nylon (66)					X
E. I. du Pont de Nemours & Co.	Nylon (66)		X	X	X	X
		Antron	X			
Firestone Synthetic Fibers Co.	Nylon (6) & (66)		X			X
		Nyloft	X			
Industrial Wire & Plastics Co., Inc.	Nylon (6)					X
National Plastic Products Co., Inc.	Nylon (6) & (66)	Nylon by National				X
Nypel Corporation	Nylon (6)	Nypel				X
Poliafil, Inc.	Nylon (66)	Poliafil				X
Polyarns, Inc.	Nylon (66)					X
United States Rubber Company	Nylon					X

F—Filament
S—Staple
T—Tow
M—Monofilament

Courtesy Textile Book Publ., Inc.

RESEARCH IN POLYAMIDE FIBERS

As an example of the technological and economic challenges to be met by new polymers seeking entry into a textile business, *Chemical and Engineering News* recently reported on the conclusions reached by several hundred polymer chemists and fiber technologists from all over the world in a symposium sponsored by the Plastics and Rubber Division of the German Chemicals Society.[3] This symposium surveyed the brilliant synthetic chemical progress in the polyamide field, that is, the field of nylons. Chemists have synthesized monomers with amide groupings with varying numbers of carbon atoms in the molecule of the monomer. Remembering that nylon 66 is so identified because both the hexamethylenediamine and the adipic acid condensed together contained six carbons each, it is obvious that condensations or high-polymer molecules may be made of monomers with any number of carbons in the chain of each simple chemical. The point of this symposium was that the polyamides, containing three, five, seven, eight, and twelve carbons, though brilliant synthetic triumphs, are lacking in two respects when it comes to serious consideration as textile fiber sources: 1) the materials or chemicals used in the synthesis are too expensive, and 2) the fibers formed offer no new and unusual properties which would in any way compete with nylon 66, the choice in the United States, or nylon 6, the preferred nylon type in Europe. Admittedly there are two other nylons currently of some importance, but they are specialties in that the nylon fibers formed, for example, from nylon 610 and nylon 11 (**Rilson**) owe their marketability to such special properties as elevated melting points, additional resiliency, and such features. These conclusions were not a death sentence but rather a

---

[3] *Chemical and Engineering News*, 40, No. 17 (April 23, 1962), pp. 57–58.

challenge to the chemical industry to seek less expensive methods of synthesis and to capitalize on some of the interesting indications of unusual properties, for example, that nylon 7 has a higher water-absorbing capacity than other nylons and would seem to have somewhat superior wash-and-wear properties.

NYLON HOSIERY

The degree to which nylon has taken over the women's hosiery business can be shown by the production statistics for 1961, which show an approximate production of 839,341,936 pairs of hose, of which approximately 10,000,000 pairs were of fibers other than nylon. Thus, nylon accounted for just over 98 per cent of the hosiery volume. The American woman, teenager and adult, uses approximately 14 pairs of nylon hosiery each year. In reviewing Chapter 4 on hosiery, it will be recalled that full-fashioned hosiery is knit flat, with loops to be added or dropped at various points in order to shape the leg accurately. The stocking then is sewn up the back, giving the characteristic back seam and the small gatherings or fashion marks indicating where changes in number of needles or loops has taken place on each side of the back seam. Thus there are narrowings near the knee and again at the ankle. A faster and cheaper way of knitting is made possible by the fact that nylon can be heat-set to accurate size and shape; thus a continuous tube of knit nylon can be shaped to fit the leg smoothly. This circular-knit hose lacks a back seam, but being cheaper and resembling the full-fashioned, it is gathering popularity rapidly. Engineers have produced a seamless-hosiery fitting machine which can form a complete seamless stocking with reinforced heel and foot and with a finished toe in 2¾ minutes. Such a stocking contains more than 2,000,000 loops. Variations in the knitted structure produce mesh hose which will not run when a yarn is broken. We have seen that one of the criticisms of man-made fibers is their luster or brightness and that consumers prefer to have such fabrics made more dull. Nevertheless there has developed a demand for what one might call *sparkling nylon,* in which, upon manipulating the physical shape of the yarn, it is made more reflective, and the surface appears to gleam with light from many sources. Some of these hose have a gold reflective tone and others are brilliant blacks or luminous pastels, in addition to the more conventional colors. Stretch nylons, utilizing stretched yarns which are about to relax into a looped and kinked structure, can be pulled to four times their length and will return to their original shape. At the same time they do not cause any feeling of binding or discomfort to the leg of the wearer.

Foreign researches interested in the effects of extremely high-frequency waves in the ultrasonic region on various chemicals and polymers created fundamental changes in the nylon molecules. The Berkshire Knitting Mills of Reading, Pennsylvania, has licensed this *Sonochemicals Process*, and the hosiery produced has been found to possess some very unusual properties, including a closer hugging of the leg in motion, a greater degree of comfort in temperature extremes (that in winter and in summer), and more porosity and softness.

It is abundantly clear that if a customer simply goes into a store and orders nylon stockings, she is overlooking the opportunity to enjoy the benefits of many of these researches. The nylon stocking is made of nylon, and it is a stocking in shape, but its properties may be unique in the experience of the average consumer.

QUESTIONS

1   What is polymerization?
2   What is a polyamide fiber?
3   Who discovered nylon? For what was he seeking?
4   What are nylon's properties with regard to
    a. sun
    b. acids
    c. abrasion
    d. water absorption and
    e. dyeability?
5   How is nylon made?

6   What value does nylon give to blends
    a. with wool
    b. with cotton?
7   Compare nylon 66 and nylon 6.
8   What does the 66 mean?
9   Give the equation for the synthesis of nylon 66.
10   Name the components.
11   Describe pilling.
12   Compare nylon with wool rugs as to serviceability.

acrylic fibers

An ever-growing family of synthetic fibers based upon the chemical compound acrylonitrile has been developed since the introduction of Orlon acrylic fiber by the du Pont Company and has now been expanded to include other acrylic fibers made by the producers shown in Table 20-1.

An acrylic is defined by the Federal Trade Commission for the Textile Fiber Products Identification Act as "a manufactured fiber in which the fiber-forming substance is any long-chain synthetic polymer composed of at least 85 per cent by weight of acrylonitrile units ($-CH_2-CH-$)." Acrylonitrile is a basic monomer
$$\underset{CN}{|}$$
also for another group of fibers which will be dealt with after the acrylics. These are the modacrylics and differ from acrylics in the amount of acrylonitrile contained therein.

TABLE 20-1 / FIBERS FROM ACRYLONITRILE

A. MANUFACTURERS OF ACRYLICS

Company	Generic Name	Trade Name	F	S	T	M
American Cyanamid Company, Fibers Division	Acrylic	Creslan		X	X	
Chemstrand Company	Acrylic	Acrilan		X		
		Acrilan-Spectran		X		
The Dow Chemical Company,	Acrylic	Zefran		X		

Textile Fibers Dept.		Zefkrome	X	
E. I. duPont de Nemours & Co.	Acrylic	Orlon	X	X
		Orlon-Sayelle	X	X

B. MANUFACTURERS OF MODACRYLICS

Company	Generic Name	Trade Name	F	S	T	M
		FIBER		TYPE AVAILABLE		
Eastman Chemical Products, Inc.	Modacrylic	Verel		X	X	
Union Carbide Chemicals Co., Textile Fibers Dept.	Modacrylic	Dynel		X	X	
		Aeress	X			

F—Filament
S—Staple
T—Tow
M—Monofilament

Courtesy Man-made Textile Encyclopedia, (New York: John Wiley & Sons, 1959)

ORLON

The du Pont Company actually began work on acrylic fibers as early as 1940 and soon had experimental fibers on the market for government inspection and for study by interested textile producers, garment manufacturers, and, in some cases, consumers. This fiber was known at the time as Fiber A. One of its early applications was in glass curtains for windows. Fiber A was named Orlon Acrylic fiber in 1948, and commercial production began in 1950. Acrylonitrile may also be called vinyl cyanide ($CH_2 : CHCN$).

A distinction must be made between the original Orlon introduced into the commercial market as Fiber A and later named as Orlon Type 81 and the type being produced today, acrylic fiber Type 42. For most applications and for dyeability, today's Orlon is superior to the original product. However, this newer Orlon is not available except in staple yarn form. The original Orlon won instant acclaim as a curtain material because of its phenomenal resistance to sun rotting; indeed, it was forecast by some that Orlon curtains should last satisfactorily, even in sunny windows, for as long as ten years. The continuous filament, however, was found to be highly flammable, nor was it possible at that time to introduce a fire-retardant chemical to make the material safer for consumer use. Another problem was that of uniform dyeing.

It was believed that the chemical reaction of this addition polymerization reaction took place somewhat as follows:

$$CH_2 : CHCN + CH_2 : CHCN + CH_2 : CHCN \longrightarrow$$

acrylonitrile
or
vinyl cyanide

$$- CH_2CHCH_2CHCH_2CH - $$
$$\underset{CN}{|} \quad \underset{CN}{|} \quad \underset{CN}{|}$$

$$or - \left(\underset{CN}{\overset{CH_2CH}{|}} \right)_n \text{ Orlon acrylic polymer.}$$

303

By an **addition polymerization** is meant one in which the monomers add on one to another without the simultaneous splitting off of or condensation of a simple chemical by-product. Basically, what happens is that the addition of one monomer to another simply fills the double bond. One term for this original acrylic reaction was **homopolymerization,** or a self-acting polymer. Most of today's acrylic fibers, including Orlon, have somewhat less than 15 per cent of another monomer. The identification of these minor monomers, or of the catalyst employed, and of the specific manufacturing conditions are parts of the patented secrets of the individual companies. Unlike nylon, the process for which has now been licensed out to other manufacturers, the patents on the other synthetics are still in force. Therefore, there is much secrecy regarding the identification of component parts and processes. Acrylic fibers are insoluble in practically all common chemical solvents. This was another block to the early development of acrylics as a potential source of fibers at a reasonable price. The problem of finding and then synthesizing sufficient quantities of solvent was a most important prerequisite to their development.

Figure 20-1 shows a probable manufacturing procedure. The acrylonitrile is a derivative of the petroleum industry, that is, it is a petrochemical. It has the ability of polymerizing with itself or with other vinyl compounds, such as vinyl chloride, to form a giant molecule consisting of some 2000 units with a molecular weight of approximately 100,000. The acrylonitrile and other monomers are heated in the reactant chamber with an appropriate catalyst and with regular stirring. The polymer precipitates from the water solution in which the ingredients were blended. This precipitate is filtered off, dried, and then dissolved in an appropriate (and still secret) solvent, from which it can be spun into the heated evaporation chamber. As the filaments extend downward, there is an upward current of warm air, or nitrogen, or other atmosphere which carries away the solvent for condensation and re-use. The last traces of the solvent are removed from the newly-formed filaments. The filaments are generally stretched to several times their original length, usually under moderate heat, approximately 250° to 350° F.

the properties of orlon

The orientation of Orlon acrylic fiber is lower than that of nylon, for example, and the tenacity is likewise considerably less, only about 2.3 gpd. The yarn breaks at an extensibility of 28 per cent. The moisture absorption is slightly over one per cent, and the fiber is more flammable than nylon. It may be necessary in some fabrics of raised nap construction, that a fire-resistant or retardant finish be incorporated into the physical structure. This precaution is as necessary with Orlon as it is with rayon and cotton in such articles of wearing apparel as sweaters and knits, if a fabric is found to be burning at too high a rate when tested by the standard method. See page 509 on Flammability.

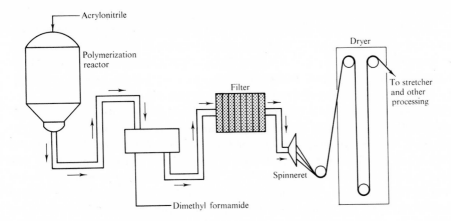

Fig. 20-1 Flow chart of orlon production. (*From Leonard Mauer and Harry Wechsler,* Man-made Fibers [*New York: Rayon Publ. Corp., 1953*], p. 33.) (*Reprinted by permission.*)

SUN EXPOSURE   Today's Orlon has greater resistance to sun rotting than other fibers on the market.

REACTION TO HEAT   The softening temperature is about 450° F. However, generally, the ironing temperature should not exceed 330° F., because direct contact at these higher temperatures will cause some yellowing of the white fibers and there will be some glazing. For safe ironing at home, use the "rayon" (really the acetate) setting of about 280° F.

CHEMICAL REACTION   Orlon has excellent resistance to dilute acids and even to strong mineral acids, as well as to practically all common solvents. Strong alkalies deteriorate it rapidly.

SPECIFIC GRAVITY   Orlon is one of our lighter fibers, having a specific gravity of 1.17. Contributing to its lightness is its unique fiber cross-section. When Orlon is spun, even from a round spinneret, the resulting fiber has a cross-section resembling that of a dog biscuit or a dumbbell. This physical cross-section does not pack or twist as compactly into yarns. Orlon yarns, therefore, even with a fairly high twist, remain fluffy or lofty. We generally refer to this property of Orlon as "exhibiting its low **bulk density.**" The result is that a yarn of wool and one of Orlon of the same diameter will have a lightness-in-weight advantage of approximately one-third in favor of Orlon, meaning that the Orlon yarn will weigh only two-thirds as much as the wool. This is one of the reasons Orlon has been such a popular fiber for sweaters; it provides warmth and covering with less weight.

DYEING   With the low moisture absorption of Orlon, the present type Orlon 42 has been somewhat difficult to dye in a wide range of colors and with a good uniformity or levelness. One of the newer methods involves the use of copper salts and elevated temperatures. By these methods, a great many acid dyes and some vats have been applied successfully to Orlon.

DIMENSIONAL STABILITY   Orlon cannot be heat-set as satisfactorily as nylon. However, reasonably fast pleats can be pressed in if the direction of pleating is at right angles to the Orlon yarn in, let us say, a blend of Orlon and cotton or Orlon and wool. This fact was demonstrated perfectly some years ago, when Orlon blended with cotton made its appearance in dresses and skirts for teenagers. The pleating was guaranteed to be permanent, but upon the first washing, the pleats went out in some portions of the skirts. It happened that these skirts were all of the ballerina type, and the pleating remained only in the front and back, where the direction of pleats was directly across the Orlon filling yarns at 90°. As the angle of the filling changed with the cut of the goods, the pleats became less sharp until at the sides there remained scarcely any evidence that pleats had ever existed. Nonetheless, Orlon is one of the synthetic fibers which does well in wash-and-wear articles, due to its resistance to wrinkles and its ability to stay fresh and clean-looking, though not as well as nylons or polyesters, such as Dacron. The dimensional stability when wet is good; thus it can be successfully washed. If Orlon is not cold stretched, however, it will shrink in boiling water. An interesting high-bulk Orlon yarn has been produced by combining two different Orlons in the yarns, a self-blend, as it were. The stretched Orlon will not shrink appreciably even at the boil, whereas the unstretched component will shrink approximately 15 per cent near the boiling point of water. Under these circumstances, the blended yarn becomes even more twisted, snarled, and lofty than normal Orlon; these yarns have been widely used in sweaters, men's and boys' hose, and similar uses.

uses for orlon

Like the other acrylics, Orlon is constantly expanding into new textile fields, while suffering minor losses in some of those in which it was used previously. For wearing apparel, Orlon is widely used for knitted outerwear, such as sweaters and scarfs, and may be either knitted or woven. It has been used in blends with wool, rayon, and other fibers for overcoatings and for relatively heavy suitings. Knitted jerseys of Orlon have had wide acceptance, due to the freedom from care and the ability of the fabric to hold its shape. A contributing factor, of course, is the saving of weight due to the lofty yarn. It has been blended with wool in men's socks and suitings and with cotton in dress fabrics and shirtings. In this latter use, it is interesting to note that even though Orlon has a lower moisture absorbency than nylon, it is more comfortable in hot weather than that sister fiber. This is due in part to the fact that moisture either in the form of body moisture from the inside or rain from the outside passes through Orlon fabrics rapidly. This is because of the low surface tension of water in contact with the polymer, causing water particles to glide along rather than to cling to the outer surface of the fibers and yarns. This tendency, combined with the capillary action of moisture creeping up small tubes and openings, provides some coolness by permitting perspiration to escape. Orlon, alone or in blends with cotton, is not as comfortable a shirting or dress fabric as all-cotton, but it is vastly more comfortable than nylon.

Household applications of Orlon include blankets and rugs; when in blends, one may find upholstery fabrics. The sun resistance of Orlon naturally makes it attractive for curtains. However, until Orlon 42 is available in filament form and capable of some protection against flammability, this fiber will not be widely used for that purpose. For draperies, awnings, tents, tarpaulins, tops for convertibles, and similar sun exposure applications, this fiber is superior to almost anything else on the market. Helpful, too, in outdoor application is its resistance to chemicals, especially to acids; in industrial areas, furniture and webbings of Orlon will vastly outwear any other material. Even though the awning or tarpaulin is not made of Orlon, its life will be enhanced if it is sewn with Orlon thread.

The production of Orlon in 1961 was in excess of 100 million pounds. The forecast for 1962 is an output of 150 million pounds.

Similar to Orlon are two fibers produced in Germany and widely used throughout the new Common Market Area (see page 513). These are **Pan** and **Dralon.**

ACRILAN

Acrilan, another acrylic fiber, is made by the Chemstrand Corporation in Decatur, Alabama. This company, formed in 1949, was jointly owned by the Monsanto Chemical Co. and the American Viscose Corp. Thus, it was a combination of one of the largest manufacturers of acrylonitrile and one of the major spinners of man-made fibers. Recently, Monsanto bought the interest of American Viscose Corp. The first Acrilan fibers came on the market in 1952, but several shortcomings were found in the fiber. For one thing, it was reported that the fiber was rather brittle and would not stand up in service when sharply bent in pressing, for example, in blends with wool in men's coats and suits. Within a few months, the objectionable features were gradually conquered one by one, and an improved Acrilan of round rather than bean-shaped cross-section came on the market and was readily accepted in 1954.

Considering the newness of this fiber and the keen competition in the field, one would not expect much disclosure as to the methods and procedures of manufacture. However, the patent literature indicates that Acrilan is essentially 85 to 90 per cent acrylonitrile, with a minor constituent, possibly of a basic nature. The fact that Acrilan is more readily dyed with acid dyes than are some of the other acrylics lends credence to this conjecture.

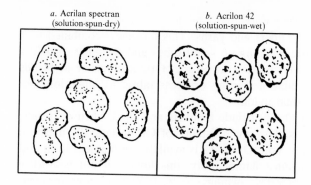

a. Acrilan spectran
(solution-spun-dry)

b. Acrilon 42
(solution-spun-wet)

Fig. 20-2 Cross-section of two types of acrilan (X500).

manufacture

In addition to the differences in chemical composition, there are variations in spinning methods between various acrylics. One of the distinct differences between the manufacture of Acrilan and that of Orlon is the Acrilan is wet-spun from solution. This is further confirmed by the cross-section of the fibers, which are essentially round but with a few surface indentations. We have noted these characteristics before as being due to the method of spinning.

properties of acrilan

Many of the physical properties of Acrilan are equal to those of Orlon. For example, the specific gravity is the same, 1.17; so is the sticking temperature, 455° F. Acrilan has approximately a 15 per cent superiority in tenacity: 2.5 gpd dry against 2.2, and 2 per cent gpd wet as against 1.8. Its extensibility is somewhat higher also. On the other hand, the moisture regain is slightly lower than that of Orlon, 1.2 per cent under standard conditions. Like Orlon, this fiber will tend to yellow after long exposure to heat. Exposure to live flame shows that Acrilan garments are safer than those of cotton, rayon, or acetate, for the rate of burning is much less. Acrilan carpets will burn under a live flame contact, but the rate of burning is slow, and Acrilan is less flammable in carpets than cotton or rayon, both of which have been on the market for many years and about which flammability complaints have been virtually nil; at least none had been received during the many years the writer was in charge of the Kaufmann Department Store's Fellowship at Mellon Institute.

In wear resistance, Acrilan, like other acrylics, is considerably lower than nylon but is higher than wool. On the other hand, one must consider the fact that the acrylics are much better preserved after long exposure to sunlight than is nylon. Thus, a nylon fabric, whether upholstery or carpeting, which has prolonged exposure to intense sunlight, such as through a picture window, may eventually deteriorate in abrasion resistance to values much less than that of Acrilan. In chemical resistance, Acrilan is comparable to Orlon in that it resists acids and most chemicals very well and is comparatively unaffected by mild alkalies. In weathering. Acrilan does not have quite the same sun-rot resistance as does Orlon, but it is in the same general order of magnitude and could be called comparable. Acrilan, however, has not been made in filament form, so that it is not an appropriate fiber for window curtains, which require the fineness and transparency of the filament yarn.

In bulk density, the bean-shaped cross-section of a dry-spun Acrilan-spectran is such that it could not give the same low-bulk density characteristic of the "dog bone" structure of Orlon. However, like other acrylics, a mixture of stretched and unstretched Acrilan fibers in a yarn produces a fabric with great bulk. This is commonly referred to in the case of Acrilan as **Hi-bulk Acrilan.** These yarns are widely used in men's and boys' socks, sweaters, and all kinds of knitted outerwear garments.

dyeing

Mention has been made that Acrilan is more successfully dyed with acid colors than some of the other acrylics, due to the chemical nature of the copolymer. **Acrilan-Spectran** has been announced by The Chemstrand Corporation[1] as a solution-dyed, high-bulk yarn with unusually even dye distribution within the fibers.

uses

As far as the consumers are concerned, a list of uses of Acrilan closely parallels that of Orlon. Acrilan seems, however, to have played a more significant part in the rug and carpet industry and in blending with wool in men's suitings than has Orlon. Acrilan carpets can be piece-dyed to order, according to the manufacturers.[2] This may be due more to a matter of trade emphasis on the part of the manufacturers of these two fibers than to any great advantage possessed by one over the other. It is claimed that Acrilan is somewhat less prone to static electricity than is Orlon, and this would possibly account for its wider use in blankets today.

CRESLAN

The American Cyanamid Corporation began its investigative work in acrylic fibers when experimental fibers X-51 and X-54 came on the market in small quantities for evaluation by textile fabric producers. In 1959, **Creslan** was announced in staple fiber form. It has fast become an important member of the acrylic fiber family. Conforming to the acrylic definition of the Federal Trade Commission this fiber has the minimum concentration of 85 per cent acryloni-

---

[1] Chemstrand Technical Information Bulletin No. AP-18, March, 1961.
[2] *Loc. cit.* Bulletin No. A-7.

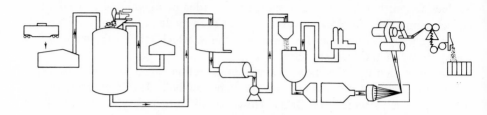

Fig. 20-3 Simplified flow chart for the production of chemstrand acrilan acrylic fiber. (*Courtesy of The Chemstrand Corporation.*)

trile and 10 to 15 per cent of another monomer, so that Creslan is, in fact a copolymer. Details of its manufacture are hidden, but its spinning method is admitted to be different. Apparently, the coagulation takes place in water and probably under intense cold. The fiber has a round cross-section and an apparent skin.

One of the early claims made for this fiber and which has been substantiated in its end-use application is its extra softness. In this respect, fine fibers of Creslan blended with high-grade wool produce fabrics of rather cashmere-like texture and feel. It may have been the acceptance of Creslan as a luxury fiber blend with wool which contributed to the disappearance of the last important **Azlon** fiber, **Vicara,** from the American market: Creslan, which gives a similar softness to woolen blends, did not suffer from the loss of strength when wet which was so characteristic of the man-made protein fibers. The properties of Creslan are much like those of the other two acrylic fibers. However, it appears to be a finer denier, for its weight or specific gravity is the same as that of the other two. Extremely fine shirtings or dress fabrics have been introduced in blends of Creslan with cotton. Many of these fabrics are almost silk-like in their feel and appearance. They will doubtless offer competition to Orlon and Acrilan in the fur-like fabrics in which these older acrylics are blended with Dynel.

TYPE 61, ACRYLIC FIBER

The American Cyanamid Company markets two types of acrylic fibers in staple and tow: Type 58, which has been identified as **Creslan,** and Type 61. These fibers are sold to the yarn and fabric producers under their type numbers. If the finished fabrics meet the standards of the American Cyanamid Company, then the manufacturer is permitted to identify the product as **Creslan.** This is one manner by which fiber producers can prevent their products from being applied to inferior goods to the detriment of the name of the fiber when these goods fail to give satisfactory service. Policing is difficult and the various fiber producers have different methods of accomplishing this. Some features of this new acrylic staple have been described by Marsh.[3] It is said to have excellent whiteness, thus producing good clear pastels. The polymer does not accept acid dyes, which are among the types most commonly used in dyeing Creslan, the Type 58 fiber. Therefore, mixtures or blends of these two acrylics in a yarn or fabric can produce cross-dyed effects of very great interest.

TABLE 20-2 / COMPARISON OF ACRYLIC FIBERS

	Orlon 42	Acrilan	Acrilan Spectran	Creslan	Courtelle (British)	Zefran
Tenacity (dry) gpd	2.2	2.5	2–2.6	2.7	3.0	3.5
Tenacity (wet) gpd	1.8	2.0		2.4	2.5	3.0
Extensibility (%) dry	25	36		33	30	33
Specific Gravity	1.7	1.17	1.17	1.17	1.17	1.19
Cross-section Shape	Dog-bone	Round	Bean	Round	Round	Round
Moisture Regain (%) Std.	1.5	1.2	1.5	1.5	2.0	2.5
Sticking Temperature (° F.)	455	455	455	408	446	490
Safe Ironing Temperature (° F.)	300	300	300	300	300	350
Chemical Resistance to Strong Acids	Good	Good	Good	Fair	Good	Good
Chemical Resistance to Weak Acids	Very good	Good	Good	Good	Good	Good
Chemical Resistance to Strong Alkali	Poor (yellow)	Poor	Poor	Poor	Fair	Fair
Chemical Resistance to Weak Alkali	Good	Good	Good	Fair	Fair	Good
Chemical Resistance to Sunlight	Excellent	Good	Good	Slight	Good	Good
Ease of Dyeing	Excellent	Excellent	Excellent	Excellent	Good	Good
Flammability	Burns	Burns	Burns	Burns	Burns	Burns

MODACRYLICS

Several interesting fibers with unique uses are classed under the generic name of **modacrylics.** The Federal Trade Commission Rules defined the modacrylic as "a manufactured fiber in which the fiber-forming substance is any long-chain synthetic polymer composed of less than 85 per cent but at least 35 per cent by weight of acrylonitrile units ($-CH_2-CH-$)." These, then, are co-polymers in

$$CN$$

which acrylonitrile may be the minor instead of the major monomer component.

[3] N. H. Marsh, "American Cyanamid New Type 61, Acrylic Staple and Tow," *Modern Textiles Magazine, 43,* No. 3 (Mar., 1962), pp. 51–54.

Prior to the passage of the Textile Fiber Products Identification Act, these fibers were included with the acrylics, but their physical and chemical nature were so different that much confusion in the mind of the consumer ensued.

DYNEL

Announced in 1949, **Dynel** really came on the market in considerable quantities two years later and is a product of the Union Carbide Chemicals Company, a division of the Union Carbide Corporation. It has been marketed only in staple yarn form.

manufacture

The chemical nature of Dynel is fairly well established as a co-polymer of vinyl chloride ($CH_2 : CHCL$) and vinyl cyanide or acrylonitrile ($CH_2 : CH$).

$$\underset{CN}{|}$$

The proportions are roughly 60–40, and the polymerization is carried out in much the same manner as that of acrylics, with catalysts and actual polymerization conditions being trade secrets. The equation is probably as follows:

$$CH_2 : CHCl + CH_2 : CHCN + CH_2 : CHCl \longrightarrow$$
vinylchloride

$$-\overset{\overset{\displaystyle H}{|}}{\underset{\underset{\displaystyle H}{|}}{C}} - \overset{\overset{\displaystyle H}{|}}{\underset{\underset{\displaystyle Cl}{|}}{C}} - \overset{\overset{\displaystyle H}{|}}{\underset{\underset{\displaystyle H}{|}}{C}} - \overset{\overset{\displaystyle H}{|}}{\underset{\underset{\displaystyle CN}{|}}{C}} - \overset{\overset{\displaystyle H}{|}}{\underset{\underset{\displaystyle H}{|}}{C}} - \overset{\overset{\displaystyle H}{|}}{\underset{\underset{\displaystyle Cl}{|}}{C}} -$$

The mechanism of the reaction is that of the typical addition polymerization. The additions are random. The polymerization reaction taking place in the autoclave produces the co-polymer, which is then passed into the mixer. There, acetone is introduced as a solvent. The solution is filtered and extruded through the spinneret. The viscous solution is forced through the spinneret by pumps and coagulated into filaments in a water bath, after which these pass through a drying chamber. The tow is transported then to a series of rolls where it is stretched to approximately thirteen times its original length, resulting in a high order of orientation. It may then be cut or may be crimped and then cut to the desired fiber length. Dynel is sold only as staple fiber.

properties

The cross-section of Dynel as referred to in Table 20-4 is extremely irregular, but it could be said to be ribbon-like, that is, vastly wider in one dimension than thick in the other. It is near-white in color and can be bleached. Some of the other properties are as follows:

TENACITY 1.5 to 3.5 gpd.
ELONGATION 42 to 30 per cent.
SPECIFIC GRAVITY 1.31.

MOISTURE REGAIN   Less than 0.5 per cent, showing that the physical properties are almost unaffected by moisture.

FLAMMABILITY   Dynel is self-extinguishing when the source of the flame is removed. It is regarded as a non-flammable material for most items of consumer use.

HEAT   The softening point is approximately 220° F., and it tends to harden and shrink and to become somewhat darker when exposed to excessive heat. Even at the coolest setting of the iron, Dynel should be ironed with a press cloth. In blends, the rayon setting may be used.

dyeing

DYEING   Special inks and rigid temperature control must be used in the dyeing operation in order to avoid heat damage to this fiber. It can, however, be colored by a rather wide number of dyestuffs with the proper technique. Though acetate dyes were the first to be used, other methods have now come to replace those dyestuffs because of the poor color fastness of the blues to such conditions as acid and gas exposure and because of some complaints about acid and sun fastness.

heat-setting of dynel

Illustrative of the potential uses of Dynel are three widely different end-use applications in which this fiber has proven to be extremely practical and popular. Dynel socks, wool-like in texture, may be boarded to a permanent shape from which they will not stretch or shrink. This is done by placing the knitted sock over the properly sized foot-form, which is heated from the inside by steam at moderate pressure, possibly 5 to 6 pounds per square inch. Dynel can be knitted or woven into a round or elliptical shape and then boarded or pre-set on an internally-heated hat form to make men's summer hats of extremely light weight and resembling fine straws. These can, of course, be of any color. The third use involving the use of heat on Dynel is wigs for dolls. This "hair" can be waved, brushed, and washed, permitting the child almost as much latitude with changing the hair style of her doll as has her mother. If wigs of various colors to suit a particular occasion or to help display a gown stay in style, they may appear also in the doll boudoirs.

uses

Industrially, and in technical laboratories, Dynel has proven to be very successful for protective garments such as coveralls, shirts, aprons, and similar outerwear. Dynel is virtually resistant to all commonly encountered chemicals and has the added advantage of non-flammability. Thus, unlike most synthetics, burning molten particles will not drop on the skin of a worker even when the source of flame is still in contact with the uniform fabric. This low flammability has contributed to the demand for this fiber for blankets. It was, for a time, rather widely used in infants' blankets, but some of the gloss has rubbed off this market due to the static electrical effects to which mothers sometimes objected on cold winter mornings when the house interior was dry and warm. Dynel can be used in blends with wool, rayon, nylon, and other fibers for suitings. Creases and pleats stay in, but the problem of pressing fabrics must be kept in mind. Sometimes if the Dynel is the predominant fiber, there is a tendency for the fabric to darken if too hot an iron is used (see properties, Table 20-3). This discoloration occurs before the softening point. Dynel proved to be an excellent filling material for insulation and for filling cushions, pillows, comforters, and similar applications. Do-it-yourself home owners have found Dynel paint rollers to be superior to brushes in the application of paints indoors. These rollers are easily cleaned if Dynel is the napped fiber. One of the widest applications of this fiber is in the imitation furs, in which the flame resistance of Dynel helps protect such soft-fibered materials against fire, because some of the other fibers used with the Dynel do have a tendency to burn.

TABLE 20-3 / COMPARISON OF PROPERTIES OF MODACRYLICS

	Dynel	Aeress	Verel
Tenacity (dry) gpd	1.5–3.5	3.2–4.0	2.5–2.8
Tenacity (wet) gpd	1.5–3.2	3.2–4.0	2.5–2.5
Extensibility (%) dry	30–42	12–16	33
Specific Gravity	1.31	1.31	1.37
Moisture Regain (%)	0.5	0	3.5–4.0
Melting Temperature (° F.)	237	240 150 (shrinks)	300
Safe Ironing Temperature (° F.)	Lowest and with press cloth damp	Lowest and with press cloth	250
Chemical Resistance—Strong Acid	Good	Fair	Fair
Chemical Resistance—Weak Acid	Excellent	Good	Good
Chemical Resistance—Strong Alkali	Excellent	Excellent	Good
Chemical Resistance—Weak Alkali	Excellent	Excellent	Good
Chemical Resistance—Sunlight	Good	Good	Good
East of Dyeing	Fair	Fair	
Flammability	Self-extinguishing		Good

VINYON N

For a brief time, from 1952 to about 1955, Vinyon N, essentially the same chemical as Dynel, was produced by the Union Carbide Chemicals Company as a filament yarn. This was temporarily discontinued, but a similar modacrylic, under the name **Aeress**, is now on the market in intermediate deniers, 75 to 200.

It is believed that this fiber is not as highly oriented as Dynel. This is unusual; the filament form of all other synthetics is more highly oriented and more crystalline than is the staple. For the properties of Aeress, see Table 20-4.

VEREL

Verel, a modacrylic manufactured by Eastman Chemical Products, Inc., a subsidiary of the Eastman Kodak Company, was introduced in 1956 in experimental lots and is currently available in staple and tow in six different types, varying in crimp intensity and permanence. One of the types is also represented as a controlled shrinkage fiber. Although the exact details of composition are not known, the properties suggest that the predominant polymer is vinylidene chloride and at least one other component in addition to acrylonitrile. Presumably, the differences in physical form depend upon variations in drawing and heat treatment; there are some variations, too, in the chemical additives in order to produce fibers more nearly suitable for certain end-use applications. It can be produced either bright or dull, depending upon whether a delustrant is used.

properties of verel

TENSILE STRENGTH   The tenacity is 2.5 to 2.8 grams per denier both wet and dry, with an elongation of 33 per cent. Specific gravity is 1.37.

MOISTURE REGAIN   Somewhat higher than most modacrylics, being 3.5 to 4 per cent under standard conditions.

SHRINKAGE   The amount of shrinkage in boiling water varies widely from one type to another, the regular type having a shrinkage of 1 to 3 per cent and Type 2 having a shrinkage of 19 to 23 per cent.

EFFECT OF TEMPERATURE   Verel fibers tend to soften at about 300° F.

CHEMICAL RESISTANCE   Verel has excellent resistance to chemicals and to most solvents, although the fiber is soluble in warm acetone.

dyeing

Verel is a very white fiber, thus permitting bright colors and pastels to be applied without bleach. Furthermore, the fiber is said to be easily dyed with a wide variety of dyestuffs.

uses of verel

This fiber has been extensively advertised in the fashion magazines as a blending material with wool for extra softness and luxury in texture. This use is probably filled by the regular Verel, which has also been used in shirts, underwear, women's, girls', and children's dress fabrics, and men's sport shirtings. To some extent, it has also been used in pajamas and nightgowns. Verel, Type 1, has a moderate yarn shrinkage in boiling water and is used sometimes for the backing yarns for artificial fur coats. Type 2, with the higher shrinkage—19 to 23 per cent in boiling water, 25 to 28 per cent in dry heat at 300° F.—provides a high-bulk yarn which has been well accepted in socks, sweaters, and other heavy knit articles. It has a cross-section much like that of Orlon. This, too, contributes to the loftiness of the yarns.

QUESTIONS

1 Define melt spinning.
2 Define solution spinning.
3 What is an acrylic fiber?
4 By what other name is acrylonitrile known?
5 How does Orlon differ from nylon in
   a. sun resistance
   b. melting point
   c. specific gravity
   d. color fastness
6 How does Orlon differ from Acrilan in
   a. sun resistance
   b. cross-section
   c. bulkiness
   d. ease of dyeing
7 What is Hi-Bulk Acrilan?
8 What is Acrilan-Spectran?
9 Compare Acrilan with wool for rugs and carpets.
10 Compare Creslan with Acrilan.
11 What is a modacrylic fiber? Name three.
12 Define modacrylic.

dacron and other
polyester fibers

A polyester has been defined by the FTC in its administration of the Textile Fiber Products Identification Act as "a manufactured fiber in which the fiber-forming substance is any long-chain synthetic polymer composed of at least 85 per cent by weight of an ester of a dihydric alcohol and terephthalic acid (β HOOC–C_6H_4–COOH)." β refers to the para position in the benzene ring. Table 21-1 lists the polyester fibers commonly in use in the United States at the present time.

T A B L E   2 1 - 1   /   M A N U F A C T U R E R S   O F   P O L Y E S T E R S

Company	FIBER		TYPE AVAILABLE			
	Generic Name	Trade Name	F	S	T	M
Beaunit Fibers, Division of Beaunit Mills, Inc.	Polyester	Vycron	X	X	X	
Celanese Fibers Company	Polyester	Fortrel	X	X	X	
E. I. du Pont de Nemours & Co., Inc.	Polyester	Dacron	X	X	X	
Eastman Chemical Products, Inc.	Polyester	Kodel		X	X	

F—Filament
S—Staple
T—Tow
M—Monofilament

DACRON

Dacron is the United States equivalent to **Terylene,** developed in England by the Calico Printers' Association. The manufacture of this synthetic linear fiber is a direct development of the initial work carried out by Dr. Carothers on polyesters. Working with straight-chain hydrocarbon acids and alcohols, the poor fiber qualities of the polymer caused him to divert his attention to the polyamides in his development of nylon. The du Pont Company purchased the patents from CPA, Ltd., and in 1953 opened its first plant at Kinston, North Carolina.

Technically, Dacron is a polyester; an ester is formed by reacting an acid with an alcohol. The raw material of principal consequence is ethylene, which is obtained from petroleum. Ethylene is oxidized to a glycol—a dihydric alcohol —which is then heated with terephthalic acid in vacuum at a high temperature. This acid has the benzene ring structure, as shown in the following equation.

$$HOOC - \left< \begin{array}{c} \\ \end{array} \right> - COOH + HO(CH_2)_2OH \longrightarrow$$

Terephthalic acid   Ethylene glycol

$$HOOC - \left< \begin{array}{c} \\ \end{array} \right> - CO \cdot O(CH_2)_2OH + H_2O$$

Hydroxyethyl terephthalate monomer

$$2HOOC - \left< \begin{array}{c} \\ \end{array} \right> - CO \cdot O(CH_2)_2OH \longrightarrow$$

$$HOOC - \left< \begin{array}{c} \\ \end{array} \right> - CO \cdot O(CH_2)_2O \cdot CO - \left< \begin{array}{c} \\ \end{array} \right> - CO \cdot O(CH_2)_2OH + H_2O$$

Dimer

$$Dacron \ is \ HO \left[-OC - \left< \begin{array}{c} \\ \end{array} \right> - CO : O(CH_2)_2O- \right]_n H + (2n-1 \ H_2O)$$

manufacture of dacron

From the reaction equation already given, it is obvious that both the acid and the alcohol have a reactive group at each end of the molecule of the monomer. That is, terephthalic acid is a dicarboxylic acid with a COOH at each end of the molecule in the para position. The alcohol is a dihydric alcohol, or glycol. Thus, the polymerization will continue until the molecule reaches the desired size, with acid and alcohol alternating along the entire chain. Although the reaction of the glycol will proceed either with the acid or with an ester, such as dimethyl terephthalate in which esterification with methyl alcohol has substituted a CH_3 group for the hydrogen on the carboxyl (the COOH groups), the reaction is usually recorded as being from the acid directly.

As shown in Figure 21-1, the monomers terephthalic acid (or dimethyl terephthalate) and the ethylene glycol are introduced into the reaction vessel, or autoclave, in which the polymerization takes place at a high temperature and "in vacuo." Various catalysts may be used. The molten polymer is withdrawn from the reaction vessel and flows onto a smooth roll or casting wheel in the form of a thin ribbon; when solid, it is cut into small chips or blocks approximately four millimeters square. The chips from several batches of polymer are generally mixed for a more uniform product, and these must be dried in order to remove any amount of moisture which may have condensed on the surface during the storage period, after which they are passed into a hopper, in which they may be heated to the molten state. This melt-spinning operation is carried out through very fine spinnerets. The emerging filaments harden rapidly and are gathered in a loose sliver and wound on cylinders.

The amount of drawing and twisting is generally specified by the customer who wishes to spin his own yarn. The usual amount of stretching is five-fold, that is, the filaments are pulled to five times their extruded length, and because the volume is unchanged, this means that the cross-section, or fineness, is one-fifth the original denier. The amount of twist given these filaments will vary depending upon the end-use application, and as a rule, the twisted yarn from the sliver is set or stabilized by passing it through an oven. Many of the industrial uses of polyesters, and particularly of Dacron, require a high-tenacity fiber. Such a fiber is given even more stretch than that used for clothing fabric purposes.

staple fiber manufacture

The procedure is identically the same for staple fiber as for filament, up to the spinning operation. The extruded filaments or fibers are much finer in the case of staple, and there are many more orifices in each spinneret. The fast-hardening extruded material is thus laid down in a rather thick tow. This is drawn to about three times its normal or extruded length and may be crimped

Fig. 21-1 Production of dacron polyester fiber. (*From Leonard Mauer and Harry Wechsler, Man-made Fibers [New York: Rayon Publ. Corp., 1953], p. 38.*) (*Reprinted by permission.*)

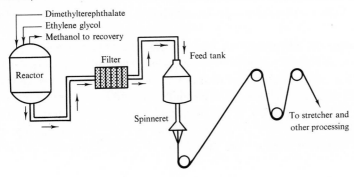

in order to match the other fiber with which it is to be blended for yarn spinning. For example, if this Dacron is to be blended with wool in a suiting fabric, the amount of crimp in the wool to be used is more or less duplicated in the Dacron in order to get a more intimate and firm blend in the yarns. This crimp is heat-set by passing the crimped yarn through the heating oven, after which it may be cut into whatever lengths may be desired for the textile process. This fiber can be produced in a wide variety of deniers, and they may be extruded as a bright fiber or a suitable delusterant may be used in the molten bath to give a dull yarn. As we have noted in other man-made fibers, the staple seems to be outgrowing the filament in volume, du Pont producing approximately 10 million pounds of filament and 25 million pounds of staple per year.

properties of dacron

Considering the immense success of Dacron as a blending fiber with wool and with cotton, it is timely to call attention again to the fact that, although a fabric is labeled with Dacron as a component fiber, all Dacrons do not behave alike. The properties of Dacron filament and staple vary because of the degree of fineness and the amount of drawing. The amount of crimp also enters into the performance of the fabric. These differences show up not only in the esthetic properties of feel, appearance, drapeability, and color, but also in serviceability, wear resistance, elongation, tear strength, and other important characteristics. Other properties, such as chemical resistance, sun resistance, and the effect of flame or heat, will not vary greatly from one Dacron to another, even from such extremes as, for example, a high-tenacity or maximum-drawn Dacron and fibers with moderate drawing and, therefore, intermediate strength.

Although reference to properties will concentrate on Dacron's high-strength filament, we must recognize that this polymer was perfected both in synthesis and in manufacture in England, where Terylene is the fiber name. More and more we are beginning to see the name Terylene on labels of goods sold in our stores. Wherever this is seen, translate it, in consumer understanding, into Dacron, or vice versa.

Dacron does not support combustion when the source of flame is removed. Of course, it is resistant to moths, carpet beetles, mildew, and bacteria. The somewhat higher moisture regain means that it is less prone to develop static electricity.

The properties affecting consumer acceptance of Dacron polyester were first made public in a weekly story in *Life* magazine. The ability of fabrics made from Dacron alone or in combination with other fibers to undergo wear and thorough wetting and then to hang out and dry rapidly with no loss of crease or permanent pleats was an exciting story. It has been said that this news story was originally intended to be devoted to Orlon as a blending fiber, but that at the time the magazine wished to feature the story, the du Pont Company was unable to

TABLE 21-2 / PROPERTIES OF COMMON POLYESTER FIBERS

| | DACRON | | | KODEL | FORTREL | | | VYCRON | |
| | FILAMENT | | Staple & Tow | Staple & Tow | FILAMENT | | Staple & Tow | Type 2 | Type 5 |
	Reg.	H.T.			Reg.	H.T.		Low-Density Monofilament	High-Density Monofilament
Tenacity, gpd (both wet and dry)	4.4–5.0	6.3–7.8	3.2–4.3	2.5–3.0	4.5	7.5–8.0	4.85	5.3–8.0	5.0–5.5
Elongation to Break, Dry (%)	19–25	10–4	25–36	24–30	25–30	8–10	45–55	30–40	35–45
Specific Gravity	1.38			1.22	1.38				1.38
Water Regain (%)	0.4–0.8			0.2	0.4				0.6
Softening Point (° F.)	480			564	485–510			410	455
Ironing—Safe Limit (° F.)	385			425	350			330	
Resistance to Acid, Strong	good			good	good			fair	
Resistance to Acid, Weak	good			good	good			good	
Resistance to Strong Alkali	good			good	poor			poor	
Resistance to Weak Alkali	good			good	good			good	
Resistance to Bleach	excellent			excellent	excellent			excellent	
Class of Dyes Used	acetate disperse & cationic with carrier			same as Dacron	same			same	
Cross-Section	round			round	round			round	

supply fiber of the newest Orlon acrylic polymer. On the other hand, they had some quantities of their new experimental fiber, Dacron polyester, alone and blended with wool in suitings and with cotton in shirtings and dress materials. As it was believed that Dacron would perform as well as Orlon, this newer fiber was substituted. So great was the success that du Pont almost completely skipped over the normal pilot-plant stage in the experimental manufacture of new fibers and leaped practically from the laboratory or, at the most, an extremely small pilot-plant production into the erection of their large Dacron plant at Kinston, N.C. Whether this is all fact or partially fiction, Dacron was produced commercially virtually without the normal intermediate steps.

TENACITY   Dacron, like the other polyester fibers, may have a wide range of certain properties, depending upon composition, process conditions, spinning method, and extent of drawing. Thus, one finds fibers available in a range of tenacities. The high-strength or HT Dacron has a tenacity of possibly 7.5 gpd, whereas normal Dacron, customarily used in clothing fabrics, has a tenacity of 4.5 gpd.

ELONGATION   The greater the tenacity, the lower the elongation or resultant stretchability of the fabric prior to break. The HT Dacron has an elongation of 7.5 per cent, whereas normal Dacron has an elongation up to about 25 per cent or slightly higher. The high-tenacity fiber is confined to filament Dacron, whereas the greater part of the staple Dacron is in the normal classification. This property of fiber elongation aids the fabric in its ability to withstand loads imposed by snagging and pulling.

MOISTURE REGAIN   Under standard conditions, the regain is only 0.4 per cent. Even at the boil, Dacron will not absorb as much as one per cent of water. We visualize Dacron fabric, therefore, as being very resistant to soiling from water solutions, easily washed, rapidly dried, and somewhat difficult to color, and having rather severe static electrical performance. It would be a most uncomfortable fabric to have in contact with the skin were it not for the fact that, as with Orlon, there is a tendency for moisture to pass through the fabric along the outside of the individual fibers, due to the low surface tension between water and the polymer plus the property of capillarity. This permits moisture vapor from the skin to escape, but it also makes these fabrics very rapidly and thoroughly wet through by rain. Rain water does not soak the fabric but goes through the openings and soaks the wearer within the garment. Anti-static treatments help in the prevention of static spark and also reduce attraction of dirt to the fabric during rubbing and wear.

ELASTICITY   Dacron fibers, when stretched within the limits of elongation, will return rapidly to their original dimension, or close to it. The degree of elasticity depends, of course, on the amount of stretch as well as on the crimp and heat-setting of the twisted fibers—a very real advantage of this fiber. This means that wrinkles will hang out rapidly, a property which makes Dacron one of the two most important filaments for glass curtains in the home, and it similarly offers advantages in blends in the wash-and-wear fabrics, whether in wool blends with Dacron for suitings or cotton or rayon blends in shirts and dress materials.

SPECIFIC GRAVITY   Dacron is slightly more dense than most of the other synthetics, being 1.38 compared with 1.14 for nylon and 1.17 for the acrylics.

MELTING POINT   Dacron melts at about 470° F. The sticking temperature is approximately 401° F., and the recommended safe ironing temperature is 275° F. Terylene, the English counterpart of Dacron, is slightly lower in all values. These polyesters are notable for their ability to resist heat damage.

MICROSCOPIC APPEARANCE   Dacron is circular in cross-section, a characteristic of melt-spun fibers. It appears clear if the fiber has been produced without a delusterant. The presence of a delusterant is disclosed by a multitude of spots which appear in the cross-section from the particles of delusterant. There are virtually no striations in the longitudinal direction, again a characteristic of melt spinning. Under a microscope, Dacron looks like a long, smooth-surfaced wire.

CHEMICAL RESISTANCE   Dacron is resistant to most common solvents, especially those used in dry- or wet-cleaning operations. It can be dissolved in a few specific solvents, and these are used in some of the chemical reactions for the identification of fibers. It is resistant to weak acids even at the boiling temperature and to cold concentrated mineral acids. The resistance to weak alkalies is excellent, but the resistance is lessened as the concentration of alkalies is increased.

BIOLOGICAL RESISTANCE   Mildew and bacteria will not affect the strength or color of Dacron. The common insect pests, carpet beetles and clothes moth larvae, will not thrive on this fiber, although they may chew their way through in order to get to or from a source of food fiber, such as wool, fur, or feathers.

DYEING   The great hydrophobic nature of Dacron means, of course, that it is difficult for moisture to get into the fiber. This fiber is commonly dyed by using higher temperatures than normally employed and a chemical swelling agent which serves as a carrier. In fact, the swelling agent enables the molecules to move a little further apart and increases their mobility within the fiber. The dye molecule comes into these larger spaces. If the carrier permits the dyeing of fabric in addition to yarn and tow, another method sometimes employed for Dacron fabric is the **Thermosol** method, which involves the application of a dyestuff and then a solvent. When the fabric has passed through a heated oven at approximately 400° F., the dyestuff dissolves and passes into the cloth.

FLAMMABILITY   Dacron burns, but generally when the source of flame has been removed, the burning stops rather quickly—not through the flame resistance of some of the ingredients in the polymer, as in the case of Dynel, but because the burning particles fall from the flame edge and the molten burning material drops away, thus removing the flame source. If Dacron is blended with a flammable fiber, the burning will progress until the fabric is consumed. Dacron, like nylon, exhibits one outstanding flammability phenomenon. Though undyed nylon is generally regarded as a non-burning material and Dacron is generally considered as one of the safer of the materials in this respect, when either of these fibers are mixed or blended with glass fiber (a non-flammable material) and flame is applied, the fabric burns almost instantaneously, leaving only a cloud of almost imperceptible ash floating in the air.

SHRINKAGE   Dacron can be heat-set or dimensionally set for wearing apparel and for knitted articles, such as sweaters and socks. If this is not done, the particles will show some shrinkage during washing. Dacron yarn will shrink about 10 per cent at the boiling point of water unless it is heat-set. This heat-setting, in addition to stabilizing the fabric dimensionally, enables the fabric to take the application of permanent pleats and permanent creases in wearing apparel. Such heat-set figures are permanent for the life of the garment, although their sharpness may have to be improved from time to time during prolonged wear and following numerous cleanings. Generally, the temperature required for permanent heat-treating, heat-setting, pre-boarding, or shrinkage control is a temperature of approximately 440°–450° F. This would be sufficient because it exceeds by about 60 degrees any temperature to which the article would be likely to be exposed during its service life or care. If the fabrics are not heat-set and then subsequently are washed at a temperature close to the boil or at least in excess of 180° F., then any wrinkles caused by the washing operation will be themselves heat-set in the fabric at that temperature. The way to remove them then would be to reheat-set the article into the desired shape and size at a higher temperature. One problem in heat-setting is that it has a tendency to stiffen the fabric slightly; therefore, finishing agents or very careful manipulation during subsequent scouring and dyeing operations will serve to soften the material again.

Knitted Dacron, specially boarded to size, has made excellent inroads into the men's and boys' hosiery trade, wherein permanence in size, color, and texture are required.

shape retention

Either in fairly crisp fabrics or those which have good softness, the wrinkles will hang out, thus minimizing the amount of ironing required. These factors all contributed to what is now known as the wash-and-wear program.

At this point perhaps it is appropriate to review the steps in consumer goods leading to wash-and-wear. Nylon and then Orlon and Dacron, widening the applications of synthetics into style fabrics, began immediately to capitalize on fabric all-day freshness; their resistance to water spots and stains, such as perspiration and accidental fluid spilling; the ability of the material to look crisp and clean; and the freedom from wear wrinkles. These features, combined with easy washing, even by hand in lukewarm or cool suds, and the fact that no ironing was needed again, made these materials of great value to the traveler and to the career woman. Thus, these users found it unnecessary to change clothing after work before going out in the evening. This was originally referred to as "all-day freshness"; then the minimum care concept became important, resulting finally in wash-and-wear. It was this feature of synthetics which prompted the modifications in cotton fabrics, especially by means of present finishes and lately the molecular changes, such as cross-lined cellulosic molecules, in order to give cellulose fibers some of these same properties and to give them likewise wash-and-wear or minimum-care properties.

It has already been stated that, like Orlon, Dacron is more comfortable than nylon in many of these articles of wearing apparel, due to the wicking action of body moisture in warm weather. This means that Dacron is quite acceptable in underwear, in which the pumping action of fabric motion during wearing aids in the removal of the humid atmosphere adjacent to the skin. Dacron tow has been crimped and formed into mattings which can be used in filling. The **fiberfill** has been used in pillows, where its resiliency, resistance to crushing, non-allergenic properties, and ease of washing and drying make it a highly successful substitute for down or feathers. The most popular blend of Dacron with cotton in the fabrics thus far produced widely for summer wear, shirtings, and dress fabrics, is a 65 per cent Dacron and 35 per cent cotton mixture. Different proportions will doubtless prove to be superior in other fabric constructions.

uses for dacron

The resistance of this fiber to sunlight and its sheerness and crispness combined with dimensional stability make this one of the most desirable of all fibers for glass curtains. Of all synthetics, it is the easiest to wash and to dry—the drying operation takes about 30 to 45 minutes. Mention has been made of the use of this fiber in blends with other fabrics (see Chapter 9). Dacron-wool mixtures, especially in a 55-wool, 45-Dacron proportion, have developed into the most widely used fabric for men's higher-quality summer suitings. Here the permanence of crease retention, resistance to wrinkling, the ability of wear-wrinkles to hang out overnight, and the coolness of the fabric make it very acceptable for suits and slacks. Many of these same qualities would be carried over into heavier-weight fabrics for winter wear. However, then the problem of static electricity might prove objectionable to some wearers. Possibly when Dacron is produced in excess, more of these winter-weight fabrics will be produced despite the problem of static.

DACRON IN WASH-AND-WEAR SUITS   Wash-and-wear summer suits have increased their sales each year since their introduction in the mid-50's. Prior to this time the most satisfactorily washable summer suits for men were the cotton seersuckers. However, these fabrics wrinkled badly, both during wear and during

325

washing, and the ironing was always a great burden. A word of caution should be given to the potential consumer of wash-and-wear Dacron suits: not all Dacron suits are washable. Figure 21-2 shows the special construction details specified by the du Pont Company for suits of their Dacron polyester fiber for satisfactory wash-and-wear performance It is significant that hydrophobic, that is, synthetic fiber threads are required. Extra care must be taken in the secure fastening-down of the edges of the linings and of other garment components. The sketch notes also that any excess fullness in the lining or facing should be avoided.

It would be an interesting study to try to determine just how many wash-and-wear suits are actually washed and how many go to the dry-cleaner along with the conventional summer suit wardrobe through lack of confidence in wash-and-wear.

Two friends of the author desired to experiment with wash-and-wear suits and finally convinced their wives that there was some practical advantage. However, the wives said that the husbands had to wash the suits themselves, at least for the first time. So the two men took one suit to the basement to experiment. Having no experience with the washing machine, the control of this mechanical monster was the first item of business. As they were leaning over the machine trying to read the directions, the suit accidentally fell into the empty tub of the agitator-type appliance. This was unobserved, and one of the men triumphantly pushed the starter button. Immediately the coat became wound around the agitator shaft, and before the men discovered how to turn the machine off, it jammed and blew a fuse, but not before one sleeve had been torn off and the fabric had been ripped down one side of the garment. The owner of the suit took it back to the store where he had bought it and in a somewhat joking manner tried to talk them into giving him an adjustment. Finally he took pity on the salesman and, in order to keep him quiet so as not to frighten away other customers, told him what had happened and bought a second suit.

WEARING APPAREL   Alone and used with cotton or rayon in lightweight fabrics, Dacron has been very successful in men's shirtings and in dress fabrics for women and girls.

INDUSTRIAL USES   Industrially, the chemical resistance and strength of this material has made it highly acceptable in filter cloths and for such heavy-duty operations as conveyor belts. Another industrial use is in the laundry trade, where it is used for calender-roll sheeting, for paddings and blankets used on presses, and for laundry bags. It has also been used to some extent as a bag for hosiery in dyeing operations, because the Dacron bag does not pick up the dye nor does it interfere with the dyeing operation of the hosiery placed in the bag for dyeing by immersion in the bath.

Another source of uses for Dacron has been in the field of sports and recreation. For example, sails and ropes of Dacron are vastly superior to those of cotton, both in durability and ease in handling, due to lighter weight and greater flexibility. In large sails, the greater stretchability of the fiber may be a handicap because sails may stretch out of size and fit in a strong wind. Nets of Dacron have shown excellent stretch, flexibility, and unusual resistance to sea water, bacteria, and other microorganisms. It will be recalled that Dacron has excellent resistance to sun rotting, another important factor in any use, such as in boating and fishing operations, where the light from the sun is not only carried to the fabric directly

Fig. 21-2   Essential tailoring details for a man's wash-and-wear Suit Coat. (*Courtesy of Textile Technical Service, E. I. du Pont de Nemours & Company.*)

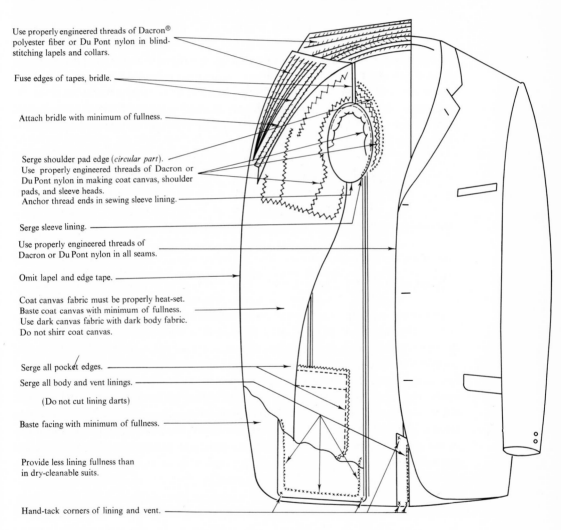

Use properly engineered threads of Dacron® polyester fiber or Du Pont nylon in blind-stitching lapels and collars.

Fuse edges of tapes, bridle.

Attach bridle with minimum of fullness.

Serge shoulder pad edge (*circular part*).
Use properly engineered threads of Dacron or Du Pont nylon in making coat canvas, shoulder pads, and sleeve heads.
Anchor thread ends in sewing sleeve lining.

Serge sleeve lining.

Use properly engineered threads of Dacron or Du Pont nylon in all seams.

Omit lapel and edge tape.

Coat canvas fabric must be properly heat-set.
Baste coat canvas with minimum of fullness.
Use dark canvas fabric with dark body fabric.
Do not shirr coat canvas.

Serge all pocket edges.
Serge all body and vent linings.

(Do not cut lining darts)

Baste facing with minimum of fullness.

Provide less lining fullness than in dry-cleanable suits.

Hand-tack corners of lining and vent.

but also by reflection from the surface of the water. It has been found that Dacron, as well as other synthetic fiber fabrics, in heavy canvas-like weaves makes good tarpaulins and covers for boats, such as lifeboats, and for hatches. Lighter in weight and with greater resistance to sunlight than cotton, these materials are also more resistant to the acid vapors from the diesel fuel burned in ocean-going vessels. Many articles of laboratory and industry protective clothing are made of Dacron. Generally, this is not all-Dacron fabric, and one must measure the economy of vastly longer life than with cotton against comfort, for the all-Dacron fabric is generally not as comfortable as a blend of that fiber with cotton.

POLYESTER FILM   The same polymer used in Dacron can be cast as a transparent film. It has been marketed under the name **Mylar** and is the most widely used film in the sandwich construction of today's metal yarns (Chapter 15, Metallic Yarns). During the time this film was under development, it was anticipated that it would be widely used as a wrapping material. However, the film had too great a strength, and it was virtually impossible for the housewife to tear or break the film. Thus, it could not be used in wrapping materials or in the protection of foodstuffs. Twisted film of Dacron makes excellent twisted cord material for outdoor furniture and for types of cordage. It also is being used in photographic film.

Flexible tubing of Dacron is being used in surgery to replace arteries and other tubular body structures. A mesh of Dacron or of twisted Mylar is being used as a lattice work to reinforce damaged body tissues, and the body tissues grow and develop through the interstices in this reinforcing lattice. These uses emphasize the non-allergic nature of this polyester polymer.

FORTREL

Fortrel polyester filament and staple yarns are produced by the Celanese Corporation of America through a license granted by the du Pont Company. The large British textile-producing company, Imperial Chemical Industries, Ltd. (generally referred to as ICI) is also interested in this Fortrel production. It is described by the Celanese Corporation as a co-polymer of ethylene glycol and dimethyl terephthalate. Thus, the reactant monomer, as in Terylene, is the methyl ester rather than the acid itself. It is mentioned, in the case of Dacron, that either might be used in this condensation reaction. Although manufacturing details have not been released, it is reasonable to suppose that they are very closely similar to those of Dacron, both for filament and tow or staple. There may be modifications in the spinning operation, the catalysts used, and perhaps in the condensation reaction itself.

properties of fortrel

Since it is similar to Dacron (see Table 21-2), however, some further specific values would be of interest. The tenacity of Fortrel continuous filament polyester yarn is 4.5 gpd, dry or wet; the tenacity of Fortrel staple and tow is 4.85. The moisture regain is the same as that of Dacron, 0.4 per cent, and the water imbibition, that is, centrifuging with water, is 7 per cent for the filament and 8 to 9 per cent for the tow or staple. The specific gravity is the same as that of Dacron. Melting point is 500° F., with the softening point essentially the same. The cross-section is round for both types of fiber. Fortrel has unusually good resistance to acids and can be used in industry as a filtering material for strongly acid solutions.

fortrel binder fiber

A special Fortrel tow of a moderate tenacity, 1.3 to 1.5, has been developed for use in non-woven fabrics. This so-called binder fiber may be used alone or with other fibers, both natural and synthetic, to produce specialty synthetic papers, filtration pads, electrical insulation sheeting, and heat-formed cores for molded rugs. These non-woven products possess the same degree of chemical resistance as Fortrel in other physical forms, and a somewhat higher melting point than many synthetics, that is, 500° F. (see Chapter 5, Non-Woven Fabrics).

K O D E L

The Eastman Chemical Products, Inc., announced its new fiber of polyester nature named **Kodel** in 1958. Since that time this fiber has been marketed in staple, tow, and, to some extent, in filament yarns. The exact nature of the polymer has not been disclosed. However, the data on the material, including tenacity, moisture regain, and melting point, indicate that it has a different base from that of the polyester fibers previously discussed. For example, the tenacity of Kodel is 1.22, much lower than that of Dacron or Fortrel, which is 1.38. Moisture regain is lower, being only 0.2 per cent, and the melting point is approximately 500° F. The fiber can be safely ironed at a temperature up to 400°–425° F. Claims are that the fabrics are dimensionally stable without being heat-set. However, there is no doubt that heat-setting will contribute to better acceptance of this fiber used alone and blended with others in wash-and-wear articles, in which dimensional stability is only one quality being sought.

V Y C R O N

Vycron, a product of Beaunit Mills, is very similar to the other polyester fibers. This fiber has excellent shape retention properties, and for that reason, garments made from it are generally shaped to size and have been given permanent creases and pleats if required; they fall, therefore, under the minimum-care classification. Being hydrophobic fibers, they are resistant to water-carried spots and stains, wash easily, and generally dry rather rapidly, depending upon the fabric construction. There are two polymers available in filament and staple which differ mainly in the effect of temperature. So-called type 2 softens at 410° F., whereas type 5 softens at 455° F.

The exact identity of the polymer composition is not known. However, the fibers exhibit the same excellent blending capabilities with wool and rayon as do some of the older polyesters.

Among the fibers of this type currently under development abroad are **Diolen** and **TreVira,** both from Germany; from Italy comes **Terital;** from France, **Tergal;** and from the Netherlands, **Terlenka.**

QUESTIONS

1 What two simple monomers combine to form the Dacron polymer?

2 What are the properties of Dacron polyester with regard to

    a. sun   d. moisture absorption

    b. acids   e. comfort in wear?

    c. abrasion

3 What is the shape of the fiber cross-section and how does this affect the serviceability?

4 To what kinds of service have blends of cotton and Dacron or wool and Dacron contributed?

5 Give the formula for Dacron. For Terylene.

6 What is Mylar?

7 How do Fortrel and Kodel compare with Dacron

    a. in strength

    b. chemical exposures

    c. light?

miscellaneous synthetic fibers

Research in polymer chemistry has led to several promising new members of the synthetic fiber family, together with the expansion of uses of one of the older fibers, **Saran.** Chronologically, Saran should be dated with the fibers of the du Pont trio; however, it has become a truly significant consumer fiber only as the result of improvements in the polymer and in its production, thus greatly widening its application from a relatively heavy monofilament to a finer monofilament and lately to staple. Among these newer classifications are the Olefins, Nitrils, Vinal, Vinyon, Polyethylene, and Teflon. In a separate classification are some of the elastic synthetic fibers of the Spandex class; their unique properties deserve a separate identification from these others.

SARANS

Saran, a co-polymer of vinylidene chloride and a lesser amount of vinyl chloride, was perfected by the Dow Chemical Company and came on the market in commercial quantities in 1940 as a rather heavy, stiff, but extremely durable and weather-resistant monofilament. The polymer was spun into filaments by several other companies, such as Firestone Industrial Products Company, a subsidiary of Firestone Rubber Company, using the name **Velon;** The Pierce Plastics, Inc., under the name **Permalon;** and in England, under the name **Tygan.**

Saran is the generic name for all these fibers, as well as a few vinylidene chloride polymers now being spun in other countries, such as Japan **(Kurehalon)** and France **(Rhovyl).** This generic name is defined by the Federal Trade Commission under the Textile Fiber Products Identification Act as "a manufactured fiber in which the fiber-forming substance is any long-chain synthetic polymer composed of at least 80 per cent by weight of vinylidene chloride units ($CH_2 : CCl_2$)."

The chemical structure of Saran is shown in the following equation:

$$CH_2 : CCl_2 + CH_2 : CCl_2 + CH_2 : CCl_2 \longrightarrow$$
$$- CH_2CCl_2CH_2CCl_2CH_2CCl_2 -_n$$

It will be noted that the characteristic of the monomers is the presence of the double bond which, by polymerization and the presence of a catalyst, forms the co-polymer which has only single bonds and is saturated. The Saran molecule is believed to contain approximately 240 to 300 units of the monomers. Varying amounts of vinyl chloride, $CH_2 : CHl$, may replace up to 20 per cent by weight of a Saran polymer, this minor constituent probably adhering in rather random order. One Saran polymer is believed to have a small amount of acrylonitrile, $CH_2 : CHCN$, in the structure.

manufacture

The polymerized product is extruded in the molten state through a spinneret with fine orifices at a temperature above the melt, approximately 350° F., and it solidifies immediately upon extrusion. This means, of course, that the cross-section of the filaments is round. The filaments are generally quickly quenched or hardened in cold water, after which they may be cold stretched to bring about a more crystalline configuration and a high degree of orientation of the molecules within the fiber.

Saran may be delustered, or it may be colored in the melt. Thus, it qualifies as a melt-dyed or "dope-dyed" filament. The initial applications of this fiber were chiefly for automobile seat covers, for the webbing and covering of porch and garden furniture requiring unusually high resistance to sunlight combined with good abrasion resistance, and to some extent for porch or outdoor carpeting or matting. These monofilaments were rather heavy, on the order of as much as 1000 to 2000 denier. This coarseness permits the production of monofilaments in other than round shapes. In other words, spinnerets may be designed to give a flat ribbon or an elliptical cross-section to the extruded filament in which the minor axis, or thickness, may be as little as one-third that of the major axis, or width, of the filament. These features provide greater covering power and permit the use of Saran filaments for fabrics and articles customarily made of rattan, straw, or split cane.

In two respects the Sarans can promise commercial success, namely, the abundance of raw material and the low cost of manufacture. These two qualities alone, however, are not enough, and acceptance of this fiber for a multitude of end-use items must depend upon the efficiency of production and the development of fibers with the kind of texture, drape, and feel desired by customers. Raw materials, principally ethylene and chlorine, are derived, respectively, from the cracking or breaking down of petroleum and from chlorine obtained by the electrolysis of seawater. The polymerization is relatively simple, and the melt-spinning operation means that there is no solvent or by-product to be recovered in order to help make the chemical reaction pay for itself. Sarans, therefore, are low in price compared with other synthetic fibers.

TABLE 22-1 / MANUFACTURERS OF SARAN

| Company | FIBER | | TYPE AVAILABLE | | | |
	Generic Name	Trade Name	F	S	T	M
The Dow Chemical Company	Saran	Rovana				X
Firestone Synthetic Fibers Co.	Saran	Velon				X
National Plastic Products Co., Inc.	Saran	Saran by National	X	X	X	X
Southern Lus-Trus Corporation	Saran	Lus-Trus				X

F—Filament
S—Staple
T—Tow
M—Monofilament

properties

Today's Sarans from four principal manufacturers (Table 22-1) are greatly different from those of twenty years ago, when they were first introduced in durable article form. The tenacity is about 2.4 gpd, and the elongation to break varies from 15 to 25 per cent. The polymer is heavy, its specific gravity being 1.68 to 1.75. This is a somewhat objectionable feature in textile products which are to be worn and carried. It is not as serious a factor for articles which are to be used as floor coverings, furniture coverings, wall coverings, or even draperies. Saran is extremely water-resistant, the regain being less than one-tenth of one per cent under normal conditions. Thus, Saran is somewhat difficult to dye, certainly from solution; pigmenting the polymer and melt dyeing are the preferred methods. These fibers have a great resistance to destructive agents, such as mildew, bacteria, and insects. Their chemical resistance is outstanding. A valuable feature, rather unique to this class of polymers, is that of excellent resistance to fire. This is a characteristic of most compounds containing an appreciable concentration of chlorine.

uses

A major application is in the upholstery of automobiles, either as the original seat covering and body interior covering material or as slipcovers or seat covers to be applied later. Porch or garden furniture pieces are frequently covered with

Saran, either in woven or braid form. Commercial establishments, such as stores, restaurants, hotels, and public transportation vehicles have used this fiber extensively. Many of these applications used deniers of from 1000 to 3000 for the monofils. In recent years, it has been possible to spin finer filaments, and staple as fine as 10 denier is now being produced. Much of this is going into fabrics for upholstery materials, where fibers are woven by the conventional method into rugs, carpets, shoes, and hats. Two properties of this fiber stand in the way of many possible applications. The most important is probably its low softening point. Saran begins to soften at 243° F. and melts at 340° F. This means that careless contact with lighted cigarettes or matches can melt holes in the garment or in the fabric. It will not, of course, burn, as previously mentioned; but in public vehicles and public places, often patrons have ruined a piece of furniture or wall covering with a cigarette butt. To touch a Saran window screen with the tip of a lighted cigarette is to melt a hole instantly. It might be said, however, that the same thing is true of nylon as a screening material, but this low softening point means to all practical purposes that Saran fibers cannot well be used in wearing apparel or in any fabric which must be ironed after washing. The second problem is that Saran has not, thus far, been made in a good, clear white. The result is that pastels and light shades are not as bright as in other synthetic fibers.

rovana

Like most of our synthetic polymers, Saran can also be cast into a film. In 1959, the Dow Chemical Company announced a new Saran fiber under the trade name **Rovana.** This is a continuous film formed into a ribbon which has been made into many accessory fabrics, such as garment trimmings, hat trimmings, ribbons, twisted belts, webbing, and many other uses, in addition to fabrics for the automotive trade and for woven wall coverings. Some novelty yarns woven with some of these colored strips of Rovana are said to give somewhat the same surface effect as sequins sewed to the garment fabric. The problem of pressing and damage to these materials is, however, serious in these novelty structures.

NYTRIL FIBER

This genus is represented by a single fiber, **Darvan,** the commercial career of which has been somewhat checkered. In October, 1955, B. F. Goodrich Chemical Company built the co-polymer of vinylidene cyanide and a vinyl acetate or other monocarboxylic acid (and having but a single COOH), which was capable of fiber formation. The polymerization reaction had been studied for some eight years by the Goodrich organization prior to this announcement to the industry, and the fiber was originally called Darlan. About a year later, the name was changed to Darvan. In 1959, the fiber process was sold to the Celanese Corporation of America. At the present time, it is understood that Darvan is being produced in England, possibly as a part of the negotiations which brought to the

Celanese Corporation the rights to manufacture a polyester fiber as their new **Fortrel.**

A nytril fiber is defined as "a manufactured fiber containing at least 85 per cent of the long-chain polymer of vinylidene dinytrile $(-CH_2-C(CN)_2-)$, where the vinylidene dinytrile content is no less than every other unit in the polymer chain." Vinylidene dinytrile is another name for vinylidene cyanide. Thus, we have the following chemical reaction portrayed in this definition:

$$
\begin{array}{cccc}
H & CN & H & H \\
| & | & | & | \\
C=C & +C=C & & \\
| & | & | & | \\
H & CN & H & OCOCH_3 \\
\end{array}
\quad\longrightarrow\quad
\left[
\begin{array}{cccc}
H & CN & H & H \\
| & | & | & | \\
-C-C & -C-C- & & \\
| & | & | & | \\
H & CN & H & OCOCH_3 \\
\end{array}
\right]_n
$$

It is believed that benzene is used as the solvent in which the polymerization takes place at a relatively low temperature and with sufficient pressure to prevent the boiling off of the benzene. The co-polymer precipitates and is filtered. The solid is then dissolved in one of several special solvents and spun into a water bath where the co-polymer filaments are hardened through precipitation. They are then stretched in several steps to give a highly-oriented filament or fiber tow which is called Darvan. Rather unique properties are claimed for this fiber; one is extreme softness in texture, and when blended with wool, it does, in fact, give a very soft-textured rich-feeling staple and fabric.

properties

The tenacity of Darvan was lower than that of most of our synthetic fibers, being 1.75 gpd under standard conditions and 1.5 gpd when wet, but Table 22-7 shows 2.2 gpd for the product now produced. It has excellent elongation properties, 22 per cent both wet and dry. The specific gravity is 1.18, approximately the same as nylon and the acrylics. The moisture regain is 2 to 3 per cent at standard conditions; thus, the problem of discomfort caused by lack of moisture absorbency becomes a factor, and also the matter of static electricity during the winter season, when house interiors are hot and very dry. It has complete resistance to moths and mildew and does not show appreciable strength loss after prolonged exposure outdoors, even in areas such as Florida. The softening temperature is around 350° F. When heated to 300° F., it retains about 50 per cent of its strength. One would characterize this fiber as having somewhat lower than moderate sensitivity to heat and as being applicable to fabrics which require little or no ironing, which may be adequately ironed for appearance' sake at the moderately low temperatures. In cross-section, the fibers are somewhat curled and appear to be rather flat. There is no great uniformity as to cross-section, so it would appear that the individual fibers are somewhat twisted and distorted along their length. (See Figure A p. 1, no. 31, p. 546.)

uses

The fiber has definite possibilities particularly because of its soft handle and good covering properties. In addition to that, it has such excellent weathering resistance and stands up so well against sunlight. In these fields, however, it is apparent that its competition in the United States was somewhat too keen, and it is being developed now and perhaps perfected for these and other uses in England.

OLEFIN FIBERS

Olefins include a great number of potential fiber-forming polymer materials. Table 22-2 shows the list of current manufacturers of olefin polymers in the United States. This family, the Olefin fibers, has been defined for the Textile Fiber Products Identification Act as "a manufactured fiber in which the fiber-forming substance is any long-chain synthetic polymer composed of at least 85 per cent by weight of ethylene, propylene, or other olefin units."

TABLE 22-2 / PRINCIPAL MANUFACTURERS OF OLEFIN FIBERS

| | FIBER | | TYPE | | | |
| | Generic | Trade | AVAILABLE | | | |
Company	Name	Name	F	S	T	M
American Thermoplastics Corp.	Olefin					X
Avisun Corporation	Olefin	Olane	X	X		
Beaunit Fibers, Div. of Beaunit Mills, Inc.	Olefin		X	X	X	
Dawbarn Brothers, Inc.	Olefin	DLP				X
		FilPak	X			
		Beamette	X			
Firestone Synthetic Fibers Co.	Olefin	Velon LP				X
Hercules Powder Company, Fiber Development Dept.	Olefin	Herculon	X	X	X	
Industrial Plastic Company	Olefin	Tuff-Lite				X
Industrial Wire & Plastics Co., Inc.	Olefin					X
National Plastic Products Co., Inc.	Olefin	Enlon	X	X		X
		Wynene				X
Polyarns, Inc.	Olefin	Polyarns				X
Reeves Brothers, Inc.	Olefin	Reevon	X	X	X	X
Southern Lus-Trus Corporation	Olefin	Lus-Trus				X
Vogt Manufacturing Corp.	Olefin	Voplex				X

F—Filament
S—Staple
T—Tow
M—Monofilament

In addition to the polyolefin fibers in Table 22-2, there are others of polyethylene fiber including **Polythene,** produced by the British firm, the ICI, Ltd.; **Velon LP** by Firestone Plastics Company; **Bolathene** by General Tire and Rubber Company; **Polyarns** by Polyarns, Inc.; **Tex** by Polymers, Inc.; **Reevon** by Reeves

Brothers, Inc.; and **Royalene** by U.S. Rubber Company. Among the trademarked propylene fibers are: **Courlene** by Courtaulds, Ltd. of England; **Beaunit polypropylene; Propylon** by Canadian Celanese, Ltd.; **Olane** by AviSun; and **Propylene** by Industrial Rayon Corporation.

These polymers have been in consumer use for a longer period of time as cast polymeric articles or as films. In other words, the textile applications are relatively new.

The reaction by which polyethylenes and polypropylenes are formed is as follows:

$$CH_2 : CH_2 + CH_2 : CH_2 + CH_2 : CH_2 + CH_2 : CH_2 \longrightarrow$$

ethylene

$$\text{or} \qquad - CH_2 - CH_2 - CH_2 - CH_2 - CH_2 - CH_2 - CH_2 - CH_2 -$$

$$CH_3 - CH = CH_2$$

propylene

It will be noted that these are unsaturated hydrocarbons. The mechanism of the reaction is that of addition polymerization, with the free bond on each carbon, now available for terminal or end-to-end linkage, replacing the broken double bond. The molecular weight of the polymer depends upon the pressure under which the operation is carried out. As a rule, molecular weights are in the general neighborhood of 20,000 to 25,000, at which point the tenacity is as high as 3 gpd. Both ethylene and propylene are obtained from the petrochemical processes, that is, the cracking of petroleum. Each of these olefin fibers is capable of being produced in more than one form. Thus, technically it should be possible to modify the olefins within limits for a particular end-use application. Certain general properties are outstanding. First, the petroleum raw material is abundant and cheap. Second, the specific gravity, varying from 0.90 to 0.96, is the lightest of any textile fiber, and it is claimed that even Orlon with its low-bulk density would require 1.3 pounds to cover the same area covered by one pound of polypropylene. Wool would require 1.46, cotton as much as 1.71 pounds for equal coverage. The tenacity varies from 2.7 to as much as 6.5, depending upon the type. Virtually the same tenacity is claimed for both the polyethylenes and polypropylenes. The moisture regain is zero, so the properties of these fibers remain wholly unaffected in the presence of moisture. The melting point is approximately 335° F.; however, in some of the polyethylenes, the melting point is approximately 80° F. lower. The softening temperature, at which softening or sticking begins, is 305° F. for the Beaunit polypropylene fiber, which when close to a flame may burn slowly. If the flame source is removed, but the fabric is left hanging, there is a tendency for the flame to regress somewhat, the molten material dropping off. Usually this melt is flaming, and more often than not it carries away from the fabric the actual burning material, so that the fiber may be said to be relatively non-flammable. A weakness is the sensitivity of these fibers to sunlight. They are about as sensitive to sun rotting as is nylon. This fiber has excellent resistance to most chemicals, including acids. This has made it popular as a protective material in laboratories and in work clothes in fabric, sheet, or film form. There is a tendency of these fibers to *creep* or gradually to extend, over a long period of time, if a weight is attached to them. Thus, a steady pull may permanently distort the garment. This is particularly true with polyethylene; the polypropylenes are somewhat more brittle and definitely have a less waxy feel than do the polyethylenes.

This is a fiber family rapidly growing in use. Applications showing promise are in carpets and rugs, and somewhat similarly in the case of upholstery fabrics, where low weight, resistance to insects and mold, freedom from pilling, and reasonably good abrasion are desirable features. The olefin fibers make excellent knit goods, such as underwear and hosiery, although the absence of any moisture absorbency does stand somewhat in the way of comfort. Good use is made in automobile upholstery fabrics, outdoor furniture, screening, the webbing of shoes, and paddings and insulators, including electrical insulation.

For a comparison of the olefin fiber properties with others of the groups still somewhat less known, see Table 22-7, page 345.

Trilok fabric is made by the United States Rubber Company as a superior "breathing" type of protective clothing. It is a tight fabric with a polyethene warp and rayon or cotton in the filling. The Polyarns shrinks 50 per cent at the boil, thus making the fabric more compact.

VINYON

Vinyon's heat sensitivity and tendency toward static electrical charge limit the use of this fiber, as in the case of the original Vinyon of nearly 25 years ago. The tenacity of the **Avisco Vinyon** is given as 0.7 to 1 gpd, both dry and wet. The specific gravity is 1.33 to 1.35. The moisture regain under standard conditions is less than one-tenth of one per cent; it is the same at 95 per cent relative humidity. In boiling water, the filaments or fibers shrink about 60 per cent. The fibers are round in cross-section and show little evidence of crystallinity in their molecular structure under the moderate degree of tension applied. The resistance to sunlight is considered to be good. Most acids and alkalies have little effect on these fibers at room temperatures. Exposure to high temperatures shows weaknesses of this fiber. It melts at 260° F., softens at 170° F., and has a tendency to become slightly sticky at 150° F. The heat-shrinking properties cause it to be applied to special uses such as heat-sealing yarns or industrial fabrics where applications to chemicals are not at temperatures in excess of 140° F. As a binder, it is used to seal layers of other fabrics together or to apply felts to the base of articles and is used also as a binding fiber in certain kinds of papers. Some three-dimensional or molded surface effects on carpets are produced by the presence of certain quantities of vinyon staple with the other fibers in the tufts. The application to dry heat or use of hot water causes the vinyon filaments to shrink, thus giving to the fabric a molded structure with high and low areas.

TABLE 22-3 / MANUFACTURERS OF VINYON

	FIBER		TYPE AVAILABLE			
	Generic	Trade				
Compay	Name	Name	F	S	T	M
American Viscose Corporation	Vinyon	Avisco	X			
Polyarns, Inc.	Vinyon	45				X
Vogt Manufacturing Corporation	Vinyon	Voplex				X

F—Filament
S—Staple
T—Tow
M—Monofilament

VINAL FIBERS

A vinal is defined by the Federal Trade Commission for the Textile Fiber Products Identification Act as a fiber in which "the fiber-forming substance is any long-chain synthetic polymer composed of at least 50 per cent by weight of vinyl alcohol units, and in which the total of the vinyl alcohol units and any one or more of the various acetal units is at least 85 per cent by weight of the fiber."

The only vinal fiber currently being manufactured in the United States is distributed by the Air Reduction Chemical Company as **Vinylon,** or as **Airco Vinal.** This is a strong fiber and has excellent resistance to abrasion. Some of its properties are considerably different from those of most synthetic fibers; for although it is hydrophobic, it is not nearly as resistant to moisture absorption as most other fibers. These facts affect its use. Because of its durability and its moderate moisture absorbency, it is being used in rain wear and in bathing suits. It is wool-like in feel and texture when spun on the wool system. One great disadvantage of the fiber is the extent to which it wrinkles in use. This feature is so severe that the fabric thus far has found little application in outerwear or in any kind of high-fashion merchandise. Nor should it be used in articles requiring ironing, because it is damaged by temperatures as low as 250° F.

TEFLON

Teflon, the trademarked tetrafluoroethylene fiber of the E. I. du Pont de Nemours & Company, posseses properties far more suitable to industrial use than to the more moderate requirements of the household. For that reason, it does not come under the Textile Fiber Products Identification Act passed by the Congress for the protection and guidance of the consumer. First made in molded form, the polymer has recently been spun into fibers.

TABLE 22-4 / MANUFACTURER OF TFE AND FEP

(Fluorocarbon)

Company	FIBER Generic Name	Trade Name	TYPE AVAILABLE			
			F	S	T	M
E. I. du Pont de Nemours & Co., Inc.	TFE-fluorocarbon	Teflon	X	X	X	
	FEP-fluorocarbon	Teflon	X			X

F—Filament
S—Staple
T—Tow
M—Monofilament

It differs from all other fibers in that the polymer is a long-chain carbon molecule in which all available bonds are filled with flourine. Tetrafluoroethylene's composition is $CF_2 = CF_2$ and the polymer is believed to have the following structure.

$$n \quad \begin{matrix} F & F \\ | & | \\ C = C \\ | & | \\ F & F \end{matrix} \longrightarrow \begin{matrix} F & F & F & F & F & F \\ | & | & | & | & | & | \\ - C - C - C - C - C - C - \\ | & | & | & | & | & | \\ F & F & F & F & F & F \end{matrix}$$

polyfluoroethylene

The basic raw materials are fluorspar, CaF_2, and chloroform. The spinning operation is complex because of the high temperature resistance of the polymer (even at 750° F., its melting point, it is too viscous to spin), and its great resistance to practically all solvents and chemical substances precludes its spinning from solution. In practice, the polymerization and spinning are both carried out in an aqueous collodial dispersion. A large opening (0.5 mm) is used, and the heavy fiber is held together by the parallel molecules. It may be bleached white in strong oxidizing mineral acids or somewhat lightened in color by heating to 500° F. It is almost impossible to dye. The tensile strength is quite high, dry and wet tenacities being 1.7. It is a very heavy fiber, with a specific gravity of 2.3. It has no moisture regain whatever, even at the boil. It has excellent resistance to all chemicals and, of course, to mildew, bacteria, and insects. Many of its uses as fabrics are for felts and woven fabric structures for gaskets, filtration media, pump packing, electrical tapes, and similar uses. It is a somewhat waxy-feeling fabric, and its low coefficient of friction is an advantage in practically all these applications.

ELASTOMERS

The elastomeric fiber is one possessing true elasticity to a comparatively great degree, that is, the fiber or filament can be stretched to many times its original length and will return to the original dimension. Generally, we say that such fibers are like rubber, but this also means that the return to the original length is as rapid as in the case of rubber. Some of the synthetic rubbers or rubber-like polymers are somewhat more sluggish than natural rubber in this regard. As a matter of fact, some automobile tires are promoted actively on the basis that the synthetic latex polymer is less rubbery and bouncy than natural rubber, thus affording a smoother ride with less bounce following a rough spot in the street or highway surface.

If rubber is to be one of our points of reference in describing the properties of these new elastomeric fibers, it might be appropriate to insert a brief discussion of rubber or lastex yarns and filaments at this point, even though none of the synthetic rubber fibers are at the present time of commerical importance in textile goods for the average consumer (though they were important during World War II, when the supply of natural rubber was cut off).

lastex

Lastex is not a synthetic but is a constructed yarn having high elasticity. This yarn has a core of latex, or thread of rubber, around which are wound filaments of rayon, silk, wool, cotton, or synthetics. The yarns are woven or knitted into fabrics in which elasticity and close conformance to the body are desirable qualities.

Among the extensive uses of lastex are foundation garments, underwear, bathing suits, hats, hosiery tops, suitings, riding clothes, and dresses. Some of these uses replace elastic webbing, but others are new uses for which lastex yarn is peculiarly suited.

Lastex has several distinctive properties.[1]

1. The fabrics would stretch in all directions, but usually lastex yarns are used only in one direction, either in the warp or in the filling, depending upon whether lateral or vertical elasticity is desired.

2. The latex core will retain its elasticity throughout the useful life of the garment.

3. Lastex yarn can be made fine enough to be woven into such delicate fabrics as laces, nets, voiles, and batistes.

4. Lastex conforms to the body contours and thus insures smoothly fitting garments.

5. The rubber is not noticeable to the eye, nor is the odor discernible.

6. Lastex is not affected by washing or by careful dry-cleaning. It can be pressed with a moderately warm iron. Generally, chlorine bleach should be avoided.

The latex of which the lastex yarn core is composed is the milky fluid obtained from the Hevea Braziliensis tree. The bark of the tree is cut, and the

[1] Bulletin of the National Retail Dry Goods Association (Feb., 1934).

fluid flowing from the wound is collected; after ammonia or some other type of preservative has been added, the latex is packed for export. Malaya and the Dutch East Indies are the principal sources of this liquid material. Ordinarily, raw latex contains between 40 and 60 per cent of water.

It is possible to extrude a round filament of latex as fine in diameter as the human hair. The filament emerging from the small round orifice is coagulated in an acid bath and is then **vulcanized,** or given a permanent set by means of heat aided by this catalyst. It is to this vulcanization of the entire round exterior that lastex owes its superior length of life as compared with the older type of rubber fiber having a square cross-section. These older fibers were cut from thin sheets of rubber and were neither as thoroughly vulcanized on all sides nor as strong as the round filaments.

The wrapping of these cores with textile filaments requires precise mechanical opertion. The fibers are tightly wrapped around the latex thread while it is under slight tension, so that the covering will not pull loose or break when the yarn is strained during use.

Lastex finds other uses which may be regarded as relating to textile applications or to clothing. A thin coating of lastex to the backs of rugs and carpets serves to pervent slipping and helps to bind the base of the pile yarns. It is also useful to cement garment seams, reinforce seams of fur coats, cement or close food containers, and waterproof paper and fabrics. Rubbers, slippers, rain coats, and similar **waterproof** articles may be made from latex.

SPANDEX FIBERS

No other family of synthetic filament fibers has had as great a growth since the Textile Fiber Products Identification Act went into effect in 1958 as the elastic-type or elastomeric filaments. To these, the Federal Trade Commission has assigned the generic name **Spandex.** The du Pont fiber **Lycra** was the first of these materials and originally was called Fiber K. So great was its acceptance, especially in foundation garments and in elasticized materials, that other producers have hastened into the field. Thus, in 1962, we have the following manufacturers:

TABLE 22-5 / MANUFACTURERS OF SPANDEX

	FIBER		TYPE			
	Generic	Trade	AVAILABLE			
Company	Name	Name	F	S	T	M
E. I. du Pont de Nemours & Co., Inc.	Spandex	Lycra	X			
Firestone Synthetic Fibers Co.	Spandex		X			
United States Rubber Co., Textile Division	Spandex	Vyrene				X
Eastman Chemical Products Company	Spandex					X
International Latex Corporation	Spandex					X

F—Filament
S—Staple
T—Tow
M—Monofilament

According to the Federal Trade Commission Regulations for the Textile Fiber Products Identification Act, Spandex is defined as "a manufactured fiber in which the fiber-forming substance is a long-chain synthetic polymer comprised of at least 85 per cent of a segmented polyurethane." Table 22-1 indicates Lycra and Vyrene elastomeric filaments as conforming to this Spandex definition. The exact nature of the processing nature and of the raw materials has not been disclosed.[2]

TABLE 22-6

| | SPANDEX | |
	Lycra	Vyrene
		(Monofilaments)
Tenacity (gpd) Dry-Wet	0.6–0.8	—
Elongation (%) Dry-Wet	520–610	700
Specific Gravity	1.21	—
Water Regain (%)	1.13	0.3
Softening Point (° F.)	300	Shrinks at 180
	Melts 440	Softens: 220
Ironing Point, safe (° F.)	Low	Cannot Iron
Resistance to Strong Acid	good	good
Resistance to Weak Acid	good	good
Resistance to Strong Alkali	good	fair
Resistance to Weak Alkali	good	good
Resistance to Bleach	yellowed	yellowed
Class of Dyes Used	easily disperse	disperse types
Cross-section	peanut	irregular

Properties. The tenacity is 0.6 to 0.8 gpd; the elongation at the break, however, is from 520 to 610 per cent. The moisture regain under standard conditions is 1.3 per cent. The fiber is very light in weight, having a specific gravity of 1.0. It has good abrasion resistance and excellent flex-life and is white in color and dull in luster. At temperatures over 300° F., the fiber has a tendency to yellow and to begin to lose strength. The melting point is 482° F. It is found that at an excessive temperature the fiber will stick to the iron sole at approximately 347° F. The cross-section of the filament is dog-bone-shaped. Further properties are given in Table 22-6, above.

[2] "Lycra, Spandex Fibers," New Product Information Bulletin NP-16 (September 1960), E. I. du Pont de Nemours and Company.

The fiber resists most solvents, including all of the common dry-cleaning solvents, and may be dissolved in dimethyl formamide at the boil. The whiteness of this fiber, even after dry cleaning and washing, combined with its excellent abrasion resistance and rather comfortable hand or feel, enables this fiber to be used uncovered in elastic fabrics. Thus, surgical stockings, girdles, elastic belts, and similar uses of elastic fabric can be made with an uncovered yarn. This does not mean that a cover cannot be put on; some wearers prefer that the original elastic yarns of which their foundation garments are made should have a coating. A garment made up of several component fabrics, with Lycra in the elasticized portions and a synthetic fiber, rayon, acetate, or cotton, in other portions, may be dyed uniformly, because Lycra will pick up some dyestuffs, although generally not the direct colors. The best colorants for Lycra are the acid and dispersed dye classes. Not all colors are fast to washing; therefore, if a good color match is to be retained in a garment, it is sometimes necessary to cover the Lycra and depend upon the covering fibers to match the shade of the rest of the garment. Some light and compact items are: brassieres, panties, and other articles of intimate attire which can be packaged in small boxes only slightly larger than a package of cigarettes and lend themselves, therefore, to self-help selling in stores.

vyrene

Little information is available as yet on **Vyrene.** However, it is believed to be essentially the same as Lycra. This product is new and has been announced as a trademarked fiber of the United States Rubber Company. It starts to shrink at 180° F. and is slightly tacky above 220° F. It is affected by hot acids and alkalies but resistant to them in the cold. It is not affected by common solvents and has the advantage of easy dyeing with acetate and dispersed colors.

uses of spandex fibers

By definition, Spandex yarns are elastic, that is, they are elastomers and retract or recover after stretching, thus giving a positive support to the body of the wearer when used in girdles, elastic belts, elasticized hose, and other articles of wearing apparel. In many of their uses, they will overlap the so-called stretch yarns, which give with the body, but which do not exert any positive support. Examples of this, of course, are Ban-Lon, Helanca, and other stretchy-type yarns, most of which are nylon. New applications of these yarns appear to be in the re-introduction of contour sheets with corner inserts of the Spandex yarn to permit a tight, snug fit. Similar uses, of course, would be in table covers, slip covers for furniture, and dust-protective textile devices. In wearing apparel, swim wear, anti-gravity suits for astronauts, outerwear, dresswear, and hosiery may be expected to receive the attention of these rather miraculous fibers. It is forecast that they will be used rather extensively in football pants, in golf-ball windings, and as protective fabrics for bathing pools and outdoor furniture.

TABLE 22-7 / PROPERTIES OF OTHER SYNTHETIC FIBERS

| | OLEFINS | | | | | |
	Saran	Polyethylenes	Polypropylenes	Vinyon	Darvan	Teflon Staple
Tenacity (gpd) Dry-/Wet	1.15–2.3	1.0–3.0	3.5–7.0	0.7–1.0	2.2	1.9
Elongation (%) Dry-/Wet	15–25	20–80	10–45		22–24	13
Specific Gravity	1.7	0.92	0.95	1.33–1.35	1.18	2.3
Water Regain (%)	negligible	negligible	negligible	0.1	2–3	none
Softening Point (°F.)	Softens: 240 Shrinks: 210–220 Melts: 340–350	Softens: 225 Melts: 240 5–8% shrinkage at 165	Softens 284–330 Melts: 330–360 4–8% shrinkage at 165	Softens: 170 Melts: 260 Shrinks 60% at boil	50% strength loss at 300	550
Ironing Point, safe (°F.)	cannot iron	cannot iron	cannot iron	cannot iron	cannot iron	High setting
Resistance to Strong Acid	good	excellent	excellent	excellent	good	excellent
Resistance to Weak Acid	good	excellent	excellent	excellent	good	excellent
Resistance to Strong Alkali	discolors	excellent	excellent	good	fair	excellent
Resistance to Weak Alkali	good	excellent	excellent	excellent	fair	excellent
Resistance to Bleach	good	excellent	excellent	good	fair	not bleached
Class of Dyes Used	pigmented	pigmented	pigmented	special classes and disperse peanut	disperse and carrier types	not dyed
Cross-section	round	round	round		irregular	round

These Spandex yarns may be wound as is customary in the case of lastex or used without winding. More sheet and lightweight batiste, satins, and laces are possible with Vyrene, due to the process developed by the United States Rubber Company for a single cover on their Spandex yarn, as compared with the double cover customary on Lycra and other elastomers. Few articles are made of 100 per cent Spandex yarn, and any percentage figure refers to the percentage of Spandex in the portion of the garment in which it occurs.

newer use for polyurethanes

Having viewed the peculiar nature of polyurethanes in filament form, that is, the highly elastic Spandex fibers, we now come to another use of polyurethane having to do with textile products. It is not a fiber, nor is it a textile-forming material. It is essentially a solid foam with infinite numbers of small openings or cells for the entrapment of air. This material is being used widely now as an insulating layer in wearing apparel and in other household and industrial applications. We generally refer to these as "foam laminates," which means that the foam layer is always firmly attached or laminated to the fabric on one or both sides of the garment structure.

FOAM LAMINATES

The fastest-growing textile specialty in 1961 and with similar expansion forecast for the next three to five years is the *polyurethane foam laminate* to knitted and woven outerwear fabrics for winter or other cold-condition wear.

More than one hundred years ago, in 1848, the chemical reaction was discovered by a German chemist who found that isocyanates and various alcohols combine together to make urethanes. Use was not made of this until the 1930's. During the years of the Second World War, our military laboratory facilities conducted research with the result that isocyanate foams were made for cushioning breakable materials to be transported by truck or to be dropped by parachute. Like all foams, solid or liquid, these consist of a vast number of air pockets or cells surrounded in this case by a film of polyurethane. This solid film corresponds to the soap bubbles in the case of a soap foam or to the butterfat and water emulsion in the case of whipped cream. The solid foams weigh about one and one-half pounds per cubic foot. They can be cut and sliced to whatever thickness is desired. Foam thicknesses of from $\frac{1}{16}$ to $\frac{3}{8}$ inch are commonly used as an insulation backing to be applied to knitted or woven outerwear fabrics. Tests have indicated the degree of insulation afforded to be protective against cold as the best of natural fibers, wool, and to be half again as effective, or more, when compared with fibrous filling materials of man-made fibers, such as Dacron, nylon, and glass fiber. Sometimes they permit air to go through the foam, because these air bubbles are somewhat continuous. Thus they permit moisture gradually to pass out through the fabric, preventing overheating in warmer weather or chilling due to moisture collection on the skin during cold-weather exposure. These foams are washable or dry-cleanable and are extremely pliable, that is, they give readily with movement of the body and with the movement of the outerwear fabric, whereas some of the protective layers previously used, notably quilted fabrics filled with fibers, have tended to make the garment somewhat bulky and thick. They can be made odorless and are not allergenic, that is, they will not produce a skin rash as wool sometimes does to sensitive persons and which is a common complaint in the case of glass fabrics if the fibers come in contact with the skin.

The high insulating value has enabled manufacturers to use somewhat lighter outer-layer fabrics without losing much by way of protection against cold. Thus, weight-saving has been effected not only through the foam, but also through the weight of the outer fabric.

These foam-back fabrics were more or less a novelty in 1959; but in 1960, some 15 million yards of knit goods were laminated to foam for winter wear. In 1961, the figure will probably have totaled four times the figure for 1960, and it is forecast that by 1965 there will be approximately 300 million yards of laminated foam fabrics produced.

Permanent foams presently applied to textiles are: **Nopcofoam** (Nopco Chemical Company), **Scott-foam** (Scott Paper Company), **Curon** (Reeves Brothers, Inc.), and products of various kinds from the General Foam Corporation of New York. A newer competitor in the field is the Dayco Corporation, whose product until recently has been utilized in foams applied to the back of automobile upholstery, furniture upholstery material, and the like. Other polymers than the urethanes are being experimented with, such as polyesters and polyethers. Some of these, however, lack the dry-cleaning or washing property of the polyurethanes; polyethers, however, cost 15 to 20 per cent less.

foam adhesion methods

The actual bonding can be done by three different methods. The one principally used is that of heat. The surface of the foam sheet is melted at a temperature of approximately 250°–300° F. by a fine gas flame; then the foam and fabric are brought together quickly between two rollers, and the tacky foam adheres to the cloth with great strength. Done quickly, there is no impermeable skin formed at the point of contact; thus the foam continues to breathe. The second method is to use an adhesive which may be sprayed on or applied in a pattern of dabs or stripes by means of a roller application to improve the breathing of the fabric. This method does not give a laminate with as much give or yield to it as the fusion method. Thus, it has been applied to woven fabrics more than to the more elastic knitted fabrics.

The third method of application is by bonding or quilting. In this case, there is no actual adhesion to the outerwear fabric, but the foam layer backed by a lightweight cloth, such as netting or scrim, is actually stitched to the outer fabric as would any other fibrous filler or padding. This construction is used principally for extreme cold conditions, where greater thickness is required and where greater bulk is not as much of a problem. A one-inch-wide strip should require a 14- to 16-ounce pull in a Scott tester to separate the layers.

There is no doubt that this flexible, durable, lightweight, and thin material forming a bond with a comparatively lightweight woven or knitted wool fabric will be an important between-seasons coat or jacket for men, women, and children.

flexible resin lamination

A unique invention recently announced is a flexible resin foam application process, developed by the Specialty Converters, Inc., East Braintree, Massachusetts. The process, according to *Modern Textiles Magazine, 43,* No. 7 (July 1962), page 22, enables one to cast a flexible foam onto any non-porous surface, such as metal foil, plastic sheeting, paper, or fabric. The base is a du Pont Hylene organic oxycyanate. The unique feature involves the internal reinforcement of the foam to increase its puncture resistance, tear strength, and dimensional stability by positioning a textile material in the center of the foam. A strong, lightweight open-weave fabric such as nylon or Fiberglas scrim can be used. The foam may then be deposited on either one or two of the smooth surfaces to give excellent wrappings, scatter rugs, table covers, display materials, and other attractive and utilitarian textile products. It also has great potentialities as a material for sound and heat insulation.[3]

[3] National Institute of Drycleaning Bulletin Service, Bulletin C-72, "Laminated Urethane Foams" (Dec. 1961).

TABLE 22-8 / TRADE NAMES YOU MAY SEE ON FOAM LAMINATED GARMENTS AND IN RETAIL ADVERTISING

Trade Name	Foam Maker	Laminator	Fabric Merchandiser	Type of Fabric†
Curon[1]	Reeves Brothers, Inc.*	Reeves Bros., Inc. and licensed laminators.	Merchandises own line of fabrics and through a number of other mills and converters under Curon name.	Mostly knit goods, some women's fabrics.
Scott Apparel Foam[2]	Scott Paper Co.*	Independent and mill owned laminating services.	Mills and converters under own names featuring Scott Apparel Foam.	Mostly knitted fabrics—some wovens.
Astrotex[3]	Scott Paper Co.	Princeton Knitting Mills*	Same	Jersey and other knitted fabrics.
Bondaknit[3]	Scott Paper Co.	Independents	Abaco Fabrics, Inc.*	Knitted fabrics.
Feathalite[3]	Scott Paper Co.	Independents	Guilford Woolen Fabrics, Inc.*	Woven woolen goods.
Vomar and Vozet	Nopco Chemical Co. & General Foam Corp.	Allied Polymer Corporation*	Fabric firm customers.	All types.
Fahrenheit	Any make	Independents	Brand and Oppenheimer Co.*	All types, including quilted lining.
Perma-Bond[4]	Any make	A. D. Gosman Corp.	For mills and converters.	All types.
Stratolite[4]	" "	Independents	Rosemont Knitting Mills, Inc.*	Knit goods.

* Designates owner of trade name.

[1] All Curon laminations by heat fusion (open flame method) under own patents obtained from Curtis-Wright Corporation.

[2] Sctt Apparel Foam applied at present time to knit fabrics by fusion; to woven fabrics by chemical adhesion. In future all Scott Apparel Foam may be applied by chemical adhesion under new procedures now in development stage.

[3] Special or regular brand names may be used by mills under Scott Apparel Foam merchandising program.

[4] Reference may sometimes be made with these or any other names to Dupont's "Hylene" line of foam chemicals. The foam is not made by Dupont. Several nationally known firms make foam chemicals.

† At the present time urethane foams are applied mainly to all types of knit goods, including bulky knits, jersey, etc. In the future, woven fabrics may predominate depending on technical developments and style demands, bringing to the fore new trade names associated with makers of woven textiles.

(Courtesy: National Institute of Dry Cleaning.)

summary of advantages of foam laminates over other filling materials

The foam laminate filler is lighter in weight, and tests conducted in various laboratories have indicated its superiority in heat insulation. Mention has also been made of the fact that it is less bulky than fillers, such as down, feathers, goose, and fluffy batts of such materials as Dacron, nylon, cotton linters, and other fibrous materials. Thus, the garments look less bulky and more trim and stylish in line. So far there has been no evidence of correlation between the actual thickness of foam required for certain temperatures and wind velocities. When this correlation is carried out, then it will be possible to provide the wearer with sufficient anti-freeze capacity in clothing for the most severe weather conditions anticipated. In other words, one would tend to skimp on the thickness of the foam liner through overconfidence and just simply not have enough thickness to do the job.

Table 22-8 shows the trade names of some of the most common lamination products. This table is from the National Institute of Drycleaning Bulletin Service, Bulletin C-72, "Laminated Urethane Foams" (December 1961).

QUESTIONS

1 What are the principal properties of the olefin fibers?

2 What are the principal properties of Saran?

3 What are the principal properties of Spandex fibers?

4 a) State the individual differences among the several olefin fibers on the market in the United States. b) To what are such differences due?

5 Why is Saran not an important apparel fiber?

6 List the principal uses of Saran and explain in what way the fiber is best suited for that particular purpose.

7 Which elastomeric fibers are natural and which are synthetic?

8 What are some of the advantages possessed over rubber by the Spandex fibers?

9 Give the Federal Trade Commission definition for olefin, Saran, Spandex, and polyester fibers.

10 List the most important polyester fibers. State for what use or uses each is most appropriate.

11 By what methods are the foam laminates commonly attached to fabrics?

12 What are the advantages of foam laminates over the conventional filling materials?

13 In what way is the most common foam laminate similar to the Spandex fibers?

14 What is the difference between Lycra and Vyrene?

furs

An inexpensive Persian lamb coat, purchased in a basement of a large department store, was returned because it tore into shreds when dry-cleaned. The consumer was justified in her complaint, though not to be congratulated on her buying wisdom or sense of value. The coat had been made up of shreds and strips cut from pelts used in better garments. It must have been like a jig-saw puzzle to assemble the pieces on the cotton net backing cloth, and so irregular were the pieces that they could not profitably be sewed together (as is customary even in coats identified as from sides, bellies, paws, and other poorer fur portions of the pelt) but had been glued with rubber cement. The dry-cleaning solvent had dissolved the cement, and some of the narrow strips hung as much as three feet below the hem line of the garment. How much better service would have been given by even a low-priced cloth coat or one of synthetic fibers, imitating genuine fur.

Furs or animal pelts were undoubtedly the first clothing adopted by prehistoric man to protect him from the elements and from the thorns and branches through which he was obliged to travel as he foraged for his food. Many of the gods and the strongest of the legendary heroes of primitive peoples are customarily portrayed as being clothed in the pelts of the strongest and most savage beasts.

The story of the fur industry in North America is one of the most adventurous chapters in our history. Indeed, much of the history of the exploration of this continent might be titled "In Search of Fur." The pelt of the beaver was for many years the medium of exchange in the whole Northwest Territory and in the fur trading posts along the Mississippi River. Furs have always been associated with romance and adventure.

A BRIEF VIEW OF FUR TRADING IN AMERICA

Newfoundland was permanently settled by an expedition sent out from England in 1578 to develop a fur trading post in the New World. The Dutch East India Company conducted a large-scale fur trading business between the years 1609 and 1684, during which period trading posts were established in what is now the state of Maine and as far south as New Amsterdam, which is now New York.

Furs were in such demand in the courts of Europe that France established fur trading posts from Hudson's Bay in the north to New Orleans in the south. The constant warfare between the French and the English which finally culminated in France's loss of her lands in America was largely caused by the desire of each nation for control of this fur trade. The rich fur trade of Canada was chartered to the Hudson's Bay Company by the government of England in 1660, and for almost 200 years this English company monopolized the fur trade in that vast area. Even today, the Hudson's Bay Company is a potent force in fur marketing trade and in the retail business in Canada. The beaver fur was used in hats.

The early history of the fur trade in the unsettled western part of the United States is largely the history of the Northwest Company, which in 1803 erected trading posts or "factories" on the Pacific Coast. Here they ran headlong into Russia's fur posts on the seacoast of California. In a few years' time, John Jacob Aster, the head of that company, bought out other companies trading and trapping in the West and in 1827 consolidated this organization under the name of the American Fur Company. Its operations were concentrated in the region of the Rocky Mountains. Strong expeditions of trappers were sent to the Pacific Coast, and more and more widespread operations were required as the beaver was exterminated from the more accessible and heavily trapped streams. After the middle of the nineteenth century, the fur trade became more scattered as to control, and many small independent operators, such as the "Mountain Men," put an end to the virtual monopolies of the American Fur Company and the Hudson's Bay Company. The trappers, who had penetrated deep into the mountains of the West and traveled the courses of the rivers, especially the Missouri, the Mississippi, and the Columbia, became guides for the wagon trains settling the West. They also became scouts and hunters for the Army as it conquered one Indian tribe after another.

The great fur trapping companies no longer ply their romantic and adventurous business, because the settling of the West removed these frontiers, the forests, and much of the fur-bearing wildlife. The fur trade today depends more and more upon the breeding and raising of these animals on a commercial scale. In general, the pelts from these ranch-raised animals are more uniform than the wild pelts brought to the market by widely scattered trappers, many of whom are Indians or half-breeds. In the United States, many farmers add to their income by winter trapping. Beavers are once more trapped legally in several of our mountainous states, including New York and Pennsylvania.

FUR TRAPPING

American furs are **prime,** or at their best, during the winter months. During December, January, and February, the fur is thicker, longer, heavier, and more free from imperfections, because nature provides this extra protection during the coldest weather. Pelts obtained at this time are at their best and command the highest prices.

Game wardens and forest rangers in national parks and forests permitting trapping enforce the observance of closed seasons to trapping, partly to protect wildlife from over-trapping or even from extinction and partly to prevent poor skins from appearing on the market. **Unprime** skins obtained during the closed season may be thin, and the fur sheds easily. Trappers are forbidden to use poison, because poison produces fever in the animal, and this, in turn, has a physiological effect on the skin and fur, causing the latter to fall out or shed.

Trapping is generally done by setting out **trap-lines.** A trap-line is simply a route often several miles in length along which traps are set at places where the game is most likely to be found, such as near water holes and in game trails. The trapper may have several of these lines covering territory licensed to him, but each one must be visited frequently to prevent hunting animals from devouring his catch. Most traps are made of steel. The toothed jaws of these traps cause much suffering and a lingering death to the catch. Improved and more humane types of traps are now available, even these must be visited frequently so as to reduce the time of suffering. Wooden traps are too bulky for use in the northern territories, where long lines are used; but they are very effective for small-scale trapping and are more humane. Snares and dead falls are rarely used today.

MARKETING OF FURS

The fur trader is rarely far from the trappers themselves, even in sparsely settled northern Canada. Like the trappers, these traders may be representatives of some of the large fur trading companies or independent operators who plan to sell their pelts at a profit.

In whatever part of the world a pelt is obtained, no matter how remote, the skin will come to one of the great fur markets of the world. These markets are creations of geography and are cities where large collections of skins from all over the world are gathered together and sold at public auction at stated times. The market may owe its existance to the fact that the city is a great distributing point and a center of population and industry. It may be far from the source of any of the pelts collected there. New York and London are the principal markets of this type. On the other hand, the market city may be located in a great fur country, and because of its distribution facilities, such as navigable waterways or radiating railroads, it is a natural collecting point. St. Louis and Montreal represent this class, and at these cities, the trappers and traders can bring their pelts from the mountains, plains, and streams. These four cities are the **"Big Four"** of the fur world. In each of these cities, many public auction companies sell pelts from all over the world, and private companies conduct the private sale of the pelts they have collected.

London is the oldest and greatest fur market of the world, and until the newer markets achieved prominence, the volume of pelt sales there was a basis for estimating the world supply of pelts, and its auction prices determined the fur prices throughout the world. The Hudson's Bay Company, Canada's principal collector of furs, once monopolized the North American pelts auctioned in this market, but today American furs come from many companies and are collected with pelts brought from abroad. Russia, Siberia, and China were the sources of many fine furs, but these do not now reach the markets of the Western world in great abundance. The Hudson's Bay Company prices even today are the standard by which the offerings from other sources are judged.

The first public auction of skins to be conducted in London occurred in the winter of 1671 in a public tavern. Several lots of beaver skins were the offering, and the bidding was closed not by the auctioneer's hammer, as today, but by the candle. The bidding on a lot of pelts continued as a candle burned and ended when the flame erased a mark previously made in the wax.

The winter sales, especially the March sale, account for the greatest number of skins. These sales attract fur brokers from all over the world, and the active competition of so many diverse interests prevents price fixing by any small but powerful group. The open market thus afforded causes traders to send their furs from all over the world. It is not uncommon for pelts to travel thousands of miles to London, there to be sold and then returned to the country of origin.

Montreal, nearly as old a fur center as London, was for many years a collecting point for the London and New York markets. In recent years, particularly with the increased trapping in Canada in the last 20 years, it has so greatly added to and improved its fur-dyeing and dressing facilities as to be ranked as one of the "Big Four" markets. Its choicest furs are disposed of directly to the world market. The powerful Hudson's Bay Company is being pressed by the French concern, Revillon Fréres, and also by the Harmony Company of Labrador.

The curtailment of trade with England during the periods of the two World Wars added to the prestige of the New York and St. Louis markets. Our domestic production and that from Canada naturally were marketed here, and large valuable shipments of pelts came from Australia, Japan, Kamchatka, and Siberia. The importance of the United States' markets was presaged by the Northern Pacific Sealing Convention of 1911, but the trade conditions of 1914–

1918 materially accelerated their growth. This treaty, signed by the United States, Russia, Great Britain, and Japan, prohibited **Pelagic** or open-sea sealing north of 30° north latitude for 15 years. The control by the United States of the seal breeding grounds, the Pribilof Islands in the Bering Sea, has afforded further protection and greatly increased the number of northern seals. Conservationists were greatly excited when, in 1955, several sea otters were seen off the coast of California. This animal, the source of the fabulous Russian otter pelts, was believed to be extinct after its ruthless slaughter during the middle of the 1880's.

St. Louis was, from the first, the frontier fur trading post, and its importance has greatly increased. New York owes its importance as a fur market to its vast transportation facilities, its merchants, and its wealth and industry. New York is the American center for fur dyeing and dressing, concentrated in a small 10-block area along 8th Avenue and between 27th and 35th Streets. The improvement of American dyes and the importation of skilled fur dressers from countries controlled first by Fascists and now by Communists have brought to New York the fur-dressing business formerly sent to Leipzig and other European cities by American fur dealers.

FUR TREATING

Just as the special treatments undergone by the textile fibers bring life and beauty to the woven fabrics, further treatments bring out the luster and beauty of furs. Many pelts are pleasing neither to the eye nor the nose when the trapper brings them to market.

Oddly enough, the fundamental steps through which pelts are processed have changed but little throughout recorded history. Machinery and modern tools have refined these steps, but they remain the same in principle.

First—the flesh and fat must be scraped away with a sharp-edged knife.
Second—the pelt is made soft and pliable by means of brine treatment. This turns the pelt into leather.
Third—the fur itself is finished by dyeing and other treatments.

The pelts as received by the fur dresser are dry and hard as boards and are commonly turned inside out as drawn from the animal. Usually the trapper has scraped off the fat with a heavy knife, so that the skin will dry as rapidly as possible.

If no further scraping is required, the skin is softened by an immersion in a brine bath or chemical treatment. Usually ten to twelve hours are sufficient to make the pelt soft.

The fur and pelt are given a drying and cleaning with maple sawdust in a large rotating wooden drum. These drums are about seven feet in diameter, and around the interior periphery are baffles which tumble the pelts. The tumbling and rolling of the pelts through the sawdust dry and cleans both skin and fur.

Fig. 23-1 Removing fat from skins: The fat or blubber on the inner surface of the skin of the Alaska Seal must be scraped away completely. (*Courtesy of Fouke Fur Company.*)

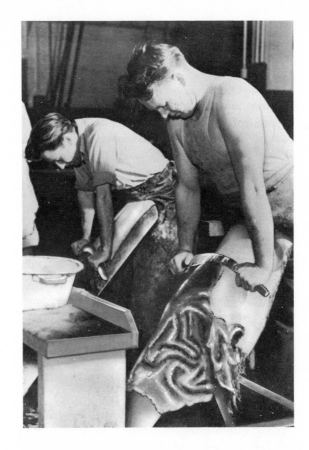

From the drum, the pelts are moved to the cage, which is similar to the drum but has wire netting instead of baffles. This shakes the sawdust out of the fur as the cage rapidly revolves. In some plants, the sawdust falls to the floor; in others the small particles are drawn off by an exhaust fan.

The small pelts, such as muskrats, moles, squirrels, and ermines, are not dried in the drum and cage but are rapidly whirled in a centrifuge. The pelts are placed in a cylindrical basket which revolves at such high speed that the moisture is thrown out through small holes in the outer surface. This type of hydro-extractor is much the same as that used in drying clothes in a laundry.

The next step is that of **fleshing,** or removing the remaining traces of flesh and fat. Whether this is done by machine or by hand, it requires great care lest a valuable pelt be ruined. The common practice is to flesh by machine skins which are being cured flat. The knife is circular in shape and revolves rapidly but is braced to prevent any vibration. The operator holds the pelt in both hands and presses it lightly against the whirling blade at the proper angle to slice off the fat without damage to the skin. The large knife used in hand fleshing is about 27 inches long and is fastened to the bench on which the operator sits. The pelt is drawn across the fine edge of this knife, and the flesh and fat are sliced off.

The pelt must now be **leathered.** Other terms for this process are **kicking** and **tramping** and suggest the arduous methods once used and which are still said to be superior to the quicker methods of today. The pelts are first dried and then dampened uniformly with a sponge or cloth. A small amount of fat is rubbed in. Dressers have their own ideas as to what fat composition is best, but almost any type from bacon fat to rancid butter will do. The Indians use bacon grease or the fat from salt pork and actually do tramp the skins. The greased pelts are piled in a tub, and the operator walks on them in his bare feet for hours. As the top pelt is lifted out, it is stretched and worked along the edge of the tub or barrel or some other smooth, hard surface, while the succeeding pelt is thoroughly tramped. The skins become softer and finer the longer they are stretched and manipulated.

The modern machine tramper duplicates the pedal method as closely as possible. A pulley arrangement raises and lowers iron columns, on the base of each of which is a rough shoe of wood and iron. These shoes both tread and kick the pelts piled in the spherically-ended receptacle. The skins are stretched by the motion of the shoe. The leathering operation varies in severity and length according to the fineness of the skin.

A second two-hour scouring in the drum and cage is necessary to clean the pelts after leathering.

Often hard spots are found in these softened pelts. These are removed by shaving with a heavy, flat-bladed knife.

Thus far, no great attention has been paid to the fur. A steel comb is used to comb out the matted fur and to remove burrs. A quick scouring in the drum with clean sawdust leaves the fur ready for dyeing if the fur is to be dyed.

DYEING FURS

It is said that the dyeing of furs dates from the Babylonian period, but technicians and scientists are still seeking improvements in the art of obtaining permanent, glossy, deep colors. The finer the fur, the more care must be exercised. The fur and skin may both be dyed; or the ends of fur may be lightly blended and made uniform in color with a brush lightly drawn over it; or the skin may be dyed so as to make it show less prominently where the fur is thin. The **blending** is applied to mink and other furs if a number of skins are to be matched for a coat. Blending is used to deepen the tone of the fur. The term may not be used as a differentiation from any other tip-dyeing operation, according to the Fur Products Labeling Act (amended May 15, 1961). Furs cannot stand the high temperatures and the hot liquids used in textile dyeing.

All skins except muskrat are fully leathered and cured before dyeing. The

Fig. 23-2 Fur Seal dyeing: Alaska sealskins are often washed and dyed by hand. It is necessary that the skins be firmly held to prevent streaking and wrinkling. (*Courtesy of Fouke Fur Company.*)

dark pelts of muskrat are used in their natural state, but the light-brown rat pelts are made into "Hudson Seal-dyed Muskrat." Muskrat pelts are leathered for twelve hours, fleshed, and hung to dry for two days before dyeing. Much of the cost of the heavy-furred, deep-black Hudson seal-dyed furs is based on the many operations of curing, dyeing, and plucking through which they must go.

Unchaining or **plucking** is the removal of the coarse hairs which conceal the beauty of the more delicate fur beneath in such pelts as otters, seals, beavers, muskrats, and nutrias. The skins are put in a hot room, the temperature of which is known to be the proper one to loosen most effectively the unwanted coarse hair without damage to the skin. The skin is placed on a wooden block, and the hairs are plucked out while the pelt is hot.

COMBINING PELTS

The techniques of combining pelts to form a coat can only be mastered after years of practice. They vary somewhat for the different animal skins and with various fur cutters. Skins are lengthened or widened, and defects are removed by skillful cutting and adjusting. The elasticity of the cured pelts makes this possible.

Separate skins are blended and combined to form a coat by skillful workmen. It is customary to use the finest skins in the front, back, and collar of a coat and to use progressively less perfect but well blended skins until the bottom of the coat is reached. Skins, especially the more perishable ones, are cut in a zig-zag pattern and sewn together in such a way that all the strain does not bear in one direction. Pelts are backed with cloth sewed to or glued onto the under side in order to strengthen the coat.

Two operations for enhancing the value of furs are **pointing** and **taping.** Pointing is the practice of planting with a needle silvery badger hairs half-way through the skin of a lower-grade fox skin and gluing them in place. A pointed fox fur may be as beautiful as a genuine silver fox, but it is not a real silver fox. Sometimes a very full-haired pelt may be taped to make it larger in size. The pelt is cut into long narrow strips, and a tape inserted between pelt strips. Leather strips may be used instead of tape. This weakens the pelt and may show when the fur is brushed or blown aside, but it may be used in muffs or in fur trimming where no great wear or strain is to be imposed.

THE USES OF FUR

Furs are used both for warmth and adornment. Today, fashion dictates furs in the summer as well as in the winter. Summer styles are usually very short coats, capes, or neck pieces, and utilize light-colored and shorter-haired types. The winter coat may be of almost any type of pelt. The cost depends on the type and quality of the skin, the coat length, the perfection of matching pelts, and other qualities of coat finish and construction. Few furs other than racoon are worn by men unless it be for a collar of lamb or muskrat. (The racoon coat was virtually a uniform for the college student in the 1920's.) The winter of 1962–63 brought a widespread use of fur pelts of mink, beaver, nutria, and rabbit as inner liners of cloth coats, with the fur facing the body of the wearer.

Fur-trimmed hats, coats, suits, and dresses are always appealing to women. In 1961, fur-trimmed sweaters were very popular. These trimmings vary widely in quality and workmanship. The popularity of certain furs, such as silver fox, squirrel, coney, beaver, and dyed muskrat is fairly constant; for most others it varies from season to season.

Other applications of fur are in blended fabrics, hats, slippers, gloves, rugs, robes, toys, and children's coats and muffs.

CLASSIFICATION OF FURS

According to Bachrach,[1] the following classification affords a good way to group the common peltries:

[1] Max Bachrach, *Furs* (New York: Prentice-Hall, 1946).

I. Rodents
    A. Water (Beaver, muskrat, nutria)
    B. Land (Rabbit, hare, marmot, burunduki, squirrel, chinchilla)

II. Felines
    A. True cats (Leopard, ocelot, European wildcat, house cat)
    B. Lynx (all varieties of lynx, American wildcat)
    C. Asiatic civet and European genet cat

III. Canines
    A. Chinese dog
    B. Wolf (under many names and from many countries)
    C. Jackal
    D. Fox (many varieties, usually named by color)

IV. Weasels
    A. Water varieties (Otter, mink, and kolinsky)
    B. Land varieties
        1. Marten, sable, and fisher
        2. Weasel, ermine, and fitch
        3. Wolverine
        4. Badger
        5. Skunk and American civet

V. Hoofed
    A. Lamb (Persian, karakul, broad tail, and krimmer)
    B. Kid
    C. Pony
    D. Camel (Guanaco)

VI. Miscellaneous
    A. Racoon-bear family (Racoons of all species)
    B. Pouched family (Opossum, Australian phalanger)
    C. Seal (Fur seal, hair seal)
    D. Mole
    E. Monkey

The following table shows a rough classification of the more common furs.

THE BUYING OF FURS

Formerly, there was a vast collection of misleading "private" names for many of our furs. Rabbit skins, being both abundant and cheap, led in this practice, and dishonest dealers sold it as every fur, even luxury mink. It was in the interest of legitimate processors and dealers, as well as the public, that the FTC adopted Trade Practice Rules in 1938, and the 82nd Congress passed a bill regulating the description and sale of fur products in 1951. The Federal Trade Commission issued the Rules and Regulations under this Act and, in 1961, an amended regulation.

TABLE 23-1 / COMMON FURS

Correct Term	Family	Description	F.T.C. Rules	Durability	Price	Uses
Astrachan	Lamb	Formerly Karakul lambs from Russia; term not now used. (See lamb)	Term not used in fur trade.	—	—	—
Badger	Weasel	Light cream or yellowish under fur, long black and white overhair. From North America, Europe, and Asia.		Good	Medium	Trimming of sport coats and pointing black furs.
Bear	Bear	Black and brown bear skins. Best from northern Canada.		Good	Medium	Warm coats for men, and robes and rugs.
Beaver Sheared beaver	Rodent	Rich fur from brown to tan. Guard hairs plucked. May be sheared to lighten weight and reduce matting.		Good	High	Sport coats, muffs, trimming and hats.
Broad tail	Lamb	Prematurely born or still-born Karakul or "fat tail" lambs. Lustrous, moire-patterned, uncurled hair. Delicate pelts.	Only young of Karakul can be described as "Broad tail."	Low	High	Coat and dress trimming.
Broad tail (processed)	Lamb	Argentine "Lincoln" lamb dressed, sheared, and dyed to simulate "Broad tail."	Must be stated if dyed to simulate.	Low	Medium	Coat or trimming.
Burunduki	Rodent	Rough, tawny, striped pelt. Related to chipmunk. Russian and Chinese best.		Poor	Low	Trimming.
Calf	Hoofed	Natural or dyed skins used as substitutes for pony. Sometimes sheared and dyed to simulate leopard.	Must be labeled if simulating other pelts.	Low	Fair	Coats for sports wear.

Name	Type	Description	Comments	Wearing quality	Price	Uses
Caracul (Natural Caracul) (Dyed Caracul) (Dyed Russian Caracul) (Dyed Chinese Caracul)	Lamb	Caracul lamb is the young of the fat-rumped sheep. The hair is longer and more curly than the Karakul. Russian Caracul is coarser than the silkier Chinese Caracul.	Caracul may be used only to describe the Caracul sheep or lamb. If fur is dyed, it must be so labeled.	Fair to Low	Medium to Low	Coats and trimming for dressy coats.
Cat (domestic)	Feline	Best skins from Holland and Belgium. Black is most valuable.		Low	Low	Trimming for children's coats.
Chinchilla	Rodent	Dense silky fur of slate blue color. Almost extinct rodent found on western slopes of the Andes. Now widely grown for market in U.S.		Poor	High	Dress and evening wraps.
Civet cat (American)	Weasel	Neither a civet nor a cat but a small skunk with narrow lyre-shaped white stripes.	Incorrect term; should be called "dipped" or natural skunk.	Low	Medium	Short coats and trimming.
Dyed Chinese civet cat	Cat	Dark greenish-gray, spotted fur of coarse texture. Usually is dyed.	Not a skunk as sometimes described.	Fair	Medium to Low	Trimming.
Coney or Rabbit Seal-dyed coney Beaver-dyed coney likewise nutria-, lapin-, chinchilla-, or galapin-dyed coney	Rodent	Best grades with heavier fur and larger skins were from Australia and New Zealand. Usually trimmed and dyed to resemble other furs. Best skins dyed to resemble Hudson-seal or beaver. Poorer ones dyed and sheared to produce *lapin* or *galapin*. Disease has almost wiped out Australian market.	Must be labeled Seal-dyed coney (or rabbit). Beaver-dyed coney (or rabbit). Terms beaverette, sealine, French seal, nutriette, etc., are not permitted.	Fair to Poor	Low	Coats for general wear and for trimming of all kinds.

TABLE 23-1 / COMMON FURS (continued)

Correct Term	Family	Description	F.T.C. Rules	Durability	Price	Uses
Ermine or Stoat (Siberian ermine) (Russian ermine) (Dyed ermine) (White weasel) (Dyed weasel) (Natural weasel) (Manchurian ermine) etc.	Weasel	Very dense, short, silky fur in white or brown. Best grades of white are from Russia and Canada. More southerly countries produce white to brown colors. Manchurian is yellow and usually dyed.	Only the true geographical source can be stated. If dyed to simulate, this must be stated. White weasels have thinner fur than white ermines. "Ermiline" or dyed coney are improper terms.	Fair to Poor	High to Medium	Dress and evening wraps, trimming, muffs, and scarfs.
Fisher (Black marten) etc.	Weasel	Rich dark brown; guard hairs are black. From Canada.	If tipped, must be labeled.	Good	Medium	Trimming and scarfs.
Fitch	Weasel	Russian fitch is white with black guard hairs; European is yellow.	Must be stated if dyed.	Fair to Good	Medium to Low	General wear and trimming.
Fox Arctic or blue	Dog	Arctic fox clear white soft dense pelt. Long silky guard hair. Blue-dyed fox is a sport breed or may be actually a blue-dyed white fox.		Fair	High	Scarfs, wraps and trimming.
Silver fox		Prized for the silver hairs for which this sport of the red breed has been bred. Character, pattern, and denseness of silver hairs determines price. Fur is blue-black. Classed as full silver, ¾, ½, ¼, or slightly silver. *Pointed* fox is a less silvered pelt with badger hairs pointed in. Best silvers are from northern countries.	"Pointed" must be labeled.	Fair	Medium to High	Jackets, scarfs, evening wraps, trimming, etc.

Name	Description	Designation		Value	Uses
Cross fox	A sport breed of red fox and silver fox having a deeper color, its value depending on the character of the dark cross pattern on the back of the neck. Far northern countries.		Fair	Medium	Trimming, scarfs, wraps, etc.
Gray or Virginia fox	Clear, gray, soft fur is best grade; may be dyed various shades of blue. United States only producer.	"Dyed Gray Fox" is correct designation.	Poor	Medium	Trimming.
Red fox (natural)	Many grades. Best has dense soft fur with long, silky guard hairs; color strong and lustrous. World-wide distribution.		Fair to Poor	Low to High	Scarfs, trimming, wraps, and jackets.
(dyed)	Color red to yellow. Paler and duller shades have coarser fibers and may be dyed red, blue, or black.	State "dyed," "tipped," "pointed," etc.	Fair to Poor	Medium	Trimming, scarfs, and wraps.
Kit or Kilt fox	Small, soft-furred desert fox, yellow in color. May be dyed.	If "dyed," must state.	Poor	Low	Sports wear trimming.
Platinum fox	A rare sport of the silver fox breed crossed with the Arctic fox. A full silver guard hair pattern over a soft, thick, platinum gray under fur. Usually some white markings on neck and legs.		Fair	High	Scarfs and wraps.
White or Polar fox	All hair pure white, thick and silky. Best in far north countries and is bluish in lower latitudes.	If "dyed," must state.	Fair	High	Scarfs, wraps, expensive trimming.

TABLE 23-1 / COMMON FURS (continued)

Correct Term	Family	Description	F.T.C. Rules	Durability	Price	Uses
Galyak (Dyed Galyak)	Lamb (Hoofed)	Prematurely or new-born Persian or Caracul lamb, kid, or pony. Hair thin, pattern flat. Skin tender.	If "dyed," must state. Term "natural" permitted if not finished to simulate other furs.	Low	Low	Trimming, coats.
Guanaco or dyed Guanaco or Guanaquito	Camel (Hoofed)	Related to vicuna. Long soft wool of reddish shade. Dyed to simulate fox. South America.	State if "dyed." "Vicuna" incorrect.	Medium to Low	Medium	Trimming, short coats, and wraps.
Hare	(see coney or rabbit)					
Japan or China mink / Dyed Kolinsky	Weasel (Kolinsky)	Silky, short hair of yellow to light brown. Dyed to simulate American mink. Best Asiatic mink.	Should be designated.	Fair	Medium	Trimming and coats.
Kid / Natural or Dyed Chinese Kidskin / Dyed Indian Kidskin / Moire Kidskin	Goat (Hoofed)	Young of the goat family. Chinese is best type. Hair flat or almost flat; finest has moire pattern. Longer-haired types used for trimming. (Note: kidskin has waves; lamb has curls).	"Caracul" kid is improper term.	Low	Medium to Low	Flat types in coats, others in trimming.
Kolinsky	(see Japan mink)					
Krimmer / Natural Krimmer or Krimmer-dyed lamb	Lamb (Hoofed)	Related to Karakul lamb but with open, circular curl instead of locked, tight curl of Persian. Gray fibers of low luster.	State "dyed" when dyed. White lambs from China and India may be dyed to imitate Krimmer.	Fair to Good	Medium	Coats for sport wear, trimming, etc.
Lapin	(see coney)					

Fur	Family	Characteristics	Labeling	Durability	Price	Uses
Leopard; Somali leopard; Asmara or Abyssinian leopard; Indian leopard; Chinese leopard	Cat	Small, short-haired, and rosette-marked. Larger pelt, less marked. Heavier. Less distinct marking and blotchy.	Baby leopard incorrect. Geographical origin must be correct.	Fair	Medium to High	Coats and trimming for sports and dress wear.
Snow leopard		Long, light, spotted fur.		Poor	Medium	Sport wear.
Leopard cat or spotted cat		Sheared South American spotted cat.		Poor	Medium	Trimming for sports wear. Jackets.
Lynx; Natural lynx; Dyed lynx; Lynx cat; Wild cat	Cat	Long, spotted, soft fur with white belly and yellow back. Reddish brown, spotted fur. Short, flat, red brown fur.	If "dyed" must state.			Sport coats and trimming.
Marmot; Mink-dyed marmot; Dyed marmot	Rodent	Best grades have straight, lustrous hair. (*Suslik* resembles marmot)	"Marmink" is incorrect.	Fair to Poor	Low	
Marten; American marten; Tipped marten; Blended marten	Weasel (Marten species)	Dense, full-furred, and with long silky guard hairs. Resembles sable. Blue-black-brown to reddish brown.	State "blended" or "tipped" if so.	Fair	Medium	Scarfs, wraps, and trimming for dress and general wear.
Hudson Bay sable or Canadian sable				Fair	Medium	
Baum marten		European: yellow-brown fur, long silky guard hair.		Fair	High	
Stone marten		White-gray under fur; dark brown guard hair.		Fair	Medium	
Mink; Natural American mink; Blended American mink; Eastern mink; Labrador mink	Weasel	Best grades dense, lustrous dark brown fur and lustrous guard hair. Eastern Canada and northeastern U.S. pelts best. Heavier pelts more durable but less beautiful. Pale skins may be blended.	State "dyed" or "blended," if so. Correct geographical origin must be given if mention is made.	Good	High	Coats, wraps, muffs, trimming for general wear.

TABLE 23-1 / COMMON FURS (continued)

Correct Term	Family	Description	F.T.C. Rules	Durability	Price	Uses
Mink Gills		Parts of pelts worked into herring-bone pattern.	As above.	Fair	Medium	As above.
Japanese mink Chinese mink		(see Japanese mink) (" ")				
Russian mink		Thin, lustrous fur with long guard hair. Flatter surface than best American types.	Correct origin must be stated.	Fair	Medium	As above.
Mole Tipped mole Dyed mole	Unclassified	Soft, velvet-like fur. Usually taupe to dark gray to black. Skin tender and light weight.	State "dyed" if so. "Tipped" or "dipped" mole accepted by trade usage.	Poor	Medium	Trimming and dressy wraps or coats.
Monkey	Unclassified	Best African grades have long, black, glossy hair. Dyed blue-black.	Must state if "dyed" to simulate.	Fair to Good	Medium to Low	Trimming; whole skins may be used for coats.
Muskrat (Musquash) Natural brown muskrat Golden sides muskrat Blended muskrat Natural black muskrat	Rodent	Yellow-brown to gray-brown. Heavy under fur and long guard hairs in best northern states grades. Color phase of brown muskrat.	If dyed to simulate must state.	Fair to Good	Medium to Low	For sports and casual coats.
Silver belly muskrat Dyed silvertone muskrat		Usually from light-colored bellies of brown muskrats. Skin tender.	"Silvered" or "Silvertone" incorrect.	Fair to Good	Medium to Low	
Hudson seal-dyed muskrat		Sheared and dyed to resemble Alaska seal skin. Heavier and fuller furred skins selected.	"Hudson seal," "Seal," "Sealskin," and "Mink" incorrect.	Fair to Good	Medium to Low	General and dress wear, coats, and trimming.
Mink-dyed muskrat		Dyed and blended to simulate mink.		Fair to Good	Medium to Low	Sport coats.

Fur	Family	Description	Notes		Warmth	Use
Nutria or Coypu Rat	Rodent	South American rodent resembling beaver; fur short; tends to mat when wet. Usually used in light-brown shade. Now abundant in lower Mississippi River.	"Nutriette" is incorrect term for nutria-dyed and processed rabbit.	Fair	Medium	Sport and casual coats and trimming.
Ocelot	Cat	Small South American wildcat; dark irregular spots and ovular rings on tan fur. Bright fur is best grade.		Fair to Poor	Medium	Sport coats and trimming.
Opossum — Pouched Family American opossum / Dyed American opossum		Natural whitish-gray to black with long black guard hair; coarse fuzzy under fur. May be dyed to simulate skunk.	State if dyed or tipped.	Fair to Poor	Medium to Low	Coats and trimming.
Australian opossum (Phalanger)		Soft, smooth steel-blue-gray to yellow-gray under fur.	Actually not opossum, but trade term; really phalanger.	Fair	Medium to Low	Trimming.
Dyed Australian ring-tail opossum		Small, taupe-gray with rusty under fur; some have ringed tail; used natural or dyed brown.		Fair	Medium to Low	Trimming.
Otter — Weasel (Large Species)		World-wide distribution of various species.				
Sea Otter		Nearly extinct. Deep blue-black to dark brown with little white hairs mixed in.	Geographical origin must be true. "Kamchatka Beaver" is incorrect for Otter.	Good	High to Medium	Trimming and sport coats.
North American		Best grades are glossy, dense blue-black to brown fur.				
South American		Coarser, shorter fur than North American; usually dark brown. Very short-furred are "Ariannas."				
Asiatic and African		Coarser, shorter brown fur.				

TABLE 23-1 / COMMON FURS (continued)

Correct Term	Family	Description	F.T.C. Rules	Durability	Price	Uses
Persian lamb	Lamb	One of the fur lamb type characterized as the "fat-tail" Karakul breed producing a patterned pelt with tight lustrous curls. Usually black or brown to gray. Light supple skin.	Statement "dyed" not required, but only peltries of this description are "Persians."	Good	Medium to High	Coats and trimming for general wear.
Bokhara Persian lamb		Best grades bred in Bokhara and Afghanistan. Pelts like "Persians."	Geographical origin must be accurately given.	Good	High	Coats and trimming.
Cross Persian lamb		Allied breeds from United States, Russia, South Africa, etc., may produce pelts as good as "Persians," but are usually more loosely curled, less lustrous, and the pattern is less beautiful.	"Half Persian" or "Persian" incorrect. "Cross Persian" is approved wording.	Fair	Medium	As above.
Persian lamb paw Pieced Persian lamb		Paws, tails, and pieces may be sewed together to make "Pieced Persian" garments.	Pieces must be stated.	Fair to Low	Medium	As above.
Pony Dyed pony Natural pony	Hoofed	Russian or Polish best grades having short, flat hair; moire patterned. Flatness of hair and beauty of pattern at premium.	Usually "dyed" black, gray, and brown; must state. If geographical origin is stated, must be correct.	Medium to Low	Medium to Low	Coats and trimming for general wear.
Rabbit	Rodent	(see Coney)				
Racoon Natural, dyed or blended American racoon	Racoon-Bear Family	Long fur with dense, wooly silver-tinted under fur. Guard hair long and black. Better grades are black and	State "Blended" if done to darken stripes. "Japan Cross Fox" im-	Good	Medium	Light-weight for coats; heavy for trimming.

Name	Description	Remarks			Uses
Asiatic racoon	silver rather than brown or red.	proper term for Asiatic racoon.			
Sable Weasel-Marten species	(see Marten)				
American sable or Hudson Bay sable					
Russian sable / Siberian sable / Dyed sable / Blended Russian sable / Chinese sable	Siberian is best grade. Color ranges downward from choice blue-brown to medium brown. Fur full and lustrous. Guard hairs silky and erect. May be sprinkled with white hairs. Chinese and Japanese sable local varieties.	State "Dyed" or "Blended" if such is case. Origin, if given, must be correct.	Fair	High	Coats and wraps, scarfs, jackets, and trimming.
Seal (Fur seal types) Unclassified / U.S. Government Alaska seal skin	Fur is dense, short, and soft. Guard hairs plucked out. Dyed brown or black. Alaska seal best.	Alaska seal bears U.S. government stamp. Use full name.	Good	High	Coats and trimming for general and dress wear.
Japanese seal (Hair seal types) / Tropical seal	Moire-patterned. Hair color dark brown to red-tan. No under fur. Usually dyed.	State "Dyed" or "Dipped" if so.	Poor	Medium to Low	Sport coats.
Hair seal / Dyed hair seal	No under fur. Hair black to white. Usually dyed.	Sometimes called "Cape of Good Hope" and "Lobos" seals if origin is true.	Poor	Medium to Low	Sport coats.
Skunk Weasel / Dyed skunk / Natural skunk	Best grade has dense blue-black under fur with long white guard hair. White stripes may be cut away or dip-dyed.	If dyed must be stated. State "Pieced" if so.	Good	Medium	Coats, jackets, trimming.
Natural spotted skunk	Known as American civet. Small, lyre-like white stripes.	"Civet cat" is incorrect.	Low	Medium	

TABLE 23-1 / COMMON FURS (continued)

Correct Term	Family	Description	F.T.C. Rules	Durability	Price	Uses
Squirrel Natural squirrel Siberian squirrel Dyed squirrel Pieced squirrel Squirrel Loche	Rodent	Siberian is best grade. Choice pelts are lustrous, soft, silky blue-gray and free from streaks. Poorer colors tend toward reddish cast. Squirrel Loche is belly of skin. Fine grays never dyed.	Only correct origin may be given. If dyed, must be stated.	Fair to Poor	High to Low	Coats, wraps, and trimming. Poorer grades dyed for linings.
Wolf Natural wolf Dyed wolf	Dog	Colors vary from brown to silver gray and black. Timber wolf is fullest furred and with longest overhair. Sometimes bleached to simulate lynx.	If dyed, must so state.	Fair to Good	Medium to Low	Trimming and jackets.
Dyed Chinese dog	Dog	Dense fur commonly dyed black or gray.	"Manchurian Wolf" incorrect term.	Good	Low	Trimming and jackets.
Wolverine	Weasel (Larger Species)	Coarse dark-brown fur with lighter brown sides.		Good	Medium	Trimming.

Source material.

1 "Selling Furs," *Good Housekeeping Magazine*, Bulletin No. 24, 1938.
2 Max Bachrach, *Selling Furs Successfully* (New York: Prentice-Hall, 1938.
3 "Money Management, Your Clothing Dollar" Household Finance Corporation, Chicago, Ill.

Fig. 23-3 Genuine fur pelts can be supple: So supple is the well-processed Alaska sealskin that a large pelt can easily be pulled through a napkin ring. (*Courtesy of Fouke Fur Company.*)

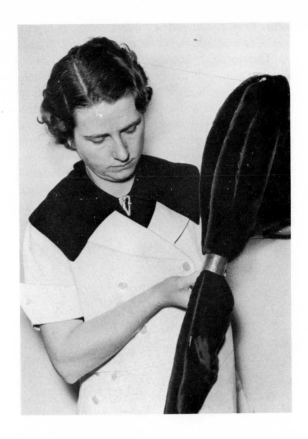

The true fur identity by name must be disclosed. If it is an imported skin or garment, the country of origin must be stated. Any degree or type of dyeing must be disclosed. If the article is made of portions of the pelt, such as sides, paws, bellies, or other waste, it must be stated, so that the customer will not be misled into the belief that the better portion of each pelt—the back—was used.

In the United States, all fur garments and the removable fur trimming from cloth coats or other apparel are subject to a 20 per cent luxury tax.

CARE OF FURS

Natural furs are more lovely but more fragile than their synthetic fiber imitations. The skin itself may be weak, as in cat, rabbit, and lamb skins. Exposure to heat and to a long period of dryness makes the skin brittle, due to loss of the natural oils. These oils must be replaced by the cleaner or fur conditioner. The outer hair and the softer under fur are subject to moth and carpet beetle damage and to wearing away and breakage from rubbing. The rough-textured automobile upholstery or seat-cover fabric is a common destroyer of fur garments from rubbing. They may become bald in the middle of the back or in the seat. Coats should never be put away wet or crushed in a crowded closet.

The storage of precious fur coats, stoles, or scarfs should be at a low temperature to avoid pelt drying. Most stores and dealers store furs in an insectproof, refrigerated vault after thorough cleaning. The same steps are used in this cleaning as in the final dressing of furs; namely, dust removal by blowing or gentle brushing, tumbling in a drum with hard maple wood flour to absorb grease and dirt, blowing to remove soiled sawdust, then cleaning and spotting in the manner most suitable to that fur. Generally, dry-cleaning solvent cleaning is frowned upon, because the solvents draw out the natural oils in the hair and pelt.

The fur-cleaning method is sometimes prescribed for the synthetic fiber fur-like garments. This, however, is not necessary if the cleaner knows how to clean synthetics.

the evaluation of textiles
for consumer use

The store laboratory received as a consumer complaint a light-blue acetate suit in which the shoulders of the jacket had become pink as the result of dry-cleaning. (This complaint pre-dated the dope or solution-dyed acetate.) The discoloration appeared to be the result either of gas-fading or of acid-fading of the dye, and the shoulder-pads obviously had something to do with the color alteration. When the jacket was opened and the shoulder pads examined, it was found that the cotton batting used as a padding had been made somewhat stiff and firm by means of spraying with a rubber-like latex. When it was dry-cleaned with a chlorinated hydrocarbon, the synthetic rubber latex gave off a small amount of free hydrochloric acid in sufficient quantity to acid-fade the light-blue dye to a pink. Through a series of favorable circumstances, the manufacturer came to the laboratory to look at this complaint, the seriousness of which could not be overestimated because it was from his new spring line. Upon viewing the laboratory test results, he immediately telephoned his factory and ordered the new shoulder pads out of the production line. "What should I do now?" he asked. "I have several million dollars worth of suits like this in stores throughout the country." When asked whether the shoulder pads and the dyestuffs in his suits had been tested for resistance to this kind of fading, he stated, with a somewhat surprised tone, "No, I have no time for testing in my operation. I have never had any of my materials tested for any kind of service whatever. I trusted the manufacturers of the fabric to supply me with the best goods; I can do no more."

The department store buyer and his customer are interested in the end-use item, the entire textile product. The many processing steps leading to the finished textile fabric which then, in turn, has been formed into the article for consumer use, are not subject to study by the retailer or the consumer. We have had reference to numerous textile test results in fibers and yarns, and in woven fabrics, in earlier chapters. The technical literature provides the textile industry with the necessary physical and chemical properties of new fibers as they are introduced into the market and with the effect of new finishes on fibers. Data are available on the differences in physical properties of yarns and fabrics, resulting from blending of two or more kinds of fibers together to form the yarn. The color fastness of the dyestuffs should have been determined at the time of application. All this information is of value to the textile customers of these suppliers of fiber, yarn, finish, dyestuff, and fabric. They are not of direct importance to the ultimate consumer, the customer of the retail store, unless there is premature failure in service. A garment is a complex structure composed of many textile parts, not only the base fabric of the garment itself, but the sewing thread, the trimming, the decorative yarns or materials; for the benefit of the consumer, it should be evaluated for consumer acceptance as a complete unit.

THE PROVING OF THE PARTS

It is vitally necessary that the basic properties of a new fiber be determined so as to gain some idea as to where in the textile picture this new fiber with its own combination of properties may best fit. Likewise, yarn properties should be of value to the textile weaver, for it may be blended, mechanically processed for bulkiness or stretching, or specially dyed. The term "textile product evaluation" is more appropriate than **textile testing** when referring to these operations and the study of the finished article. By **evaluation,** we mean that in addition to carrying out the specific fabric property tests, the laboratory technologists endeavor to weigh the various results in terms of their intricate influence one upon the other; from this composite picture, they try to estimate the suitability of the fabric performance for the end-use product, as well as the workmanship and other features of the product itself in terms of its potential consumer satisfaction. In other words, the data are evaluated in light of the previous experience of the laboratory with this and other textile materials for similar types of end-use items. Judgment and experience are necessary, in addition to technical competence and accuracy. Some garment manufacturers, especially in infants' and boys' and girls' wear, endeavor to have some of their products field- or use-tested by selected groups, so that the performance of the article in service can be compared with the laboratory test data. This is a measure of the ability of the technologist to forecast the potential use value in terms of laboratory figures. No laboratory tests exactly duplicate wear conditions for garments in service.

There is no such thing as an average wear value. For example, we have several abrasion or wear tests which have been adopted as standard procedures by the American Society for Testing Materials, but none exactly simulates consumer-use wear. How can they? Laboratory wear tests do not include the addition of grease and dirt stains which almost inevitably accompany worn garments in service. The kind of abrasion given fabrics by different wearers varies greatly. Elbow damage, wearing at the back, wearing in the seat, wearing around the cuffs of trousers, abrasion by women's handbags on the sides of skirts and jackets—all these vary from user to user. It would be absurd to think that any one abrasion test can give industry the entire answer. But they are all indicative of potential durability of the fabric.

STANDARDS AND TESTING

Faced with problems of selecting the best among several different dresses for a child, the customer may say, "Well, suppose I take the most expensive. That surely should be the best in serviceability." Similarly, she may select the more expensive of two water-repellent raincoats for herself as being probably the more water-resistant. Actually, price often has very little to do with the relative durability or serviceability of the items. In any assembly of products of varying price lines, there comes a point of maximum durability; then as the price continues to ascend, the durability may actually decrease as fineness and delicacy of material, amount of handwork in assembling the garment, or increased importance of fashion and neatness become of greater significance than wear and ordinary serviceability. A case in point is, of course, found in the case of bed sheets: Type 140 muslin, selling at a price between the Type 128 lightweight muslin and the more luxurious percales, is generally recognized as the utility product with greatest wear. Durability falls down or decreases as the fineness of the fabric in the percales becomes more important than resistance to wear. It is more guess than fact perhaps, but in our experience, we have concluded that in a group of articles selling at different prices, the one giving the greatest amount of serviceability is somewhere around two-thirds of the way up the price scale. Above it, additional fabric fineness often means somewhat less durability.

Another area in which customers sometimes lose themselves is in the matter of thread or yarn count. Surely, the higher the count, or number of yarns per square inch, the greater the serviceability. Again, reference to the example of bed sheets should be convincing that count is not the only factor. The count does not tell us the length of the individual filaments, to say nothing of the twist. Fiber composition does not guarantee any special degree of durability. We now know[1] the concentration of fibers present in the fabric, but we do not know the relative amounts of the two or more fiber types in the individual yarns.

Suppose the label states a breaking strength. Is breaking strength important to the ultimate consumer? The strength of a new fiber type, that is, its tenacity, is certainly significant in forecasting the usefulness of this material for textile

[1] Textile Fiber Products Identification Act, 1961.

use. Fabric breaking strength is a good engineering test on which a purchasing agent may depend as one of the factors influencing him in his selection of goods which he may use in making garments, slipcovers, tarpaulins, or some other textile product for which strength of material is really important. In consumer use, damage through a clean pull is very rarely found. Tearing strength is much more significant. The cotton fabric which has been given a resin treatment for wash-and-wear promotion has a higher breaking strength than the fabric going into garments without the resin treatment being applied, but the tear strength is often materially lowered in the wash-and-wear treated fabric because the fabric is now more brittle.

samples not uniform

Another complication is that tests are generally made on samples, and it is understood that the final product as shipped will be similar to the samples on which the tests have been made. They cannot be identical; textile products rarely are. We recognize the variations inherent in the natural fibers through growing conditions, exposures, harvesting problems, and the many machine operations required to prepare the natural fiber for use in a textile fabric. Reference has been made in the several chapters dealing with the man-made fibers to the need for blending of different batches in order to achieve as uniform a product as possible. It is similarity in service rather than identical performance toward which the technologist is constantly working. Individual yarns will differ in fiber arrangements and filament counts from place to place through the length of the yarn; blending of two or more fibers will give slightly different compositions everywhere through the yarn. Textile products by their very nature cannot be identically the same, yard after yard and batch after batch.

Even if it were possible to produce gray goods which were identical, the processing steps through which the fabric must go to make them acceptable to the consumer impose further differences. Successive treatments for water repellency are made as uniform as possible in the degree of protection of the fabric. Different dye lots will vary slightly in color, perhaps even in color durability. The effect of bleach on cotton filaments of greater maturity, of higher twist, and of greater fiber tenacity may not be as severe as the same concentration of bleach used on another cotton seemingly identical in every way. These questions are not intended to disillusion the student against testing of fabrics or their evaluation, but rather further to emphasize its importance, realizing that individual test values are of relative significance only and that the composite or over-all value is the main issue.

conflicting claims

Sometimes a customer may be further confused by the fact that comparing the "best value" listings of men's shirts, for example, will show one consumer goods rating agency as giving a vastly different order or performance for a dozen or more different shirt brand names when compared with the listing of another rating agency; or perhaps the label claims made by the department store or a mail-order house for its own brand of shirts seem at variance with the ratings appearing in the magazines to which the consumer subscribes. The point here is that all may be right. Results in tests are relative, and much depends then upon the order of importance habitually given by the various laboratories to individual test procedures. To one laboratory, the tear strength may be considered most important; to another, breaking strength may be primary; to a third, appearance, texture, and workmanship of the shirt may outweigh the factor of wear. In all the laboratories, the same tests have probably been carried out, but their order of significance through the years of experience of the laboratories may differ. Then, again, we have to face the ever-present bugaboo of the impossibility of having identical samples. Suppose, for example, that manufacturer "B" (the shirt was evaluated in all laboratories) had one shirt sample lot which was over-bleached. Laboratory results would show a lower breaking strength. On the other hand, that particular sample might have a higher rating than usual on the basis of its beautiful whiteness. The degree of quality control maintained by the manufacturer determines largely the uniformity of the rating of his products in laboratories year after year and the consistency of the popularity of his product among store customers. It may be consistently good or consistently bad, depending on whether his quality control is toward a fine value or toward a price item which may be so questionable in value as not to bear any brand name at all.

chaotic testing

Suppose the producer of each fiber type were permitted to test the strength of his products under the conditions most favorable to his product and, perhaps, most unfavorable to his principal competition. Knowing what we do of the moisture regain of fibers and fabrics and the effect of moisture on their strengths, would we not expect the cotton-goods producer to test cotton under conditions of high humidity, where cotton or average cotton is stronger than it is when dry and rayon is weaker? On the other hand, the rayon and acetate producers would undoubtedly prefer to test their materials as close to dryness as possible. If one synthetic fiber softens at around 220° F., whereas another will not soften until the temperature of 350° F. is reached, would not one expect the second manufacturer to say that all ironing tests should be made at temperatures in excess of 330–340° F., because "a hot iron is generally preferred by the consumer because it does a good job more rapidly than a cool iron"? If one fiber tends to elongate more slowly under the steady application of load, would we not expect the manufacturer of the more easily extended or stretched fiber to prefer that all breaking-strength tests be made at a relatively rapid rate of load application to which his fiber would adapt itself and the other fiber would tend to snap or break at a lower figure, simply because it was slower in adapting itself to the stretch rate?

Before textile test results can be depended upon, they must be standardized and performed under uniform conditions in all laboratories engaged in the evaluation of textile products. Tests having to do with the strength of fibers, yarns, or fabrics are customarily carried out under so-called standard conditions of temperature and humidity. These standards have been established by the American Society for Testing Materials (ASTM) and call for the temperature of 70° F. and a relative humidity of 65 per cent. The ASTM is recognized as the authority for all textile tests of physical properties, that is, of a strength and wear nature. Its sister organization, the American Association of Textile Chemists and Colorists (AATCC), is primarily concerned with test methods having to do with the chemical behavior of the textile product, including color fastness of the dyestuff and permanence of finish. Several of the test methods appear in the yearbooks of both organizations; furthermore, they confer jointly on the subject of test methods through Sectional Committee L-14 of the American Standards Association and cooperate in the formulation of the Commercial Standard CS-59, the revision of which has been under way for some time, since the last revision of this Commercial Standard for Textile Testing was in 1944.

There are no standard methods of laboratory evaluation for many of the esthetic properties which are first looked for by the consumer in the evaluation of textile products. Such properties, therefore, as hand, texture, draping quality, and similar beauty factors as yet have no standard laboratory test procedures. It is expected, however, that if a fabric successfully passes the evaluational tests under these existing standards of the technical societies and of the L-22 Textile Standard recently promulgated by the American Standards Association, these esthetic properties will persist for a reasonable period of time during the use-life of the product; that is to say, it will not vary greatly in hand, drape, or appearance after a reasonable number of washings and wearings.

The test or evaluation results provided by a private test method used by one mill, or by a single commercial testing laboratory, or by a store laboratory, have no real significance within the responsibilities of the technical societies in advancing the science of merchandising evaluation, not only in textiles but in any other kind of commodity. The technical society strives to develop simple procedures which simulate use conditions or those which experience shows can indicate with fair dependability the useful life of the product in the hands of the consumer. Having admitted that laboratory methods do not duplicate and perhaps fall short of simulating use conditions, nevertheless, the procedures, after having been tried and tested in many laboratories in order to determine their reproducibility and dependability, may finally be given a tentative approval in the yearbook of the Society, either the AATCC or the ASTM. After a few years of trial and error throughout the textile industry, the users of the testing procedure will then cast their ballot as to whether the method remains on the tentative listing or whether it can be adopted as a full standard testing procedure.

END-USE REQUIREMENTS

According to Stoll,[2, 3] the following table (Table 24-1) provides a classification of the end-use requirements of textile materials. The author then proceeds to fill into this table each characteristic the user would associate with each of the

TABLE 24-1 / THREE CATEGORIES OF CONDITIONS DETERMINING END-USE REQUIREMENTS OF TEXTILES

End Item	Environmental Conditions	Customer Preference
Apparel More than 50 major use groups with several hundred individual items	*Climatic* Hot-day (desert), hot-humid (jungle, temperate (warm to cool), wet-cold, cold-dry (arctic), high altitude	Preferences and tastes of customer and individual consumer
Household Textiles, Home Furnishing More than 20 major use groups	*Biological* Mold, fungus, insects	Economic and social position of consumer
Medical, Surgical, Sanitary Supply	*Mechanical* Terrain, vegetation, wind, dust, sand, abrasive rocks, snagging vegetation	Special physiological and psychological requirements of individual user
Military and Special Protective Textiles	*Chemical* Salt spray, smoke, smog, soot	Predispositions; allergies, idiosyncrasies
Industrial and Technical Textiles More than 50 major uses	*Sociological* Tradition, economy, fashion, jurisdiction	

From: *End-use Requirements vs. Material Properties of Textiles,* by R. G. Stoll, Res. & Dev. Report, Textile Series Report No. 83, Dept. of the Army, OQG (1953), p. 4.

nine categories. Under esthetic appeal (1.00) would fall first the characteristics pertaining to the eye under the general heading "appearance," given the classification number 1.10, to which are appended at least four sub-characteristics: texture, 1.11; color, 1.12; luster, 1.13; and translucency, 1.14. The next most important esthetic property is generally the feel or hand and draping quality, with classification number 1.20; associated with it would be the sub-characteristics, such as density, softness, stretchability, stiffness, resilience, contour (smooth

[2] R. G. Stoll, Chapter 10, "End-Use Requirements Versus Fiber Properties," in S. B. McFarlane (ed.), *Technology of Synthetic Fibers* (New York: Fairchild Publications, Inc., 1953), p. 256.

[3] R. G. Stoll, "End-Use Requirements Versus Material Properties of Textiles," Research and Development Report, Textile Series No. 83, Dept. of the Army, OQMG, U.S. Dept. of Commerce (1953), p. 5.

or rough), friction, warmth to touch, etc. The third esthetic appeal to be satisfied is that of odor and taste (1.30) or, more exactly, lack of odor and taste.

TABLE 24-2 / CLASSIFICATION OF END-USE
REQUIREMENTS OF TEXTILE MATERIALS

1.00 Aesthetic appeal	⎤ Functional characteristics
2.00 Ease of handling	⎜ determining:
3.00 Form stability	⎬ *Appeal*
4.00 Physiological requirements	⎜ *Suitability*
5.00 Special functional requirements	⎦ *Adaptability*
6.00 Retention of esthetic appeal	⎤ Characteristics determining:
7.00 Resistance to chemical degradation and disintegration	⎜ *Durability*
8.00 Resistance to mechanical fatigue and wear	⎬
9.00 Ultimate strength and resistance to fortuitous wear and tear	⎜ *Wear resistance* ⎦

Numbers 1.00 through 5.00 represent those requirements which determine if the material has the desired appeal and the proper suitability and adaptability. Numbers 6.00 through 9.00 are concerned with the durability and wear resistance of textiles in the widest sense of the terms.

Ease of handling and care (2.00) would include, under tailoring or garment-making quality, the various sub-characteristics contributing to the ease of handling of the material by the maker of the garment. It would include cleanliness and also launderability and cleanability with their sub-characteristics, most of them determinable by appropriate laboratory procedures.

Form stability would include, as 3.10, resistance to shrinkage in the various kinds of handling, cleaning, and wearing. It would also include wrinkle resistance, stretchability, and compressibility during various kinds of care and exposure.

physiological requirements

The physiological requirements (4.00) are generally consumer wants in an end-use item and would include factors contributing to comfort (4.10), retention of comfort after a reasonable period of service and cleaning (4.20), and water resistance or water absorbency, depending upon the end-use requirement of the textile product (4.30), that is, whether the item is a dish towel or a raincoat. The question as to comfort or one's tactile or bodily reaction to a textile material is affected by many fiber and textile properties, such as weight, touch, tendency to cling, heat transmission, water absorption, static electrical effects, and others of lesser significance. This is still a field of research worthy of the skill and technical knowledge of physicists, chemists, physiologists, and psychologists, to explain more fully why fabrics of one fiber are more comfortable than those of another or to determine why certain fiber lengths or degrees of fineness, when woven or knitted into certain fabric constructions, feel different to the wearer. Other research fields lie in the explanation of the effects of finishes and of dif-

TABLE 24-3 / CLASSIFICATION OF PROPERTIES RELATED TO END-USE REQUIREMENTS OF TEXTILE MATERIALS

A. FUNCTIONAL CHARACTERISTICS DETERMINING APPEAL—SUITABILITY—ADAPTABILITY

1.00 Esthetic Appeal

1.10 *Appearance*
1.11 Texture
1.12 Color
1.13 Luster
1.14 Translucency
1.20 *Hand and Drape*
1.21 Density—compact to open
1.22 Softness—soft to hard
1.23 Stretchability— stretchy to nonstretchy
1.24 Stiffness—stiff to pliable
1.25 Resilience—springy to limp
1.26 Contour—smooth to rough
1.27 Friction—harsh to slippery
1.28 Touch—warm to cold
1.30 *Odor and Taste*

2.00 Ease of Handling

2.10 *Tailoring Quality*
2.11 Sewability
2.12 Resistance to slippage and fraying
2.13 Ease of ironing and pressing
2.14 Shape retention
2.15 Resistance to marking
2.20 *Cleanliness*
2.21 Resistance to soilage and staining
2.22 Ease of spot removing
2.30 *Laundering and Cleaning*
2.31 Ease of washing and cleaning
2.32 Resistance to laundering and cleaning
2.33 Speed of drying
2.34 Ease of and resistance to ironing and pressing

3.00 Form Stability

3.10 *Resistance to Shrinkage in:*
3.11 Sponging
3.12 Pressing
3.13 Laundering
3.14 Cleaning
3.15 Humidity
3.20 *Crease Resistance*
3.21 Wrinkle resistance
3.22 Wrinkle recovery
3.23 Crease retention
3.30 *Stretchability (Uniaxial-Biaxial)*
3.31 Resistance to stretching
3.32 Recovery from stretching
3.40 *Compressibility*
3.41 Resistance to compression
3.42 Recovery from compression

4.00 Physiological Requirements

4.10 *Comfort Factors*
4.11 Weight
4.12 Drapability
4.13 Touch
4.14 Heat transmission by:
4.141 Conduction-convection
4.142 Radiation
4.143 Evaporation-convection
4.15 Absorption
4.16 Air and water vapor permeability
4.17 Static
4.18 Odor and taste, inherent and effected by perspiration and wearing
4.19 Dermatological congruity
4.20 *Retention of Comfort Requirements After:*
4.21 Laundering
4.22 Cleaning
4.23 Wearing and other service actions
4.30 *Water Resistance*
4.31 Absorption
4.32 Repellency
4.33 Impermeability

5.00 Special Functional Requirements

5.10 *Special Environmental Requirements*
5.11 Extreme climatic conditions
5.12 High altitude
5.13 Under water
5.14 Bactericidal properties
5.15 Insect-repellent properties
5.16 Proofness against gas and war chemicals
5.17 Protection against radiation
5.18 Fire resistance
5.19 Special camouflage characteristics
5.20 *Suitability for Special Industrial Requirements*
For example, adhesion with rubber, plastic coatings and synthetic resins; special degree of purity with regard to aging and catalytic action (free of metallic traces); special properties for industrial packings, as in bearings, fittings, etc.; special electrical properties; special filtering properties; dust proofness, translucency; resistance to special chemical and catalytic attacks; etc.
5.40 *Special Properties for Medical, Surgical and Sanitary Requirements*
For example, degree of purity, capacity of absorption, surface activity, antiseptic action, therapeutic properties

TABLE 24-3 / CLASSIFICATION OF PROPERTIES RELATED TO END-USE REQUIREMENTS OF TEXTILE MATERIALS (continued)

B. FUNCTIONAL CHARACTERISTICS DETERMINING DURABILITY—WEAR RESISTANCE

6.00 Retention of Esthetic Appeal	7.00 Resistance to Chemical Degradation and Disintegration	8.00 Resistance to Mechanical Fatigue and Wear	9.00 Ultimate Strength and Resistance to Fortuitous Wear and Tear
6.10 *Fastness of Color and Bleach*	7.10 *Laundering and Cleaning*	8.10 *Fatigue*	9.10 *Breaking Strength (Static) Dry, Wet and Under Other Service Conditions*
6.11 Wash fastness	7.11 Chemical degradation of the fiber material with normal use of detergents	Fatigue = Decrease of inherent resistance to wear, without causing actual fiber breakdown	9.11 Uniaxial tensile loading
6.12 Fastness to cleaning, dry and wet	7.12 Degradation (oxidation or reduction) as a result of too concentrated use of detergents and bleaching agents	Effect of:	9.12 Biaxial tensile loading
6.13 Fastness to pressing, dry and wet	7.13 Catalytic degradation	8.11 Stretching	9.13 Multiaxial tensile loading (bursting)
6.14 Lightfastness	7.14 Degradation through high temperature during washing, drying and pressing	8.12 Compression } Static and	9.14 Tearing strength
6.15 Resistance to gas fading	7.15 Damage by undissolved detergents	8.13 Complex mechanical actions (flexing etc.) } Dynamic	9.15 Resistance to crushing, puncture, shearing and cutting
6.19 Fastness to storage	7.20 *Resistance to Aging by Climatic Conditions*	8.20 *Moderate Wear*	9.16 Seam strength
6.17 Fastness to perspiration	7.21 Photochemical degradation	8.201 Shine	9.17 Knot strength and strength of splicings
6.18 Fastness to crocking	7.22 Fatigue from too high, too low or markedly variable humidity	8.202 Roughening	9.18 Adhesion resistance of coated and laminated fabrics
6.19 Fastness to storage	7.23 Degradation from extreme cold or hot climate	8.203 Pilling	9.20 *Impact and Ballistic Strength* Same condition as above, but at high speeds.
6.20 Fastness to weather	7.30 *Resistance to Deterioration by Microorganisms*	8.204 Threadbareness } Produced by:	9.30 *Fortuitous Destruction by Complex Mechanical Service Action such as:*
6.30 *Resistance to Spotting*	7.31 Fungi	8.205 Slight fraying	9.31 Crushing of the fabrics (in washing machine, extractor, mechanical dryers, and pressing)
6.31 Water	7.32 Bacteria	8.206 Seam failures	9.32 Cuts, tears and other mechanical damages from rough and defective places in washing machines
6.32 Perspiration	7.40 *Resistance to Aging by Other Chemical Service Actions*	8.21 Fabric against fabric abrasion	
6.33 Lime Soap	7.41 Perspiration	8.22 Abrasion against smooth surfaces	
5.34 Rust	7.42 Gases and vapors in the atmosphere	8.23 Internal abrasion by flexing, folding, stretching, compression	
6.35 Fungi and molds	7.43 Chemicals in connection with special technical and industrial end uses		
6.36 Others			
6.40 *Resistance to Mechanical Changes of Appearance*			
6.41 Marking			
6.42 Glaziness in pressing			
6.43 Shine in wear			
6.44 Roughening and pilling in washing and wearing			

6.45 Deformation of weave and texture by yarn slippage and snagging and snarling

6.50 *Retention of Hand and Drape*
6.51 Laundering
6.52 Cleaning
6.53 Wearing

7.44 Aging from presence of deleterious concomitant substances, for example, residues of acid, formation of acid by oxidation, autooxidation of oil, traces of metal, etc.

7.50 *Resistance to Chemical Disintegration*
7.51 Dissolving or hole formation by acids (in cellulose materials)
7.52 By alkalies (keratin materials)
7.53 By organic solvents
7.54 By stain removers and drugs
7.55 Damages by other dissolving chemicals

7.60 *Heat and Fire Resistance*
7.61 Degradation by heat
7.62 Softening temperature
7.63 Melting temperature
7.64 Decomposition temperature
7.65 Flammability
7.66 Afterglow

8.24 Mechanical wear by normal laundering and cleaning methods

8.30 *Severe Wear*
8.301 Runs in knitted fabrics
8.302 Fraying of edges, creases and folds
8.303 Hole formation by continued wear on localized areas and projections
8.304 Tears and breaks in worn areas
8.31 Abrasion against rough and harsh surfaces
8.32 Internal abrasion under high flexing, stretching, compression loads
8.33 Laundering damages by excessive mechanical surface and internal abrasion

9.33 Breaking of frozen fabrics by winding and flexing

9.40 *Resistance to Chewing by Insects*
9.41 Moths
9.42 Household insects
9.43 Termites
9.44 Mice and other animals

From *End-use Requirements vs. Material Properties of Textiles*, by R. G. Stoll, Res. & Dev. Rept., Textile Series Rept. No. 83, Dept. of the Army, OQG (1953), p. 6a.

ferences in the reactions of the subjective test personnel, the men, women, and children who wear these articles of clothing. The machine readings of some tests do not always agree with human experience.

special functional requirements

Special functional requirements are those one considers when moving from one environmental condition to another, thus requiring clothing of a different construction, weight, fiber, or finish for health, comfort, or long serviceability with minimum care. It is the kind of exposure which naturally affects the military forces more than the average citizen of the United States, whose maximum environmental or climatic change is usually to flee the Northern winter for Florida, Arizona, or California sunshine. Likewise, any citizen who was moving from, let us say, the warmth and humidity of Washington or Philadelphia to year-round living in one of the northcentral states, where the air is dry and the temperature is extremely cold in the winter, would require a different clothing pattern. Similarly, an Air Force detachment might be shifted from the hot Texas plains to a base along the Arctic Circle, where the texture of clothing and garment design must meet special requirements of protection. Special-function design for protection against insects, reptiles, or chemicals fall under this category of special environmental requirements.

resistance to chemical and mechanical action

Repetitious or not, the point cannot be stressed too greatly upon the buyer and user of textile products that the many features which made the article attractive and appealing at the time of purchase should be sufficiently fast or permanent to be retained through reasonable periods of use and care. No one will even pretend that the esthetic appeals nor the original strength or color of the textile fabric will be maintained throughout the life of the article. Use does bring about wearing out—the goods are truly consumed—but sudden failure of the article should not occur. Four characteristics determine durability and wear resistance. The first of these—retention of esthetic appeal—provides the textile industry with a whole series of testing procedures to determine the retention of eye appeal, such as the fastness of the color, the resistance to spotting, the resistance of the fabric to changes brought about by mechanical action, such as pressing, shining, pilling, glazing, weave deformation and fulling, and the retention of hand and drape through various cleaning operations and wear. This would also include the development of odors resulting from a finish which may have broken down during the life of the garment in question, or it might include such odor problems as the smell of sour milk when casein fibers are exposed to warm air during shipment.

Resistance to chemical action (7.00) should include the chemical destruction suffered by some fibers in normal cleaning and washing, the damaging action of certain dry-cleaning solvents or spotting agents on some fibers, or the effect of too great a temperature in drying. Included in this classification of damage would be effects of climatic conditions, microorganisms, perspiration, and water or fire, for objectionable damage can be short of complete destruction of the article.

Resistance to mechanical fatigue and wear (8.00) is simply one way of stating the resistance of the garment to wearing out in service. The first category used by Stoll is certainly not of importance to the average consumer. We recognize fatigue in ourselves, and we talk of fatigue in metals, but we fail to recognize that fatigue can also occur in textile materials far short of actual breaks in the fabric or individual yarns. If garments are allowed to rest, particularly if they are kept clean, they will last longer. Every washing operation causes the individual fibers and the yarns to swell, to move about within the geometric confines of the fabric weave, and, thus, in relaxing, to expose new fibers and yarn surfaces to the wearing conditions and to the abrasive action of wear, giving reversed twist and perhaps greater elasticity when loads are applied in wearing. The physicist is interested in fatigue. Standards for textile materials overlook it, for it has comparatively little interest to the consumer. We are interested, however, in the effects of moderate or severe wear on the fabric. Does it shine? Does it pill, rough up, or fray? Do seams fail? Do folded edges, such as hems, sleeves, or pockets, become thread-bare? Is a soft-textured garment damaged by a coarser, harder, more abrasive one frequently worn with it?

The last item in Stoll's table, ultimate strength and resistance to fortuitous wear and tear (9.00), refers to test results achieved only by complete destruction of the sample. Ultimate strength means final strength, just as ultimate consumer refers to the final consumer or user of the article. Also, the physical strength determinations made on textiles for the benefit of the consumer are of this type, and they provide comparative figures for various fabric constructions and textile materials useful in forecasting the kind of durability the consumer may expect in service. Thus, the various kinds of tensile or breaking strengths, tearing strengths, bursting strengths, seam strengths, and knot strengths come under the category of breaking strengths, either dry or wet; abrasion tests and snagging devices determine the ultimate wear compared with various degrees of wear or abrasion under category 8.00, resistance to mechanical fatigue and wear. Reference has often been made to the effect of moths and other insects, termites, bacteria, and mildew to textile materials. These exposure conditions also come under the classification of ultimate resistance to fortuitous exposures in use.

practical limitations to testing

Textile-testing programs of most laboratories tend to follow the basic requirements of Dr. Stoll's table but with different emphases and slightly different classifications in some cases, depending largely upon the end-use item itself.

385

Articles are evaluated for their original esthetic properties, for the degree of retention of these properties, for the relative permanence of special functional finishes which may have been used, and for a rating as to ultimate strength and durability. The determinations are made on the fabric, as distinguished from delicate, highly precise measurements the textile physicist may make on individual yarns or fibers. The serviceability classifications are those which experience has shown to be of main interest to the consumer. They are the bases for frequent consumer complaints if the garment falls short in any important respect from the test levels described in the Standard L-22; of course, only those tests are made which are appropriate to that end-use item. Volume II of American Standard Performance Requirements for Textile Fabrics[4] list 40 different tests or test methods to be used with the L-22 Standard.

THE ESTABLISHMENT OF TEXTILE STANDARDS

The rapid development of new synthetic fabrics and the simulation of one fabric by another with the use of the many new finishing agents have made the purchase of textiles more and more difficult at every "customer" level. The weaver or the knitter of goods can test the yarns he buys for conformance to his specifications. The manufacturer of garments also can test the dyed and finished fabrics. His problem is more difficult, however, because the identity of the fiber, the fabric strength, shrinkage, color fastness, and the type and permanence of special-purpose finishes are only a few of the factors which should influence his selection. It is an unfortunate fact that a great many manufacturers, especially of women's and children's wear, simply buy their materials by price, color, and design. Little technical inspection is made of the goods, and the manufacturer frequently has no specifications as to quality and performance of the materials he uses.

It is too often overlooked by retail customers that the selection problems which confuse them are equally confusing to the stores from which they buy the merchandise. It was to make easier the selection problems of their buyers that during the past forty years, and particularly since 1930, many large retail establishments built up their own scientific laboratories for the testing, analysis, and evaluation of merchandise. Among the stores which maintain their own laboratories are: Sears Roebuck & Company, Montgomery Ward & Company, R. H. Macy & Company, T. Eaton and Company, G. C. Murphy Co., Kaufmann Department Stores, Inc. (now a member of the May Co.), J. C. Penney Company, and Marshall Field and Company. For the most part, these laboratories are housed on the property of the store. Kaufmann's, however, only moved its laboratory facilities to the store in 1958, after 27 years of maintaining a fellow-

[4] American Standard Performance Requirements for Textile Fabrics, Vol. II, American Standards Association (1960).

ship at Mellon Institute in Pittsburgh, Pennsylvania. Gimbels utilizes to a great extent the technical services and facilities of a commercial laboratory which for many years occupied space in its Philadelphia store. Some of the finer stores in the United States avail themselves occasionally of the services of one or another of the excellent commercial laboratories by paying for the tests made on their merchandise. In other cases, stores belonging to a central buying office are benefitted by the association's own technical service.

In order that the results of tests may have real meaning, they must be reproducible. This necessitates the definition of standard conditions of testing, the standardization of the testing procedures, and the development of a common method of interpretation of results based upon an adequate number of determinations or measurements. Unless there were such standards, two operators using the same method of test would be liable to obtain different results, and a single operative re-testing a fabric at a different time of year might not duplicate his previous result, obtained by exactly the same technique but with different room conditions of temperature and humidity.

Merchandise specifications and standards of quality depend first of all upon standardized methods and conditions of test. It is fitting that the more common textile test methods should be described briefly.

conditions for testing

Virtually all the physical properties of textile materials are affected by the amount of moisture in the air and, to a lesser degree, by the temperature. It seems that the relative humidity affects the moisture content of a fabric more than does the actual amount of moisture in the air.[5] The relative humidity is expressed as the percentage of saturation of the air as compared with its maximum possible moisture content at that particular temperature. Large, well-equipped laboratories have a conditioned room in which the physical testing of fabrics is conducted. This room is kept at the standard conditions of 70° F. and 65 per cent relative humidity. Laboratories which do not have these facilities may test with each series of tests a standard cloth sample and compare these results with the standard or blank sample. It may be sufficient in evaluating several samples of the same type, such as sheeting, to make all the tests as nearly as possible at the same time.

moisture content of fabrics

Textile materials always contain a certain amount of moisture, depending upon the condition of the atmosphere around them. The moisture content is of less importance to the buyer of finished goods than to the purchaser of raw fibers,

[5] John H. Skinkle, *Textile Testing* (New York: Chemical Publishing Co., Inc., 1940), p. 12.

yarns, or gray goods, who may be buying by weight. Stores and their customers commonly consider the moisture content in terms of per cent of moisture by weight. The textile technicians concerned with the processing of fibers use the term "per cent ragain," which may be described as the weight of moisture divided by the dry weight of the sample and multiplied by 100.

Skinkle shows the relationship of the two in the following equations:[6]

$$M = \frac{100\ (a-b)}{a} \qquad\qquad R = \frac{100\ (a-b)}{b}$$

wherein M = per cent moisture
 R = regain
 a = weight of fabric sample with moisture
 b = weight of sample after drying

The interrelationships of the two terms are shown as follows:

$$R = \frac{100\ M}{100-M} \qquad\qquad M = \frac{100\ R}{100+R}$$

The most satisfactory method for determining either of these values is by means of an oven. These ovens are found in most chemical laboratories. The sample is suspended in the oven or placed in a weighed, dried weighing bottle in the oven to dry at 105°–110° C. (220–230° F.). The weighing must be carefully made in a weighing bottle to prevent the rapid re-absorption of moisture by the bone-dry sample.

yarn count or thread count

This is simply the process of counting the number of warp yarns and filling yarns per linear inch. Textile technologists refer to the warp-yarn count as the number of **ends** per inch, or **sley,** and to the filling or **weft** yarns per inch as the **picks** per inch, or **shot.** In knit goods the corresponding values are **wales** per inch and **courses** per inch. The actual count must be made some distance from the selvage and from torn ends. Three and preferably five different areas should be counted.

The most common method of counting is by means of a small magnifying glass, or pick glass, mounted in a stand over a square exactly one inch or half an inch along each side. When the fabric is very closely woven or is heavily napped or otherwise hard to count, it is common practice to ravel the edges to about ⅛ inch to make the yarns more readily seen. When a great many cloths are to be counted, some laboratories project the image of the sample on a screen by means of a textile projector. The yarn count is one of the useful methods for comparing the qualities of competitive fabrics.

[6] *Ibid.*, p. 12.

fabric weight

The actual weight per unit area of a cloth aids the customer in evaluating it. It must be borne in mind, however, that two systems of weight determination are in general use; namely, the weight in ounces per **square** yard and the weight in ounces per **running** yard, based on the actual width. For example, the standard width of woolens and worsteds is 54 inches, so that a 16-ounce worsted fabric is one in which a piece 1 yard long and 54 inches wide weighs 16 ounces. This fabric may be calculated into weight per square yard from the unit-length weight by the formula:

$$S = 36R/B$$

where S = square-yard weight (ounces per square yard)
R = running-yard weight (ounces per running yard), or 16 as above
B = width of cloth in inches, or 54 as above
Thus $S = 36 \times 16/54 = 10.66$ ounces per square yard.

The linear-length weight may be similarly calculated from the weight per unit area by the equation:

$$R = SB/36$$

Usually small, carefully measured pieces are weighed when oven-dry and calculated to the standard regain for that particular fiber. It is desirable to weigh enough pieces so that the total area represented by the samples is not less than 30 square inches.[7]

miscellaneous fabric tests

Fabrics have a variety of qualities which are either built into them in their construction or given them by special finishes. These qualities are built into the fabrics for specific uses and services which the garments must undergo, and the measurements of these qualities are important techniques of textile laboratories.

CRIMP   Crimp may be defined as the deviation from straightness of yarns as they lie in the cloth, expressed as the percentage of length in the cloth.[8] The crimp is controlled by the weaving operation and by finishing methods such as calendering and stretching. Crepes in particular show the effect of crimp. The new textured yarns exhibit high degrees of crimp.

This factor is measured on individual yarns as they lie in the fabric and as straightened out by the application of a standard weight, or from the strength-stretch curve.[9]

THICKNESS   The purchasers of fabrics in retail stores are often impressed with the comparative thicknesses of, for example, two different blankets or two

[7] A.S.T.M. Standards on Textile Materials (Philadelphia: A.S.T.M. 1963), p. 54.
[8] *Ibid.*, p. 61.
[9] *Ibid.*, p. 64.

rugs. Actually, the thickness of fabrics is not often determined except in the case of firm or rather rigid types. When the thickness of a blanket or other soft fabric is to be measured, it is more satisfactory to measure the cross-section of the sample microscopically. The reason for this is that a thickness gauge will more or less depress a soft fabric, depending on the size of the presser foot, the weight applied, the speed of the application of the force, the time elapsing during the test, and other factors. A blanket may be overnapped to such a degree that it is much thicker than another selling at the same price, but it will probably not last as long nor remain as warm as the thinner but slightly more dense sample.

POROSITY   Porosity is determined by measuring the total volume of the sample and calculating the total fiber volume, the difference being the amount of air space. The latter figure when expressed as the percentage of the total volume gives the porosity of the fabric. Skinkle[10] shows the formulae by which the determination is made.

POROSITY CALCULATION

S = total volume of fabric sample in cubic centimeters
F = total volume of fiber in cubic centimeters
P = porosity in percent

$$\text{By definition } P = \frac{100\ (S-F)}{S}$$

To calculate S, one must know the area and thickness of the fabric.
  A = area of sample in square centimeters
  T = thickness of sample in centimeters

$$S = AT \text{ (by definition)}$$

To calculate F, one must know the density of the fiber in grams per cubic centimeter and the weight of the sample plus moisture or the regain at standard conditions.
  W = weight of sample at standard regain in grams
  D = density of fiber in grams per cubic centimeter

$$F = W/D \text{ (by definition)}$$
$$\text{Then } P = \frac{100\ (AT-W/D)}{AT}$$

[10] John H. Skinkle, *Textile Testing* (New York: Chemical Publishing Co., Inc., 1940), p. 70

Porosity is of value because it gives an approximation of the comfort of a fabric, that is, the warmth or coolness, lightness, and permeability of the cloth. The greater the porosity, the lighter the cloth will be. A high porosity value may distinguish either a warm or a cool fabric, depending upon its permeability. For example, a summer suiting will have a high porosity and a high permeability value, due to the large size of the air spaces between the yarns and the removal of loose fibers which customarily obstruct these interstices. An overcoating might have just as high a porosity, but the air would be confined to dead spaces in the napped fabric, and the permeability would be low.

PERMEABILITY   The permeability of a fabric to air may be determined by several types of rather expensive equipment. In brief, they depend upon the following techniques:

1   Forcing air through the sample at a constant rate and measuring the resultant back pressure.

2   Forcing air through the fabric at constant pressure and measuring the rate of flow.

3   Forcing a known volume of air through the fabric at a standard pressure and measuring the time required.

A second kind of permeability of importance in the laboratory determination of garment comfort is the permeability of water vapor. Underclothing and hosiery are more comfortable when they permit the passage of water vapor. The various methods for testing this quality all involve standardization of techniques and delicate measurements of weight changes due to the passage of moisture through the test sample. In general, the methods involve the gain in weight of sulfuric acid or other hygroscopic chemical in a dish covered with the test sample and exposed to a standard atmosphere, or the loss of weight of a dish of water similarly covered and exposed to a standard atmosphere. The method of Black and Matthews[11] is a simple one and requires no special atmosphere. One dish of water is left uncovered, and a similar one is covered with the fabric sample for the same time. The loss through the fabric divided by the loss from the open vessel gives the permeability.

No single method has yet been adopted as a standard test procedure for determining the air or water vapor permeability of a fabric.

THERMAL PROPERTIES   Associated with the thermal properties of a fabric, that is, its ability to resist or to permit the passage of heat, are two factors already discussed in this chapter, namely, permeability and porosity. The warmth of a fabric depends principally upon the dead air entrapped between the fibers; however, for comfort, some air permeability is required so that the body moisture can evaporate.[12]

---

[11] C. P. Black and J. A. Matthews, "Physical Properties of Fabrics in Relation to *Research*" (December, 1943).

[12] H. F. Shieffer, "Factors Relating to the Thermal Insulation of Fabrics," *Textile Research* (December, 1943).

SERVICE-SATISFACTION-WEAR   The serviceability of any cloth is judged by the length of time it continues to have the qualities or properties for which it was purchased. It is not a determinable quantity.

Wear is rarely the same as serviceability and is also an indeterminate quantity because the conditions of wear vary widely and cannot be exactly reproduced in the laboratory. So many factors are simultaneously involved during the wear or use of a fabric that the relative importance of any one of them cannot be measured. Despite this dark picture, wear testing is of value, because competitive cloths can be compared by laboratory procedures, although the length of service life or wear-resistance cannot be forecast in the several samples.

Contributing to wear are the following factors:

1   Direct force or impact on the cloth.

2   Friction of yarn against yarn in the flexing and bending of the cloth —important in sized or coated fabrics, or loosely-woven cloths.

3   Abrasion or rubbing is of several types:

A.   Friction of cloth on cloth is a local phenomenon, such as wear of the sleeve against the side of a garment.

B.   Friction of the fabric against other object surfaces. This includes lining wear and abrasion by hard-surfaced upholstery materials and other of the infinite number of possible abradant objects.

C.   Friction of the fibers against dust and dirt in the cloth itself. This is primarily a cutting action and depends on the care given by the wearer.

Abrasion is the most important factor in the wearing quality of a cloth. In testing by an accelerated method, the test must not be more severe than the fabric might reasonably be expected to withstand. This means that the abradant material used may be the cloth itself, canvas, emery cloth or emery paper, a steel surface, or a standard screen. Although rubbing rarely occurs without some twisting, it is better from a practical testing point of view to use some machine having a reciprocating motion so that the wear can be determined in both directions of the cloth.

Influencing the results obtained by all the various wear testers are the following:

1   Type of motion—most common is reciprocating motion.

2   Nature of the abradant—emery cloth most widely used.

3   Pressure of abradant on cloth sample.

4   Tension on sample—varies widely, as creeping tendencies vary greatly.

5   Completeness of lint removal.

6   Determination of the end point or of the amount of abrasion.

A.   Number of strokes required to wear a hole or to accomplish a predetermined amount of wear.

B.   Loss in strength after a certain number of strokes.

C. Change in thickness after a definite number of strokes.

D. Loss of weight after a definite number of strokes.

E. Change in physical properties for which the test cloth was designed after abrasion period.

There is no single standard abrasion test method, but the one most widely used by department store laboratories and commercial testing laboratories has been the Wyzenbeck machine.[13]

In recent years, a subcommittee of the American Society for Testing Materials, Committee D-13, Textile Materials, has been actively at work in the development of more exact and realistic methods for determining the abrasion of wear resistance of fabrics, so that their end-use may be more accurately forecast. The annual report of the Society[14] gives in detail all the test methods currently standard or on the tentative list awaiting formal approval. These standards-in-waiting, as it were, are those requiring further inter-laboratory proof in order to determine the amount of correlation obtainable by different laboratories. Even today, the determination of abrasion is not directly to be correlated with service life. Laboratories generally make the tests on as many types of equipment as the laboratory has, reaches some kind of an average comparison among the various methods, and makes its report. Three types of abrasion machines most commonly used in the fully-equipped laboratory are:

1 the Stoll-Quartermaster Abrasion Machine

2 the Taber Abrasor

3 the Accelerotor

STOLL-QUARTERMASTER ABRASION MACHINE   This is the most elaborate and costly of the abrasion testers, and it is rarely found in college home economics departments laboratories. The machine was designed primarily by Dr. Reiner Stoll, a brilliant German textile engineer, for and with the aid of the Research and Development Branch of the Quartermaster Corps of the Department of Defense. Not only can the machine give abrasions or rubbing on flat surfaces, but it also can give edge-wear, that is, abrasion on the edges of creases and pleats.

TABER ABRASOR   This is a small machine which gives results rather quickly. A sample of fabric approximately five inches square is attached to the base plate by means of an embroidery ring. When the machine is operating, this base plate turns in a clockwise direction, each complete movement being automatically recorded, and as the sample turns, two abrasive wheels, one on either side of a small protective plate in the middle of the sample, rub a circular path. The speed of the machine is constant, but the weight of the abrasion wheels and

---

[13] E. H. Harvey, "Wyzenbeck Precision Wear Tester Meter," *American Dyestuff Reporter,* 21, No. 177 (1932).

[14] A.S.T.M. Standards on Textile Materials (Philadelphia, 1963).

their texture for rate of cutting may be varied. The value of this machine is that it shows very quickly whether it is the warp or the filling yarns which are most subject to abrasion in any fabric sample.

ACCELEROTOR   This machine, developed by the American Association of Textile Chemists and Colorists, performs several other functions in addition to the wear abrasion test. It can be used either wet or dry, and with modifications it can be used for a vastly speeded-up washing operation. In the abrasion test, the test fabric is given a narrow coating of special adhesive along the cut edges so as to avoid raveling. The fabric is put in the test cylinder, around the inner periphery of which is a strip of sandpaper. The sample is whirled and thrown against this sandpaper by a rapidly revolving (3000 RPM) paddle wheel. Tests usually take one minute, and the degree of abrasion is determined by the weight loss of the fabric during the procedure of the test. Some of our more delicate weaves, such as satin and others with long floats, are generally whipped to small amounts of short fiber resembling tow.

EVALUATION OF FABRICS UNDER THE TEXTILE STANDARD L-22

Probably no college or university textile laboratory will have all of the pieces of textile testing equipment referred to in the Standard L-22 listing. It is obvious, too, that not all these tests are ever to be made on each end-use product. For example, a dress or blouse, or a fabric intended for these purposes, may be subjected to the following tests.

Breaking strength, wet and dry
Resistance to yarn slippage
Tongue-tear strength
Yarn shifting
Maximum dimensional change (shrinkage)
Color fastness to atmospheric fading
(after washing and after dry-cleaning)
Color fastness to laundering
Color fastness to dry-cleaning
Color fastness to crocking, wet and dry
Color fastness to perspiration
Color fastness to light
And with future reference to tests on
Abrasion and on Pilling when agreed-upon
procedures have been developed.

On the other hand, with a more rugged fabric, such as a dungaree material for women's and girls' wear, the user would be concerned with such performances as breaking strength; yarn slippage; dimensional change; color fastness to laundering, to crocking, dry and wet, to perspiration, and to light; and again with possible reference to abrasion when generally agreed-upon tests are available. One should note that absent from this list are many of the usual tests carried out in store laboratories and in those of colleges and universities. All these tests, such as count, twist, construction, weight, etc., have been made on these same materials at one or more stages of their development and have been discussed earlier. The testing procedures referred to in L-22 are those having to do with the performance of the material during service. They are made on actual merchandise in the ready-to-be-bought-and-used-condition. If the fabric has been found to be too light in weight, too uneven, too low in yarn count, or not adequately pre-shrunk, or if luster, texture, feel, draping quality, and other esthetics have not been fully realized, then the product would not be suitable for the garment in question. Also, it must be recognized that with the wide number of synthetic fibers and blends available in many of these end-use items, one could not put down a definite figure for weight of fabric or for yarn count, except in a case where one fiber and one fabric construction have so absorbed the end-product industry or important sections of it that an individual standard should be written for that fabric and no other. Such examples referred to in this standard deal with tricot in several end-products for women's and girls' wear, such as knitted slip fabrics (acetate and tri-acetate tricot) Standard No. 22.10.30-1960 and women's and girls' knitted (opaque) slip fabrics (nylon and polyester tricot) L-22.10.31-1960.

The following table lists in order the test methods contained in and thus to be used with the L-22 Standard. They are referred to by number, with a very brief indication as to the significance of the test to the consumer and the method by which each is carried out.

The reader may be rather surprised at first to find a Number 1 rating to be the lowest in performance. Number 1 is not the winner in these tests. It is reasonable to assume that as the techniques of textile production continue to develop and the art of evaluation becomes more critical, even higher numbers of ratings may become necessary in many tests.

PERFORMANCE TESTS IN TEXTILE FABRICS
STANDARD L-22

1. color fastness to crocking (rubbing).   AS L14.72-1960[15]; AATCC 8-1961[16]

This test determines whether color can be transferred from the surface of the dyed material to another surface by rubbing when wet or dry. The appliance

[15] American Standard L14.72-1960.
[16] American Association of Textile Chemists and Colorists, Test Method 8-1961.

used is the Crockmeter, which rubs a white test cloth against the dyed or printed fabric. In the case of prints, each color must be tested. There are five ratings as to depth of color transfer: Class 5 (negligible) to Class 1 (color equivalent to worst rating, or line 1, of AATCC chart[17]). The test is of value in all outerwear fabrics, upholstery, slip covers, etc.

2. color fastness to perspiration.   AS L4.56-1960; AATCC 15-1960

This test determines the fastness of dyed fabrics to perspiration.

Two artificial perspiration solutions are prepared: acid, to simulate fresh perspiration, and basic, to simulate perspiration after bacterial exposure. The Perspirometer or other device is used to hold the solution-wetted dyed fabrics in close contact with the multifiber test cloth until dry. Five classes of color change of the dyed sample are based on the International Geometric Gray Scale.[18] The same scale is used also to measure the depth of staining of the test cloth.

3. color fastness to light.   AS L14.53-1960; AATCC 16A-1960

The dyed fabric sample and a standard fabric dyeing or a light-sensitive paper reference sample are exposed simultaneously to an accelerated fading light source, a calibrated carbon arc light, until "just appreciable fading" is noted. The apparatus is the FDA-R Fade-Ometer, in which the samples and the "standards" are mounted in exposure frames of aluminum on the track revolving about the arc light. The mounting frames permit the covering of parts of the exposure area, so that the samples may be exposed for 10, 20, 40, 80, 160, and 320 hours, depending on the severity of sun exposure to be demanded of the end-use item. It is often inconvenient to continue the test through longer periods of exposure.

The degree of color fastness is in terms of "Standard Fading Hours" (SFH). Eight degrees of color fastness are recognized, from Class 1 (not as fast as Standard L-2), the lowest, to Class 8 (as fast as L-8). Another classification is in terms of the Fade-Ometer hours required to produce appreciable fading. Only the prescribed time intervals should be used.

4. color fastness of dyed textiles to atmospheric oxides of nitrogen.
AS L14.54-1960; AATCC 23-1957

The test is to determine resistance to color change of dyed textile fabrics when exposed to atmospheric oxides of nitrogen (gas fading of acetates).

The apparatus used is the Gas Fading Test Chamber, using a gas flame,

---

[17] AATCC Chart for Measuring Transference of Color (p. 79 of the Technical Manual of the AATCC, 1961).
[18] *Ibid,* p. 77.

the fumes of which pass into an upper chamber, within which the control samples and the test specimens are rotated. The exposure period in terms of cycles is determined by the amount of fading of the control samples. Thus, when Sample 1 shows a certain amount of fading, one cycle is deemed to have been completed. A second control Sample No. 1 is then placed in the chamber, and the test is repeated. The readings of the fabrics under test are based on the number of cycles they will withstand without an appreciable color change. Beginning with Class 5, which is excellent and shows no appreciable fading after eight exposure-cycles, the gradients then go down to Class 1, or poor, which shows appreciable fading on a single cycle; fine measurements of an actual color change are based on the International Gray Scale.

5. color fastness of textiles to commercial laundering and domestic washing. AATCC 61-1961T

These are tests identified in the Technical Manual of the AATCC and in the Standard as "Accelerated Tests," with Tests 1A, 2A, 3A, and 4A applying for different degrees of washability. They are specifically designed for evaluating the wash fastness of textiles which are expected to withstand frequent launderings. One 45-minute test for each category has been found by laboratory correlation to be equivalent to the color loss and abrasion action of five average hand, commercial, or home launderings, respectively.

The tests are carried out in the Launder-Ometer, using multifiber test cloths stitched to the dyed samples as indicators of color bleeding or transfer during washing operations. Test No. 1A, carried out at 105° F., is to approximate the action of five hand washings. Test No. 2A is conducted at 120° F.; Test 3A at 160° F.; and Test 4A also at 160° F., but with the addition of a small amount of chlorine bleach. The series provides hand, mild home or commercial, average commercial, and heavy commercial laundering classifications. Color change is graduated in terms of the International Gray Scale and the staining by the scale for measuring the transference of color to the test cloth.

6. color fastness to water.   AS L14.83-1960; AATCC 63-1957

Certain products made of dyed textile fabrics must, on occasion, be exposed to waters of various kinds, including distilled water, sea water, or chlorinated pool water. The test is understandably given only to products which would be expected to encounter such water or waters during service.

The specimen is immersed in the appropriate water solution and is backed by a multifiber test cloth. The two are then compressed between glass plates until dry. Evaluation is made of the change of color of the specimen and staining of the multifiber test cloth. The Perspirometer is conveniently used for this test. Readings are from Class 6, which is negligible or no staining, to Class 1, which is row 1 on the staining scale of the AATCC chart. The color-washed specimen is measured on the International Geometric Gray Scale.

7. color fastness to dry-cleaning.   AATCC 85-1960T

The purpose of the test is to determine what happens to the fabric color under repeated dry-cleaning operations. It is not applied to spotting or to stain removal techniques which may be used by the commercial dry-cleaner.

A chlorinated hydrocarbon solvent (perchlorethylene) is customarily used. The test can be carried out in the Launder-Ometer. One cycle in the machine totals 30 minutes at a temperature of 115° F., after which the specimen is removed, excess solvent is pressed out between paper towels, and the sample is allowed to air dry. After this, it is pressed carefully. Color change is determined on the International Gray Scale.

8. durability of applied designs and finishes to dry-cleaning.   AATCC 86-1957T

This test is to determine the effect of dry-cleaning on applied designs or finishes on textiles.

The apparatus used is the Launder-Ometer with perchlorethylene solvent in the glass jars. The perchlorethylene can be substituted for by Stoddard solvent for determining the effect of naphtha on some of these finishes. The evaluation of the samples is purely subjective, judging the test effect on the handle or body of the fabric.

9. quantitative analysis of textiles.   AATCC 20A-1959T

This refers to a group of solvents and other extracting materials used to remove specific non-fibrous constituents, such as finishing agents, stiffening agents, and other materials in some textile fabric products. It also provides an orderly procedure for the identification and quantitative analysis of the natural and man-made fibers.

10. resistance to wetting (spray test).   AS L14.60-1956; AATCC 22-1961

The test is applicable to a textile fabric which may or may not have been given a water-repellent finish. It measures the resistance of fabrics to wetting by water and is primarily designed for measuring the water-repellent efficiency of finishes applied to plain-woven fabrics intended for rainwear and made of cotton, rayon, acetate, or synthetic fibers. It does not determine the water penetration resistance of fabrics under severe impact, such as in heavy rains.

Water is sprayed against the taut surface of the test specimen under controlled conditions to produce a pattern of wetting, depending upon the resistance of the finish to water absorption.

The evaluation varies from a reading of 100, which shows no wetted area; then a rating of 90, an occasional dark spot where water has penetrated; through 80, 70, 60, etc.; to a zero rating, which is rather uniformly darkened over the entire test area. The tests should be run not only on new fabrics but also after a cycle of washings or dry-cleanings.

11. resistance of textiles to insects.   AS L14.64-1960; AATCC 24-1956

The methods of test are designed to evaluate, by biological procedures, the resistance of textiles containing wool or other fibers susceptible to the attacks of clothes moths and carpet beetles. Each insect specie requires a slightly different method of evaluation. In the case of carpet beetles, the weight of the excrement is determined after fourteen days of exposure to larvae. The weight of fabric loss is determined in the case of the clothes moth test, and the test larvae at the start of the exposure must be 25 to 27 days old.

The procedures include methods of rearing and caring for these two types of insects from the egg through the adult stage.

12. resistance of textiles to mildew and rot. an evaluation of textile fungicides.
AS L14.55-1960; AATCC 30-1957T

This is a dual purpose test: first, to determine the behavior of textiles with respect to mildew; and second, to evaluate mildew preventives which are offered to the textile trade. Various test procedures utilized by laboratories representing the textile industry are included. Even these may be varied, depending upon the specific conditions of use required of the textile product. Soil contact tests are intended for fabrics which, in service, will be in contact with the soil. A few of these are: protective tarpaulins, tents, ground cloths, and other materials exposed to weather. The second group of tests involves exposure of the test cloth to direct inoculation of the fabric with cultures of the more common organisms damaging cellulosic fibers. These bacteria themselves represent a method of rating because of the difference in severity of attack on cellulose by the various organisms.

13. evaluation of fire-resistant textiles.   AATCC 34-1952

This test is applicable to industrial fabrics, such as cotton duck, tentage tarpaulins, awnings, canvas upholstery coverings, canvas theater scenery, etc., and the term fire-resistance is meant to include resistance to flame and to charring or smoldering.

The test specimen is hung vertically in the test chamber and is exposed to a standard flame for a measured time and under carefully controlled conditions. The specimen is then evaluated for degree of burning, for tendency to after-flame, and for the length of char remaining after any after-glowing has taken place.

14. resistance to water penetration (rain test).   AS L14.74-1956; AATCC 35-1961

This test measures the resistance of fabrics to the penetration of water by impact and can, therefore, be applied to any textile material whether or not it has been given a water-resistant or water-repellent finish. In principle, it predicts the probable rain-penetration resistance of fabrics in use and is particularly useful for wearing apparel or protective garment fabrics. The degree of protection depends not only upon the water-repellency of the fibers and yarns but also on the fabric construction.

The AATCC Rain Tester is the apparatus used for this test, and the severity of the "rain" can be controlled by the height of the water head in the storage column, very mild showers being produced with a water head of one foot and a veritable tropical rain storm by the eight-foot head. The method is suitable for the testing not only of a single fabric but also of a rainwear assembly, consisting of several layers of rain-protective material. Thus, the fabric may be subjected to the mildest exposure, and then, progressively by one-foot head intervals, the exposure may be increased until water intensity is reached at which penetration occurs.

15. dimensional changes in wool textiles: accelerated tests.   AS L14.11-1956; AATCC 41-1952

This is an accelerated test for the evaluation of the shrinkage of wool and of part-wool woven fabrics.

The procedure involves the use of a wash-wheel in which 20-inch squares of samples are washed under controlled conditions. The first step is to determine the relaxation shrinkage of the fabrics through spraying with water, extracting and then pressing to dryness, and measuring for the shrinkage under this mild wetting operation. The second step then is to determine the shrinkage due to fulling or felting action under a controlled wash test.

16. evaluation of the wrinkle recovery of fabrics.   AATCC 66-1959T

The test is a measure of the recovery of fabrics from creasing as an indication of the ability of the fabric to free itself of wrinkles when hung following wearing under high humidity conditions and compression of the mussed or wrinkled garment.

The appliance used is the Wrinkle Recovery Tester developed by the Monsanto Chemical Company[19] and adopted by the AATCC as a Tentative Test Method in 1959.

The test specimens are cut to specified size and are creased back with the fold at right angles to the long axis. The fabric is then compressed in this crease for a period of time prescribed by the test, after which the fold is placed in the jaws of the small measuring device one end of the strip being allowed to hang free. As it hangs, the material shows a greater or lesser tendency to straighten out, and it is the angle of recovery which indicates the ability of the textile to hang free of wrinkles after wearing. The procedure permits the rating of fabrics as to their ability to conform to minimum-care classifications in use.

[19] Bulletin T30-45.1, Monsanto Wrinkle Recovery Tester, Monsanto Chemical Company, Textile and Paper Resins Dept., Springfield 2, Mass.

17. relaxation and felting shrinkage of wool knit fabrics: accelerated test.
AS L14.89-1956; AATCC 74-1953

This test is to aid in the evaluation of knitted wool and part-wool fabrics which may have been given a treatment or finish to render the wool resistant to shrinkage, particularly after washing and drying sweaters, socks, knitted underwear, and knitted outerwear apparel. The procedure does not include any restorative steps or forces; that is to say, there are no attempts to pull or work the garment back to its premarked size or shape. Some garments might respond more easily to body movement and would tend to work back to the original dimensions or at least a comfortable fit, even though distorted in washing; whereas others might be slower to go back to shape through a lower degree of elasticity in the fabric construction. Thus, the test is not indicative of the degree of consumer satisfaction but rather measures the effectiveness of finishes in preventing the immediate shrinking.

In general, the test samples should be at least 12-inch squares and are first evaluated for their relaxation shrinkage by wetting them and allowing them to dry under controlled conditions after removal of excess water by spinning. Having determined the relaxation shrinkage, the fabric is then sudsed and washed in a standard wash-wheel, spun until nearly dry, then dried flat without pressing; the shrinkage is calculated on the basis of the measurements of the test sample before and after treatment.

18. determination of the electrical resistivity of fabrics. AATCC 76-1959

The resistivity of the fabric influences the accumulation of electrostatic charge on a fabric. This is an increasingly important characteristic of some fibers, notably the synthetics, due to the nuisance value of a static spark and the effect of electrostatic deposition or the dirt-catching capacity of some of these materials.

An electrical resistance meter is used to measure the resistivity under constant conditions of temperature and humidity.

19. determining the absorbency of bleached woven cotton cloth.
AATCC79-1954T

Some end-use fabrics have as a very important quality or requirement the ability to absorb moisture rapidly and to accumulate a high water content. This property is important also in the case of fabrics to be dyed in deep shades or to be given a special finish of some kind for functional purposes, such as a resin finish for a minimum-care fabric.

The measurement is simply that of letting a drop of water from a standard burette fall from a prescribed height onto the top surface of the test specimen and timing the disappearance of the reflection of the water drop, which is taken as the time required for complete wetting by that drop. Generally, a minimum of 10 drops are timed, and it is important that the evaluation be carried out at standard conditions, that is, 70° F., 65 per cent relative humidity, the conditions of the usual laboratory condition room for the testing of textiles.

20. wash-and-wear fabrics—appearance after home laundering.
AATCC 88-1960T

The test is to give a visual rating of the smoothness of wash-and-wear fabrics after repeated home launderings. Wash-and-wear fabrics of minimum acceptable performance must be capable of shedding or erasing through relaxation not only the wrinkles formed during wearing but the mussing or wrinkling accompanying the washing operation in a normal wash load.

Recognizing the fact that certain fabric constructions or garment constructions may require more delicate conditions of washing, even approaching hand-washing methods, the test includes two washing temperatures, 105° F. and 140° F. As in previous washing tests and in consumer use, the garments may be dried by various methods. Accordingly, the test fabrics should be evaluated for these several methods of drying. Thus, the following list of washing procedures comprise this method of evaluation.

> Test No. 1 —Washed by hand, 105° F., drip dry
> Test No. 2 —Machine washed, 105° F., drip dry
> Test No. 3 —Machine washed, 105° F., tumble dry
> Test No. 4 —Machine washed, 105° F., line dry
> Test No. 2A—Machine washed, 140° F., drip dry
> Test No. 3A—Machine washed, 140° F., tumble dry
> Test No. 4A—Machine washed, 140° F., line dry

The washed and dried samples are then examined under prescribed lighting conditions[20] and compared with standard photographs or contourgraphs demonstrating five classes of appearance, ranging from Class 5, which shows negligible wrinkles or no change in surface appearance, to Class 1, which shows a badly mussed appearance equivalent to photograph No. 1.

21. damage caused by retained chlorine.   AATCC 92-1958T

This is an accelerated test to determine the potential damage which might be caused by retained chlorine. Certain resin finishes applied to cottons and rayons for the purpose of wrinkle control or minimum-care properties have the ability to store up chlorine from the hypochlorite type of bleach. It is a cumulative effect, and after several bleachings, this absorbed chlorine may eventually weaken or discolor the fabric.

In principle, the test involves the exposure of the test fabric to a chlorine solution under prescribed conditions, then calculating the extent of damage

[20] Cranston Print Works Co., Cranston, Rhode Island.

caused by the chlorine by comparing the tensile strength of the orignial fabric with that of the exposed samples.

22. dimensional restorability of woven textiles after laundering.
AATCC 95-1959T

This test procedure is intended to determine the extent to which hand ironing, or wearing a garment after laundering, can restore it to its original dimension or to a comfortable fit after moderate shrinkage in washing.

The marked sample, usually 20 inches on each side of the square test area, having been laundered, flat-bed pressed, and re-measured to indicate its dimensional change, is then re-wet and pressed under tension until dry. The dry relaxed specimen is then measured, and the dimensional change is calculated and reported as a percentage. The tension presser apparatus thus simulates hand ironing and pulling to shape, as well as the tensions applied to the fabric during wearing if it has shrunk much out of fit.

23. dimensional changes in woven or knitted textiles (excluding wool).
AATCC 96-1960T

This test method is intended to determine the dimensionsal changes in woven or knitted fabrics made of fibers other than wool, which may be expected when the textile product is washed and dried under normal conditions. With the variety of blends now on the market and with the additional complexities of textured and novelty yarns, shrinking and stretching have become increasing problems to the consumer. The test includes four washing test procedures of varying severity and five drying procedures. Some textiles which require restoration of shape by ironing or stretching cannot stand a test of accelerated character and must be given repeated washings by ordinary procedures because serious dimensional change may be long delayed.

The apparatus used is a cylindrical wash-wheel of the reversing type, and the pressing equipment is a flat-bed press measuring 24 inches in width by a minimum of 50 inches in length. The dryer is of the rotary tumble type. One of the restoration procedures requires a tension presser. (A tension presser is manufactured by the United States Testing Company, Inc., of Hoboken, New Jersey.) The specimen may be evaluated by one or more of the several laundering procedures, listed as follows:

SHRINKAGE OR STRETCH IN TEXTILES

Washing Procedure	Drying Procedure	Restoration Procedure
I 100–109° F., 30 min.	A Drip Dry	1 Tension Presser
II 120–129° F., 45 min.	B Flat-Bed Press Dry	2 Knit Shrinkage Gauge
III 160–169° F., 60 min.	C Screen Dry	3 Hand Iron
IV 203–212° F., 60 min.	D Line	
	E Tumble Dry	

According to this list, the procedure can be indicated simply by a combination of figures and letters. Thus, if a fabric has been washed at 160° F., tumble-dried, and tension-pressed, the designation would be "Washed by III-E-1." The shrinkage is calculated in each direction to the nearest one-half per cent.

24. standard general methods of testing woven textile fabrics.   AS L14.68-1951; ASTM D39-49

This test method, since it deals with physical properties, is within the domain of the American Society for Testing Materials rather than the AATCC. The test method in question deals with several factors having to do with dimensions, the weights, the constructions, and the load elongations of woven textiles fabrics and should, therefore, be carried out under constant conditions (70° F., 65 per cent RH).

DIMENSIONS   Fabric dimensions, particularly the length of the fabric, are determined by laying the fabric on a flat surface without tension and measuring parallel with the selvage for lengthwise and at right angles to the selvage for widthwise dimensions.

THICKNESS   For thickness, a standard thickness gauge is used; the fabric is placed on the anvil of the gauge without tension, the presser foot is gradually lowered upon the fabric and allowed to come to a rest for 10 seconds, then the dial is read.

WEIGHT   The weight is to be determined on an accurate calibrated scale, and it may be reported in ounces per square yard or in ounces per running yard. In the L-22 test document, for one group of fabrics, the tricot knit, the weight is reported in a somewhat different way, that is, by the number of square yards of fabric required to weigh one pound.

YARN COUNT   The number of ends or warp yarns per inch, and the number of picks or filling yarns per inch, are counted. These are usually reported separately, with the warp count being given first. There is an exception to this in the official grading of bed sheets, in which the count in the two directions is totaled, and the sheet is described by the type number for which standard the fabric in question qualifies. Thus, if a sheet has a total count of 134, it must be described as Type 128, because it does not meet the count for the next standard, which is 140 yarns per square inch.

CRIMP   The proper number of yarns are to be separated and raveled out to a distance of at least two inches beyond the test mark without any stretching of the yarns; then, the actual counting of the number of crimps can be made in terms of the yarn number for the kind of fiber used.

BREAKING STRENGTH   The breaking strength machine is generally so devised that the test sample can be gripped securely between two parallel jaws. The lower one, which is motor-driven and goes downward at a constant rate of speed, thus imposes tension or pull on the fabric.

As the lower jaw descends, the pendulum arm moves outward along the arc and to it is fastened the recording needle indicating the number of pounds tension the fabric is bearing. At the point at which the fabric breaks, both the pendulum arm and the needle come to rest. The machine may also be equipped with a recording device which indicates the elongation pattern of the fabric between the start of the load and the final break. The most common device is the Grab Test Machine, in which a sample six inches in length and four inches in width is subjected to pull. The other type of test involves a raveled strip, usually of one-inch width, of intact yarns, each extending through the full length of the test specimen. The breaking strengths are made of both the warp and filling yarns and may be made wet as well as dry for a more accurate evaluation of some of those fibers which are suspectible to damage when wet.

TEARING STRENGTH   There are two methods of conducting tear tests, the Trapezoid Method and the Tongue Test. In each case, the sample is prepared according to the directions given for that machine or method. In each case, also, there is a tear of approximately one-half inch in depth on the bottom of the test specimen, and the tear strength is then the resistance to tearing of the material from the top of this point of weakness to the top of the test specimen when it is completely torn in half.

TWIST   The amount of twist, or number of twists per inch of both warp and filling yarns, is customarily determined in the analysis of the construction of fabrics. The twist-counter device is customarily used, and its direction of operation can be controlled so that it will untwist in either the S or Z direction.

BOW   Bowing or misalignment is often referred to as being **off-grain** and is quite visible in prints, but in solid colors, it is sometimes difficult to see whether a fabric is absolutely smooth or whether there is a distortion and twisting of the fabric between the two selvages. In this case, an end yarn is identified and followed through the test distance. One way of marking this is to trace a filling yarn clear across the fabric and then, using a straight edge, to trace the distortion or bow in the selvages on both sides; sewing measurements should be made on points ten yards from each end of the fabric and intermediate points. (This off-grain is the most bitter condemnation of fabrics by teachers of sewing.)

25. standard methods of testing and tolerances for knit goods.
AS L14.67-1951; ASTM D231-46

These methods of test apply particularly to knit goods which are intended to enter into manufacturing processes. Such materials may require special finishing or processing which will give them a different degree of performance than the fabric originally possessed. Under these conditions, the tests on the finished fabric are the official ones and supersede these, which are primarily for the manufacturer of garments and other articles. These tests can simply be listed as width, weight per square yard, count (number of wales or courses per inch), thickness, bursting strength, moisture regain, and crease determination. The bursting-strength machine imposes a load in the form of a round ball or an expanding spherical surface from a heavy rubber diaphragm against the flat surface of the fabric. It is, of course, intended primarily for knit goods on which regular tensile-strength tests cannot be conducted. When woven goods are tested, the yarns stretch slightly as the load increases, until the fabric is broken across the weaker set of yarns, generally the filling.

26. resistance to yarn slippage in silk, rayon, and acetate woven fabrics.
AS L14.102.1957; ASTM D434-42

This method of test applies to the measurement of the resistance to slippage of filling yarns on warp yarns or vice versa in silk, rayon, acetate, or synthetic fiber fabrics, and in combinations of these fibers. The resistance to slippage is the number of pounds of pull across a seam per inch of width necessary to produce an elongation of ¼-inch in excess of the normal stretch of the fabric under the same load. The standard breaking-strength machine of pendulum type is appropriate for this test, and it must have an autographic direction, for the test calls for the sewing together of two test pieces with either the warp or the filling yarns, whichever tends to show the greatest amount of seam slippage, being perfectly parallel. The test, then, is with the edges parallel to the seam, and not only the breaking strength of the seam but the amount of stretch and slippage will be recorded by the automatic recording device.

27. standard methods of test for air permeability of textile fabrics.
AS L14.51-1949; ASTM D737-46

This test procedure determines the air permeability of textile fabrics.

The tests must be made under standard conditions and basically employ a suction fan drawing air through a known area of fabric, using a circular orifice, the size of which determines the pressure drop across the fabric and enables the operator to measure the volume of air going through the fabric in a unit period of time.[21]

28. tentative method of test for yarn distortion in woven fabrics.
AS L14.103-1957; ASTM D1336-54T

The test method applies to the measurement of yarn distortion in woven fabrics of either warp or filling yarns after surface friction has been applied. The resistance to shifting is measured by the distance in one-hundredths of an inch, between the distorted yarn groups at the widest opening after shifting under a specified load.

---

[21] H. F. Schiefer and P. M. Boyland, "Improved Instrument for Measuring the Air Permeability of Fabrics," *Journal of Research,* National Bureau of Standards, 28, No. 5 (May 1942), p. 637 (Research Paper RP 1471).

Two definitions are required in this test:

1. YARN DISTORTION   **Yarn distortion** of the woven fabric is that condition whereby the surface appearance of the fabric is destroyed through the displacement of warp or filling yarns by shifting or sliding.

2. SHIFT MARK   **Shift mark** in a woven fabric is the opening or blister created in the fabric by sliding one set of yarns, warp or filling, across the other. The apparatus consists of a series or set of cylindrical rubber grippers, and the fabric is gripped between the two rounded contacting surfaces. The fabric shift tester is suitable for this test, using reciprocating arm attachments for the exertion of the force.

29. shrinkage in laundering and dimensional restorability of warp knit fabrics
ASTM D1487-57T

This test determines the total shrinkage of laundering and the dimensional restorability under specified forces. This method is only a means of obtaining reproducible results and cannot, at this stage of development, set up any tolerance or specifications. A domestic-type automatic washer is the preferred washing device; a rotary tumble-type dryer may be used, or the fabric may be drip-dried; pressing can be done by hand iron or by the tension presser. The restorability is that degree of dimensional recovery after the tension-presser operation, as compared with the sample after washing, tumble drying, flattening, and measuring.

The appendix contains reference to other tests which are either tentative within the technical societies, such as ASTM, or which are so-called private test methods. These procedures will doubtless be researched considerably by the responsible technical societies in order to establish more precise inter-laboratory agreement. This is customary in all these American Standards Association testing methods. These methods will simply be listed according to the name and responsible organization with no details, for they can be found in the Technical Society Yearbook and in the second volume of the L-22 Standard, if any laboratory is called upon to make such tests.

1   Proposed Method of Test for Dimensional Change of Knitted Fabrics in Laundering and Dimensional Restorability of the Laundered Fabric. ASTM Appendix 10.

2   Absorbency Tests. Total Absorption of Water (Haven's Method). American Viscose Corporation.

3   Thickness and Resiliency Tests for Blankets. American Viscose Corporation.

4   Shrinkage in Dry-Cleaning of Woven Fabrics. CS-59-44[22]

5   Strength of Cloth, Tearing; Tongue Method. CCC-T-191B Method 5134[23]

[22] Commercial Standard CS-59-44, Textiles—Testing and Reporting.
[23] Federal Specifications CCC-T-191B.

6 Weathering Resistance of Cloth; Accelerated Weathering Method (National Weathering Unit) CC-T-191B, Method 5804

7 Color Fastness to Sublimation—TDI No. 1, Textile Distributors Institute, Inc., New York.

8 Resistance to Needle-Cutting—TDI No. 2

9 Determination of Odor in Fabrics—TDI No. 3

10 Seam Strength of Garments or Textile Items, United States Testing Company Method.

TEXTILE STANDARDS FOR INSTITUTIONAL USERS

Under the sponsorship of the American Hotel Association, the Project L-24 —Textile Standards for Institutional Users—was announced in 1953 by the American Standards Association. These standards, available to such purchasers as hotels, hospitals, motels, steamship lines, dormitories, and other large purchasers and users of textiles of all kinds, were completed in December of 1955. As in the case of L-22, all elements of the textile industry combined in the task of arriving at workable, realistic standards which, on one hand, offered satisfactory service and use and, on the other hand, recognized not only the traditional fabrics and constructions entering into different end-use items but also the impact of the man-made fibers. The test methods were those of the National Societies, that is, ASTM and AATCC, and the commercial standards CS-59-44 and CCCT-191A.

Bradley[24] has incorporated the textile standards for L-24 with a textile purchasing guide for each end-use commodity, combined with a brief description of each item. He points out the significance of the standard and gives suggestions for purchasing each commodity, along with a typical wording to be used on all purchase orders for such products. For example, the recommendations for purchasing woven shower curtains suggested that the following wording be placed on all purchase orders for curtains to be obtained under this standard:

The woven shower curtains listed on this purchase order shall meet or exceed American Standard L-24.2.10 minimum performance requirements.

The significance is that this standard recognizes the minimum nature of the data and suggests strongly that when a manufacturer exceeds the standard in any particular, these superior features should be noted. If the purchaser and vendor are in agreement as to what the superior features should be, this information should also appear on the purchase order. Otherwise, the standard alone refers to the desired level of performance. This guide also includes directions for care, washing, cleaning, storage, grease-spotting, and supplies necessary to keep the goods in satisfactory condition.

[24] L. A. Bradley, *Hotel Textile Purchasing Guide* (American Hotel Association, 221 West 57th Street, New York 19, New York).

wash-and-wear not needed by institutions

The minimum performance requirements for institutional purchasers are necessarily somewhat higher than those in L-22 for the homemaker consumer because of the far greater wear and frequency of cleaning required of bedding in hotels, hospitals, and other institutions. The constant freshness and fine appearance, as well as cleanliness, of uniforms and work clothing worn in the presence of guests or customers require more regular and more severe washing methods. Generally such institutional purchasers will have their own laundry facilities and, in many cases, their own dry-cleaning plant. Under these conditions, it would appear that minimum-care or wash-and-wear garments would scarcely be necessary for these large-scale purchasers. There are several reasons for this conclusion.

1   A wash-and-wear uniform which has merely been touched up with an iron, which is the principal benefit of such minimum-care fabrics, would not pass inspection by the supervisor in comparison with uniforms which had been washed and carefully pressed according to standard practice in the restaurant, hotel, or hospital.

2   Some of the benefits of minimum-care garments are lost when they are washed and dried under too severe conditions. As a matter of general practice, approximately a half-load both in washer and drier is recommended in order to avoid water-wrinkles. Thus, such fabrics would not be satisfactorily washed in the ordinary wash load of the institution.

3   Regular laundry practices call for frequent use of bleaches, which might be damaging to the resin in resin-finished cottons, either through discoloration or strength loss. White nylon also would be discolored with too frequent use of chlorine bleach.

4   Even when washed, dried, and ironed under the most advantageous conditions, resin-treated cotton wash-and-wear articles would be at a disadvantage with regular cottons and probably with many other textile fibers, due to the loss of strength resulting from the resin treatment. The tear strength of such fabrics is generally recognized as being approximately 30 per cent less compared with untreated cottons from the same grey-goods construction. It might be noted that institutional housekeepers have complained that it is very difficult for them to find maids' or waitresses' uniforms which have not been given a wash-and-wear finish, despite the fact that a plain cotton of the same construction would be a far better purchase from the standpoint of durability and serviceability.

color code washing guides

L-24 was the first Standard to use the sewn-in labels as guideposts to the proper method of washing or cleaning garments purchased under this standard. Thus, the color purple designates garments and articles which can be washed at 160° F. with bleach; green, washable at 160° F. without bleach; blue, 120° F.

without bleach; yellow, 105° F. without bleach; and red, dry-cleaning.

The manner in which the color code will be used is shown by the quotation from Bradley's[25] Purchasing Guide.

Wash 160° F.—No Bleach

Wash 160°F.—no bleach—are completely washable with the exception that some property of color or pattern will not withstand bleaching. In addition to laundering conditions, the label will contain the minimum information as listed in the preceding subsection. The chlorine retention tests will not be specified for these products because normally no bleach should be used. The 1/16" wide color-band running the width or length of the label which identifies the products in this classification is green.

Woven shower curtains, some bed spreads, and screen-printed table napery are examples of products which could bear this label.

[25] *Ibid.*

women's and girls' selections in clothing

The point has been developed that fashion merchandise is in a unique position in the textile market because:

1 Its purchasing is confined to a relatively small group of potential consumers;

2 Its appeal is predominantly to the senses, and only the esthetic properties of the fabric or garment are of significance in the final choice;

3 It defies any attempt at standards or pre-testing of the material for utility;

4 It is generally discarded for obsolescence rather than wearing out.

Nevertheless, a more intense study of textile properties and buying problems should be directed toward the more stable lines growing out of fashion merchandise. Even staple products purchased year after year, often of the same fabric construction as the fashion favorites, are, at present, in a state of rather rapid change due to advances in textile technology and in the art of finishing.

In establishing any kind of judgment of consumer preference between fibers, in brand names, within certain price-line limitations, or in view of technical information available to the customer, all buyers at retail or in the home should recognize several basic hypotheses:

1 Real skill in buying textile products depends not only upon knowledge as to what are the desirable properties of fiber and fabric, but what are the individual requirements of the consumer, himself, who is making the purchase.

2   There is no textile fiber, fabric construction, or fiber composition which is best for *all end-use* applications or, in fact, for suits, for women's dresses, for children's play clothes, for men's shirts, or for any other item of merchandise at *each price line* carried by the store.

3   We cannot view textiles simply as materials, for, in use, they are inseparable from the finished product, the commodity into which the various textile elements have been combined.

4   Those qualities both esthetic and functional which influence the customer to make the purchase should last through the useful life of the article.

Numerous preference studies have been carried out by various services in the U.S. Department of Agriculture; these marketing research reports give much information on what facts influence customer purchasing of many commodities of women's and girls' wear and, at the same time, disclose the fact that the esthetic qualities still predominate in the initial impact on the customer. These studies have been made in state experiment stations and in the home economics departments of various land-grant universities. Meyers and Levine[1] reported that

cotton had a high ranking with teenage girls and was the fiber with which they claimed to have the greatest familiarity. Nine out of ten girls named one or more things they liked about cotton. A few of them, four out of ten, mentioned something they disliked about it. Most frequent criticism was the tendency of these fabrics to wrinkle.

Wool was widely preferred for outerwear and for winter clothes; about 6 out of 10 noted some feature about wool which they disliked, major faults being scratchy or irritating texture and the need for dry-cleaning the garment. This economic fact is often overlooked by customers. The most widely used synthetic fiber was nylon, which was greatly preferred in slips, blouses, summer dress-up (dressy) dresses, and anklets. Nylon was most frequently praised for its laundering qualities, for the relief from heavy ironing requirements, for its speed of drying, and for durability, lightness, and coolness. On the other hand, others claimed it to be warm, especially in summer weather, and to have a tendency to stick and cling. Transparency of nylon fabrics was another feature criticized by teenagers. Oddly enough, very few seemed to have as much familiarity with rayon as they should have had, and both rayon and Dacron received few comments or criticisms, due to lack of familiarity with the behavior of these fabrics in service. Orlon was recognized because of its use in sweaters.

With regard to comments on functionability in this study and in others, mothers seemed to be more concerned with launderability, durability, and expense. Girls were most likely to speak of weight and of appearance.

[1] Trienah Meyers and Daniel B. Levine, "Teenage Girls Discuss Their Wardrobes and Their Attitudes toward Cotton and Other Fibers," Report No. 155, Agricultural Marketing Service, Market Research Division, U.S. Department of Agriculture (1955).

TABLE 25-1 / FREQUENCY OF POSSESSION
OF NINETEEN CLOTHING ITEMS
BY 4400 GIRLS

Item	Per Cent Owning	Thousands of Girls
Winter skirts	98	4,400
Anklets or bobby socks	97	4,400
Summer blouses	96	4,400
Summer skirts	94	4,300
Dress-length slips	94	4,300
Winter blouses	93	4,200
Pajamas	91	4,10⌐
Stand-out petticoats	88	4,000
Shorts	87	3,900
Full-length coats	86	3,900
Slacks	84	3,800
Short coats	78	3,500
Summer every-day dresses	71	3,200
Sports jackets	71	3,200
Summer dress-up dresses	67	3,000
Winter dress-up dresses	51	2,300
Winter every-day dresses	39	1,800
Raincoats	32	1,500
Multipurpose coats	25	1,100

Table 25-1 indicates the percentage of respondents to a census population report.[1] Respondents holding at least one item in each clothing category as indicated by the survey are included.

Table 25-2[2] demonstrates the reasons for preference of several fibers for ready-made summer dress-up dresses on the part of the girls and of mothers. The girls preferred cotton for the various reasons of care and laundering—58 per cent of the answers—weight and comfort accounting for some 47 per cent. Appearance and styling were shown to be important to 34 per cent. Cotton also ranked higher than any of the other fabrics in variety and selection—18 per cent —demonstrating rather clearly the versatility of this fiber and its ability to be utilized in such a wide number of fabric constructions. It will be noted, incidentally, that many of the answers total more than 100 per cent. This is because the respondents gave more than one reason for preference. In the case of nylon, appearance and styling were the predominant factors—65 per cent—with care and laundering and weight and comfort coming next. Rayon and linen had a most surprising preponderance of answers in appearance and styling—81 and 85 per cent, respectively; but these two fibers did not rate nearly as heavily as did the

[1] United States Bureau of Census, Population Report, Series P-57, No. 195, October 1955.
[2] Report No. 155, Agricultural Marketing Service (1955).

TABLE 25-2 / SUMMER DRESS-UP DRESSES

Girls who had ready-made summer dress-up dresses and said they liked certain fibers best, and mothers who said they liked certain fibers best: "Why do you prefer (fiber liked best) for dress-up summer dresses?"

FIBER PREFERRED FOR SUMMER DRESS-UP DRESSES[1]

Reasons for Preference	GIRLS				MOTHERS	
	Cotton	Nylon	Rayon	Linen	Cotton	Nylon
	Per Cent²	Per Cent²	Per Cent²	Per Cent²	Per Cent²	Per Cent²
Care and laundering	**58**	**41**	**16**	**21**	**63**	**74**
Easy to wash and care for	40	26	6	12	42	58
Easy to iron	16	3	4	9	16	9
Washable; no dry-cleaning required	13	6	4	1	15	13
Good appearance after laundering	9	1	1	—	8	—
Starches well	7	—	3	—	3	—
Less expensive to keep clean	3	—	—	—	7	1
Doesn't require frequent washing	3*	1	2	3	2	2
Requires little or no ironing	*	20	*	—	3	39
Dries quickly	*	6	—	—	—	9
All other care and laundering	—	—	1	1	1	1
Weight and comfort	**47**	**35**	**19**	**13**	**30**	**14**
Light weight, cool	42	34	6	10	28	10
Doesn't scratch, itch, stick, cling	3	*	9	2	1	1
Comfortable	3	—	—	*	1	—
Fits, hangs, drapes well	2	1	6	2	*	4
Appearance and styling	**34**	**65**	**81**	**85**	**38**	**43**
Looks nice, good, pretty	15	23	22	24	14	15

Looks neat, fresh, crisp; doesn't wrinkle	13	21	11	40	18	14
Good for dress-up wear, dressy, fancy	8	34	61	44	9	26
Good styling, lines	2	1	1	6	1	2
Good for everyday wear; simple, informal	2	—	—	2	6	1
Not too sheer, thin	1	1	1	—	1	—
Grownup looking	*	7	4	1	16	6
Variety and selection	18					
Variety of styles; large selection	8	3	—	—	5	2
Variety of colors, prints, patterns	7	3	4	1	10	5
Variety of fabrics, weaves, materials	4	1	—	—	4	—
Durability	8	6	12	15	22	13
Durable; doesn't fray, ravel, split, tear	4	3	5	10	18	11
Holds colors; doesn't fade, run	3	2	1	2	5	2
Holds shape; doesn't shrink, stretch	3	1	10	4	*	3
Suitable for more occasions, seasons	5	2	*	6	3	1
Less expensive	5	1	—	5	9	4
Popular in style	2	—	1	—	2	—
Suitable for teenager's type, personality	2	1	—	2	8	2
Practical	*	—	—	—	1	—
Easy to sew, mend	—	2	—	6	1	—
All other	*	2	—	6	*	—
Not ascertained	4	5	2	2	6	6
Number of cases	589	242	70	69	211	81

[1] Numbers preferring other fibers too small for separate analysis.
[2] Percentages (left column) add to more than their group totals (right column), and these add to more than 100 because some respondents gave more than 1 answer.
[3] Asterisk indicates less than 1 per cent.

others in care and laundering or in weight and comfort. These latter two fibers, rayon and linen, rated 12 and 15 per cent, respectively, in durability, whereas, nylon, the most wear-resistant of all fibers, had a rating of only 6 per cent. This is not to be construed as a criticism of the wear of nylon, but simply that other factors were rated as more important in the case of this synthetic. The mothers' ratings were confined to cotton and nylon. They proved to be more conscious of care and laundering than were their daughters; cotton scored 63 per cent, and nylon, 74 per cent, in this phase of textile experience. Second was appearance and styling—38 per cent for cotton and 43 per cent for nylon. Mothers rated both these fibers higher on account of durability than did their daughters.

Tables such as this one cannot simply be dismissed as a somewhat haphazard check on the preferences of consumers of textile products. They reveal many interesting facts which should benefit not only other consumers but also producers of textile fabrics for these specific end-use articles. What the user likes is a positive approach to which textile performance studies may well be directed and evaluated. There remains a wide open field of research along this same line dealing with many textile commodities in which the consumer reaction to products produced under a program of performance standards may be evaluated against what amounts to untested merchandise selling at approximately the same price range or perhaps at a price bracket immediately below the standard products' retail value. Such studies must, of course, await the wider acceptance and use of textile standards in staple merchandise lines.

EFFECT OF CASUAL LIVING ON WOMEN'S AND GIRLS' WEARING APPAREL TYPES

One has only to sit in a classroom in any college or university with women students to see the extent to which skirts and sweaters have become almost the uniform of the undergraduate. Similar trends are to be seen in high schools. When dress regulations permit and the weather becomes warmer, blouses and Bermuda shorts will replace the heavier sweater and skirt. Rarely will dresses be seen on more than a few of the students. At one time the working girl would no more think of going to the office or the store or other places of employment clad in anything other than a dress or a suit than would the young businessman think of going to his place of employment without matching trousers and suit coat. Today both sexes appear more and more in what one might describe as a mix-up assembly; sweaters and skirts will be worn by these girls, slacks and sports jackets by the young men. One might say that casual living has made casualties of formal attire.

Older women also have responded to this urge toward greater comfort and convenience. Many women who still would never think of going downtown to shop without being impeccably dressed in suit or dress and hat and gloves think nothing now of appearing in the suburban branch of the same store clad in sweater and slacks or even shorts. Thus, the shopping facility has moved out to meet the customer, so as to make it both easier and more comfortable for her to make her selection. This more informal way of life is a general characteristic of today's suburbia, but at the same time that the pendulum is swinging so far to the comfort or "at ease" side, it is also swinging equally far to the other side, so that retailers have noted with considerable pleasure that there is increased attention being given to formal attire by both men and women on special occasions. Thus, it seems to be the afternoon dress or the street dress which is the principal casualty of this modern way of life. The challenge is ever present for the textile industry to rebuild demand for many of these special dress and suit fabrics by artful dyeing and printing and through new textures, new fabrics, and more attractive blends.

Fig. 25-1 Production of women's, misses' and juniors' clothing. (*From Consumer Clothing Expenditures* [*An Analysis of Trends*], *Ruth Jackendoff, The Wool Bureau, Inc. 360 Lexington Ave., New York 17, New York.*)

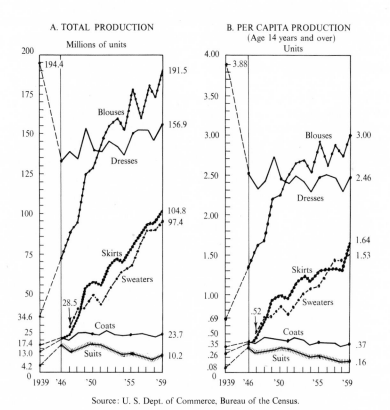

Source: U. S. Dept. of Commerce, Bureau of the Census.

417

Figure 25-1A shows the total production in millions of units of various articles of women's and girls' outerwear from 1939 to 1959. Note the almost vertical growth of blouses from 34.6 million units in 1939 to 191.5 million in 1959, and in the case of skirts, from 13 million to 104.8 million. Sweaters increased from 28.5 million in 1946 to 97.4 in 1959. Dresses, on the other hand, lost ground sharply from 194.4 million in 1939 down to approximately 133 million in 1946 and 156.9 million units in 1959. Suits and coats showed little growth and almost a uniform flat line at 23.7 for coats and 10.2 for suits in 1959.

The companion graph (B), also from Miss Jackendoff's presentation at the workshop of fashion merchandising of the Fashion Institute of Technology in New York, June 3, 1960, shows the per capita production of the clothing for girls and women over 14 years of age. The per capita possessions of any textile class in college would probably show a higher number of items in the possession of the students than these figures show for 1959. The reason is that these graphs represent the number produced per capita during each of these years, and there is no evaluation of the accumulation of these items over a period of several years, so any conclusions arrived at by an individual class should be in terms of the number of these items purchased by each student per year over whatever period of years they may remember clearly.

GARMENT SIZES

Women's sizes will be discussed in greater detail in Chapter 29. However, a considerable part of the pleasure and comfort associated with any wearing apparel is that it be the proper size, not too constrictive so as to interfere with one's body movement but not so baggy and full as to give an unpleasing appearance. With the improvements in the arts and technology of textile finishing and much better control over the shrinkage of garments in washing and in service, there is now little excuse for anyone to have to buy an out-sized garment in order to compensate for natural shrinkage of the fibers or fabrics during washing. One possible exception to this would be in articles which must be or are likely to be dried in an automatic household dryer, especially knitted cottons. In outerwear for women and girls, there are five standard size ranges:

1. misses, 10 to 20
2. junior, 7 to 15
3. women's, 32 to 52
4. half, 12½ to 26½
5. stout, 34½ to 52½

Another great step forward was made in satisfying the problem of women selecting dresses made by different manufacturers when, in 1944, the National

Bureau of Standards issued the voluntary Commercial Standards CS-13-44 for the body measurements and size classifications for women's dress patterns.

WOMEN'S DRESSES

Similarity of replies for other items may be shown in the following table. Two questions with no reference whatever to specific items, but dealing entirely with evaluation of the fibers, were:

1   Tell everything you like about each fiber.
2   Tell everything you dislike about each fiber.

Responses to these questions appear to have been colored by the time of exposure or experience, because most of the girls were fairly familiar with cotton, wool, rayon, and nylon, but knew little about Orlon and Dacron.

cotton likes

Easy to wash, easy to take care of, easy to iron, cool in summer, warm in winter, durable, and nice appearance and style were the type of answers. Sixty per cent of the girls said that there was nothing they disliked about cotton; the major criticism among elder consumers was that it wrinkled easily.

nylon

Favorable comments were: ease of care and laundering, freedom from ironing, quick drying, appearance, and styling of nylon; its weight, comfort, and durability were also praised. Criticisms of nylon were that it was too warm in the summer and stuck or clung to the body, or that it was too thin and sheer. Some comment was made as to lack of durability (possibly seams). Other comments were in regard to fraying, raveling, loss of shape, stretching, loss of color, and development of pills.

wool

Warmth was the outstanding virtue by more than 70 per cent. Appearance, wrinkle resistance, durability, shape retention, ease of care, and a variety of wide selection were other praiseworthy features.

Criticisms were minor: about one-third said they had no criticism of wool; about 40 per cent said there was some skin irritation; 20 per cent said it was difficult or expensive to care for.

rayon

Surprisingly, there was not much knowledge about this fiber, possibly because it was not clearly identified in the minds of the girls; therefore, they would not express an opinion favorable or unfavorable. Twenty per cent stated there was nothing that they liked about rayon; about the same number said that there was nothing they disliked about it. The main features listed against it were difficulty of care and lack of durability.

nylon, orlon, and dacron

Few volunteered to having had much experience with these fibers, but ease of care and laundering, light weight, comfort, and durability were the major advantages claimed for them. One criticism was that the yarns stretch and pill, and they did not hold their shape.

The mothers' comments were not greatly different, except that they tended to give nylon much more credit for wrinkle resistance than wool, which was contrary to the response of their daughters.

Although the evidence is that not only the teenagers but their mothers respond principally to esthetic properties of the garment and fabric in making the original selection, greater attention to their needs is now being provided by labels. The National Retail Merchants Association, of which more than 3,000 retail stores are members, was trying to simplify shopping and to give more information to the customer in three different programs, all involving labels.

1   The use of a distinctive color of label showing the size of the dress, this to be uniform for all articles for women and girls.

2   Graphic labels showing the kind of washing operation the garment will withstand.

3   A label identifying the article as conforming to the Textile Standard L-22.

4   Fiber content disclosure.

Customers are paying more attention to labels now than formerly. A study of textiles by Drake and Grimes[3] reports that women participating in this study concluded that some labels should give the source of the dress, such as the brand or manufacturer's name or the name of the store. They wanted information as to whether the dress should be dry-cleaned or washed, also data as to the fabric content and size placed so it could be found readily. It will be noted, therefore, that the name, the washability, and the size are already parts of the various programs of the National Retail Merchants Association, and the fourth item is now the law of the land, since the Textile Fiber Products Identification Act went into effect on March 3, 1960, and is under the Federal Trade Commission for administration.

This study reported the following information available on some labels on 4538 dresses in stores.

[3] Phyllis Drake and Mary Anna Grimes, "Labeling of Ready-made Street Dresses," Bulletin 943, Texas Agricultural Experiment Station, College Station, Texas (November 1959).

TABLE 25-3 / INFORMATION ON SEWN LABELS ON 4,538 DRESSES IN STORES [4]

| | DRESSES WITH INFORMATION | | PRICE OF DRESSES | | | |
| | | | UNDER $20 | | $20 AND OVER | |
Information	Number	Per Cent	Number	Per Cent	Number	Per Cent
Number of dresses	4,538		3,366		1,172	
Brand	2,594	57	1,919	57	675	58
Size	2,740	60	2,370	70	370	32
Dry-clean or wash	23	(1)	17	(1)	6	(1)
Iron temperature	32	(1)	15	(1)	17	1
Fiber name	251	6	195	6	56	5
Fiber per cent	92	2	58	2	34	3
Fabric name	19	(1)	12	(1)	7	(1)
Manufacturer's name	136	3	84	2	52	4
Store name	287	6	61	2	226	19

(1) Less than 1 per cent.

[4] Phyllis Drake and Mary Anna Grimes, Texas Agricultural Experiment Station, Bulletin 943 (November 1958).

Manufacturers and retailers alike agreed that these directions for care often were not followed: the careless use of bleach, excessive heat when ironing, and similar infractions of the rules resulted in many consumer complaints. The possibility of such misuses is very rarely considered in advance by the customer when making the purchase; in other words, he does not consciously look for or anticipate bleach resistance or resistance to heat in ironing; but having ruined the garment, he then considers he has a complaint which can be brought back to the store and hence to the manufacturer.

Although the study of consumer complaints conducted by the author and his associates of the Commodity Standards Fellowship at Mellon Institute[5] was based on textile complaints from 1938 to 1950, the table on consumer complaints concerning women's dresses confirms the general opinion held by manufacturers and retailers as to the care with which consumers actually read the labels, or the use to which they put them after purchase. The date of these tables, dealing chiefly with rayon and acetate, was 1950.

SWEATERS

The large sweater wardrobe of today can be credited largely to the beautiful appearance and textures and the almost unlimited colors available in sweaters knitted of the new synthetic yarns at moderate prices. First nylon, then Dacron, and now Orlon and its sister acrylics have been in vogue and have offered keen competition to wool in sweaters. The development of stretch yarns (Chapter 7) and the specially textured yarns have improved the softness, the loftiness, and the fit of these synthetic fiber sweaters and at the same time have reduced their

[5] Maintained by the Kaufmann Department Stores, Inc., Pittsburgh, Pa.

TABLE 25-4 / USE VERSUS ABUSE AS SOURCES FOR CUSTOMER COMPLAINTS

Cause of Customer Complaint	L-22 Standard Test Applicable	WOMEN'S RAINWEAR			WOMEN'S SKIRTS			WOMEN'S JACKETS			WOMEN'S BLOUSES			WOMEN'S COATS		
		Rayon	Acetate	All	Rayon	Acetate	All	Rayon	Acetate	All	Rayon	Acetate	All	Rayon	Acetate	All
1. Perspiration causing breaks & holes[1]	13–17				1	1	2	2	2	4	13	14	170			1
2. Perspiration causing color damage[1]	13										5	5	19			
3. Perspiration causing bleeding[1]						2	2	1	2				3			3
4. Washing causing shrinkage	41	5	4	21	1	2	10	1			2	2				11
5. Washing causing color change[2]	19	2		4	1	1	8	1		15	19	29	87	1	1	11
6. Washing causing fabric breaks	7				3		4	3		15	14	15	60	1	1	4
7. Ironing causing damage	19						4		1		28	44	83			6
8. Bleaching and staining	19	3		8	6	3	16	1	2	15	3	311	328	2		21
9. Chemicals causing holes			2	2	1	4	11	1	2	26	12	20	60	2		9
10. Strain in wear (rips, cuts, etc.)	7		2	4	1	2	24	3			2	9	43			
11. Abrasion in wear (holes and shine)	7	2		8	3	1	17	3		6	22	40	118	1		14
12. Heat or burning (except ironing)	27		1	3						15	8	15	45	2		65
13. Moth and carpet beetle damage							1				1	4	8			3
14. Seam failure in use							3						4			19
15. Sun rotting of fabric											2	3	6			
16. Sun fading of dye	15	1	1	1			1				2		17			26
17. Gas or fume fading	9		3	4		4	4		2	10	1	1	31		9	10
18. Garment construction[3]	43	1			3		6				15	24	58		1	20
19. Shifting of yarns							2					18	101		1	16
20. Processing defects & loss of finish[4]	32–31	2	8	18	2	5	11	1			17	60	49	3		2
21. Inadequate or wrong labeling[5]		5		5			1		1	250	16	20	28		1	22
22. Dye crocking in service	19	4	2	12	2	1	7	4			10	27	56	1	1	6
23. Miscellaneous[6]		3		18	3	5	21	3	1	24	19	19	64	3	2	50
TOTAL		28	21	108	27	31	155	24	11	365	211	690	1438	13	16	308
Customer at Fault		43%	33%	46%	63%	52%	66%	67%	64%	67%	61%	73%	72%	54%	6%	51%
Merchandise at Fault		57%	67%	54%	37%	48%	34%	33%	36%	33%	39%	27%	28%	46%	94%	49%

Data from Commodity Standards Fellowship of Kaufmann Department Stores, Mellon Institute, Pittsburgh, Pa.

[1] Including careless use of anti-perspirants.
[2] Excessive strain while wet.
[3] Including faulty seams, wrong fit, etc.
[4] Holes in discharge prints, chlorine retention, finish odor, water penetration, etc.
[5] Leading to customer misuse of article.
[6] Dermatitis, mildew, pilling (for other causes than above) etc.

TABLE 25-4 / USE VERSUS ABUSE AS SOURCES FOR CUSTOMER COMPLAINTS
(continued)

Cause of Customer Complaint	L-22 Standard Test Applicable	WOMEN'S PLAYCLOTHES & SLACKS			UNDERWEAR & FOUNDATION GARMENTS			WOMEN'S BATHING SUITS			WOMEN'S SUITS			WOMEN'S UNIFORMS		
		Rayon	Acetate	All	Rayon	Acetate	All	Rayon	Acetate	All	Rayon	Acetate	All	Rayon	Acetate	All
1. Perspiration causing breaks & holes[1]	—			1	1		2			1	2	3	6	1		33
2. Perspiration causing color damage[1]	13–17			1							1		2			
3. Perspiration causing bleeding[1]	13												15			
4. Washing causing shrinkage	41	3		8	2	1	15	2		8	2	2	15			7
5. Washing causing color change[2]	19	1		7	1		2	4	1	8	1	1	4		4	8
6. Washing causing fabric breaks	7	2		2	6	1	16	1	2	6			3		8	11
7. Ironing causing damage	19	2	2	7		2	4	1		1			4			11
8. Bleaching and staining	19	2	1	7	2	2	4	3	1	9		4	4	1		9
9. Chemicals causing holes	—			3	2	2	5	1	1	8		3	9	5	1	46
10. Strain in wear (rips, cuts, etc.)	7	2	1	6	3	2	12	6	10	38	2	2	5	1	2	13
11. Abrasion in wear (holes and shine)	7	1		7	4		4	5	9	31	1	1	5		1	8
12. Heat or burning (except ironing)	27						1				1		15	1		1
13. Moth and carpet beetle damage	—						1									
14. Seam failure in use	—							3	3	7		1	4			1
15. Sun rotting of fabric	15	1		5						3	1		2			
16. Sun fading of dye	9			2						4			3			
17. Gas or fume fading	—	2	1	5				6	1	17		28	29		1	2
18. Garment construction[3]	43						2		1	1		1	5			2
19. Shifting of yarns	—			1	1	1	3	4	2	5	2		2		1	7
20. Processing defects & loss of finish[4]	32–31	1		2	5	1	8	1	4	5	2	7	14	1	1	6
21. Inadequate or wrong labeling[5]	—							6		15			2		5	1
22. Dye crocking in service	19	2		9	2	2	2	10	3	31	3	2	12	2		6
23. Miscellaneous[6]				3	1		12	9	4	41	3	5	26	1	5	10
TOTAL		19	10	76	30	13	93	62	46	239	26	61	168	16	23	176
Customer at Fault		68%	40%	64%	70%	62%	71%	37%	52%	49%	35%	30%	43%	94%	70%	84%
Merchandise at Fault		32%	60%	36%	30%	38%	29%	63%	48%	51%	65%	70%	57%	6%	30%	16%

Data from Commodity Standards Fellowship of Kaufmann Department Stores, Mellon Institute, Pittsburgh, Pa.

[1] Including careless use of anti-perspirants.
[2] Excessive strain while wet.
[3] Including faulty seams, wrong fit, etc.
[4] Holes in discharge prints, chlorine retention, finish odor, water penetration, etc.
[5] Leading to customer misuse of article.
[6] Dermatitis, mildew, pilling (for other causes than above) etc.

TABLE 25-4 / USE VERSUS ABUSE AS SOURCES FOR CUSTOMER COMPLAINTS
(continued)

Cause of Customer Complaint	L-22 Standard Test Applicable	WOMEN'S DRESSES			WOMEN'S ROBES OR PAJAMAS			WOMEN'S SLIPS			GIRLS' DRESSES			CHILDREN'S SHIRTS & BLOUSES		
		Rayon	Acetate	All	Rayon	Acetate	All	Rayon	Acetate	All	Rayon	Acetate	All	Rayon	Acetate	All
1. Perspiration causing breaks & holes[1]	—	72	61	337	2		8		2	3			7			2
2. Perspiration causing color damage[1]	13–17	26	42	93			1									
3. Perspiration causing bleeding[1]	13	21	14	47			2									
4. Washing causing shrinkage	41	31	22	116	8	1	18	12	11	38	1	3	4	1		1
5. Washing causing color change[2]	19	39	48	190	11	2	47	2	1	11	1		21	1		16
6. Washing causing fabric breaks	7	59	12	87	11	4	20	11	8	26			1	1		4
7. Ironing causing damage	19	7	112	142	2	10	16		17	29	2	5	9	1	5	9
8. Bleaching and staining	19	33	87	206	3	5	20	2	1	12	1	1	13	1	2	12
9. Chemicals causing holes	—	22	17	125	1	3	11	1	2	9	1		25			18
10. Strain in wear (rips, cuts, etc.)	7	102	29	331	3	2	16	10	10	41			15	1		11
11. Abrasion in wear (holes and shine)	7	34	22	106	2		11	3	5	21			8	2	1	11
12. Heat or burning (except ironing)	27	3		8	1		2			2			4		1	1
13. Moth and carpet beetle damage	—			10			2									
14. Seam failure in use	—	2	3	17	1		2		1	2	2		3			
15. Sun rotting of fabric	—			15												
16. Sun fading of dye	15	7	5	38			4						1			
17. Gas or fume fading	9	6	193	201		18	18					3	3			
18. Garment construction[3]	—	28	13	61	3	2	11	5	1	11	4	2	11	3		4
19. Shifting of yarns	43	35	17	68	1	5	14	9	1	64	2	2	4	1		2
20. Processing defects & loss of finish[4]	32–31	94	34	182	23	2	34	1	6	5	3	2	11	5	1	9
21. Inadequate or wrong labeling[5]	—	7	1	9		1	3			4			2			8
22. Dye crocking in service	19	86	14	200	4	2	24	1	4	5	5	2	16		8	8
23. Miscellaneous[6]	—	51	18	143	4	2	26	2		21	1		11	1		2
TOTAL		765	764	2632	80	59	310	59	75	505	23	21	166	17	19	118
Customer at Fault		59%	61%	64%	55%	46%	56%	69%	76%	63%	26%	38%	62.7%	41%	53%	72%
Merchandise at Fault		41%	39%	36%	45%	54%	44%	31%	24%	37%	74%	62%	37.3%	59%	47%	28%

Data from Commodity Standards Fellowship of Kaufmann Department Stores, Mellon Institute, Pittsburgh, Pa.

[1] Including careless use of anti-perspirants.
[2] Excessive strain while wet.
[3] Including faulty seams, wrong fit, etc.
[4] Holes in discharge prints, chlorine retention, finish odor, water penetration, etc.
[5] Leading to customer misuse of article.
[6] Dermatitis, mildew, pilling (for other causes than above) etc.

TABLE 25-5

Women and girls who had sweaters in their active wardrobes: Percentage distribution of number of sweaters currently owned

Background Characteristics	NUMBER OF SWEATERS OWNED							Average	Cases
	1 Per Cent	2 Per Cent	3 Per Cent	4 Per Cent	5 or 6 Per Cent	7-8 or 9 Per Cent	10 or More Per Cent	Per Cent	Number
Women sweater owners	21	21	16	11	13	11	7	4.0	1,798
Age group:									
Under 30 years	9	12	14	11	18	21	15	5.7	501
30–39 years	16	19	14	16	17	11	7	4.2	437
40–49 years	27	21	16	13	11	8	4	3.5	349
50 years and over	33	34	18	7	5	2	1	2.4	511
Girls 14 to 17 years[1]	3	7	7	11	22	24	26[2]	7.4	1,676

[1] Girls 14 to 17 were interviewed in a separate study and are not included in any of the other groupings.
[2] Fifteen per cent of the teenage girls owned 10 to 12 sweaters; 11 per cent owned more than 12 sweaters.

TABLE 25-6

Women and girls who had bought sweaters in the past year: Percentage distribution of number of sweaters bought

Background Characteristics	NUMBER OF SWEATERS BOUGHT							8 or More	Average	Cases
	1 Per Cent	2 Per Cent	3 Per Cent	4 Per Cent	5 Per Cent	6 Per Cent	7 Per Cent	Per Cent	Per Cent	Number
Women sweater buyers	56	20	9	6	3	2	2	2	2.1	892
Age group:										
Under 30 years	44	19	13	10	4	3	3	4	2.6	286
30–39 years	51	22	12	5	4	3	1	2	2.1	254
40–49 years	65	22	6	3	1	2	—	1	1.7	183
50 years and over	74	18	3	3	1	—	1	—	1.4	169
Girls 14 to 17 years[1]	14	14	14	14	11	10	6	17[2]	4.8	1,362

[1] Girls 14 to 17 were interviewed in a separate study and are not included in any of the other groupings.
[2] Eight per cent of the teenage girls bought 8 or 9 sweaters in the past year; 9 per cent bought 10 or more.

weight. These sweaters are much less expensive than wool sweaters of similar texture and softness, such as fine lambs' wool and cashmere. Hoxtem[6] showed the number of sweaters owned by women under 30 years of age, 30 to 39 years of age, 40 to 49 years of age, and 50 years and over, and of girls from 14 to 17 years; also the number of sweaters bought in the preceding year by women and girls in these same age categories. This, Table 25-5, indicated 15 per cent of the teenage girls owned 10 to 12 sweaters and that 11 per cent owned more than 12 sweaters. Table 25-6 showed 8 per cent of these girls bought 8 or 9 sweaters in the past year and 9 per cent bought 10 or more.

Cotton sweaters and lightweights still are popular for spring and summer wear.

It must be kept in mind that sweaters are invariably a knitted garment. Most sweaters are of the weft-knit structure in which a single yarn is knit or fed at a time to a great number of needles in the weft or cross-wise direction, or filling-wise in woven fabrics, to produce a flat knitted article or a cylindrical one (see Chapter 4 on knitting). This forms a series of yarn loops in the horizontal direction. Much of the elasticity of the garment depends upon the tightness of the knitted loops and thus on the ability of the fabric to yield with the body movement. The knitted fabric is versatile, and the intricacy of designs is virtually unlimited, for it requires the feeding in of different colored yarns to the needles at predetermined intervals to produce the desired pattern effects, or having the needles pick up extra yarns. The knitting machine also has the advantage of being able to produce a garment shaped to the body by varying tensions or by adding to the number of needles or taking needles away.

It is important that the sweater be washable, if possible. Many are used for active or semi-active sports; others replace the conventional jacket when traveling or on informal occasions. The yarns are of loose structure and tend to pick up lint and dust rather readily within the interstices of the individual yarns. Therefore, the more complete cleaning afforded by washing is the better way of keeping them fresh in appearance. Such sweaters should, of course, not shrink or stretch when wet or during drying; the colors should be fast not only to washing but to sunlight as they dry. One of the consumer complaints heard rather frequently about sweaters, particularly those composed of synthetic fibers, is the tendency of the material to ball up or pill in areas of abrasion, for example, inside the elbow, under the armpits, and perhaps in the middle of the back, where the yarns have been worn against a rather rough upholstery. Pilling was once a much more serious problem than it is now. The original nylon sweaters pilled badly, but when a somewhat heavier nylon filament was used instead of the finer denier corresponding in fiber size to cashmere, the tendency to pill was greatly reduced.

[6] Esther M. Hoxtem, "Women's Attitudes toward Wool and Other Fibers," U.S. Department of Agriculture, Agricultural Marketing Service, Marketing Service Division, Marketing Research Report No. 153, 1957.

Pills can be removed from sweaters, whether of wool, cashmere, nylon, Orlon, Dacron, or any of the newer fibers, by means of a very gentle brushing with a stiff nylon brush or a pet brush, such as used for grooming a dog or a cat. Care must be taken not to tear filaments out of the yarns. An electric razor, used with care, can also remove these pills readily.

men's and boys' wear

The garment industry manufacturing men's and boys' wear is characterized by large factory units buying goods by the hundreds of thousands of yards and generally using a high proportion of staple fabric constructions year after year. Thus, it is easier for them to set up staple lines which may differ slightly from one season to another in color or texture, depending upon the market, but basically the same fabrics are often used over a long period of time. This means that a manufacturing company can set up its own standards of quality or performance to be met by the fabrics they buy. Similarly, large retail units, such as Sears, Roebuck & Company, Montgomery Ward, J. C. Penney, and large department stores and chains, can set up their own specifications for private brand lines. This is important because men's and boys' wear, both inner and outer apparel, are subject to greater wear demands in terms of time than are articles worn by girls and women.

Utility and comfort are of great concern; if any shirts, slacks, or suits fail to meet both criteria, they are simply relegated to the closet and rarely worn.

GROWTH OF CASUAL WEAR

Casual dress has had a terrific impact on manufacturers of white dress shirts traditionally worn with a necktie. Today the men's shirt department in the average department store sells approximately two sports shirts to every dress shirt. The Bureau of the Census reports a threefold output of men's and boys' sports shirts between 1946 and 1959. Slacks and sports shirts or shorts with shirts are the campus dress for spring, summer, and fall; sports shirts and slacks with an odd jacket or sweater, instead of the traditional suit, constitute the usual daytime attire for the winter season. The sports jacket and sports shirt with slacks have even appeared in town wear, although the well-dressed professional man or young business initiate must wear a suit and shirt with tie to be properly dressed.

A Bureau of Agricultural Economics study[1] reports various age groups' answers to the question: "In the long run, which do you think is most economical —to buy a separate jacket and trousers or to buy a suit?" In the 16- to 19-year age group, 52 per cent favored the jacket and trousers, to 36 per cent for those 45 years and older. Preferences for suits rose with the age group, beginning at 27 per cent for those 16 to 19; 42 per cent, 20 to 29; 50 per cent, 30 to 44; and then down to 40 per cent for those 45 years and older, the latter probably being influenced by a more sedentary life and greater amount of leisure time.

TABLE 26-1 / RELATION BETWEEN AGE AND REPLIES TO THE QUESTION: ''IN THE LONG RUN, WHICH DO YOU THINK IS MOST ECONOMICAL—TO BUY A SEPARATE JACKET AND TROUSERS OR TO BUY A SUIT?''

OWNERS OF SPORTS JACKETS[1]

Considered More Economical	16 to 19 Years Per Cent	20 to 29 Years Per Cent	30 to 44 Years Per Cent	45 Years and Over Per Cent
Jacket and trousers	52	42	39	36
Suit	27	42	50	40
No difference	7	10	6	14
Didn't know	10	5	4	10
Not ascertained	4	1	1	( )[2]
Total Per Cent	100	100	100	100
Number of cases	63	311	218	108

[1] Two men whose ages were not ascertained are omitted from this table.
[2] Less than one per cent.

The men who thought a suit more economical than jacket and trousers combination indicated that there were more uses for the suit, that it was appropriate for more occasions. No other reason approached this in significance, as is shown in the following table.

[1] Men's Preferences among Wool Suits, Coats, and Jackets, Agricultural Information Bulletin No. 64, U.S. Department of Agriculture, 1951.

TABLE 26-2 / REASONS MEN GAVE FOR
THINKING A SUIT MORE ECONOMICAL
THAN JACKET AND TROUSERS
COMBINATION

Reasons Given	Owners of Sports Jackets Who Thought a Suit Was More Economical Per Cent[1]
More use for a suit; suit appropriate for more occasions	61
Initial cost of suit lower or just as low	17
Suit coat and trousers could be worn either together or separately	11
Suit lasts longer	8
Suit could be worn all year round, while sports jacket could not	5
Preferred suit; didn't like jacket and trousers combination	2
Other reasons	5
Didn't know	1
Not ascertained	4
Number of Cases	256

[1] Percentages add to more than 100 because some men gave more than one reason.

Of a group of 247 stating that a jacket and trousers combination was more economical than a suit, 36 per cent indicated that there was more variety and the appearance of a larger wardrobe, because the jacket and/or trousers could be worn separately and in different combinations. A lower cost and more occasion to wear this combination were also important factors. It is reasonable to assume that the last ten years, since this study was completed, have seen an increased swing toward the casual wear, as the advantages of synthetic fiber combinations with wool or cotton have given the casual jacket or sports jacket even more sales appeal than they had previously. It must be remembered that this study included only wool jackets, and the extremely lightweight blended fiber, colorful sports jackets of recent summers were unknown in 1951.

See Appendix for collateral statistical data.

TABLE 26-3 / REASONS MEN GAVE FOR
THINKING A JACKET AND TROUSERS
COMBINATION WAS MORE
ECONOMICAL THAN A SUIT

Reasons Given	Owners of Sports Jackets Who Thought a Jacket and Trousers Combination Was More Economical Per Cent[1]
More variety, appearance of larger wardrobe because jacket and/or trousers could be worn separately and in different combinations	36

Initial cost lower	34
More occasion to wear sports jacket and trousers; more use for a sports jacket	16
Jacket and trousers could be replaced separately	14
One sports jacket outlasts several pairs of trousers	10
Cleaning cost less	5
Longer-wearing; wears longer than a suit	3
Other reasons	3
Didn't know	1
Not ascertained	4
Number of Cases	247

[1] Percentages add to more than 100 because some men gave more than one reason.

For men's and boys' suits, wool is still the most wanted fiber. Durability, appearance, texture, and comfort are associated with wool. The old enemies, the clothes moth and carpet beetle, can now be controlled by permanent insect-proofing treatment which lasts the life of the garment. The protection against cold given by wool, due to its moisture absorbency, cannot be equalled by any other fiber—natural or synthetic. The superior resistance to wear-wrinkles of some of the synthetic fibers, such as the polyesters and acrylics, have led to the use of these fibers blended with wool to bring about a combination of desirable features. The tailorability and moisture absorbency of wool, combined with the wrinkle resistance and permanence of creasing or pressing of the synthetic fibers, are featured in blended fabrics in men's suits for summer wear. Blends also permit lighter weight fabrics; for coating fabrics, the fiber weight per unit has decreased from 3.40 pounds to 2.88 and in suits from 2.94 to 2.50 pounds between 1952 and 1958. The problem of static electrical effects with synthetic fibers still remains an obstacle for widespread adaptability of these same blends for winter wear, when home interiors are so dry and static is so prevalent.

MEN'S AND BOYS' SHIRTS

In 1946, sports shirts accounted for 35 per cent of the shirts cut, whereas they totaled 63 per cent in 1955. The man-made fibers—rayons and synthetics—now account for about 35 per cent of the fibers used in sports shirts. The most successful of the synthetic fibers in shirts has been Dacron, due to its good wrinkle resistance and its ability to be heat-set to a permanent shape and size. Other polyesters, such as Kodel, Fortel, and Vycron, are also useful in blends for shirts as well as for women's dresses. A very popular summer fabric for shirts has been the blend of 65 per cent Dacron and 35 per cent cotton. This has been used not only in sports shirts but also in white dress shirts in weights as fine as batiste. The cotton content increases the moisture absorbency and somewhat reduces the transparency of the material.

In 1955, 13,805,000 dozen sports shirts were cut. Comfort, launderability, dimensional stability (resistance to shrinkage, in particular), retention of color, and satisfactory wear have been the factors influencing the selection of fibers for men's and boys' shirts, both in the dress and sports categories. Especially in sports wear, the fabric variety in texture, color, and pattern have been pre-dominant. Rayon, alone and in blends with acetate, has been important in the sports shirt field. These garments generally require special resin finishes[2] in order to improve the wrinkle-resistant and crease-retentive properties. Prominent among the resins used in the past has been the thermosetting aminoformaldehyde type. This has caused some consumer complaints after use, because of the development of formaldehyde and fish odor in cases where the resin applied by the finisher had not been properly cured. Cross-linking reagents have proved to be better for shrinkage control than either the urea formaldehydes or the melamine formaldehyde types. However, the use of these resins has increased the danger of chlorine retention; thus, they should not be used on whites or shirts with a predominantly white background. The selection of a resin for rayon or cotton shirts in order to give them the minimum-care characteristics possessed by the synthetic fibers also results, in many cases, in a somewhat more brittle fiber, and the shirt fabric then is more susceptible to tearing in use. The cross-linked cellulosic fibers, such as **Corval** and **Topel,** are beginning to appear on the market blended with cotton or with rayon in lovely white fabrics in which these molecularly rearranged cellulosic fibers seem to possess good dimensional stability.

shirt sizes

Men's shirts are sized according to Federal Specification DDD-S-301. The size designations are generally not only on hang tags but are also stamped in the collar band, as 16-35, the first figure being the collar size, the second, the sleeve length. The collar size measurement is made from the front of the thread sewing the collar button in place around the collar to the front of the button hole, and the sizing is in half-inch increments, generally from a 15-inch collar size to a 17½-inch in most well-stocked departments. The sleeve length is measured from the midpoint of the back of the collar (for example, a mark put 7½ inches from the button of the collar to the back of the shirt for a size 15) to the tip of the sleeve cuff when laid out in a straight line (Figure 1). Sleeve lengths are most commonly found to range from 32 to 36 inches; 32, 33, and 34 being in the shirts of 15- to 16-inch neck size, and 34 to 36 being in the 16 to 17½-inch neck size. Again, smaller and larger shirts may be found. Boys' shirts are similarly marked as to size. Sports shirts are generally indicated only as small, medium, and large, with some extra large (XL) selection. Commercial Standard No. CS 135–46 covers these shirt dimensions. If a manufacturer, in order to save material and cut costs, chooses to vary from the standard sizes, it is most likely to be at the expense of the girth around the chest and waist and in the length of the shirt. Thus, cheap shirts will sometimes feel and look as if

[2] For greater detail, see Chapter 9.

Fig. 26-1 Size measurement of man's and boy's shirt.

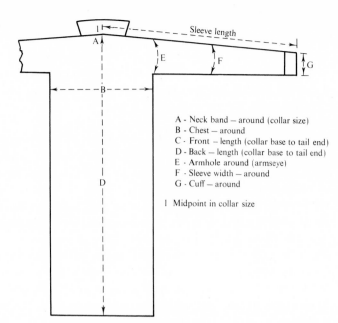

A - Neck band — around (collar size)
B - Chest — around
C - Front — length (collar base to tail end)
D - Back — length (collar base to tail end)
E - Armhole around (armseye)
F - Sleeve width — around
G - Cuff — around

I Midpoint in collar size

skimpily cut. The seam construction likewise will be inferior in these shirts.

The most common shirting materials for dress shirts for men and boys are lightweight poplins, broadcloths (1 × 1 for the cheaper shirts and 2 × 2 for the more costly), and Oxford and basket weave. During the last two years, batiste of very light weight has been popular in both dress shirts and sports shirts for men, but this lacks the durability required in boys' wear.

According to the Bureau of Census, United States Department of Commerce,[3] the American male regardless of age is affected by the casual trend, so that most of his purchases are in small units, such as a pair of slacks, one or two sports shirts, or a sports jacket, whereas in the more formal period, prior to 1946, the annual purchase of a suit was practically automatic, and dress shirts were purchased in lots of three to six at a time, generally during the store's annual sale month. It is significant, too, that these annual items lend themselves readily to specification purchasing by the store, particularly if it has an active private brand program. The men's and boys' clothing departments from skin out, so to speak, are among the most active private brand promotion areas in many large stores and in the mail order houses. Figure 26-2 shows from 1939 to 1959 the great change in production of these casual items. In slacks or separate trousers, the number of units has increased from 40.3 million in 1939 to 93 million in 1959.

[3] Ruth Jackendoff, Director, Problems of Economics and Statistics, Dewoven, Inc., Paper "Consumer Clothing Expenditures," presented at the Fashion Institute of Technology, New York, June 3, 1960.

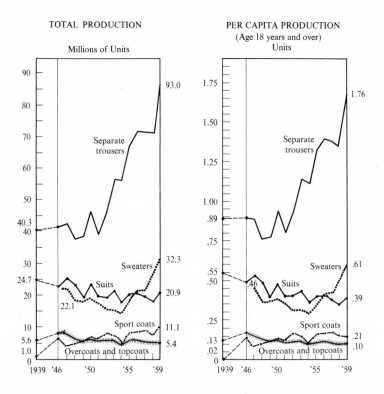

Fig. 26-2 Production of men's clothing. *(From Consumer Clothing Expenditures [An Analysis of Trends], Ruth Jackendoff, The Wool Bureau, Inc., 360 Lexington Avenue, New York 17, New York.)*

The number of suits in the same period has declined from 24.7 million to 20.9 million, despite a population increase of approximately 18 million in the same period. Also, sports coats, selling a million in 1939, have reached about 11.1 million in 1959. Interesting, too, is the growth shown by men's sweaters since the introduction of the synthetic fibers in the early 1950's; a declining market suddenly reversed, and the number of sweaters jumped sharply to 32.3 million produced in 1959. The second part of this curve shows these same figures in another way. It is based on the per capita production in terms of men and young men 18 years and older.

Figure 26-3 shows the relative importance of the various age groups in the men's wear market and illustrates the merchandising importance in the periodic appeals to youths, particularly the 15- to 18-year-old boys in high school, to dress right. It is a sharply ascending group forecast for 1960 to 1970. According to this chart, based on the Bureau of Census figures by Miss Jackendoff, this group will increase 49 per cent in the next ten-year period, whereas the next larger group, 65 and over, will increase about 18 per cent. Habits and customs learned in youth will carry over into later life. There is no reason why style rightness and casual comfort cannot exist side by side. They both express one way of life, only varying one's dress according to different hours of the day and different days of the week. Retailers regard this group of 15 to 24 as the most style-conscious of the ages of man. At the same time, this group is condemned for its sloppy attire with blue jeans, T-shirts, and other ways of self-expression. The two extremes in dress by the same boy (or girl) during a single day can be startling to family and friends.

SYNTHETICS IN UNIFORMS

Impetus to much better use of synthetic fibers, alone or in blends, in men's outerwear came about in 1962 when the United States Air Force adopted a summer uniform containing man-made fibers as a mandatory uniform for all airmen. This move from all-cotton was the result of a long period of research and testing. The former summer uniform, a cotton twill, was replaced because a 50-50 blend of polyester and cotton was superior in crease retention, more comfortable in warm weather, and lighter in weight. The shirting fabric was a

Fig. 26-3 The men's wear market: millions of men, by age groups (men aged 15 years and over). (*From Consumer Clothing Expenditures [An Analysis of Trends], Ruth Jackendoff, The Wool Bureau, Inc., 360 Lexington Ave., New York 17, New York.*)

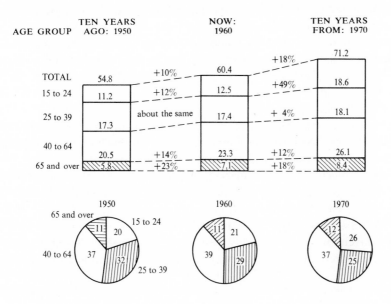

plain weave 4.5 ounces per square yard in weight; the trouser fabric, a right-hand twill, 6.5 ounces per square yard.

Partly due to this, the fiber content in uniform fabrics has changed greatly over the past seven years. In 1955, cotton accounted for 50 per cent; wool, 30 per cent; and man-made fibers, only 20 per cent. In 1961, man-made fibers accounted for 65 per cent; cotton, 25 per cent; and wool, 10 per cent.

The potential impact of this change, according to LaPedes,[4] suggests that the 50-50 blend will perform satisfactorily in all kinds of men's work clothing and even in leisure clothing articles, as well as service uniforms. He estimates that this blend might account for 30 million yards per year in a field which has been using approximately 85 million yards of a similar fabric construction and weight in the past. Although static electrical effects did cause a slight accumulation of dust particles attracted to the high-polymer fibers, soiling was not considered to be much different, and it was noted that the uniforms could be worn more days between laundering and pressing, due to better wrinkle-resistance and crease-retention. This, in turn, would lengthen the life of the fabric and garment and would lower the cost of care and cleaning. The presence of the polyester fiber does increase the pilling tendencies, but the 50-50 blend was not abnormally high in this regard.

Another potential outlet for these blends lies in its application to civilian goods in the every-day uniforms of industrial workers. It was reported by the author that in the United States there are now over 210,000 gasoline filling stations and the number is constantly increasing; each employs an average of four men; thus, there are almost one million men to wear these company uniforms while working. When we combine these with the service industries and other delivery men, police and fire departments, and public service employees, it means a bitter battle for this market. If fast colors can be obtained for the wide range of shades required by the high school and college band market, and if all the trimmings and findings of such uniforms are equally cleanable or washable, a great potential market competition will open not only with cotton but also with wool. There is said to be over 200,000 of these bands, numbering anywhere from 25 to as many as 200 musicians.

Of course, no man likes to be in uniform constantly, but there is no reason why a satisfactory work shirting fabric and slack fabric should not be adaptable to garment patterns for recreational wear.

In this competitive civilian market, we must recognize that cotton, too, has conducted serious researches and has developed new types of cellulosic fiber. Some of these have been discussed in the chapter on cotton (Chapter 10). The so-called cross-linked cotton molecules of vinyl cellulose fiber may be used alone or with conventional cotton greatly to increase the serviceability of a fabric over that of one entirely of cotton. Likewise, the crease retention and the dimensional

[4] Clarence LaPedes, "What Every Mill and Manufacturer Should Know about Fabrics for Uniforms," *American Fabrics,* 57 (1962), pp. 78–82.

stability of an all-cotton fabric are superior in the blend. Similarly, the incorporation of other cellulosic fibers, such as **Avril,** the American Viscose Corporation's strong, springy, wear-resistant, cross-linked rayon, in a cotton blend has produced an improved fabric. The other cross-linked rayons, the **polynosic** fibers, will find a place in this civilian market.

Thus far, the Air Force has not adopted a new blend for its winter uniforms. They still use all-wool. Strictly from a standpoint of performance, an excellent serge was used for the base construction with numerous modifications in percentage of wool, rayon, nylon, or polyester. Eventually, a three-fiber blend of 70 per cent wool, 20 per cent viscose, and 10 per cent nylon was adopted as being superior to wool in wind resistance, effects of abrasion, and specific volume. It was equal to wool in compressibility, crease retention, and breaking strength; inferior in drop absorption time (moisture absorption), flex stiffness, and crease recovery. The three-component blend did not dye with a satisfactory levelness for acceptance by the inspection department.

We may think from time to time that the specifications for textiles are rigid. We should like to quote two paragraphs from LaPedes' article on uniforms, as follows:

Lint-free static-free fabrics. Since the mad race for the development of rockets has been given top priority in the American Defense effort, a new field for the use of synthetic fibers has been found. This is the need for static-free and lint-free clothing for workers in this industry. This has resulted in the use of fabrics made from filament polyester and filament nylon; "white room," "lint-free room," "clean room" are three synonymous terms describing the area built especially to manufacture and/or assemble electronic parts, precision instruments, etc. They are designed to be absolutely free of air contamination, such as lint, skin flakes, dust and other solids.

An example of such exacting requirements is an Eastman Kodak plant which is built to a tolerance of ½ micron of air contamination per cubic centimeter. On entering some of these plants, the employee must show cleaned, shined shoes. He walks across a tacking mat and his person is swept with a blast of air in an air lock. After being thus cleaned, he is permitted to go to the locker room where he changes all his clothes; even his underwear is cotton-free. The requirements for the outer fabric are not only that the fabric itself be lint-free but also that it must prevent lint leaking through it from hair, under garments, etc. Polyester or nylon wiping cloths are used. Also knit nylon gloves. Static is sometimes a problem more serious than lint because in many cases, volatile fuels are employed. Fabrics are, therefore, given a durable, anti-static finish. In addition, a commercial anti-static finish is added in each washing.

WEAVE PREFERENCE TO BE CONSIDERED

This adaptation to civilian goods of new blends cannot be left simply to whim or to engineering or performance claims. The element of fashion is misleading not only in women's and girls' wear but in men's and boys' as well. A blend

Fig. 26-4 A large cotton fabric weave room: Weave Room, White Oak Plant, Cone Mills Corp. A view of the largest denim mill in the world. (*Courtesy of Cone Mills Corporation.*)

must be either in the fabric construction which has been traditional or which is currently most popular for that particular end-use item. We may all have our own opinions as to where these decisions as to popularity arise. Are they dictated to the consumer by the retailer? Are they dictated to the retailer and the consumer by the fabric manufacturer or garment manufacturer? Are they dictated to the fabric manufacturers by the weaver upon the advice of the fiber producer? Are they the result of consumer wants, telling each of these parties what he or she wants in fabrics for specific end-uses? Probably all elements play a part. It would seem that two elements or sources of pressure are probably predominant. The first is the influence and guidance given by each manufacturing element in turn to his customers or his suppliers so as better to utilize the know-how of all concerning the performance capabilities of the product being incorporated into a more nearly perfected fabric or garment form. By this is meant that the fabric producer should influence the fiber producer, but conversely, the latter guides

TABLE 26-4 / USE VERSUS ABUSE AS SOURCES FOR CUSTOMER COMPLAINTS — MEN'S WEAR

Cause of Customer Complaint	L-22 Standard Test Applicable	MEN'S DRESS SHIRTS			MEN'S SPORT SHIRTS			MEN'S TROUSERS		
		Rayon	Acetate	All	Rayon	Acetate	All	Rayon	Acetate	All
1. Perspiration causing breaks and holes[1]	—	2	2	4		1	1			1
2. Perspiration causing color damage[1]	13–17		1	4		2	2	1		1
3. Perspiration causing bleeding[1]	13	1	1	2		1	1			
4. Washing causing shrinkage	41	1	2	14	1	3	4	2	1	19
5. Washing causing color change[2]	19	4	3	19	1	1	3			5
6. Washing causing fabric breaks	7		2	10	3	2	5	1		3
7. Ironing causing damage	19	4	7	10	1	12	13		1	3
8. Bleaching and staining	19	3	2	40	2	3	10	4	1	32
9. Chemicals causing holes			1	96	1	2	5	1		29
10. Strain in wear (rips, cuts, etc.)	7	2	2	33	1		2	2	1	43
11. Abraison in wear (holes and shine)	7	3	3	28	1	1	4			55
12. Heat or burning (except ironing)	27			2			1			4
13. Moth and carpet beetle damage	—			1						16
14. Seam failure in use	—									1
15. Sun rotting of fabric	—									
16. Sun fading of dye	15							2		3
17. Gas or fume fading	9					1	1			
18. Garment construction[3]			1	7					1	6
19. Shifting of yarns	43	1		1						1
20. Processing defects & loss of finish[4]	32–31	1	2	7	1		3	2	1	9
21. Inadequate or wrong labeling[5]	—		1	1						
22. Dye crocking in service	19	1		9	1	4	6			6
23. Miscellaneous[6]		2		24			2	2		17
TOTAL		20	29	312	13	33	64	18	7	254
Customer at Fault		80%	86%	84%	85%	85%	80%	61%	71%	83%
Merchandise at Fault		20%	14%	16%	15%	15%	20%	39%	29%	17%

Data from Commodity Standards Fellowship of Kaufmann Department Stores, Mellon Institute, Pittsburgh, Pa.

[1] Including careless use of anti-perspirants.
[2] Excessive strain while wet.
[3] Including faulty seams, wrong fit, etc.
[4] Holes in discharge prints, chlorine retention, finish odor, water penetration, etc.
[5] Leading to customer misuse of article.
[6] Dermatitis, mildew, pilling (for other causes than above) etc.

the fabric weaver. The end result to be obtained would be specified to the buyer and finisher, who, knowing the performance built into the fabric, would guide the cutter or garment manufacturer into the best or, at least, an acceptable weave for the end-use article being made. The garment manufacturer then tries to sell his product in competition with others to the store buyer, who considers himself the purchasing agent for the consumer. In this field of trial and error and of constant experimentation, real pressure is put upon the manufacturers of fibers, because they must see that quality standards are maintained; otherwise their products will not be satisfactory for certain end-use products. One cannot claim that all blends are equivalent nor that there is one blend best for a considerable number of end-use items. We would not expect the same fiber blend to be equally suitable for heavy and light-weight fabrics nor for a plain weave and a heavy twill. At the same time, we would not expect fabrics for different end-uses to be dyed to the same color permanence (see Chapter 25, Textile Standards). What confuses the issue still more is that when we speak of rayon, we are not defining it very accurately, there being some 200 different rayons, all pure cellulose, and it has been said that the du Pont Company today has close to 4000 variations of its three basic fibers, when one counts in differences in denier, luster, length of fiber, strength, package designed to serve the requirements of the mills making such products, and other commercial variables.

textiles for the household

Textiles for household furnishings, equipment, and decoration present a wider variety of properties required by their end-use applications than textiles for any other use by the ultimate consumer. This is logical when we remember that some household textile applications are predominantly decorative, with only a moderate degree of serviceability required, and this serviceability generally applies more to resistance to damage of washing, dry-cleaning, or sun exposure than to actual wear or rubbing in service. Still other household textile products must be durable as well as decorative. These would naturally include upholstery, slipcover materials, carpets, and rugs; for these, wash fastness is not a factor, except in the case of washable slipcover materials, because of the size as well as the nature of the fabric construction or because the article is not removable from the furniture or perhaps from the floor for separate cleaning or cleaning by any other means than sponging in location. The most desirable physical properties of towels and toweling is certainly a thirstiness for water. This applies to all towel materials, terry toweling for the bath or linen or cotton toweling for wiping the dishes. All dish toweling must absorb moisture quickly and hold it without smearing the surface of the article to be dried. On the other hand, the less total absorbency possessed by curtains and draperies the better. For the sake of ease of washing, resistance to soiling, and speed of drying, drapability is a factor to be considered in the selection of curtains, draperies, and also table napery. Many other examples of conflicting properties which will appear in individual items are discussed in this chapter.

Little wonder, then, that not only does virtually every common textile fiber, natural, man-made, and synthetic, appear in household fabrics, but the many fiber lengths and fiber diameters available in each type of textile product find some application in these household textile products. For example, longest and finest diameters of cotton may be the select materials for table napery, whereas other cotton fibers too short to be spun into any textile product may be found in the filling materials of quilts and comforts, quilted bed pads, ironing board pads, and other hidden uses. The finest of flax will be in luxury table settings, the coarsest in toweling and wiping cloths; continuous filaments of fine denier are found in curtains; stiffer, short-fiber Dacrons of heavy denier in carpetings. Similarly, rayons and acetates of filament yarns will be found in curtain materials; shorter-fiber spun yarns of a wide variety of deniers will be used in carpetings, upholstery covering, and toweling, either alone or blended with other fibers. Blankets may differ in grade of wool or in the denier of Dacron, Acrilan, Orlon, or other fibers in that textile product. Sheets and pillow cases of the finest percale do not contain the same cotton fibers or yarns as those in durable muslin.

Household fabrics are a real challenge to the customer in her selection of the best material for a specific end-use. The type of wear and serviceability required by the individual family should influence greatly the selection of any of these household fabrics. Certainly for the family with several active children, the utmost in durability of furniture and floor covering should be required above any other consideration. Type 140 muslin sheets and pillow cases will be of greater value to this customer with a family than would be luxury and soft-textured percales. Towels of utilitarian colors requiring the minimum of laundry care are preferable to bright and bold colors. The house with the large picture window or with a great deal of sun exposure requires different curtain and drapery materials than one in which direct sunlight is at a minimum. Dacron glass curtains are preferred for the sun exposure resistance. Rayons, acetates, nylons, and even silks may be satisfactory window decorative treatments where sun is not a factor. Individual room conditions, such as the chance of oil and grease staining of carpets, should play a part in the selection of the fiber of which the rugs are to be made; thus, wool from which oil and grease are easily removed is preferable in the dining room, whereas nylon, Acrilan, and other synthetic fibers are not as satisfactory. It must be repeated that the selection of household textiles, as well as wearing apparel, is a matter of a study of care conditions and of individual needs and wants if value is to be achieved.

Household Fabrics, or **Household Textile Products,** are both terms used rather loosely, for they cover several very distinct groupings of textile products. The properties sought in some of these textiles may, at times, be diametrically opposite to those desired in others, for their purposes are so widely different. The first broad breakdown should be those textiles which once were characterized generally as **Domestics.** These are the products which serve the home, just as on the farm one regards domestic animals as those which serve the home and household either by providing food or textile materials or physical protection. The next group would be **Household** and **Decorative Fabrics,** and last, **Floor Coverings.** It is apparent that virtually every textile fiber we have studied will find numerous applications among these end-use items.

DOMESTICS

The Domestics are generally found in any department store on a single floor, and in smaller stores they are generally grouped under the attention of a single buyer. Even among these service fabrics, there are several distinct classifications; we refer to the linen department in a store as meaning the department to which we go for real linen fabrics, such as scarfs, doilies, tablecloths of fine linen damask, and linen napkins, but also the term includes rather loosely another category of table "linens" which may be of almost any fiber, generally cotton or rayon. These are the table covers such as luncheon sets, bridge table covers, napkins, scarfs, and similar products. Surprisingly, towels may often be found under this general classification. Here, again, there are some true linen fabrics, either fine hand towels or rather coarse-textured but very absorbent dish towels, but included with them under the linen end-use category are cotton turkish towels, heavy huck towels, and usually bathroom equipment, such as the shower rugs and mats, shower curtains, shower curtain and window curtain ensembles, and, indeed, a wide variety of products.

Generally under Domestics are included the fabrics used in the bedroom. Sheets and pillow cases are sometimes again loosely referred to as bed linens, though linen is rarely found today. Mattress covers, comforters, ticks, quilted pads—all these are found under the Domestic heading. Sometimes yard goods are included in this department; if this is true, it can include any textile fiber we have studied, for the yard goods are used for making all kinds of apparel as well as household textiles.

The blanket department is generally identified separately from other bedding supplies because of the very special properties sought for in blankets as compared with the other fabric products. Today's blankets are more complex than ever before, because formerly the staple fiber used for most blankets was wool. Now vast inroads have been made by the synthetics. To complicate further the purchase of blankets, we have a wider spread in weight, with many similar lightweight summer blankets being sold, and, of course, the electric blanket has proved a boon to many persons who have difficulty keeping warm at night but who cannot tolerate the weight of normal bedding. Comforters and bedspreads are also included with the blankets in that department.

towels and toweling

The well-appointed bathroom or powder room will have an adequate supply of huck guest towels, sometimes referred to as face towels. These are generally of cotton, though the finest grades are of linen or linen and cotton mixtures, linen being preferred because of its lower lint-carrying ability. These towels are generally woven in a diamond pattern, which is often referred to as the honeycomb or huckaback weave. Characteristic of this fabric is that the yarns are given a low twist; this gives a relatively soft but very absorbent fabric. Much of the quality depends upon the way in which the towels have been hemmed. This may be done at home, or they may be bought in the hemmed size. Huck towels come in such dimensions as 17 × 32″, 18 × 32″, 18 × 34″, and 18 × 36″. The fabric can also be purchased in stores in 18-inch widths.

TERRY TOWELS AND WASH CLOTHS   The terry cloth previously described in Chapter ★★ is a characteristic weave of the turkish bath towel. Although there are numerous well-known brand names in the terry cloth field, the brand name alone without any specification or manufacturing detail does not tell one the full story of what the quality of a towel may be, even though the primary purpose of each is rapid moisture absorbency. It is not unusual for a manufacturer to produce twenty or more different terry towels, when one includes such variables as basic fabric construction, height and density of the loops, and changes in the dimensions of the towels. The purpose of the loops, of course, is to give as much loosely twisted yarn volume as possible within the area of the towel. The looser and more absorbent the terry loops, the more rapid will be the moisture absorbency, and, at the same time, the greater the number of piles or loops per square inch, the higher the total water-capacity rating of the towel will be. Therefore, the more expensive towels will have the longer pile, or terry loops. These are, however, somewhat more fragile than the shorter loops, because they can more easily be caught and pulled loose. Shorter loops tend to make the fabric seem somewhat more scratchy, and the total capacity of the fabrics holding of water will be reduced. The poorer grades of terry are made with a single thread in each loop. Better grades have a double-thread construction in which each loop has two parallel threads virtually without twist for greater absorbency. The selvage should be firm, and the filling yarns should bind in the warps clear to the edge of the selvage. In improving the selvage wear of terry towels, some manufacturers are making a few of their products with Dacron as a reinforcing yarn in the selvage for increased abrasion resistance. Decorative yarns of Dacron and of Mylar metallic yarn are used in some terry towels as well as in huck towels. The polyester fibers and polymers are preferred because they are color fast to the vat dyes used in the dyeing of the towels. Other decoratives are patterned borders or colored borders or stripes. Colored towels are usually self-color bound and generally match the huck towels and colored guest towels in the bathroom ensemble. The finest quality towels are made on the Jacquard loom and are decorated by weaving complicated figures in these towels.

The sizes vary greatly: usually the face towel sizes are 16 × 28″ and 18 × 36″, medium sizes are 20 × 40″ and 22 × 44″, and over-sized bath towels are 24 × 48″ and 32 × 64″. Beach towels, bath sheets, and terry yardage for beach robes and for bathrobes are much larger in size. Normally there is a fairly high amount of shrinkage in terry towels, as much as 14 to 15 per cent in some cases. If the size of the towel is great enough, then the shrinkages will not interfere with their serviceability, but the uneven edges are very unsightly where the greater shrinkages in the decorative stripes on many of these terry towels cause ripples down the sides. These towels should never be ironed and are much more fluffy, absorbent and attractive in appearance when they have been tumble-dried, despite the fact that this drying method does contribute to the shrinkage. One must not forget that the bold dark colors are less fast in washing than lighter shades; there may be a gradual loss of color depth over a period of time, especially if these towels are washed at a high temperature, and, of course, colored towels should never be exposed to chlorine bleach or hanging outdoors in the sun.

DISH TOWELING   Among several requisites for a satisfactory towel for the drying of dishes and especially of glassware is a high count in proper balance so that the fabric will absorb as much moisture as possible and so that its strength is the same in both directions. Thus, linen is generally preferred, but, of course, cotton will also be acceptable. Some of the most common fabrics are **crash,** a plain-weave fabric; **damask,** the cotton Jacquard-loomed fabric; **glass cloth,** cotton with a hard twisted yarn comparatively free from linting; **cottonade,** somewhat resembling woolens in weave; and **osnaburg** in plain weave, a strong fabric of very coarse yarns. Non-wovens are beginning to enter this field; they have good wet and dry strength and enjoy the further advantage of reducing linting. An interesting new combination of asbestos with cotton in the proportion of 80 per cent cotton to 20 per cent asbestos is sold under the name **Carosel,** manufactured by the United States Rubber Company. **Tex-knit** is 75 per cent asbestos, 25 per cent cotton and is sold for ironing-board covers.

Viscose rayon alone or blended with cotton or linen has become important in the dish-towel field because of its increased resistance to linting. In addition to the softness and evenness, the rayon contributes high luster and has excellent moisture absorbency. Towels of a 100 per cent rayon have proven to be very satisfactory. One objection is the tendency of the fibers to shrink lengthwise as they are swelled with water. Because these fibers are notably hydrophilic, the towels may shrink as much as 10 per cent in length when wet. Much of this, however, can be restored when the towels are ironed, especially with a lengthwise tension. The ASA Standards on towels made of rayon require that the maximum permanent lengthwise shrinkage shall not exceed 8 to 10 per cent.

The National Cotton Council reports in detail on the continued volume of cotton in this field of Domestic and also in such heavier cotton fabrics as bath mats generally of pure cotton or with a combination cotton and rayon pile.

shower curtains

These generally form the center of color and pattern interest in the bath-room, although the modern trend is more and more to have them correlated with the coloring of the walls, whether these be of tile or of a washable wall-

TABLE 27-1 / AMERICAN STANDARD PERFORMANCE REQUIREMENTS FOR WOVEN TOWELING FABRICS
L22.30.12-1960

Property		MINIMUM REQUIREMENTS			Test Number (See Volume II)
	Identification:	122.30.12-B Washable 160 F	122.30.12-W Washable 160 F No Bleach	122.30.12-C Washable 120 F No Bleach	
BREAKING STRENGTH					ASTM D 39—49, Grab Method (AS L14.68-1951)
Dry (See Note 1)		50 lb	50 lb	50 lb	
Wet		35 lb	35 lb	35 lb	
MAXIMUM DIMENSIONAL CHANGE (See Note 2)					AATCC 96-1960, Table II
Warp		10%	10%	10%	Test No. III
Filling		5%	5%	5%	Test No. II
COLORFASTNESS TO					
Laundering		Test IVA (See Note 3)	Test IIIA (See Note 3)	Test IIA	AATCC 61-1960
Alteration in Shade		Class 4	Class 4	Class 4	
Staining		Class 4	Class 4	Class 4	
Light		L5-40 hr	L5-40 hr	L5-40 hr	AATCC 16A-1957 (AS L14.53-1960)
SIZING (Maximum)		5%	5%	5%	AATCC 20A-1959, Section 4

PRESSING

Whenever the pressing temperature specified in any testing procedure is too high for heat-sensitive fibers, pressing should be done at temperatures as high as possible without glazing or fusing.

RETENTION OF HAND, CHARACTER, AND APPEARANCE

A fabric shall not change substantially in hand, character, or appearance as a result of three launderings by the applicable shrinkage procedure. In addition, the fabric shall not lose more than 5 per cent of its weight as a result of this treatment.

COMPONENTS

All textile components and components other than textiles incorporated into the textile article shall conform to applicable performance requirements of this standard in order not to cause alteration in appearance of fabrics meeting these requirements after appropriate refreshing tests. If the provisions of this standard do not cover refreshing requirements suitable for removable components, other L22 end-use standards may be specified.

SPECIAL PERFORMANCE CHARACTERISTICS

When a claim is made for a special performance characteristic not covered by this standard, see Part IV of these standards.

NOTE 1: Fabrics known to exhibit a wet strength which is within 90 per cent of the dry strength need not be subjected to a wet test.
NOTE 2: Trade Practice Rule for Shrinkage of Woven Cotton Yard Goods as promulgated June 30, 1938, by the Federal Trade Commission.
NOTE 3: If there is no nylon, wool, or silk in the fabric under test, staining of these fibers in the test cloth shall be disregarded.

From: American Standard Performance Requirements for Textile Fabrics, l, Am. Stds. Assoc., approved Feb. 11, 1960, p. 144.

paper surface. Some shower curtains are simply sheet plastic or sheet rubber; others have a plastic sheeting or rubber sheeting over a textile fabric base. Still others are of a woven fabric which has been given a satisfactory and permanent water-repellent finish. Some of the fabrics used either alone or in combination with a water impermeable layer are ducks, taffetas, and satins. The standard curtain size is 70 × 70″ and is generally sold today alone or together with a small-size window curtain of matching material. This imposes the extra demand on the material that it have satisfactory sun-fastness for window exposure. This fact was not previously considered as of very much value to the consumer until gay prints came into style in these articles.

table linens

Linen is still the preferred fiber for dining-room use, especially in fine table damasks, because of its increased luster and appearance through many years of service. These have been previously described in some detail in Jacquard weave, Chapter 3. Other fibers are found in more casual use, such as bridge table covers, the standard size being 34 × 36″. Other table settings may be of linen, crash, lace, or embroidery; sets of runners or place mats may be used, runners being 18 × 36″ or 18 × 72″, the place mats generally 12 × 18″ or 14 × 20″. Matching napkins are usually small, 14 × 14″.

bed sheets

Bed sheets are an example of practically a 100-per-cent one-fiber product, and cotton accounts for almost all of the bed sheets used in the homes of America. Linen sheets are smooth and comfortable but are very high-priced and are distinctly a luxury item found in few homes. From time to time, attempts have been made to promote nylon sheets, but the reaction of the public has been unfavorable: they are too slippery and too warm, the bed covers slip off, and, over a period of time, they tend to discolor in laundering, becoming grey- or yellow-looking.

Bed sheets and sheeting were the first of the consumer products for which a voluntary standard was adopted by distributors and consumers. This standard defines four types of sheeting in terms of the number of yarns per square inch. Sheets are of plain weave and have been previously referred to in the discussion of this weave where the advantage of fabric balance was emphasized. Thus, when the type is expressed in number of yarns per square inch, such as Type 128 (lightweight muslin), Type 140 (heavy muslin), Type 180 (utility percale), or Type 200 (fine percale), the figure represents the total of warp and filling threads per square inch. The closer the actual count is to an equal number in both directions, such as 64 × 64 for Type 128, 90 × 90 in the percale, or Type 180, for example, the more even will be the strength of the sheet in both directions unless there is a distinct disparity in the size of yarns. Usually such dif-

TABLE 27-2 / AMERICAN STANDARD PERFORMANCE REQUIREMENTS FOR WOVEN TABLECLOTH AND NAPERY FABRICS

L22.30.11-1960

Property	MINIMUM REQUIREMENTS				Test Number (See Volume II)
Identification:	L22.30.11-B Washable 160 F	L22.30.11-W Washable 160 F No Bleach	L22.30.11-C Washable 120 F No Bleach	L22.30.11-H Washable 105 F No Bleach	
BREAKING STRENGTH					ASTM D 39–49, Grab Method (AS L14.68-1951)
Dry (See Note 1)	75 lb	75 lb	75 lb	75 lb	
Wet	40 lb	40 lb	40 lb	40 lb	
TONGUE TEAR STRENGTH	2.5 lb	2.5 lb	2.5 lb	2.5 lb	CCC-T-19 lb, Method No. 5134
YARN SHIFTING Maximum Opening Load	0.05 in. 2 lb	0.05 in. 2 lb	0.05 in. 2 lb	0.05 in. 2 lb	ASTM D 1336-54T (AS L14.103-1957)
MAXIMUM DIMENSIONAL CHANGE (See Note 2)					AATCC 96-1960, Table II
Warp	8%	8%	8%	8%	Test No. III
Filling	6%	6%	6%	6%	Test No. II
					Test No. I
COLORFASTNESS TO					
Atmospheric Fading After Washing (See Note 3)	Class 4	Class 4	Class 4	Class 4	AATCC 23-1957 (1 cycle alternate evaluation) (AS L14.54-1960)
Laundering	Test IVA (See Note 4)	Test IIIA (See Note 4)	Test IIA	Test IA	AATCC 61-1960
Alteration in Shade	Class 4	Class 4	Class 4	Class 4	
Staining	Class 4	Class 4	Class 4	Class 4	
Crocking					
Dry	Class 4	Class 4	Class 4	Class 4	AATCC 8-1957 (AS L14.72-1960)
Wet	Class 3	Class 3	Class 3	Class 3	
Light	L5-40 hr	L5-40 hr	L5-40 hr	L5-40 hr	AATCC 16A-1957 (AS L14.53-1960)

PRESSING

Whenever the pressing temperature specified in any testing procedure is too high for heat-sensitive fibers, pressing should be done at temperatures as high as possible without glazing or fusing.

RETENTION OF HAND, CHARACTER, AND APPEARANCE

A fabric shall not change substantially in hand, character, or appearance as a result of three launderings by the applicable shrinkage procedure. In addition, the fabric shall not lose more than 5 per cent of its weight as a result of this treatment.

COMPONENTS

All textile components and components other than textiles incorporated into the textile article shall conform to applicable performance requirements of this standard in order not to cause alteration in appearance of fabrics meeting these requirements after appropriate refreshing tests. If the provisions of this standard do not cover refreshing requirements suitable for removable components, other L22 end-use standards may be specified.

SPECIAL PERFORMANCE CHARACTERISTICS

When a claim is made for a special performance characteristic not covered by this standard, see Part IV of these standards.

SEAM STRENGTH (Garment or Textile Items)

Each original seam shall possess a breaking strength of at least 64 pounds (U.S. Testing Company Method).

RAVELLING TEST (Seams in Garments or Textile Items)

Fabrics containing filament yarns shall be tested for seam strength after three launderings, using the applicable shrinkage procedure, or after dry-cleaning by AATCC Test Method 86-1957. Seam failure due to excessive free-edge ravelling indicates the need for another type of seam.

NOTE 1: Fabrics known to exhibit a wet strength which is within 90 per cent of the dry strength need not be subjected to a wet test.

NOTE 2: Trade Practice Rule for Shrinkage of Woven Cotton Yard Goods as promulgated June 30, 1938, by the Federal Trade Commission.

NOTE 3: Use corresponding test methods as provided in the columns under laundering.

N*95 4: If there is no nylon, wool, or silk in the fabric under test, staining of these fibers in the test cloth shall be disregarded.

From: American Standard Performance Requirements for Textile Fabrics, 1, Am. Stds. Assoc., approved Feb. 11, 1960, pp. 142–143.

ferences are avoided for the reason that the sheet must be even in appearance if it is to appeal to the consumer. As a general rule, the warp and filling counts will not differ in the sheet by more than 10 per cent; thus, a 60 × 60 count would be too low arithmetically for a Type 128 and would not be accepted; the difference in count would be too much. On the other hand, the 61 × 67 would barely pass. Another safeguard in this Standard is that the breaking strength in terms of pounds per inch (minimum breaking strength by grab test) for the Type 128 muslin is 55 pounds in the weaker direction; for Type 140, it is 70 pounds. As for the combed or carded Type 180 percale, a strength of 60 pounds is required, and in the combed Type 200, 60 pounds for the weaker direction, as shown in Table 27-3.

TABLE 27-3 / AMERICAN STANDARD
SHEETS AND SHEETING

	Type 128 Combed or Carded Yarns	Type 140 Carded Yarns	Type 180 Combed or Carded Yarns	Type 200 Combed Yarns
Combined thread count, warp and filling	128	140	180	200
Warp breaking strength, pounds	55	70	60	60
Filling breaking strength, pounds	55	70	60	60
Maximum added sizing, per cent	6	4	2	1
Weight, ounces per square yard	4	4.6	3.6	3.6

Another set of Standards dealing with sheets is that of sizes of sheets for the various sizes of beds most commonly used in the United States. These dimensions are in terms of torn length of sheet and make allowance for a one-inch turnover at the foot and a three- or four-inch turnover for hemming at the top of the sheet. Thus, the actual sheet dimension in length will be five inches shorter than the torn length. It should also be mentioned that some manufacturers use the same hem size at both ends, sometimes a two- or sometimes a three-inch turnover.

The size of the sheet to be selected should be adequate to provide a firm placement of the sheet with enough material both at sides and top and bottom for turning under the mattress. A skimpy sheet requires too much pulling and tugging, with the danger of tearing after the sheet has been to the laundry and has lost a significant amount of its original strength through repeated washings and bleachings. The principal wear area of a sheet is at the shoulder level. Here occurs the maximum combination of abrasion and weight load, and an advantage for those sheets having equal hems at both ends is that the sheet can be reversed lengthwise to distribute the wear in service more evenly.

blankets

It is known that a well-insulated house is cool in summer and warm in winter. The insulating capacity of the materials stuffed into the walls and laid under the roof depends greatly on the amount of air enmeshed in the spaces between the fibers or within the hollow cells. This trapped air acts as a barrier to the rapid passage of heat through the insulating material. It prevents the sun's heat from warming the house in summer and prevents the escape of the furnace heat into the outside air in winter. Of course, the insulating fibers or the other solid structural materials have a degree of resistance to heat conduction. In a similar manner, the warmth of a blanket depends on the air retained in the finely napped construction: a blanket does not add warmth; it retains it. Tests have proved that an equally heavy felted blanket is not as warm. A well-napped cotton blanket, when new, retains heat well, but the fibers are not as elastic as wool and, after repeated launderings, the air spaces are gradually reduced and the warmth retention decreases. Blankets of Acrilan, Orlon, and other synthetic fibers retain their nap structure longer than do the natural fibers.

Blankets are not purchased as frequently as are most other staple articles, but their selection is of great importance. They are quite expensive; all-wool blankets range in price from $7.50 to $28.00, while the synthetics are slightly lower. When a customer buys a blanket, she is interested in warmth, weight, durability, attractiveness, and price. Her selection will depend on the order of importance of these factors as far as her own needs are concerned. If she wants the greatest amount of warmth combined with comfort, she will select a light-weight all-wool blanket or one of synthetic fiber. If a moderate price is of special importance to her, she will probably buy an all-cotton blanket or a cotton-wool mixture. Whatever her selection may be, a knowledge of the characteristics of the fibers and of the desirable qualities of blankets will be of great help.

Wool blankets are woven of yarns in which the individual fibers are loosely gathered together with very little twist, so that they lie in every direction. The yarn count in the warp and filling must be well balanced, that is, of approximately the same number of yarns to the inch. The warp yarns must be strong in order to withstand the friction and tension of weaving. The filling yarns are made looser and are then rendered still more fuzzy by pulling or napping with teazle burrs or fine wire brushes. The well-napped blanket offers a construction characterized by a great deal of air-holding capacity. The loose fuzzy fibers actually seem to reach out to hold the air.

With these construction facts in mind, the several factors influencing the customer's choice may be elaborated on.

WARMTH   A fabric with an open weave permits the cold air to pass through it quickly. If the fabric is so constructed that a considerable amount of air is enmeshed between the fibers, the cold air from the outside will pass through so slowly that it is warmed before it reaches the body. The blanket with the greater air-holding capacity is the warmer.

COMFORT   Warmth and comfort are not synonymous. A heavy, felted blanket may have enough warmth, but it is not comfortable to the person under it. The lighter the blanket, the more comfortable it is, and an all-wool blanket of very light weight, properly napped, would be even warmer than the heavy blanket. A well-napped cotton blanket is warmer than a felted wool blanket of the same weight because it has greater air capacity. The extent to which the blanket can be napped depends on the looseness of the twist of the filling yarns, the strength of the core around which the loose fibers are loosely twisted, and the amount of napping which can be done without weakening the filling yarns beyond serviceable limit.

Another factor influencing comfort is the moisture absorption capacity of the fiber itself. Wool can hold as much as 30 per cent of its own weight of moisture without its feeling wet and cold. Cotton can hold much less water and will feel damp in wet weather. The synthetics hold practically no moisture and would give little protection as out-of-door bed covers and would feel clammy in humid weather.

DURABILITY   Whatever the yarn composition may be, there are certain factors that govern the durability and serviceability of a blanket.

1. *Length of Fibers.* Short fibers pull out easily. The napping process may have worked the fibers loose and actually weakened the filling yarn. Long fibers are more securely caught in the yarns and will not slip or pull out so rapidly. Cotton fibers pull out easier than wool. Pinch some of the nap between the thumb and forefinger and lift the blanket; the nap should not pull out even when the weight of the blanket is suspended.

2. *Tensile Strength of Fibers.* Weak or brittle fibers will break off during use and during washing. It is important that strong fibers be used in blankets. The strength of the individual fibers varies over a wide range.

3. *Yarn Tensile Strength.* The warp yarns must be strong enough to withstand the tension in the loom and compact enough to withstand the friction during weaving. Warp yarns are often multi-ply, that is, two or more yarns are twisted together to form the warp yarn. The filling yarns are made more loose so that the nap can be brushed up easily.

4. *Construction.* A balanced fabric having an even distribution of warp and filling yarns is desirable for long wear. A loosely-woven blanket which has been excessively napped in order to make it look firm and compact is much too weak for good service and washability. There are not enough yarns to give adequate strength, and the chances are that the filling has been still further weakened during the raising of the profuse nap. The minimum strength for the warp and filling respectively should be 30 and 20 pounds. A good idea of the closeness of the weave can be judged by looking through the blanket with a bright light on the other side.

SIZE   The matter of the proper size of the blanket affects both its comfort and its durability. Too small a blanket does not adequately protect the sleeper in cold weather. In addition to that, it is subjected to excessive pulling in order to tuck it in at the foot and sides or to cover the shoulders of the sleeper. The blanket should be large enough so that it can be tucked in at the foot and on each side. Remembering that the average double bed is 54 inches wide and the mattress is about 5½ inches thick, it is obvious that the narrow 54-inch and the short 76-inch blankets are inadequate.

In Table 27-4 are given sizes of blankets in relation to the width and length of the bed.

TABLE 27-4 / BED AND BLANKET SIZES IN INCHES

	Width of Bed	Width of Blanket	Total Allowance	Allowance at Each Side
Double	54	66	12	6
Double	54	70	16	8
Double	54	72	18	9
Double	54	80	26	13
Twin	39	54	15	7.5
Twin	39	60	21	10.5
Twin	39	66	27	13.5
Single	36	54	18	9
Single	36	60	24	12
Single	36	66	30	15
Narrow Single or Day Bed	33	54	21	10.5
Narrow Single or Day Bed	33	60	27	13.5
Day Bed or Cot	30	54	24	12
Day Bed or Cot	30	60	30	15

	Length of Bed	Length of Mattress	Length of Blanket	Total Allowance
	78	76	76	0
	78	76	80	4
	78	76	84	8
	78	76	90	14
	72	70	76	6
	72	70	80	10
	72	70	84	14

Laurene Hempstead, "The Selling Points of Bedding," *Retailing*, Fairchild News Service, 1930.

The American Standards Association has recommended eight standard sizes for blankets, as follows: 60 × 80, 60 × 84, 60 × 90, 66 × 80, 70 × 80, 72 × 84, 72 × 90, and 80 × 90.

FIBER IDENTITY—LABELING   The labeling of blankets falls under the Wool Products Labeling Act. Accordingly, the Federal Trade Commission has ruled that if the blanket contains less than 5 per cent wool, the finished blanket cannot carry the word "wool" in any form. Blankets bearing the word "wool" must be labeled as follows:

1   By fiber content wool to be described accurately as wool, means reprocessed or re-used.

2   Above 98 per cent shall be labeled "All Wool."

3 "Virgin Wool" or "wool" means that only new wool not previously used in fabric is contained in the blanket. The Wool Products Law (1941) forced the labeling of wool fabrics into giving the content of reprocessed and re-used wool.

APPEARANCE   A fine-grade virgin wool is lustrous and clear in appearance, and the colors are uniform and clear. A delicate pastel shade is usually more pleasing than a bright, glaring color. The finishing of the ends is a factor influencing the blanket's appearance. The most attractive and durable binding is pure-dye silk ribbon. Taffeta or a binding of nylon, acetate, or rayon satin remains bright even after repeated washings, but it must be washed with care. Acetates may gradually change color due to contact with the wool. Mercerized cotton sateen is strong and durable but tends to become dull. A blanket-stitched edge is practical and inexpensive.

data on blankets

Comparatively little of the actual test data on blanket performance has been made available to consumer. The National Consumer-Retailer Relations Council (1935–1950) prepared a check list suggested as a basis for informative labels on blankets. This check list was proposed as a guide for manufacturers, retailers, and consumers.

care of blankets

No matter how well-made an article may be or how carefully it was selected, it can not be considered to be serviceable unless it can be cleaned without loss of strength or impairment of its appearance. Blankets are no exception, but they must be cleaned and cared for according to definite methods because of the nature of the fibers and construction of the cloth.

Blankets may be dry-cleaned or washed. In washing blankets, it is necessary to avoid heat, excessive manipulation while wet, and too great pressure. An abundant lukewarm suds of a neutral soap should be used. The blanket should be washed quickly with as little manipulation as possible, it should never be twisted, rubbed, or wrung. The suds should be squeezed out and the blanket thoroughly rinsed in two or more lukewarm waters. Excess water should be squeezed out. Wet blankets must be carefully hung to dry in the shade; it is advisable to lay the blanket across two parallel lines, and it may be shaken gently while it is drying. The binding should be stretched flat after the blanket is dry and can then be ironed at a moderate iron temperature. The nap may be fluffed up by gently brushing it with a soft brush.

Blankets must be cleaned before being stored away. Moths are attracted by dirty woolens. Pack blankets rather loosely in a moth-proof drawer or box. A handful of para-dichlorobenzene thrown on top of stored woolens affords good protection against moth damage if the container is kept closed.

the role of synthetics in blankets

As we have seen, wool has been a natural fiber for blankets in almost every sense of the term, and yet there are certain disadvantages to the fiber which one cannot minimize. First, the problem of insect damage requires special storage conditions; these necessitate some extra-care provisions on the part of a consumer. In certain climates wool will mildew, again requiring special care. Probably the principal disadvantage, however, is in the tendency of wool blankets to shrink. This is still a problem today in spite of the shrinkproof treatments which can be given to wool and wool fabrics, the difficulty being that these treatments are almost inevitably accompanied by a slight harshening of the fiber, and it will not have the same degree of softness and luxury feeling which one associates with a really fine blanket fabric. Most people know how to wash wool blankets, but even now mistakes are made occasionally and the wool is given the full treatment: hot water, bleach, excessive drying, and other features. Lower-priced wool blankets have not had the fibers fully bleached in many cases, and they do not produce the clean rich-looking pastel shades now so popular in blankets made of the synthetic fibers.

All blanket manufacturers produce several grades of blanketing materials, and even those depending primarily upon wool for their quality blankets do make cheaper lines with rayon blended with nylon or an acrylic fiber. These give excellent thermal properties, bright colors, dimensional stability in washing, and lightness in weight. Blankets can be made of almost any of the more common synthetic fiber fabrics: nylons, polyesters (Dacron), acrylics (Orlon or Acrilan or Creslon), Dynel, and several others. Because they are staple fibers and can be processed like wool, they require no great amount of change in manufacturing. Furthermore, the fibers are uniform, much more so than in the case of natural products, as we have already seen. The pricing of the synthetic fibers is subject to less variation and manipulation than that of the natural fibers, and it can be depended upon for a year or more in advance, thus enabling the manufacturer to calculate his costs closely. When one combines these inherent advantages possessed by the synthetics, there is little wonder that these fibers, especially the acrylics, have met the competition of quality wool blankets head-on. They have gone into the field of highest quality, rather than working up through lower grades into the top price ranges. The brightness of color, especially of pastels, possessed by these acrylics cannot be matched by wool. In addition to that, the fibers retain their loftiness in the nap; thus their thermal properties are maintained to a high degree. There is no tendency to shrink nor full. Insects cannot damage them, nor are they subject to mildew attack. Their tensile strength is fully equal to that of wool. Being somewhat more bulky, the actual fiber weight of a blanket of the same nap height and apparent density is lower in the case of the synthetics than it is in wool. Static electricity is still a problem, however; also, these synthetic fiber blankets are not as good protection

TABLE 27-5 / REASONS FOR LIKING LAST BLANKET ACQUIRED AND USED, BY FIBER [1]

Reasons	Wool Per Cent	Wool and Rayon Per Cent	Wool and Nylon Per Cent	Other Wool Mixtures Per Cent	Cotton Per Cent	Cotton and Wool Per Cent	Cotton and Synthetics Per Cent	Other Cotton Mixtures Per Cent	Synthetics and Synthetic Mixtures Per Cent
Comfort characteristics	82	76	75	77	72	74	75	65	81
Warm (general)	62	42	47	43	29	39	37	27	38
Lightweight, not too heavy	23	26	25	31	23	20	23	25	35
Warmth without weight	12	18	11	16	4	8	14	9	15
Soft, feels soft; feels good next to body	10	9	14	10	15	8	19	18	14
Heavy, heavier, thicker	2	—	2	1	3	3	4	2	—
Right weight, right weight for climate	2	2	3	2	4	6	—	9	—
Doesn't scratch, irritate skin, not sticky	1	4	5	6	13	12	9	5	5
Not too warm; good for summer, cooler	2*	—	1	1	4	1	4	2	1
Care and laundering characteristics	32	49	47	44	51	51	54	38	65
Washes well	9	19	14	8	9	13	18	5	19
Holds shape; doesn't stretch, shrink	7	13	14	13	9	14	18	16	18
Colorfast, colors stay bright, white doesn't discolor	5	3	3	3	4	4	9	4	3
Washes easily, easy to clean, easily laundered	4	6	8	7	18	9	7	5	16
Doesn't mat, get harsh, stiff after washing	3	7	4	5	3	6	2	2	8
Soil resistant; doesn't show soil, stays clean longer	2	3	3	1	2	1	—	2	1
Washable	2	2	5	6	7	4	4	2	4
Can be washed at home	2	3	—	3	3	4	2	—	4
Can be washed in washing machine	1	3	6	5	3	1	4	4	1
Easy to care for	1	—	1	2	1	2	—	—	—

Reason given									
Dry cleans well	1	—	—	—	—	1	2	2	—
Dries quickly	*	3	1	3	4	1	5	4	18
Appearance	19	17	16	16	8	10	21	12	3
Like color; comes in pretty/wide variety of colors	12	11	10	11	6	8	11	5	—
Looks nice, pretty, beautiful, attractive	6	5	4	5	2	1	7	5	3
Like binding, satin binding	1	2	—	—	—	1	4	—	—
All other appearance characteristics	1	—	2	—	*	—	4	2	—
Durability: Wears well, durable	18	14	4	11	9	19	4	5	5
Performance characteristics	4	4	8	8	3	4	11	5	7
Wool fuzz doesn't come off; not linty	2	3	7	6	2	3	4	2	5
Doesn't slip, slide; stays on bed	1	1	1	1	1	*	2	2	—
Stays fluffy	1	—	—	2	*	1	5	2	3
Properties pertaining to electric blankets only: Single/dual control, can control heat	4	6	6	9	4	2	—	15	4
uniform temperature	2	2	4	2	2	4	2	2	—
Size: Size wanted, super size	1	1	2	—	1	—	—	—	3
Construction characteristics: Smooth, closely woven, firm weave	1	1	4	3	1	1	—	—	3
Mothproof; no moth problem	1	1	—	—	—	1	2	—	7
Price: Less expensive; right price, on sale	1	6	1	1	4	4	—	2	1
price, on sale	2	2	1	2	3	1	4	2	—
Nothing particularly liked	1	—	—	2	1	1	—	—	1
All other reasons	1	1	—	—	2	1	—	2	3
Not ascertained	—	—	—	—	—	—	—	—	—
Number who have used last blanket acquired	1,153	118	93	88	307	340	57	55	74

1 Percentages may add to more than group totals and these add to more than 100 because some users gave more than 1 reply.

2 Asterisk denotes less than 1 per cent.

Courtesy U.S. Dept. of Agriculture.

as wool when used out-of-doors or at camps or lodges when the room or ambient conditions are low in temperature and high in humidity. In these circumstances, wool will out-perform the synthetics, if one is to translate the fiber properties into the physical performance of the fabric. No test figures have been seen, however, to substantiate this theory. The thermoplasticity of these fibers should affect only those who are foolish enough to smoke in bed and thus run the risk of melting holes in the blanket.

consumer preferences in blankets

The preference study of consumers among blankets edited by Levine[1] showed comparatively little familiarity of the public with blankets of synthetic fibers other than nylon. About 6 per cent of the homemakers did not use blankets, giving as a reason that they considered themselves one of the families to be allergic to wool blankets, and they found them scratchy. Other homemakers said their houses were sufficiently warm without any blankets; some said they were too expensive. Many who had quilts felt that they were adequate to take the place of blankets. Of those having blankets of wool, 83 per cent had chosen them because of comfort; 18 per cent because of durability; 19 per cent because of appearance; and 32 per cent because of ease of care and laundering. Practically none were influenced by price.

TABLE 27-6 / OWNERS WHO DISLIKED SOME ATTRIBUTE OF LAST BLANKET ACQUIRED, BY FIBER

Fibers	Dislike Something About Blankets	Number Who Have Used Last Blanket Acquired
	Per Cent	Number
Wool	19	1,153
Wool and rayon	19	118
Wool and nylon	19	93
Other wool mixtures	12	88
Cotton	13	307
Cotton and wool	15	340
Cotton and synthetics	19	57
Other cotton mixtures	20	55
Synthetics and synthetic mixtures	20	74

Another group of blankets about which the survey asked questions was the synthetics. Eighty per cent of those having blankets made of synthetics named various comfort characteristics; 65 per cent laundering ease; 7 per cent the in-

---

[1] Daniel B. Levine, "Homemakers Appraise Cotton, Wool and Other Fibers in Household Furnishings," U.S. Department of Agriculture, Marketing Research Report No. 279, November 1958.

expensiveness; 3 per cent the appearance. Of those who had last purchased a regular blanket of cotton, 72 per cent gave comfort as the reason; 51 per cent mentioned care and laundering; 4 per cent selected it because it was cheap; and 8 per cent said they liked the appearance.

TABLE 27-7 / REASONS FOR DISLIKING LAST BLANKET ACQUIRED AND USED, BY FIBER

Reasons	Wool	Wool and Cotton
	Per Cent	*Per Cent*
Care and laundering characteristics	38	27
Doesn't hold shape; stretches, shrinks	22	12
Has to be dry cleaned	7	—
Mats, gets harsh, stiff after washing	5	4
Difficult to wash	4	6
Not colorfast, faded, color ran	2	2
Doesn't wash, launder well	2	—
Not soil resistant, spots easily, picks up lint	2*	2
All other care and laundering characteristics	2	4
Comfort characteristics	30	27
Scratches, irritates skin, not nonallergenic	22	20
Too warm	6	—
Too heavy, bulky	3	6
Not warm	1	—
Too thin, not heavy enough	1	—
All other comfort characteristics	1	2
Performance	15	25
Wool, fuzz comes off; gets linty	14	25
Slides off bed	1	—
Not mothproof	7	—
Durability	7	20
Binding wears out	6	18
Doesn't wear well	1	2
Properties pertaining to electric blankets only:		
Electrical difficulties; afraid of it; can't see dial in dark, etc.	5	2
Size: Not big enough	4	2
Appearance: Dislike color	2	2
Price: Too expensive	2	—
All other reasons	—	6
Number of users expressing dissatisfaction with fiber	215	51

[1] Percentages add to more than the group totals and these add to more than 100 because some users gave more than 1 reply.

[2] Asterisk denotes less than 1 per cent.

Courtesy U.S. Dept. of Agriculture.

DECORATIVE FABRICS

Though some of the Domestics have decorative features, glass curtains and draperies are regarded as primarily decorative. One cannot separate the esthetics or decorative features of color, texture, pattern, design, drapability, and other properties from the textile fabrics used in covering furniture. Thus, upholstery materials must be decorative and at the same time have satisfactory durability to stand up well in use.

TABLE 27-8 / TWO DECORATIVE PRODUCTS
USE VERSUS ABUSE AS SOURCES
FOR CUSTOMER COMPLAINTS

Cause of Customer Complaint	L-22 Standard Test Applicable	CURTAINS			DRAPERIES		
		Rayon	Acetate	All	Rayon	Acetate	All
1. Perspiration causing breaks & holes[1]	—	—	—	—	—	—	—
2. Perspiration causing color damage[1]	13–17	—	—	—	—	—	—
3. Perspiration causing bleeding[1]	13	—	—	—	—	—	—
4. Washing causing shrinkage	41	—	1	7	—	—	4
5. Washing causing color change[2]	19	1	1	10	3	—	6
6. Washing causing fabric breaks	7	9		9			
7. Ironing causing damage	19	—	—	—	—	—	—
8. Bleaching and staining	19	2	—	2	1	—	1
9. Chemicals causing holes	—	1	—	9	1	—	2
10. Strain in wear (rips, cuts, etc.)	7	4	1	17	1	—	1
11. Abrasion in wear (holes and shine)	7	3	1	5	1	—	1
12. Heat or burning (except ironing)	27	—	—	—	—	—	—
13. Moth and carpet beetle damage	—	—	—	—	—	—	—
14. Seam failure in use	—	—	—	—	—	—	—
15. Sun rotting of fabric	—	14	5	33			1
16. Sun fading of dye	15				2		4
17. Gas or fume fading	9					5	5
18. Garment construction[3]	—			3	1		2
19. Shifting of yarns	43	3		9	1		1
20. Processing defects & loss of finish[4]	32–31	4		4			
21. Inadequate or wrong labeling[5]	—						
22. Dye crocking in service	19			5			
23. Miscellaneous[6]		1		9	2		3
TOTAL		42	9	122	13	5	31
Customer at Fault		48%	44%	48%	54%	0%	48%
Merchandise at Fault		52%	56%	52%	46%	100%	52%

Data from Commodity Standards Fellowship of Kaufmann Department Stores, Mellon Institute, Pittsburgh, Pa.

[1] Including careless use of anti-perspirants.
[2] Excessive strain while wet.
[3] Including faulty seams, wrong fit, etc.
[4] Holes in discharge prints, chlorine retention, finish odor, water penetration, etc.
[5] Leading to customer misuse of article.
[6] Dermatitis, mildew, pilling (for other causes than above), etc.

The data shown in Table 27-8 refer to 122 pairs of glass curtains and 31 pairs of draperies reaching the laboratory in the form of customer complaints prior to 1950. Admittedly, these two items are of little significance today. However, the table does demonstrate many of the essential differences between the two fibers which made it important for the Federal Trade Commission to revise the Rayon and Acetate Rules in 1950, and it explains also some of the requirements later proposed by the FTC in the labeling of household fabrics under the Fiber Identification Law. It will be noted that even at that time the number of curtains identified as rayon totaled 42, of acetate, 9, and the remainder of the 122 pairs of curtains received from store customers were of other fibers. Of the draperies, 13 were rayon, 5 acetate, and the total of 31 included other fibers. In both curtains and draperies, approximately 50 per cent responsibility rested on each side of the counter; that is, the merchandise was at fault in 52 per cent of the cases and the customer in 48 per cent.

RUGS

Last but not least, we have the broad expanse of the floor to consider. Here, knowledge of carpets and rugs, their constructions, their advantages, their shortcomings, and the properties of the various fibers now going into these important products must all be kept in mind when one begins to furnish or to refurnish a home or an apartment. There are many references on the subject of furniture and rugs correlation.

There are doubtless many consumers who today still remember the sad experiences with rayon carpeting during World War II when wool was unobtainable. In bearing old grudges, these consumers are doing themselves a great disservice by not experimenting with or studying something about the new rayon carpets, because with the advent of the high-tenacity rayons and of the permanently crimped fibers such as Avisco Super-L rayon (American Viscose Corporation) for heavy-duty carpeting in hotels, modern rayons have demonstrated good resiliency, greatly improved wet strength, uniform denier, a smooth soil-resistant surface, which has been made further resistant to soiling by the use of titanium dioxide pigment in the fiber. The general denier used in the high-tenacity carpet rayons is 12 to 15, which is about the same fiber size as most of our carpet wools. It is probable that rayon carpeting will be still more serviceable in the uncut-loop type than in the cut-loop. It is reasonable to suppose also that Arnel will become increasingly important as a carpet fiber, possibly in blends with other fibers.

Of the true synthetics, nylon has achieved the greatest success, probably due to its high reputation as a durable fiber in wearing apparel and its well-demonstrated ability to withstand abrasion or rubbing better than any other textile or material we know. Low moisture absorbency and non-flammability are also important factors in nylon's role as a carpet material. Mention has been made in the case of blankets of the superiority of the pastels in these household fabrics compared with wool. Nylon does not have the resilience of wool upon the removal of a load; its thermoplasticity, or tenderness toward dropped matches and lighted cigarette butts, and its relative high price compared with other fibers offer obstacles to its use on a large scale alone. Today, nylon-wool and nylon-rayon-wool combinations are very common.

Previous mention of the fact that one of the soil-resistant treatments for nylon carpeting is the use of dulling agents, such as TiO_2, suggests the fact that semi-dull and bright nylons are somewhat more prone to soiling than wool; also, oil and grease stains on any synthetics are more serious than on wool, rayon, or cotton fibers. Another problem with nylon carpeting has been that of pilling. To some extent this has been corrected by changing of deniers, by the mixing of harder- and softer-textured nylon filaments in the pile, and, of course, by varying the twist.

acrylics in rugs

The acrylics, especially Acrilan, are important synthetic fibers. The Chemstrand Corporation developed Type 41, Acrilan, specifically for the carpet trade. This may be blended with Acrilan 16, and in a single dye bath, cross-dyed effects can be created. A recent Acrilan innovation[2] is in multi-colored yarns. This is achieved by spinning into a single yarn four colors of Acrilan fibers, thus creating various tones of the same shade or hue in a piece of carpeting. It is claimed that decorators may find their problems of correlation of colors much simplified by this new creation.

Acrilan facing on interlocking plastic tiles appropriately termed **Plushtiles** offers a new method whereby a soft-surfaced floor covering may be applied. Some of the more unusual and wear-demanding applications of Acrilan carpeting materials are in minature golf courses and around small wading pools and children's playgrounds. This type of application, which offers a smooth-surface effect, requires that the Acrilan be laid down in a series of fiber webs until sufficient thickness has been arrived at and then that this mass be passed through a needle loom, stitching the various webs together into a compact sandwich. Acrilan is being used alone and also blended with other fibers. Other acrylics coming into the carpet field are: Creslan, Zefran, and Verel. Thus far, Orlon has not been utilized for this purpose to a great extent. The clothing industry is apparently taking up practically all the volume of this fiber.

The acrylics seem to show less static than nylon and some of the other synthetic fibers. Although their durability is not as high as that of nylon, they are said to be longer-wearing than wool under similar construction and fiber size. About the time the acrylics came on the market in carpeting, there was a whispering campaign against them, especially Acrilan, on the basis of its flammability. However, Acrilan is less flammable than viscose rayon or cotton carpeting, both of which have been in use for many years and without any notable number of complaints. There is a vast difference in the fire hazard between a textile article

[2] G. L. Solomon, "Quality and Taste Levels Rise for Carpets, Draperies and Upholstery," *Modern Textiles Magazine, 44,* No. 1 (January 1963).

hung in the near upright position—along which flame can crawl rapidly—and the same fibers laid out flat on the floor with comparatively little air circulation through them. Nevertheless, these fibers will burn slowly, but whether the damage is somewhat more widespread than the melted hole which one gets with nylon is simply a question of degree of damage in terms of the whole area.

Table 27-9 shows the calculations based on data from several sources of the usage of various fibers in United States carpets and rugs for 1960–1961 and 1962 (estimate).

TABLE 27-9 / FIBERS USED IN CARPETS
AND RUGS

Fiber	1960	1961	(Estimate) 1962
	Per Cent	*Per Cent*	*Per Cent*
Wool	64	57	52
Nylon filament	7	18	24
Nylon staple	10	8	10
Acrylics	6	5	7
Rayon	9	8	4
Cotton	4	4	3

This is estimated to represent at wholesale prices approximately 745 million dollars.

olefins

Not included in these figures are the olefins, the polymers of polypropylene or of polyethylene. These fibers are still too new for their consumption to be of significant proportions; however, it is reported that **Herculan,** a continuous filament propylene yarn, is being used extensively, and polyethylene yarns are also being experimentally used in carpets, especially in novelty yarns utilizing the high shrinkage characteristics of this fiber, producing a relatively short but compact and highly crimped pile. These are low-priced polymers, and their physical characteristics are such that they should give relatively good wear. They are quite resistant to soiling, but two obstacles would be the very low melting point and a general slippery feel to the yarns. Another vinyl derivative, Saran, the copolymer of vinyl chloride and vinylidene chloride now available in finer deniers, is being used at least by one manufacturer in pile carpeting, with the ease of stain removal being one of the principal sales points. Its fine wear-resistance is another. The fiber, however, lacks the softness or feeling of resiliency characteristic of most successful pile fibers. It will be noted that Dacron has not yet become a significant factor in carpeting. The fiber is more expensive than some of the other polymers, and its utilization in wearing apparel has been so great that there is no incentive to carry out further investigations on a large scale in extending the market to floor coverings. The natural properties of the fiber, however, are such that it should be a good material for pile surfaces.

TABLE 27-10 / PRINCIPAL RUG AND CARPET TYPES

	Velvet	Modern Pile	Wilton	Chenille	Axminster	Jacquard
Figure No.	27-1	27-2	27-3	27-4	27-5	27-6
Loom Type	Harness	Harness	Jacquard Backing	Two looms	Multi-spool loom	Jacquard
Stuffer Yarns	Yes	No	Yes	Yes	Yes	Yes
Shot Across	Yes	No	Yes	Yes	Yes	Yes
Chain Yarn	Yes	No! Needled	Yes	Yes	Yes	Yes
Pile Type	Cut	Loop or Cut	Cut or Loop (Brussels)	Cut	Cut	Loop or Cut
Main Characteristics	Back is plain solid color face pile. Even in height.	Back fabric latex-coated. Pile loops stitched to backing.	Heavy back excess face yarns buried. Figured patterns.	Unlimited size. Most dense pile. Colors unlimited.	Back is stiff and ribbed. Face is gaily figured. Cannot roll crosswise.	Wide pattern selection and pile height. Variable weights.
Relative cost	Medium	Low	Variable	High	Low	High
Warp Yarns*	Jute	Jute or cotton	Cotton	Cotton	Jute or linen	Cotton
Stuffed Yarns*	Jute	—		Jute	Cotton	Jute
Binder Yarns*	Cotton	Jute or cotton			Cotton	Cotton
Chain Yarns*	Jute	Jute or cotton	Cotton	Jute or cotton	Linen or jute	Jute
Face Pile	Wool, rayon, and synthetics	Wool, rayon synthetics, and blends	Wool, synthetic and blends, also cotton	"Chenille fur" is filling on 2nd-loom wool	Wool and synthetic, also rayon	Wool and synthetics
Service	Fair to poor	Fair	Good	Excellent	Fair	Good

* Compositions given are common to the trade. They may be interchangeable or substituted for by nylon, H.T. rayons, paper fibers, etc.

backings, special backings or ground structures

More and more the latex-backed carpetings are being found on the market. These latex coatings of various elastomers, including natural rubber, help hold the pile loops or fibers in place; likewise, they afford greater protection against back abrasion than do some of the traditional constructions with backing yarns of jute, hemp, linen, cotton, and other fibers. Another fiber which is entering into the backing in recent years has been a twisted paper, a kraft paper slit and then twisted into a yarn called **Kraftcord.** It tends to make carpet backing somewhat more stiff than the natural fibers; also the resistance to shrinkage is greater. Note in the various sketches of carpet constructions the stuffer and filling yarns in the backing construction. These are the yarns referred to as being of hemp, paper, and similar materials. Rather recently, a very high-strength, water-resistant and dimensionally stable backing yarn has made its appearance as a kraft paper yarn twisted around a fiberglas core.

Another change in the backing of rugs has been the increased use of laminated. foamed backings. Thus far, this backing has been used more on scatter rugs and small throw rugs in order to reduce the tendency to slip on waxed floors and also to give a washable backing, so that the rugs themselves may be washed and dried in conventional equipment.

UPHOLSTERY FABRICS

Generally, fiber types best suited for carpets and rugs will likewise be well-suited for use in upholstery fabrics. After all, the primary purpose of each is to afford surfaces which have wear-resistance, attractiveness, colorful appeal, and easy cleanability (and if possible, spot and stain resistance). The degree of wear will vary due to the conditions of use. Thus, it is only natural that those synthetic fibers which have proved successful for the rug manufacturer are likewise those of greatest interest to the manufacturer or weaver of fabrics for upholstery materials. New nylons, such as **Enkaloft,** made by American Enka Corporation; **du Pont 501;** Allied Chemical Corporation's **Caprolan;** Chemstrand's **Cumuloft;** and **Nyloft,** made by Firestone Tire and Rubber Company, are among the newer fibers going into the rug and into decorative fabrics. A nylon from Guilford Mills, Greensboro, North Carolina, is known as **Trilon** and consists of continuous filament Caprolan imprinted in many colors. An interesting suede-like fabric of nylon is Chemstrand's **Islon.** This is bonded to a foam backing and illustrates one of the many new uses for these urethane foams: not only has the foam appeared as a backing material in upholstery fabrics to help keep them firm and to give additional warmth, but foam has replaced some of the traditional springing and foam rubber in upholstered chairs and sofas. Of interest to decorators is du Pont's **Pattina,** an expanded vinyl sheeting resembling leather. This has been used to some extent in shoes. Recently, it has been made into garments and luggage and leather-like coverings for furniture.

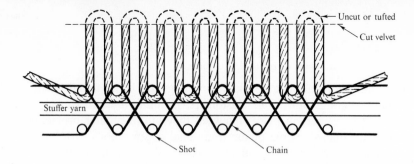

Fig. 27-1   Velvet rug construction: sketch of a row of the pile yarns (2-shot).

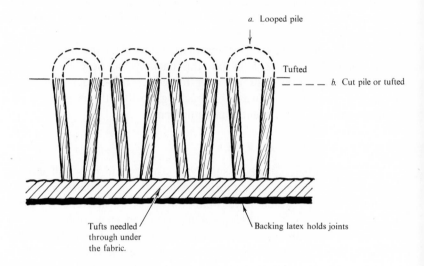

Fig. 27-2   Modern pile construction.

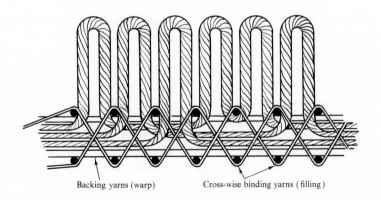

Fig. 27-3   Wilton rug construction.

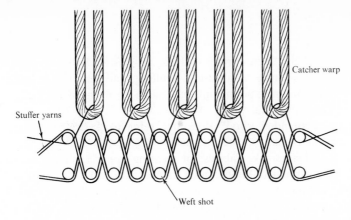

Fig. 27-4 Schematic view of chenille rug construction: The various yarns and interlacings are widely separated in order to show the construction in the rug hall.

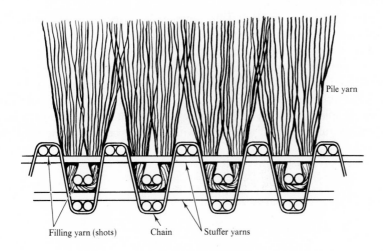

Fig. 27-5 Axminster rug construction (3-double-shots type).

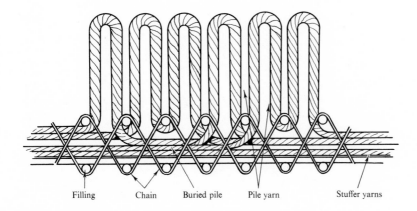

Fig. 27-6 Rug construction by the frame jacquard method.

It is a polymer of the Olefin group and has an elastic cloth backing. The fabric has tremendous resistance to abrasion, scuffing, and marking It has even been used successfully on an experimental basis as a covering for furniture in a high school for as long as seven years.

The term **"expanded vinyl"** does not refer to a stretch fabric, although moderate stretch is one of the characteristics of this material referred to in connection with leather-like fabrics for wearing apparel, shoes, and upholstery materials. The expanded vinyl-coated fabrics are vinyl coatings to which a cellular structure has been given by a heat-treating or baking process. The result is that the customary polymer coating has achieved a softnes and texture somewhat resembling that of natural leather with a thin honey-combed interior brought about by a rising or vertical expansion mechanism which might be compared with the rising of a dense dough in the baking process to create a soft, cellular loaf of bread.

Another application of the Olefin polymer is in the form of a novelty yarn of polyethylene around a core of a non-shrinkable yarn, which is then woven into a fabric with this coated yarn as the pile. A novelty effect is created upon dyeing, because the polyethylene winding tends to shrink, and the core yarn is thus spread and crimped, creating a textured effect of great permanence. Mention has been also made of the comparative prevalance now of metallic yarns as decorative or splash features in the figures woven into many of our upholstery materials. Generally, colored aluminum with a Mylar coating is the fiber chosen.

steps to fiber identification

From time to time, it is necessary for a consumer to find out the fiber type or types present in a textile material. Generally, it may be necessary only to determine whether or not a sufficient quantity of a thermoplastic or synthetic fiber is present in either the warp or filling direction to require special care in ironing. On other occasions a purchaser may wish to verify or to refute some statement made in the selling of the fabric as to its chemical composition or, under the Textile Fiber Products Labeling Act, to complete a more technical identification test often required of laboratories in commercial testing establishments and those in textile mills for the detailed analyses of their own and competing products. Home economics laboratories are often called upon to make such determinations as a part of research projects conducted in the institution or for the aid of the local consumer, whether they are individual or institutional customers or representing the service industries, such as laundries' and dry-cleaners' interests. Though several of the qualitative (identification-type) tests can be conducted with relative ease, the identification of individual fibers within a generic group or the determination of amounts of fibers through quantitative analyses are highly technical and beyond the scope of anyone but a skilled analytical chemist.

The physical tests on fabrics give some information as to the way they will probably perform in service. The actual satisfaction and serviceability they can be expected to give depend to some degree on the identity of the fibers. It is important that the wearer should know of what the garment is made so as better to use and care for it. To some extent, this is fulfilled by the Textile Fiber Products Identification Act. The sales person who knows of what fiber or mixture of fibers a garment is made will not be likely to sell it for a service condition to which the fibers are not suited. Likewise, the informed customer will not subject it to extremely severe conditions and will be more sure to see that it is properly washed or dry cleaned.

In several chapters, especially in Chapter 9 dealing with textile finishing, it was made clear that fabrics are confusing in appearance, and even experienced laboratory technicians and department store buyers cannot be sure of identifying the fibers of which many modern fabrics are made. Rayon satin resembling silk satin is still rayon, with the natural advantages and disadvantages of that fiber. Likewise, cotton finished to resemble linen is still cotton. Napped rayon blankets look like wool blankets, but they are not the same, and the most skilled buyer cannot distinguish between wool and the synthetic in blankets. Many of the so-called silk-linen dresses of a few years ago were remarkable chiefly in that they were neither silk nor linen but all rayon. The finest quality fabric may give poor service if it is improperly used and cared for.

TYPES OF IDENTIFICATION TESTS

1   Burning tests—reaction to heat, burning; odor and ash characteristics.
2   Color tests—reactions to stains and dyes.
3   Chemical tests—solubility in chemical solutions.
4   Microscopic examination.
5   Specific gravity—weight.

The fibers in each direction should be separately tested, because many fabrics have a different textile fiber in the filling yarns than in the warp; also, the yarns in either direction, or both, may be composed of more than one kind of fiber.

burning tests

The test specimen for the burning test is a small cluster of yarns from the warp direction and a similar cluster from the filling direction to be burned separately. If it is known or suspected that the fabric is a mixture or blend of two or more kinds of fiber, then individual fibers from both warp and filling should be tested separately. The specimen is brought very slowly into contact with a small flame, with careful observation as to the way in which the fibers curl or soften as they become heated. The odor produced by burning and the persistence of burning after the sample is removed from the flame should be observed. By persistence is meant whether the flame dies out instantly or whether the fibers continue to burn and melt. The final observation is the texture and appearance of the hard ash, if any. The odor can be compared with that of known fibers,

TABLE 28-1 / REACTION OF TEXTILE FIBERS TO HEAT AND FLAME

Test Procedure: A speciment of the fiber is moved slowly toward a small flame, and the reaction of the fiber to heat is observed. One end of the specimen is then pushed directly into the flame to determine the burning characteristics of the fiber. After removal from the flame, the fiber's burning characteristics are again observed, and the burning odor is noted. (The burning odor can be compared with that of known fibers.) The specimen is then allowed to cool, and the characteristics of the ash are checked.

Groups of fibers, short lengths of yarn, or small pieces of fabric can be used as test specimens unless the product to be tested contains a combination of yarns or a blend of fibers. In such cases, individual fibers selected from the textile material with the aid of a magnifying glass may be used.

CAUTION: This test should be made with care to prevent burning of the fingers and to avoid inhaling excessive amounts of smoke from the burning sample.

TYPICAL BEHAVIOR OF FIBER SPECIMEN

	Fibers	When Approaching Flame	When in Flame	After Removal of Flame	Typical Ash Characteristics
NATURAL	Cotton	Does *not* fuse or shrink away from flame.	Burns *without* melting.	Continues to burn *without* melting.	Does *not* leave knob or bead.
	Flax	Does *not* fuse or shrink away from flame.	Burns *without* melting.	Continues to burn *without* melting.	Does *not* leave knob or bead.
	Silk	Fuses and curls away from flame.	Burns slowly with some melting.	Burns very slowly; sometimes self-extinguishing.	Leaves soft, fluffy, black ash.
	Wool	Fuses and curls away from flame.	Burns slowly with some melting.	Burns very slowly; sometimes self-extinguishing.	Leaves soft, fluffy, black ash.
MAN-MADE	Acetate	Fuses away from flame.	Burns with melting.	Continues to burn with melting.	Leaves brittle, black irregular-shaped bead.
	Acrylic	Fuses away from flame.	Burns with melting.	Continues to burn with melting.	Leaves hard, brittle, black, irregular-shaped bead.
	Modacrylic	Fuses away from flame.	Burns very slowly with melting.	Self-extinguishing.	Leaves hard black irregular-shaped bead.
	Nylon	Fuses and shrinks away from flame.	Burns slowly with melting.	Usually self-extinguishing.	Leaves hard, tough, gray, round bead.
	Nytril	Fuses away from flame.	Burns slowly with melting.	Continues to burn with melting.	Leaves hard, black, irregular-shaped bead.
	Olefin	Fuses, shrinks and curls away from flame.	Burns with melting.	Continues to burn with melting.	Leaves hard, tough, tan, round bead.
	Polyester	Fuses and shrinks away from flame.	Burns slowly with melting.	Usually self-extinguishing.	Leaves hard, tough, black, round bead.
	Rayon	Does *not* fuse or shrink away from flame.	Burns *without* melting.	Continues to burn *without* melting.	Does *not* leave knob or bead.
	Saran	Fuses and shrinks away from flame.	Burns very slowly with melting.	Self-extinguishing.	Leaves hard, black, irregular-shaped bead.
	Spandex	Fuses but does *not* shrink away from flame.	Burns with melting.	Continues to burn with melting.	Leaves soft, fluffy, black ash.

Excerpt from: "Identification of Fibers in Textile Materials," Technical Information Bulletin X-156, E. I. duPont de Nemours & Co., Inc., December 1961.

if a collection is available. A word of caution should be given, however, against inhaling excessive amounts of smoke from the burning samples, especially the synthetics, some of which have a decidedly acrid odor. Care should be taken against burning one's fingers, and generally a long pair of forceps is the preferred holder. A collection of woven fiber residue at the end of the forceps sometimes gives false clues as to odor and amount of smoke produced. For greater detail on fiber burning, see Table 4 Appendix C.

color tests

The identification of fiber type by the use of color staining is applicable to undyed white or near-white fibers and fabrics. These color tests are of two types: 1) a standard coloring agent or chemical giving a specific color to one type of fiber, such as Millon's Reagent for the identification of protein fibers, and 2) mixtures of stains or dyestuffs developing characteristic colors for the identification of several fibers. Although it is true that many dyed fabrics and yarns can be stripped of their color, the chemicals involved may alter the dyeing characteristics of the chemical polymer making up the fiber. Likewise, all finishing agents must be removed prior to the staining test, and this may lead to inaccuracies in color development during the testing procedure. Among the most common finishing agents to be removed would be starch or glue sizes, both of which may be removed successfully by heating the sample to 140° in a solution of enzyme. According to Wolfgang,[1] "Oil wax or plastic sizes (e.g., polyvinyl alcohol or polyvinyl acetate) can be removed by boiling the sample in a solution containing 5 per cent soap and 5 per cent sodium hydroxide. Resins can be removed by boiling for one hour with a one percent hydrochloric acid solution."

The author particularly recommends five commercially available identification stains, the results of which are listed in Table 28-2, entitled "Colors Developed on Fibers by Five Identification Stains." The sources of these are as follows:

Calco—identification stain No. 2—American Cyanamid Company—good distinction between Orlon 42 and Dacron.

du Pont identification stain No. 4—E. I. du Pont de Nemours & Co.—good distinction between Nylon 6 and Nylon 66.

Geigy—identification stain—Geigy Chemical Corporation—good distinction between nylons.

Texchrom—identification stain—Fisher Scientific Company—can be applied cold and therefore excellent for staining microscope slides.

Test Fabrics—identification stain—Test Fabrics, Inc.—good distinction between cotton and viscose rayons.

[1] William G. Wolfgang, Chapter 4, "Fiber Identification," in J. J. Press (ed.), *Man-made Textile Encyclopedia* (New York: John Wiley, 1959), pp. 151–154.

TABLE 28-2 / COLORS DEVELOPED ON FIBERS BY FIVE IDENTIFICATION STAINS

Fiber	Calco #2	DuPont #4	Geigy	Texchrom	Test Fabrics
Cotton	Greyish olive	Greyish green	Deep powder blue	Pale blue	Dark greyish olive
Viscose	Dark bluish green	Dark greenish blue	Purplish blue	Very pale blue	Blackish blue
Cuprammonium	Dark green	Dark blue	Hunter green	—	—
Corvel	Dark grey green	Metallic blue grey	Bright metallic blue	Mauve	Royal purple
Topel	Light grey	Light green grey	Bright metallic blue	Light mauve	Purple
Fortisan	Medium grey	Light greyish tan	Lavender	—	—
Fortisan 36	Pale rose grey	Silver grey	Blue lavender	—	—
Acetate	Orange yellow	Deep orange	Yellow green	Yellow green	Gold
Arnel	Lemon yellow	Gold orange	Bright brownish yellow	—	Canary yellow
Wool	Dark greyish purple	Dark greyish purple	Navy	Dark yellow	Dark red
Silk	Black	Blackish purple	Navy black	Yellow brown	Dark reddish purple
Vicara	Brown	Reddish orange	Dark green	Yellow green	Dark red
Vinyon HH	—	—	Dull orange brown	—	—
Dynel	Dark greyish yellow	Light brown	Dark tan	Pale green	Yellowish brown
Darvan	Rose grey	Light tan	Rose tan	—	Pale tannish yellow
Verel	Yellow grey brown	Orange brown	Dark rose tan	—	Tannish yellow
Orlon 42	Tannish white	Pale orange tan	Pale yellow ivory	Pale yellow green	Pale reddish orange
Orlon 81	Unstained	Unstained	Yellow white	Very light bluish green	Yellow grey
Acrilan	Light reddish brown	Light brown	Greenish grey	Pale green	Light brown
Creslan	Tan	Tannish orange	Pale greenish blue	—	—
Zefran	Brown	Wine	Hunter green	—	Brown
Kuralon	Brownish wine	Wine orange	Blackish green	Violet	Orange brown
Nylon 6	Purple brown	Brownish wine	Blackish green	Pale orange yellow	Reddish brown
Nylon 66	Burgundy	Reddish brown	Bright dark green	Light yellow green	Orange brown
Dacron 54	Pale emerald green	Light greenish yellow	Light rose tan	Pale blue	Light greenish grey
Dacron 64	Light chartreuse	Light orange tan	Pink grey	—	Yellowish grey
Kodel	Pale green	Orange yellow	Light grey	—	Light greenish grey
Saran	—	—	Bright orange brown	—	—
Polyethylene, low pressure	Very light beige	Light yellow blond	Very light orchid	Unstained	—
Polyethylene, high pressure	Very light beige	Light yellow blond	Very light orchid	Unstained	—
Polypropylene	Light beige	Yellow blond	Light orchid	Unstained	—
Rhovyl	Mustard yellow	Brownish orange	Reddish brown	Very light blue	—

From: J. J. Press (ed.), *Man-Made Textile Encyclopedia* (New York: John Wiley & Sons, Inc., 1959), p. 153, Table VI.

The staining of the yarn might give the color of the composite mass, that is, the blending of color from two or more different fabrics present. For this reason, it is more accurate to separate the individual fibers into a tasseled end and to observe these individual fibers for their color under the low-power microscope.

chemical tests

This technique is applicable to research and testing laboratories, and for accuracy, a clean fiber or yarn completely free of any finishing agent is required. Ideally, in a blend, one would seek to have a solvent or a chemical which would react quickly and completely with one fiber but not affect the other. An extensive list of chemicals and solvents would be required in order to separate from one another the wide number of textile fibers now on the market, and as certain groups tend to expand with new polymers coming into commercial production, it is reasonable to suppose that the differences between them will become increasingly minute, so that the search for specific chemicals must constantly go on. Many of these chemicals are hazardous, and the operation should be carried out in a hood, with the laboratory technician or chemist completely protected by means of chemical-resistant gloves, aprons, gowns, etc. The eyes should be protected with goggles.

The du Pont Company has published an interesting and usable list on chemical solubility of textile fibers. This is shown in Table 28-3. It will be noted that when each solvent is used in turn on an unknown fiber or group of fiber samples, there is a specific solvent for each of the nine classes of fibers. Caution in the use of these chemicals must be rigidly observed, and one must weigh possible inaccuracies arising out of chemical damage during the bleaching and finish removal if that has been necessary.

microscopic examination

The characteristic structures of the various fibers as shown by the microscope have been described in the chapters dealing with each of the textile fibers. A brief summary of the method, however, may properly be repeated.

In many cases it may be necessary to remove or strip the dye from the fabric or yarn so that the structure of the fibers may be observed more clearly. No one chemical is universally succesful, and several chemicals and reagents may have to be tried before one is found to do an acceptable job. Sodium hydrosulfite may be used to remove acid and substantive dyes. The fabric is placed in a three per cent solution and brought to a boil. The operation is continued until the dye is removed. The fabric is then further rinsed in clear water and dried. Caustic soda in an approximate 0.5 per cent solution will strip some dyes. However, this method cannot be used if any protein fiber is contained in the blend, since this concentration of alkali will dissolve protein fibers. Household hypochlorite bleach may be used for some dyestuffs; however, chlorine may cause some yarns and fibers to yellow.

TABLE 28-3 / CHEMICAL SOLUBILITY OF TEXTILE FIBERS

Test Procedure: A specimen is placed first in one and then another of the liquids using the numerical sequence shown below. (The liquid-to-specimen weight ratio should be at least 100 to 1.) In each liquid, the specimen is stirred periodically for 5 minutes, and the effect of the liquid on the specimen is carefully noted. Special illumination may be required to observe the results of the test.

Small clumps of fibers, short lengths of yarn, or small pieces of fabric can be used as test specimens; however, if there is any doubt about the results, individual fibers should be tested. Such fibers must be carefully selected from the textile material to assure that specimens of each fiber present are tested. Selection of the individual fibers can be facilitated by use of a magnifying glass or microscope.

Effect of Liquid: I = Fiber insoluble   P = Fiber partly soluble or partly disintegrated   S = Fiber soluble or completely disintegrated.

CAUTION: These are hazardous liquids and should be handled with care. Chemical laboratory exhaust hoods, gloves, aprons, and goggles should be used for fiber solubility work.

Chemical Agent	Concentration (% by weight)	Density (at 75° F.)	Temp. (°F.)	Acetate	Nylon	Silk & Wool	Olefin & Saran	Acrylic	Modacrylic & Nytril	Spandex	Cotton Flax Rayon	Polyester
1. Acetic Acid, glacial	—	—	75	S*	I	I	I	I	I	I	I	I
2. Hydrochloric Acid	20	1.096	75	I	S	I	I	I	I	I	I	I
3. Sodium Hypochlorite solution (pH 11)	(5% Avail. Chlorine)	—	75	I	I	S**	I	I	I	I	I	I
4. Xylene (meta-)	—	—	282††	I	I	I	S***	I	I	I	I	I
5. Ammonium Thiocyanate	70	—	266††	I	I	I	I	S	I	I	I	I
6. Butyrolactone	—	—	75	S	I	I	I	I	S§	I	I	I
7. Dimethyl Formamide	—	—	200	S	I	I	I & S	S	S	S	I	I
8. Sulfuric Acid	75	1.665	75	S	S	S & I	I	S & I	I	P	S§§	I
9. Cresol (meta-)	—	—	200	S	S	I	I	P	P	P	I	S

† If not otherwise specified, the concentration was approximately 100%. Where lower levels of concentration are specified, water was used as the diluent.

†† At the boil.

* Vigorous agitation may be required to dissolve triacetate fibers in the specified time. A more rapid dissolution can be accomplished at a temperature of 100° F.

** Silk and wool fibers can be separated by dissolving the silk in concentrated (37 to 38%) hydrochloric acid at 75° F. Wool fibers are not soluble.

*** Olefin and saran fibers can be separated by dissolving the saran in dioxane-1,4 at 200° F. Olefin fibers are not soluble.

§ Modacrylic and nytril fibers can be separated by dissolving the nytril in 60% nitric acid (density = 1.362) at 75° F. Modacrylic fibers are not soluble.

§§ Rayon fibers can be separated from cotton and flax fibers by dissolving the rayon in concentrated (37 to 38%) hydrochloric acid at 75° F. Cotton and flax fibers are not soluble. Cotton and flax can be distinguished by their longitudinal appearance when observed with a microscope.

Courtesy E. I. du Pont, Technical Information Bulletin X-156, December 1961.

Generally, laboratories lack a satisfactory microtome for the preparation of cross-sections of the fibers. Thus the actual cross-section is rarely seen except in photographs. Examination of the longitudinal section of the fibers is generally not too revealing unless the fiber has a distinctive pattern: the twist in the case of cotton; a distinctive outer wall structure, such as scales on wool or "nodes" on silk fibers; or the long dark lines along the length of the fibers showing indentations from the irregular cross-section of such fibers as Arnel or Viscose. Figure 1, Appendix C shows the cross sections of important fibers, pp. 546.

TABLE 28-4 / SPECIFIC GRAVITY OF TEXTILE FIBERS

Test Procedure: A single-filament or single-fiber specimen is placed in a series of specially prepared liquids of known specific gravity. If the specific gravity of the fiber is greater than that of the liquid, the specimen will sink in the liquid; conversely, if the specific gravity of the fiber is lower, the specimen will float. (The fiber's surface must be free of air bubbles since they can affect the results of the test.)

A suitable series of liquids for this test may be prepared by mixing, in various proportions, carbon tetrachloride (specific gravity of 1.60 at room temperature) with xylene (specific gravity of 0.87 at room temperature). Before using any of the liquids for fiber identification, their specific gravity should be checked with a calibrated hydrometer.

		Fibers	Specific Gravity†
MAN-MADE	Acetate	Secondary (ACELE*) and triacetate ("arnel")	1.32
	Acrylic	All (including ORLON* and ORLON SAYELLE**)	1.14 to 1.19
	Modacrylic	"Dynel"	1.30
		"Verel"	1.36
		Nylon 6 and nylon 6-6 (including ANTRON***	
	Nylon	and Du PONT Type 501)	1.14
	Nytril	"Darvan"	1.18
	Olefin	Polyethylene and polypropylene	0.92
	Polyester	DACRON*, "Fortrel", "Terylene", "Toray-Teto-	
		ron"	1.38
		"Kodel"	1.22
		"Vycron"	1.37
	Rayon	All	1.52
	Saran	All	1.70
	Spandex	LYCRA*	1.21
		"Vyrene"	1.35
NATURAL	Cotton	All (including mercerized and not mercerized)	1.52
	Flax	Bleached	1.52
	Silk	Boiled-off	1.25
	Wool	Cashmere, mohair, and regular (Merino)	1.32

* Du Pont's registered trademark.
** Du Pont's registered trademark for its bi-component acrylic fiber.
*** Du Pont's registered trademark for its trilobal multifilament nylon yarn.
† These are average values; hence, individual determinations on the same fiber specimen may produce values that vary by as much as 0.02.

From Identification of Fibers in Textile Materials, Bulletin X-156, December, 1961, p. 8 (Wilmington, Delaware: E. I. du Pont de Nemours & Co.).

Reprinted with permission.

specific gravity

Another confirmatory test used by many laboratories is that of determining specific gravity of the unknown fiber or fibers. Table 28-5 from the du Pont publication, X-156, shows the specific gravity of some of our fiber groups.

Thus, using a series of mixtures from 100 per cent carbon tetrachloride (with a specific gravity of 1.60 at room temperature) to 100 per cent Xylene (specific gravity of 0.87 at room temperature), a sinking value or specific gravity value can be obtained for a wide number of samples shown in Table 28-5. Thus, starting with 100 per cent carbon tetrachloride, we would have the specific gravity, 1.60, at which Saran would sink.

> 1.45—Saran, cotton, flax, and rayon would all sink.
> 1.30—all of the foregoing plus Verel, Dacron, Fortel, Terylene, Vycron, Vyrene, acetate, Dynel, and wool.
> 1.15—all of the foregoing plus Darvan, Kodel, Lycra, silk, and possibly acrylic or nylon.
> 1.00—all of the foregoing including those listed as possibilities.
> 0.87—all of the foregoing plus olefins.

textile product
consumership

The general consensus is that the average store customer—the housewife—like other members of her family, tends to make her textile product selections more on the basis of the esthetic or appearance factors than on durability or potential performance in service. Many of these esthetic qualities defy actual testing in terms of figures and precise ratings. They are essentially **subjective** reactions and, to a considerable degree, depend upon the taste and selective ability of the individual. We must use words to describe the drape or hang of a skirt or the graceful folds in a curtain and drapery material. We must use words to describe the relative dullness or luster. Fabric textures are often more a matter of feel or tactile sensory response than of precise measurements. Similarly, we say that one fabric feels cool or comfortable to the skin and that another does not. The advertisements of new textile products and finishes appearing in the fashion magazines or in the columns of the daily paper or on store display signs emphasize the fashion rightness, beauty, texture, and price, with attention being called very seldom to the durability of the fabric or of its color or finish. Recently, the so-called "minimum care" fabrics (often referred to as wash-and-wear) have begun to call the attention of the customer to the serviceability of these new materials, principally the synthetic fibers. These are **objective** reactions with differences measurable by laboratory testing procedures and to which numbers or rating values can be assigned. With these new fibers and with the chemical changes which have been imposed upon the natural fibers, principally cotton and wool, and upon other cellulosic fibers, such as linen and rayon, some of the potential use-experience or consumer influence is beginning to be felt at the point and time of sale.

CUSTOMER VS. CONSUMER INFLUENCES

Despite these changes, which are still small in comparison with the total textile volume sold in our large department stores, we can safely conclude that when the individual makes a purchase, it is with the esthetics principally in mind. These can be defined as the **customer influences.** After purchase and when the article has been used for some months, then the same individual becomes more critical and begins to compare the garment's performance with what she expected or hoped for. These are the **consumer elements** and influence the individual in her future action. Does she re-purchase? Does she silently condemn the product? Does she return it for credit or replacement? The housewife is a realist and probably bases her return of merchandise more upon failure of the article to meet her expectations than upon the extent to which it falls short of perfection in service. For perfection would mean almost indefinite serviceability and with no attrition or visible damage to fabrics, texture, color, or finish during normal wear. Expectations should be modified, too, as the weight, texture, or delicacy of the new article differs from that which the customer may previously have purchased and been accustomed to using. Thus, the realistic customer or housewife will recognize that today's nylon stocking, being much finer in filament and, therefore, much more transparent than those with which she first became familiar, would not expect the same degree of wear as she did from pre-World War II nylon full-fashioned stockings. She would not expect the same serviceability from a sheer blouse that she experienced from a heavier, firmer poplin. And, certainly, today's 8-ounce summer suiting will not wear as long as the former 11- or 13-ounce wool suiting for men's summer tropicals.

ATTRIBUTES OR CHARACTERISTICS OF TEXTILES

The fabric or the end-use products made from it will have a combination of properties or attributes influencing not only customer selection but also consumer experience in use.[1] Some of these properties are due to the individual fiber or fibers making up the yarn structure. Others have been imparted through the art and science of fabric finishing and dyeing. Generally, the first characteristic

---

[1] Many of the prominent leaders in the field of teaching of Consumership or Home Economics disregard this duality of interest. It is a fact that the more knowledge one has of the properties of textiles and other commodities, the more proficiently would one fulfill the double responsibility of the ultimate consumer, the housewife, in *buying* and using, or *consuming,* the products.

should be that whatever the combination of properties, both esthetic and functional, which were orginally possessed by the textile, it should be reasonably permanent, so that the wearer or user will continue to enjoy the product. Two notable exceptions to this permanence are, of course, India madras prints, which are widely advertised as "readily fadeable" or "guaranteed fadeable," and blue denims, which, due to some quirk in human nature, must be stiff and deep-toned dyed initially but which become increasingly pleasing to the wearer as they soften both in texture and in color tone through frequent wearing and washing.

No single textile product would ever have all of the fabric properties appearing in the following table. Some of those appearing together are direct antipathies; others are comparatively insignificant when one considers which properties are most wanted or expected in terms of serviceability in use.

TABLE 29-1 / PROPERTIES OF TEXTILE PRODUCTS

Group I: Esthetic or Sensory Factors

Fashion or style rightness
Feel—smooth or rough
Texture—soft or firm
Comfort—cool or warm
Transparency—sheerness or opacity (denseness)
Drapability—grace of fold or rigidity
Dimensional stability (resistance to shrinking, stretching, or distortion in use)

Group II: Service Properties

Permanence of esthetic properties
Breaking strength
Tear strength
Bursting strength
Weight
Wear or abrasion resistance
Yarn-slippage resistance
Seam strength
Crease retention
Wrinkle resistance
Odor resistance
Sun-damage resistance
Color-fastness to washing
Color-fastness to sunlight
Color-fastness to cleaning
Color-fastness to crocking
Color-fastness to bleach
Resistance to chlorine retention
Resistance to insects
Resistance to mildew
Resistance to perspiration
Resistance to bacteria
Flammability resistance
Water repellency
Water absorbency

The Agricultural Marketing Service of the Market Research Division of the United States Department of Agriculture has carried out several research studies on consumer preferences and consumers' attitudes toward various fibers for certain end-use products. One of these, reported by Nolan and Levine,[2] was made in a Pennsylvania city, and, in order to discover the relative importance of characteristics of fabrics in the minds of the consumers interviewed, a somewhat abbreviated list of factors was prepared, as follows:

> Ability to hold shape
> Amount of shrinkage
> Appearance of the weave
> Color-fastness
> Color
> Cost
> Degree of sheerness
> Degree of warmth or coolness
> Degree to which it will show or pick up soil
> Degree to which it will wrinkle
> Durability
> Ease of pressing or ironing
> Feel on skin

The homemakers were asked to rate these various factors as "one" for most important, "two" for least important. The relative rankings of fourteen characteristics for fabric in dresses for selected situations showed the following summary:

TABLE 29-2 / RELATIVE RANKINGS OF 14 CHARACTERISTICS OF FABRIC IN DRESSES FOR SELECTED SITUATIONS

	STREET DRESS		SPECIAL OCCASION DRESS	
Fabric Characteristics	Winter	Summer	Winter	Summer
Ability to hold shape	1	6	1	2
Amount of shrinkage	6	5	12	9
Appearance of weave	13	13	9	12
Color fastness	3	2	8	5
Range of color	11	9	3	4
Cost	2	8	4	6
Degree of sheerness	14	10	14	8
Degree of warmth or coolness provided	4	1	11	3
Degree it will show soil	8	11	6	11
Degree it will wrinkle	5	3	2	1
Durability	9	12	13	13
Ease of cleaning	7	7	5	10
Ease of pressing	10	4	10	7
Feel on skin	12	9	7	9

F. L. Nolan and D. B. Levine, *Consumers' Concepts of Fabric*, Marketing Research Report No. 338, U.S. Department of Agriculture, p. 9.

Courtesy U.S. Dept. of Agriculture.

[2] F. L. Nolan and Daniel B. Levine, *Consumers' Concepts of Fabric*, Marketing Research Report No. 338, U.S. Department of Agriculture, Agricultural Marketing Service, Market Research Division, Washington, D.C. (1959).

Another interesting tabulation from this survey deals with the characteristics which influenced the choice of the last dress bought by some 2133 homemakers interviewed in this study.

TABLE 29-3 / REASONS FOR SELECTING DRESSES PURCHASED

Reason		Per Cent
Appearance		48
Style, trim	30	
Color	18	
Fit and usefulness		25
Fit	13	
Comfortable	4	
Versatile	4	
Need	4	
Fabric and care		25
Fabric	9	
Practical	7	
Washable	5	
Easy care	4	
Gift or other		2
Total		100

Courtesy U.S. Dept. of Agriculture.

It is interesting to note that appearance, color, feel, wrinkle resistance, and ease of cleaning were the principal influences guiding the choice of these consumers. Other studies carried out by this Service and independent studies carried out by colleges and universities, as well as by industry, are in general agreement that the esthetics are the guiding factors in attracting the customer and in influencing the garment selection and purchase.

CONSUMERSHIP — BUYING WITH A PURPOSE

The vast array of dresses, suits, coats, shirts, carpets, draperies, curtains, towels, and every other type of textile product tends to confuse and perhaps even to terrify the completely uninformed store customer. She tends to fear the unknown, such as the strange-sounding new fiber names, to mistrust the labels claiming particular virtues for a new fabric finish, and maybe even to worry about this season's new texture if it differs greatly from the kind of material with which she has had previous experience. Even cottons no longer always feel or look the same. They may not feel like cottons, and the labels often state that they will do things which she knows from her own limited experience cottons have never done before, such as to resist wrinkling and hold pleats and creases. She may fall back upon the kind of goods with which she has had satisfactory experience in the past or search out a familiar brand name if her experience has been a happy one. On the other hand, she may be an eager experimenter who will react most trustingly in response to the most enthusiastic claims. She may be one who fears or mistrusts labels and advertising claims and falls back on unlabeled, unidentified merchandise which may cost a little less than those whose price must reflect some of the extra research and testing which have gone into their development.

Too often, all these are one-time customers. They are not the stable market for whom the buyer has made his selection in the garment market. They are not the consumers, the repeat customers. Knowledge or even appreciation of textile performance are not easily achieved. Fiber, fabric, and manufacturer's names, and claims for performance challenge even the experienced home economist and store buyer, to say nothing of the salesperson. These goods have been bought by the store for the purpose of pleasing a majority of the buying public who are regular customers of the store. They will not please every customer; they will not satisfy the consumer unless she makes her selections carefully with her own particular needs in view. Whether buying for herself or buying for her family, she is generally regarded as the purchasing agent for that unit of our society. If she is a good purchasing agent, she should buy with the interest of her family in mind, not only in terms of cost and of what she expects by way of performance but with the idea of value for the money expended.

the concept of value

Value rarely enters into the conscious action of the housewife, but it is the guiding factor behind most of the store's own buying practices, especially in private brand merchandise. For several years, the Commodity Standards Fellowship[3] utilized an equation expressing such a concept of value in judging the best among the offerings of several potential resources supplying such things as men's shirts, women's blouses, bed sheets, and a host of other textile products to be sold in the store under the store's own brand program. Price was one factor, but it was not the major influence in the final selection in every case. Each manufacturer's offering was evaluated in the laboratory, not just tested. The tests gave figures and ratings which were then evaluated by comparing all of the important features of the article and estimating the degree to which each test rating contributed to the total of the features considered to be of greatest consumer importance. Each individual total was then divided by the cost of the article tested. Sometimes the least expensive merchandise appeared to offer the best value in potential serviceability, as indicated by the laboratory tests. In some cases, the more expensive item was selected.

Some such mathematical equation can be set up by each individual consumer if she has the ability and experience to study thoroughly in advance her own habits in use and cleaning, the state of her wardrobe, and her expectations (or hopes) in terms of garment performance, not, however, overlooking the prices of the several garments in which she may be interested in the store as possible additions to her wardrobe or to that of her family.

[3] Maintained by the Kaufmann Department Store at Mellon Institute, 1931–1958.

definition of value

Value may be defined as the degree to which her present needs and wants and particular care requirements may be satisfied per dollar retail cost by each of the various dresses or other articles under consideration. Expressed as an equation, then,

$$\text{Value (V)} = \frac{N \text{ (Needs)} + W \text{ (Wants)} + C \text{ (Care)}}{D \text{ (Dollars)}}$$

Generally, a **need** is an important requirement the article must meet or an important role the article must fill in the textile use pattern of the individual person or family. A **want** is something secondary; it is desirable but not imperative. **Care** involves method of cleansing, potential frequency of cleansing, ease of ironing, color permanence, and any special storage or care conditions required of the material or article.

As an example of this calculation, let us assume that a college freshman in Home Economics is considering the purchase of a light blue dress, primarily for afternoon parties or for trips to town, but suitable also for wear to class on occasion. It must be a dress which would be comfortable in comparatively warm weather, such as late spring and early fall. The style must be suitable for this college freshman, but she must also take into account the possibility that it may have to be used by her younger sister, who, at present, is somewhat heavier than she is, though both can wear the same size. The selection has come down to two dresses: one an all-cotton poplin, rather loose-fitting dress at $15.95; the other, a somewhat more sheer, Dacron and cotton blend, sheath type at $19.95. From the needs or primary requirements, this girl selects appearance, style, size, drapability, general utility, durability, crease retention, and sheerness as her bases of selection. Among the wants, or secondary factors, to be considered are the coordination of each dress in terms of her wardrobe, the trimming, the workmanship observed, potential resistance to soiling, retention of its dimensions, colorfastness to light, the presence of a Standard Label, comfort, and the hand-me-down potential of each dress. In terms of care, the washability of the fabric, the possibility of removing trimming, and the ease of ironing were the three important factors. Only now does she draw up the following table.

TABLE 29-4 / VALUE COMPARISON
OF TWO ''DRESSY'' DRESSES

Needs	Cotton $15.95	Dacron-Cotton $19.95
Appearance	10	10
Style	8	10
Size	10	10
Drape	10	10
General use (utility)	10	7
Durability	7	10

Crease retention	7	10	
Sheerness	8	10	
Total	70	77	

Wants

Coordination—wardrobe	10	8	
Trimming	8	10	
Workmanship	7	10	
Soil resistance	10	8	
Dimension retention	8	10	
Color fastness to light	8	8	
"Standards" label	7	10	
Hand-me-down use	10	6	
Comfort	10	10	
Total	78	80	

Care

Washability (label)	8	10	
Ease of trim removal	8	10	
Ease of ironing	8	10	
Total	24	30	
N + W + C = Total	172	187	

Based on files of personal laboratory reports.

Taking the totals of "needs," "wants," and "care," for each dress and dividing by the appropriate dollar value, the equation for dress No. 1 (the all-cotton) will be

$$V = \frac{70 + 78 + 24}{16} = 10.7$$

The second dress will have as its equation:

$$V = \frac{77 + 80 + 30}{20} = 9.03$$

(Note that the dollar values have been rounded out to the nearest whole dollar for ease of calculation.) These differences are well within the error of estimation on the part of the shopper. The lower-priced dress is the higher value in terms of the money this young lady has to expend.

In some cases, treating the three analytical categories separately, the shopper may be better able to evaluate her own buying patterns and habits than if all three were added together; it may be that an individual may find that the "wants" or the "special care" requirements are of much less importance than the "needs," and she can assign her own private weighting or significance to these other two analytical summations. Perhaps a more experienced shopper than this college freshman would have put considerable trust in the name of the manufacturer if she had had experience with garments made by this firm before. She might also have had experience with the Dacron-cotton blend. She may well have misjudged the quality of the trimming of the two garments, and perhaps that on the more expensive dress would not be as good. It is possible, too, that in her generosity she gave too great a penalty to the $19.95 dress for its more limited hand-me-down features. She would have loved the sheath-type herself, but how terribly would her sister have looked when she inherited it next year.

TABLE 29-5 / CHARACTERISTICS OF FABRIC WHICH INFLUENCED CHOICE OF LAST DRESS BOUGHT, REPORTED BY 2,133 HOMEMAKERS

Characteristics of Fabric	Number	Per Cent[1]
Appearance of weave	844	40
Color of dress	507	24
Feel on skin	444	21
No characteristic of fabric	371	17
Degree of warmth or coolness	261	12
Wrinkle resistance	249	12
Ease of cleaning	223	10
Durability	171	8
Ability to hold shape	139	7
Ease of pressing	39	2
Amount of shrinkage	4	2
Color-fastness	3	2

Courtesy U.S. Department of Agriculture.

F. L. Nolan and D. B. Levine, *Consumers' Concepts of Fabric,* Marketing Research Report No. 338, Department of Agriculture.

[1] Percentages add to more than 100 because respondents named more than one characteristic.

[2] Less than 1 per cent.

If we are to believe 2,133 homemakers, the three esthetic appeals of appearance, color, and texture had the greatest influence on the purchase of the latest dress bought. But it is the consumer aspects in which this same study indicates consumers expect better satisfaction as the price bracket goes up. The wise consumer will also refer to her knowledge of potential serviceability of fibers (Table 29-6).

TABLE 29-6 / CHARACTERISTICS OF FABRICS WHICH WOULD BE EXPECTED TO IMPROVE IN A DRESS COSTING $15 COMPARED WITH ONE COSTING $8, AND ONE COSTING $25 COMPARED WITH ONE COSTING $15

Characteristics	PER CENT EXPECTING IMPROVEMENT IN DRESS COSTING—	
	$15 Compared with $8	$25 Compared with $15
None	15	9
Ability to hold shape	62	76
Amount of shrinkage	39	40

Appearance of weave	32	40
Color-fastness	37	38
Range of colors	12	17
Degree of sheerness	9	12
Degree of warmth or coolness	13	18
Degree it will pick up soil	20	25
Degree to which it will wrinkle	43	54
Durability	56	63
Ease of cleaning	19	27
Ease of pressing	19	22
Feel on the skin	21	35
Number reporting	498	496

F. L. Nolan and D. B. Levine. *Consumers' Concepts of Fabric,* Marketing Research Report No. 338 Dept. of Agriculture, p. 19.
Courtesy U.S. Department of Agriculture.

WOMEN'S AND GIRLS' APPAREL

Probably in no textile product is competition as keen as in outerwear for women and girls. One could scarcely class the wide variety of eye-catching advertising appeal as guides to **consumer selection.** They are designed more to tantalize the curiosity and create a desire for ownership. To attract attention, most advertisements, therefore, emphasize the esthetics of the product and may be described more as lures than as guides. Nor is this a wrong thing to do; nor should the industry be condemned for it as long as the product is made honorably and is not described in a deceptive manner. The fact is that customers will only respond in mass to these appeals as have been shown in Table 29-3. Of the buying influences commonly available for textile products, advertising and display are the primary elements affecting women's and girls' wear selection not only in suits, coats, and dresses but also in lingerie and casual wear. Brand names and names of famous designers identified with a garment rank next in importance. Federal legislation as it applies to the fibers of which a garment is made attracts some customer attention. Informative labels, particularly those dealing with care in use or cleansing, have some effect on the initial selection of a garment. The advisory services of magazines are of little importance for any kind of fashion merchandise, and standards likewise will probably never be significant in the field of fashion merchandise for women.

fashion demands speed

More than in any other kind of textile product, speed in presentation, promotion, and selling is essential in women's and girls' wear of a fashion or style nature. Although high fashion is confined to the wealthy throughout the world, its effect is often reflected within a few months or even weeks in more moderately-priced outerwear and, eventually, even in many of the staple price lines. High-fashion dresses, suits, and coats (the more appropriate high fashion words are doubtless gowns and ensembles) are generally thought of in terms of the line and drape and also of the texture and the garment length as dictated by the leading designers of Europe and the United States. Fashion also dictates the colors for the forthcoming spring and fall merchandise. These new colors and names must be coordinated with the other articles of wearing apparel and with the accessories, such as hats, gloves, shoes, and even hose and hair tint. The colors selected by the dictates of fashion, when combined with the coordinated texture and drape, may at times require certain fibers, fabric constructions, kinds of finish, and other influences affecting the fabric quality desired. Therefore, not only are the designs of the leading couturières closely-guarded secrets prior to their showing to the buyers throughout the world and to their favorite individual clients, but the type, shades, and textures may also be concealed from competitors.

Just as a new design may be copied quickly and adapted by garment manu-facturers in simulating the garment lines of famous designers, the textile industry can copy the details and textures of the new fashion fabrics. Paris, New York, or Rome "originals" can be identified from copies by the meticulous handwork in the garment, or the original may be made of an exclusive fabric. Copies directed to a somewhat larger style market must be adapted to cheaper and faster types of garment manufacture than the original in order to sell to the retailer outlets. This copying, or **piracy,** as it is often called, goes into production rapidly, and the textile industry will hasten to simulate the texture and perhaps to produce the same shade, but not necessarily with the same quality dyestuffs or with the same care in finishing. Just as the individual or originating couturière seeks fast acceptance of his designs, the textile companies and the garment manu-facturers who simulate the original, possibly for one store in each of the major cities, wish to have the product purchased by the retail buyers and sold to the public before the copy may itself be copied for a still wider market. What is high fashion one year may, if it is sound and popular, be found in the more expensive gown and suit departments in the finer stores the next year, and some-times even later the effect of the fashion can still be seen in a wider variety of garments at popular prices. Perhaps the same colors and general textures will still be noticed in this expanded market. One may call this the ripple effect of fashion. The greater the impact of fashion, the more widely it will be found in time throughout the world, just as the larger the stone thrown into a still pond, the more rapid the transmission of ripples on the surface and the wider the ripple pattern will be.

standards cannot apply

With speed of marketing so vital, it is understandable that there will be no time for the testing of colors, textures, and finishes in fashion merchandise between the time it is first seen in the market and the time it reaches the consumer's home. The advisory agencies dealing with performance facts likewise can be of no benefit to the consumer in the field of fashion merchandise. Admittedly, this would seem to be a disservice to the customer; however, textile problems returned to stores generally indicate that fashion merchandise is rarely returned because of poor serviceability. To begin with, the garments are much more carefully made than are the more widely commercially available products. They are worn less often and are generally discarded because of obsolescence rather than garment failure in service.

foreign competition in staples

A recent evaluation made by two students in a home economics laboratory demonstrated how little difference there is between low-priced blouses of United States manufacture and those from Japan and Hong Kong. Tables 29-7, 8, and 9 are self-explanatory.

TABLE 29-7 / BLOUSE MEASUREMENTS

Size 14 (R)	UNITED STATES		JAPAN		HONG KONG	
Girth Measurements	No. 1	No. 2	No. 3	No. 4	No. 5	No. 6
1. Bust*	38"	39"	39"	37½"	40"	39"
2. Waist**	38"	39"	33½"	34"	38"	34"
3. Neck Base	14½"	13½"	13½"	23¾"	15½"	14"
4. Armscye	17¼"	16½"	16"	16¾"	17½"	17"
5. Upper Arm*	14"	15"		13"		
6. Vertical Trunk*	20" Front	19½"	18"	15½"	23"	19½"
(Collar Base)	23½" Back	22½"	20½"	16"	24"	20½"
Width and Length						
1. Cross-back Width**	19"	19½"	19½"	18½"	19"	19"
2. Cross-chest Width**	19"	19½"	19½"	18½"	21"	20"
3. Scye Depth	7½"	7½"	7"	8¼"	7½"	7½"
4. Armscye to Waist	8½"	8½"	8"	7"	7½"	8¼"
5. Arm Length, Shoulder to Wrist**						
6. Arm Length, Shoulder to Total**	14"	14"		9½"		
7. Underarm Length*	11½"	11½"		4¼"		
White Ones First*	$1.99	$1.99	$ .97	$ .97	$ .97	$ .97

* To the standard bust measurement, cross-back width and cross-chest width, was added 4" for ease, because they are sport blouses and require ease.
** We have eliminated the waist and arm lengths since they did not pertain to these blouses.

Conclusions—There is no consistent skimping of material in the 97 cent imported blouses.

TABLE 29-8 / OBSERVATIONS ON WORKMANSHIP OF SIX BLOUSES

1. American Blouse—White
   1. Skimpy button holes
   2. Hem not finished properly—just stitched
   3. Seam under left arm does not meet
   4. Improper french seam on hem of left sleeve
   5. Neckline not back stitched at center fronts
   6. Right shoulder seam reverses direction
   7. Facing shows at neckline
   8. Neckline: first seam allowance not taken into second seam

2. American Blouse—Colored
  1. When buttoned, collar does not meet
  2. Puckers along center front when buttoned
  3. Skimpy button holes
  4. Hem: (a) stretched and pulled in places
          (b) center front ends not properly finished
          (c) where other seams—sloppy: ends show
  5. Underarm seams do not meet
  6. Left shoulder seam reversed—(outside)
  7. Stitching to hold collar in place—misses collar in most places.
  8. Right shoulder seam reverses direction—(inside)
  9. Left sleeve: underarm seam bad—french seam does not enclose all edges.

3. Japan Blouse—White
  1. Button holes—*very* bad
  2. Right side of collar ¼" longer than left side
  3. Stitching to hold collar in place—misses collar in most places
  4. Dart tucks at waist—not back stitched
  5. No back under-facing—collar
  6. Seam stitching—stitch size too large (darts—side seams)
  7. Side seams: (a) poor seam construction
          (b) at hem raw edges exposed

4. Japan Blouse—Colored
  1. Button holes—*very, very* bad
  2. No button at highest point of bust
  3. Center front design line—corners pucker
  4. Right underarm seam—does not meet
  5. Too much bulk underarm
  6. Left side seam—finish puckers material
  7. Exposed raw edge along hem
  8. Darts folded wrong way—side seams
  9. No back-facing along neckline
  10. Facing around neckline—finish poor
  11. Side seams—poor seam construction
  12. Did not clip around facing seam

5. Hong Kong Blouse—White
  1. Center front: (a) neckline does not meet
          (b) seam stitching not straight
  2. Yoke—stitching not straight: should be clipped
  3. Facing shows around neckline
  4. Underarm seams do not meet
  5. Too much bulk underarm
  6. Facing shows around armscye
  7. Shoulder seam on left side does not meet yoke seam
  8. Drill marks around darts
  9. Button holes—bad
  10. Poor side seam construction
  11. Side seams crooked
  12. Seam finish around armscye poor—raw edges show

6. Hong Kong Blouse—Colored
  1. Center front—off grain
  2. Button holes—poor
  3. Left underarm does not meet properly
  4. Too much bulk underarm—especially left side
  5. Dart, hem stitches—too large
  6. Poor side seam construction

7. Reverse seam on left shoulder
8. Miss stitching around left armscye—facing not stitched in places
9. Dart stitching on left side—greatly puckered

Conclusions—All blouses were hastily constructed with fractions of cents at stake. It could not be said the U.S. blouses were better.

TABLE 29-9 / SUMMARY RATING OF 6 TEST BLOUSES

	UNITED STATES		JAPAN		HONG KONG	
	No. 1 White	No. 2	No. 3 White	No. 4	No. 5 White	No. 6
1. Tensile Strength (Scott Tester)						
Warp	2	2	4	3	3	3
Fill	3	4	3	3	3	3
2. Tabor Abrasor—Wear	4	3	5	4	5	5
3. Accelerotor—Wear	1	2	4	5	5	5
4. Yarn Strength (Twist)	5	5	3	5	3	5
5. Standard Size	5	4	3	2	3.5	3.5
6. Construction	3	3	1	2	1	1
7. Shrinkage on washing	5	5	5	5	5	5
8. Colorfastness—Light		5		4		5
9. Color to Perspiration Acid (Perspirometer)						
Acidic		5		3		3
Alkaline		4		2		2
10. Color to Crocking (Crock-Metor)						
Dry		5		5		4
Wet		5		4		2
Average	3.5	4.0	3.5	3.5	3.6	3.8

Scale:
5 = Very good
4 = Good
3 = Satisfactory
2 = Poor
1 = Very poor

Conclusion—A rating scale more precise than this would be needed to show much difference between these products.

CARE OF TEXTILE PRODUCTS

Care of textile products is an important element in consumership. On page 484, we noted that the extra care requirements of one dress compared with another entered into the equation by which the calculated value of the two could be determined for the guidance of the prospective purchaser. We often hear such cautions as: "Be careful of your new dress today," or "Take care; it is going to rain, and don't get the new suit spotted or wrinkled." These refer, of course, to care during wearing, but by care we also mean the conditions of cleaning and maintenance and the storage of these textile products when they are not being worn. Here, too, the better the care, the longer the wear.

If we are going to classify our textile purchases as to care conditions, the first classification would normally be whether or not the textile product could be washed. One classification, therefore, would include those which are washable; the second, those which must be cleaned by dry-cleaning procedures. Then the question arises, "What do we mean by washable?" and further in this chapter, we will learn some of these differences in degrees of washability. One of the most troublesome definitions to arrive at in technical committee meetings on wash-ability of textile products is just what is meant by the term "washable." It is more or less agreed upon now that the word without any qualification is about as absolute a term as one can use. In other words, washable means that the article can be washed under any normal conditions and that no special care need be given in the drying or pressing. Any other term, however, would have some kind of qualifications in the form of special directions. Is it hand washable only? Can it be washed in a moderate temperature of, let us say, 120° F? Or can it be washed at a hot temperature, such as 160°? Must it be drip-dried, or can it be dried in a tumbler? If machine washable at an elevated temperature, can it be washed equally well and safely in a tumble-type or agitator-type of automatic machine? At what temperature can it be pressed with safety? Does the term washable refer only to the fabric of which the article is made? Does it also in-clude trimming and decoration and, one might add, sewing thread? Are these elements as color-fast and as dimensionally stable as the main fabric of which the garment is composed? If it is a slipcover which can be washed or upholstered furniture covering which can be sponged with an aqueous solution of detergent, are all the elements equally washable?

gradations in washability

In the chapter on Textile Standards, reference is made on page 409, to the color-code designation between degrees of washability of textile products under the L-22 and the L-24 Textile Standards. This information will not be repeated here, but note in review that this program does not depend upon paper or card-board tags and labels, such as those seen here, but refers to permanently sewn-in identifications for the permanent guidance of the housewife, the dry-cleaner, and laundry, all of whom may be called upon to service her garments. Five degrees of washability are indicated. Figure 29-1 shows in symbolic form the sure-care symbols adopted by the National Retail Merchants Association for the five kinds of washability. These labels are appearing on more and more articles of clothing, especially for boys and for children, and should be a boon to the harrassed mother.

special conditions for care in washing

These brief conditions are based on the tables dealing with fiber properties. In studying textile fibers and fabrics, we note a few general cautions.

Fig. 29-1

Sure Care Symbols

Follow these symbols to WASH or DRY-CLEAN and IRON your clothes or home furnishings with satisfactory results. Look for the labels with these simple guides to happier washdays.

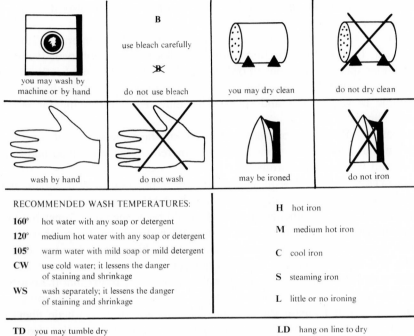

| you may wash by machine or by hand | B use bleach carefully do not use bleach | you may dry clean | do not dry clean |

| wash by hand | do not wash | may be ironed | do not iron |

RECOMMENDED WASH TEMPERATURES:

160°   hot water with any soap or detergent

120°   medium hot water with any soap or detergent

105°   warm water with mild soap or mild detergent

CW   use cold water; it lessens the danger of staining and shrinkage

WS   wash separately; it lessens the danger of staining and shrinkage

H   hot iron

M   medium hot iron

C   cool iron

S   steaming iron

L   little or no ironing

TD   you may tumble dry

DD   drip dry

DR   dry rapidly, (for example, remove excess moisture between towels)

LD   hang on line to dry

DF   dry flat

HERE ARE HOW THESE SYMBOLS MIGHT LOOK ON LABELS: WHAT THEY TELL YOU.

Wash by machine or by hand in hot water with any soap or detergent. Use bleach carefully. Tumble dry. Do not dry clean. Iron with hot iron.

Wash by hand in warm water with any soap or detergent. Do not bleach. Dry clean. Little or no ironing.

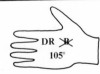

Wash by hand in lukewarm water with mild soap or detergent. Do not bleach. Dry rapidly. Dry clean. Do not iron.

Courtesy of National Retail Merchants Association

COTTON   Cotton is regarded as the fiber capable of withstanding the most vigorous of all household washing methods. The presence of resin finishes makes them susceptible to oil and grease stains, and they should then be treated more like synthetics in the tumble-drying operation, that is, using a light load in order to avoid heat-setting of wrinkles. The presence of resins also makes them susceptible to permanent discoloration from chlorine bleach, also described as Javelle water, hypochlorite, etc.

WOOL   Wool should be washed at a relatively low temperature and in a short cycle. It should not be tumble-dried, at least in a heavy load. It must be stored under special conditions in order to avoid moth and carpet beetle damage.

SILK   Generally, silk is not washable, due to the type of finish. It is often susceptible to water spots and stains. This may require steaming for removal or concealment.

RAYON   Rayon is now regarded as having the same degree of washability as cotton, but it is not as strong when wet; therefore, the wash load and drying load should be judged accordingly.

ACETATE   Acetate requires low ironing temperatures and should never be stored in contact with wool, due to the risk of color change.

SYNTHETICS   Synthetics in general should be washed at a somewhat lower temperature, mainly due to the fact that being hydrophobic fibers, they do not absorb the wet dirt as readily. Low-temperature washing is an advantage in terms of time and ease of handling but does not get the garments as clean as would the high temperature. Special drying conditions generally direct that these articles be dried with a very light load in order to avoid heat-set wrinkles previously referred to. Oil and grease stains should be removed from synthetic fibers immediately in order to avoid permanent spots and stains. This applies also to the use of these fibers in rugs and carpets; nylon, Acrilan, Saran, Orlon, etc.

Fortunately, the unhygienic ideas about washing nearly all clothing in lukewarm water seems to have passed.

GLASS   A knowledge of glass fiber tells us that it must be washed under very mild conditions to avoid rubbing when wet. This practically requires hand washing or, at the most, the use of a tumbler washer to wash not more than two curtains at a time. Glass fabrics should not be put in the dryer but should be hung to drip-dry. They cannot be ironed with safety, lest the turned edges crack due to lack of resiliency.

BLENDS   A good rule in the case of any combined or blended fabric is to treat the garment or article as if it were made completely of the more delicate and heat-sensitive or color-fugitive material.

laundering

The pattern of permanence of consumer complaints with regard to laundering of apparel is said by some to have diminished since the introduction of more of the synthetic fibers and of wash-and-wear treated cottons and rayons during the past ten years. However, the total "refreshing operation," involving washing, drying, and ironing, still constitutes a major source of consumer irritation and disappointment. In 1950, the summary of consumer textile complaints compiled by the Commodity Standards Fellowship of the Kaufmann Department Stores at Mellon Institute, Pittsburgh, Pennsylvania, had 1,438 blouse complaints among just over ten thousand textile complaints in all. Of the 1,438 consumer complaints about women's blouses (rayon, acetate, cotton, linen, and nylon), 87 were caused by excessive shrinkage, 60 by color fading, 83 by breaks or tears in the material, and 328 by glazing or melting due to excessive heat in ironing. Second to iron damage, among 23 listed causes of complaint, was the presence of breaks and holes under the arms as a result of perspiration or careless use of anti-perspirant solutions. The seriousness of the ironing problem still persists, because all the new fibers which have in recent years entered the blouse and dress industry are thermoplastic, with heat characteristics not differing greatly from that of acetate. The advantage possessed by fabrics today is that all of the sales promotion effort has gone into the minimum-care phases of home laundering, that is, one need not press the garment—simply touch it up with a cool iron.

It was found in this department store textile service program that consumers themselves were often "forgetful" as to just what had happened during the washing operation. It is no exaggeration to say that of some 3000 to 3500 textile washing complaints, never had the consumer admitted that she had washed the article by any other method than by hand, using Lux or Ivory Flakes, and pressing with a cool iron, and never was bleach used. Other store laboratory technicians, some commercial testing laboratories, and those representing the service industries know well that most consumers try to hide behind the hand-washing method as an excuse. Of course, washing machines were used in many of these cases, but this is not a condemnation of the washing machine, rather of the probability of poor sorting on the part of the consumer. The trouble lay with one or more of these errors: more delicate, fragile fabrics mixed with heavier ones; mixing of colored with white articles in a wash load; the use of too heavy a dryer load; and, in many cases, an excessive heat in the ironing. The automatic washing machines today have such detailed directions for proper use and offer varieties of washing formulations, times, and temperatures that if the operator selects the proper set of conditions, no washable fabric should be damaged in that phase of the cleaning operation.

HEAVY DUTY WASH LOAD   In preparation for washing at home or in a coin-operated laundry center in the neighborhood, housewives should be as careful in the sorting of garments as is the commercial laundry to which are sent the heavier and more difficult-to-handle washing chores. The first sorting should be a separation of all the whites from colored articles. These whites will then be separated into three general classes: heavy, medium, and light. Heavy-duty, thoroughly washable white cottons, linens, and rayons, such as table wear, bedding, white uniforms, and the heavier, more durable white clothing items form the first category. These articles can be washed at the highest temperature afforded by the hot water heater in the home. Generally, this would be somewhere between 140 and 160° F., and usually bleach can be used if necessary. A heavy-duty soap or Syndet may be used.

For this wash pile with heavily soiled articles, such as heavy knit sweat shirts, white coveralls of twill or corvet, duck trousers, denim articles, or other deeply soiled fabrics, the Ruud Manufacturing Company[4] recommends a longer washing time; if necessary, a second washing cycle with new detergent and hot water can be done.

MEDIUM WASH LOAD   Resin-treated cottons of the wash-and-wear or minimum-care groups, most white synthetics, and colored garments of known wash-fastness may be washed together, but using about a half-washer load and preferably a temperature about 120°, with 130° maximum. Caution: White nylons should never be washed with any colored garments, due to their tendency to pick up color from wash water. Under no circumstances should a chlorine-type bleach be used with this group of fabrics because 1) many of the resins tend to pick up chlorine and eventually to go into holes; 2) chlorine bleach will discolor whites in some of these resin treatments and some of the new synthetic fibers; and 3) there is danger of the chlorine affecting the color even of a washable colored article.

LIGHT WASH LOAD   The third category—the most delicate of the whites— must be hand-washed, using soap flakes or a neutral detergent. By hand washing is meant the washing operation at a temperature comfortable to the flesh. This is usually about 105° F., but some individuals can withstand a temperature up to about 115°, which should be the maximum used.

In general, the colored articles which have been separated from the white, and especially those of which the color-fastness is not yet established either through experience or through a guarantee on the label, are best washed at a relatively low temperature and short cycle. Such a condition would be as follows: the water does not exceed 120° F., a mild or neutral soap or detergent is used, and the washing cycle does not exceed three to five minutes. It may be necessary for certain garments to be washed alone or certainly with no articles of another color.

Wool should always be washed alone and preferably by hand with the minimum of manipulation while wet if fulling and shrinkage are to be avoided. Many household fabric articles, such as shag rugs, slipcovers, draperies, quilts, pillows, porch and garden furniture covers, glass curtains, shower curtains, and others will have specific directions for their best method of washing and drying. Authorities[5] on washing urge the use of fabric softeners in the washing formula for a cleaner product and for better appearance of wash-and-wear articles.

[4] "All About Modern Home Laundering," Ruud Manufacturing Company, Pittsburgh, Pennsylvania, 1953.
[5] Twelfth National Home Laundry Conference of American Home Laundry Manufacturers' Association, page 47, and other of these annual reports.

drying

In the drying operation, a few general cautions should be given. Only in the case of the heavy utilitarian fabrics should the dryer be operated at full temperature and with a full load. Generally, the synthetic fiber fabrics will dry so rapidly that drip-drying may be the preferred operation. However, they can be dried in the dryer and handled at the same time as wash-and-wear cottons and rayons, for example. However, the dryer should not have in it more than about a four-pound load; this is about one-half the capacity of the dryer. If a longer time and a heavier load are used, then there is danger of the wrinkles forming which would then be heat-set in the fabrics and garments, and they would require a vast amount of care in ironing. The advantage to the light load in drying is that in most cases the articles then need no ironing whatever, even slacks if taken to almost complete dryness and then put on forms and allowed to complete the drying in the air. Similar care should be taken of wool articles, such as blankets; these should never be taken to complete dryness; generally not more than fifteen minutes of tumble drying with a light load and with intermediate to high temperature is sufficient.

ironing

As noted in the reference to glosses at the start of this chapter, ironing is a major problem. In the booklet, "All About Modern Laundering,"[6] five conditions of ironing are given. These may be compared with the Sure Care Symbols, page 493.

1   Dry ironing, which is using a hot, dry iron on dampened fabrics.
2   Steam ironing, using steam and with a gliding, ironing stroke similar to that used in dry ironing.
3   Steam pressing, using steam but with a tapping or up-and-down motion, bringing the iron in contact with the fabric and withdrawing it again.
4   Steaming, holding the iron two to three inches above the fabric so that the surface of the garment is enveloped in steam but without the iron touching the material.
5   Do not iron.

In all three of the steam iron operations, a press cloth may be used, especially on smooth-surfaced fabrics which might develop a shine and wherever there are double thickness of cloth which again might shine or glaze along the edge, such as lapels, cuffs, welts, pocket tips, This ironing chart is from "Take It Easy—101 Helpful Hints for Easy Ironing."[7]

In ironing any thermoplastic fiber, even for a quick touch-up, it is advisable to do most of the ironing on the wrong side of the garment in order to avoid

---

[6] *Op. cit.,* pp. 62, 65.
[7] "Take It Easy—101 Helpful Hints for Easy Ironing," Mary Proctor, Proctor Silex Corporation, Philadelphia, Pa.

stiffening and glazing. This is particularly true in all double thicknesses. As a general rule, the following end-temperatures should be observed:

Linen—500 to 550° F.
Cotton—400 to 450° F.
Rayon—400 to 450° F.
Wool—350 to 400° F.
Silk—300° F.
Most synthetics and those with synthetics in the blend—250 to 300° F.
Dynel—do not iron.
Glass fiber—do not iron.
Saran and Olefines—do not iron.

One other source of rather frequent complaint of damage resulting from ironing is a by-product of today's crease-retentive, wrinkle-resistant, minimum-care fabrics. A beverage or food may be spilled on the front of a child's dress or boy's shirt; because the fabric does not absorb the moisture, there may be no perceptible stain. After one or two wearings, the garment may begin to look a little mussed, and the housewife will touch it up with a warm iron. If the beverage contained an organic acid, the scorching temperature of cotton or rayon may be reduced, so that the fabric can no longer be ironed with safety at the cotton setting, or over 400° F. The beverage or food might contain sugar, which might caramelize slightly to give a yellowish color, or may be oily in nature and leave a gray stain in the polymer of the fiber or of the resin used in resin treating. It is always safest to wash such garments by hand, which can be done quickly, drip-dry, then press where needed. If there is any indication whatever of a spill spot, such as a dullness in the fabric, somewhat roughened texture, or a slight stiffness, wash it out before pressing.

stain removal

The removal of stains from wearing apparel, carpets, and upholstery is an important factor in the proper maintenance of such textile products. It is not an experiment to be made blindly, however, because the success of the operation depends upon the chemical characteristics of the textile fiber, finishing agent, and dye as well as of the agency causing the stain. The textile student should remember the chemical properties of fibers.

It is advisable to depend upon a reputable dry-cleaner to remove stains. Knowing the causative agent, or stain source, the housewife should clearly identify and label the stain in order to make experimental identification tests by the *spotter* unnecessary. The spotter in the dry-cleaning establishment commonly removes those stains remaining after the garment has been cleaned. The cleaning process removes most spots and loosens many of those remaining so that the expensive labor cost of hand-spotting is thus reduced. The spotter commonly uses a soft brush to tamp the stain-removing agent into the stained material, a bone spatula or a glass stirring rod to rub it in, and a chamois skin, white blotter, or piece of absorbent fabric to absorb the soiled solvent or the excess of the cleaning solution. A glass stirring rod may have small chipped spots which, when rubbed on the garment, will cut the yarns.

These tools and the technique of the use of each are not always available to the consumer, but brief descriptions of the method for the removal of common stains may prove useful to students and users of textiles.

The suds from the synthetic detergent (Syndet) make a useful spot-cleaning material if it is not necessary to wash the entire garment or tablecloth or other textile material. Simply rubbing the spot gently with the suds will generally remove most stains of oily nature unless they are heavily colored due to natural juices or coloring material in the staining liquid. Whenever the presence of a few remaining crumbs from potato chips or buttered popcorn or other oily foodstuffs indicates that there might have been quantities spilled on the carpet or on an upholstered chair by a young TV follower, it is well to sponge the area or shampoo it with a synthetic detergent just as a matter of precaution, lest any of the fat remain in contact with the synthetic fiber and the rug and upholstery be damaged. If such oily materials stand for a time, they combine with the polymer and oxidize, and a permanent gray stain develops. This combination and stain do not occur on wool carpeting nor on rayon or cotton.

PRECAUTIONS   Stains should be removed promptly before they have been *set* by exposure to light and air, by hot water, or by ironing.

It is advisable to test the effect of all liquid stain-removing agents (even cold water) on the fibers and dye by applying the treatment to a small piece cut from a seam or on a concealed portion of the garment.

The use of acids, except in very dilute solution, should be avoided in working on cotton, linen, and rayon fabrics. If acid solutions are used, they should promptly be neutralized and thoroughly rinsed out. Bleaches should be used with care, because they weaken the fibers and may destroy the color if the fabric is dyed.

Silk and wool, being protein fibers, are affected by alkalis. Dilute acids have little or no harmful effect. Hot water and excessive rubbing both cause physical damage to these fibers, making wool felt and shrink and causing silk to become dull. Rubbing will often tear the fabric.

Rayons are weakened when wet and must be carefully handled. No spotting agent or cleaner containing acetone, ethyl acetate, or a strong acetic acid solution should be used on acetates because of the solvent action of these chemicals on the fibers. Dilute acids are not as harmful to rayons as to the primary cellulose fibers (cotton and linen). Alkaline solutions and bleaches are harmful unless they are rinsed out promptly and thoroughly. Chlorine bleaches should never be used on wool, silk, or nylon.

If the dye has been affected by an acid treatment, it may sometimes be restored by a dilute ammonia solution. Damage due to alkalies is often restored by dilute acetic acid.

The synthetic fibers have been shown to be resistant to most chemicals and to practically all of the solvents commonly used in spotting or cleaning operations, either in commercial plants or at home. It must be remembered that they are highly resistant to moisture absorption; therefore, water-carried stains should not generally penetrate them deeply. They are, however, very subject to the oil and grease stains previously mentioned, which may be removed with a synthetic detergent or with a household dry-cleaning solvent.

TECHNIQUES IN HOME "SPOTTING"   The materials which may be used in the home are classified as absorbents, solvents, or bleaches, plus a few specific chemicals for use in certain chemical and medicinal stains.

A fresh, damp stain may often be removed or be greatly reduced in intensity by spreading over it an absorbent, such as chalk, talc, Fuller's earth, or corn meal.

Liquids such as water, ether, alcohol, carbon tetrachloride, naphtha, benzol, acetone, chloroform, and gasoline are solvents. Those which are flammable (all except water and carbon "tet") should only be used out-of-doors and away from all flames, even that of a cigarette. Quick-drying solvents may leave *rings* if carelessly applied. It is best to keep an absorbent material beneath the stained fabric and to work the solvent from the edge toward the center of the spot. The vapors from carbon "tet" and chloroform are toxic. These solvents may be used safely out-of-doors.

Javelle water, potassium permanganate, hydrogen peroxide, oxalic acid, and hydrosulfites are the most widely-used bleaches. The first-named is commonly bought as "chlorine bleach," or it is prepared in the laboratory by dissolving one-half pound of washing soda in a quart of cold water and then adding one-fourth pound of chloride of lime (bleaching powder). The solution is filtered and tightly bottled for future use.

The application of all chemicals should be performed with care. It may be done by stretching the fabric over a small bowl and dropping the solution on the stain from a medicine dropper. The alternative method is to place an absorbent fabric pad (corresponding to the cleaners' chamois pad) under the stained material and to work the chemical into the stain with a crack- and chip-free glass stirring rod. Whatever the method of treatment, chemicals must be rinsed out as quickly as possible. Just as with solvent cleaners, the stain must be rubbed lightly from the edge toward the center to avoid rings.

Brief outlines of the best methods of removing the more common stains are given below.

removal of some common stains

ACIDS   Soak washable goods in water to check the effect of the acid. Stains may be removed by neutralizing the acid with ammonia fumes or baking-soda solution, followed by another rinsing.

ADHESIVE TAPE   Apply ice cubes to reduce stickiness; rub gently with the ball of the thumb to remove adhesive; last traces may be removed with carbon tetrachloride or kerosene.

AIRPLANE GLUE   Except for acetates, acetone or amyl acetate may be used. Sometimes rubbing alcohol is successful.

ALCOHOLIC BEVERAGE   Apply cold water immediately. If necessary, apply cold water with a small amount of glycerine added. Rinsing with white vinegar will remove any last traces; then the stain should be rinsed again with pure water.

ALKALIS   Soak washable goods in water. Color change caused by alkali may be restored by the application of mild acids, such as acetic acid, white vinegar, or lemon juice.

BLOOD   Hot water sets the protein in blood. Cold water alone or with a small amount of ammonium hydroxide is effective with washable fabrics. Non-washable fabrics require spotting with cold water and hydrogen peroxide; starch paste has been recommended for blankets.

BLUING   Cold water reduces most fresh stains, but the next step in the treatment depends on the type of bluing employed. Prussian blues (liquid bluing) may yellow fabrics, and this stain is removed like *Rust*.

BUTTER   (see Fats)

CANDLE WAX AND PARAFFIN   Scrape away as much as possible with a dull knife and remove the last traces with methanol (wood alcohol), carbon tetrachloride, benzol, or acetone. The colder the wax, the easier it is to chip or scrape away. A hot iron placed on a blotting paper on top of the spot helps remove the paraffin from the fibers.

CANDY   The syrup and sugar may be removed by washing. Chocolate stains may be removed by methods listed under *Chocolate*. Dyes must be bleached out.

CHEWING GUM   Cool with ice cubes in a plastic bag, and then scrape off the excess with a dull knife. The remaining substance is a mixture of sugar and chicle or a resin substitute. Alternate treatments with water and carbon tetrachloride remove the sugar and chicle, respectively.

CHOCOLATE AND COCOA   Laundering will often remove most of the stain. Javelle water (hypochlorite bleach) may be used on cotton or linen fabrics (peroxide on wool or silk), or an organic solvent may be used. Methanol made alkaline with ammonia is very effective.

COD LIVER OIL   Carbon tetrachloride is effective, but bleaching with hydrogen peroxide may be necessary for old stains. Washing is sometimes all that is required, especially if nail polish remover and soap suds are first rubbed on the stain.

COFFEE   Washing is effective with new stains. If small, rub with Syndet suds. Pouring boiling water through the fabric is equally good. A bleach such as Javelle water may be needed for old stains. *Sugar* and *cream* may be removed in the usual way.

DYES   Soaking for several hours in cold water or washing and then drying in the sun may be effective. Often hydrosulfite or Javelle water bleaches are required. Use alkaline hydrogen peroxide on silk and wool.

EGG   Cold water followed by a thorough washing or by the use of a grease solvent is recommended. Egg contains a fat (yolk) and an albumin (white).

ENAMEL, PAINT, LACQUER, AND VARNISH   The stain is caused by the pigment and by the solvent or vehicle. Scrape off as much paint as possible and then treat by washing or with a solvent such as turpentine, benzol-acetone mixture, oil solvents, or methanol. The new latex paints may be washed off with detergent, if fresh.

FATS, BUTTER, LARD, MILK PRODUCTS   Washing with soap or Syndet suds, particularly a naptha soap, is effective. Grease solvents such as benzol, carbon tetrachloride, ether, etc., are good when used alone or in combination with an absorbent powder. These stains must be removed promptly from all synthetic fiber garments, rugs, and fabrics to avoid a permanent stain. Resin-treated cottons are stained also.

FINGERNAIL POLISH   If the fabric is acetate, nothing can be done. For all other fibers, acetone or amyl acetate, followed by sponging with ethyl alcohol, will remove the bright color.

FRUITS AND BERRIES, COOKED   These stains have more sugar and less tannin than have those of fresh fruits. Warm water or boiling water will remove most fruit stains.

FRUITS AND BERRIES, FRESH   These stains are often very persistent. Water loosens many stains, but soap sets some of them. Bleaches such as potassium permanganate, oxalic acid or hydrosulfites are good for specific stains. Glycerine may be rubbed in first and then alcohol used as a solvent.

GLUE   Soaking in warm water will remove glue stains or soften them so that a later treatment with dilute acetic acid may remove the last traces of the stain.

GRASS AND FOLIAGE   The fresh green stain of chlorophyll is soluble in ether or alcohol. Old stains may be removed by vigorous washing followed by treatment with Javelle water or potassium permanganate. Amyl acetate may remove last traces.

HAIR OIL   Backs of chairs are often stained with hair oil. The arms may be stained with perspiration or oil from the skin. These dark spots are best removed by means of a stiff suds of synthetic detergent or by means of a dry-cleaning solvent.

INK   Among the types of ink which may stain fabrics are the following:

Ball Point Ink: A synthetic shampoo or a suds of Syndet may be rubbed on the stain and allowed to stand ten to fifteen minutes, after which it should be rinsed off. If the stain remains, vaseline or sodium hydrosulfite may be rubbed in, after which it should be sponged with carbon tetrachloride. Some ball point inks respond better to glycerine being rubbed on, followed with a shampooing.

Writing Ink: Removable by absorbent powders, followed by oxalic acid and ammonium hydroxide.

Printing Ink: Synthetic detergent suds may loosen stains; soaking in turpentine and then sponging with ether or methanol is effective. Rubbing with lard and then washing may remove the pigment.

India Ink: It is difficult to remove the carbon black, but the waterproofing agent is removable by solvent extraction, using amyl acetate. Synthetic detergent followed by sodium hydrosulfite may remove last traces.

Marking Ink: It is almost impossible to remove completely, but bleaches may reduce the intensity of the stain. The removal of all ink stains may be expedited by soaking the stained fabric area overnight in Yogurt.

ICE CREAM (see Fats)   The combination of fats, sugar, and fruits or other flavors requires specific methods for each.

IODINE   Photographers' "hypo" solution removes iodine stains. Methanol may be sponged on fabrics which may be harmed by water.

IRON RUST   *Erusicator*—rust remover is best, but sodium hydrosulfiite on a damp stain may work. Dilute hydrochloric acid may be applied and washed out thoroughly.

LACQUERS (*see Enamels*)

LIPSTICK   Ethanol (ethyl alcohol), rubbing alcohol, or carbon tetrachloride may be used on non-washable garments. Javelle water or hydrogen peroxide may be effective on washable fabrics. Some stains are removed by rubbing with lard and followed with suds.

LIQUOR AND WINE   Treat as in the case of fruit stains.

MEAT JUICES   Treat as in blood stains.

MERCUROCHROME   This is a difficult stain to remove. The application of potassium permanganate followed by sodium hydrosulfite or oxalic acid may be effective. A thorough rinse with a mild alkali or cold water is required to remove the chemicals.

METAL STAINS   Stains from copper or brass may be removed by dilute acetic acid, vinegar, or lemon juice and rinsing well.

MILDEW   Washing may remove surface stains. Old stains are removed by dilute acids (salt or lemon juice), by Javelle water, by oxalic acid, or by the steps followed in the removal of mercurochrome.

MILK (*see Fats*)   Washing is usually sufficient; but if not, proceed as for grease and fats.

MUD   Do not touch until dry, then brush off. Washable goods may then be laundered, if necessary. Methanol is useful in cleaning non-washable fabrics.

MUSTARD   The more permanent stain is due to *turmeric*. Washing is sometimes effective. Applying warm glycerin to the stain and then washing will often be found useful. Hydrosulfite bleach can be applied to stubborn stains.

OILS   Solvents for oils, greases, and fats may be used.

PAINT (*see Enamels*)   Turpentine is particularly effective with paints, especially if the fabric is first dampened with ammonia. The newer latex will wash out if fresh.

PENCIL MARKS   A soft eraser may be used on firm-textured fabrics. Dipping in chloroform and brushing may be used with effectiveness.

PERFUME   Alcohol followed by cold water should remove the stain.

PERSPIRATION   Careful sponging with cool water or soaking may remove stains from washables. Last traces may be bleached out with Javelle water or other bleaches. Treatments for **acids** and **alkalis** may be followed, also.

RESINS AND GUMS   Organic solvents must be tried until the most suitable one is found.

RUBBER CEMENT   Apply vaseline to loosen, then sponge with carbon tetrachloride or benzene.

RUST (*see Iron*)   With the fabric dampened by steam, squeeze lemon juice on the stain and rinse.

SCORCH   Brushing wool may restore it if the fibers are not burned through. Silk cannot be restored. Slight stains on cotton, linen, and rayon may be washed out. Moistening the spot and allowing it to dry in the sun may remove it. Hydrogen peroxide spread over the stain and ironed through a pressing cloth is a good method for white fabrics.

SHOE POLISH   Washing followed, if necessary, by potassium hydroxide removes most stains due to black polish. Sponging with alcohol or with carbon tetrachloride is the safest method for silk and wool. Wash out white shoe dressing stains.

SKIN OIL   Stains on collar and cuff edges may be loosened by rubbing on "Halo" or "Drene" shampoo or a suds of synthetic detergent, leaving it on 10 to 15 minutes, and washing.

SOAP MARKS   Fabrics which have been ironed while soap was still on them may be yellowed. Washing, especially with **Calgon** in the suds, is effective in removing the stain.

STOVE POLISH   Organic solvents or a thorough washing may remove the stain caused by the graphite or carbon black in the polish.

SOFT DRINKS   Soft drinks of the cola type or those containing sweetened citrus fruit base may leave slightly colored or stiffened areas. These should be sponged first with cool water, then with a synthetic detergent suds. Rubbing alcohol or a mixture of alcohol with glycerine (50–50) will remove the last traces of discoloration. Heat will set the stain; therefore, hot water and subsequent pressings should not be used.

SUGAR AND SYRUP   Try washing or gentle sponging. If the fabric is not washable, steaming may loosen these stains.

TARS   Moisten with gasoline, chloroform, benzene, or carbon tetrachloride, scrape off softened tar, then rub with a cloth saturated with the solvent used. Tars may contain some solids, such as graphite, road dust, etc. If the stain still appears dark, rub in a food oil, lard, or colorless margarine and proceed with the oil removal.

TEA   Launder, if possible. It may be necessary to alternate treatments with potassium permanganate and hydrosulfite or oxalic acid. If the stain is kept moist with lemon juice and exposed to the sun for a couple of days, it will be removed.

TOBACCO   Treat as with tar. Sponging with alcohol may be effective. Potassium permanganate or oxalic acid will remove stubborn stains.

URINE   No one treatment is universally effective, due to the chemical variations in the solution. Sponging with soap and water or with a salt solution and then rinsing are effective methods. Dilute ammonia alone or with hydrogen peroxide may then be applied for a minute and then rinsed off.

WALNUT   Washing with a heavy soap solution followed by Javelle water is fairly effective. Javelle water (chlorine-type bleach) should not be used with silk or wool.

WATER SPOTS   These can only be removed from finished silks or stiffened sheer fabrics by dampening or steaming the entire garment and pressing while damp. Careful brushing may remove the stain if it is small.

Small spotting kits for home use can be found in some stores. These generally consist of three liquids: 1) a detergent, 2) a dilute acid, and 3) a solvent mixture. There are specific directions for the dilution of these various liquids prior to application.

On one occasion our Fellowship laboratory had a call from an irate consumer who had removed the color from her sofa's upholstered fabric in an attempt to remove a beverage stain with one of these sets. Upon inquiry, it was found that she had not read the directions but had simply applied the No. 1; when it did not work, she had quickly applied No. 2; when that failed to remove the stain, No. 3 was applied; all full-strength. The result was that the color was ruined in the affected area.

Spot removal is invariably a chemical process; if color damage or fabric damage are to be avoided, care must be taken, and above all, hard rubbing must never take place.

home dry-cleaning

Dry-cleaning is simply the cleaning of garments with an organic solvent, virtually free from water. Thus, the garments do not become wet. In some dry-cleaning systems, a small amount of moisture is used to help put the dry-cleaning soap into solution and to gain somewhat better penetration through a slight wetting action on the fibers. This method is known as the "charged system" and is most commonly carried out with naphtha as the cleaning solvent. Many dry-cleaning plants today, especially those in congested areas of the city of the "neighborhood type," use a chlorinated hydrocarbon solvent, such as carbon tetrachloride, perchloroethylene, or trichloroethylene. The latter two of the chlorinated hydrocarbons solvents are generally used now in the so-called coin-operated dry-cleaning plants which are beginning to appear, separately or in conjunction with coin-operated laundries, because these are completely safe from fire and the only danger is from breathing in of an excessive amount of fume. However, if the system is tight and the redistillation of the dirty solvent is efficiently operated without any leakage of vapor, then these should be satisfactory from the standpoint of safety. Any garment which is to be stored should be perfectly clean before being put away. This is especially true in the case of woolens which are subject to insect damage. Washing and dry-cleaning both destroy the eggs of clothes moths which may be laid in the fabric.

At one time, householders endeavored to do some dry-cleaning at home. This operation, however, was never too efficient and was fraught with considerable hazard. It was inefficient, because rarely was there enough solvent used to rinse the garment completely. Thus, soiled solvent was left in the goods, and upon evaporation it redeposited the dirt. Naphtha, the most inexpensive of the solvents, had too great a fire hazard and, in fact, its storage in the home was a violation of local fire ordinances and endangered the status of fire insurance. The addition of approximately 20 per cent of carbon tetrachloride raised the flash point of naphtha, that is, **Stoddard Solvent,** sufficiently so that it was generally regarded as safe from the standpoint of flammability. However, carbon tetrachloride is a more volatile solvent; that is, it evaporates at a lower temperature when such mixtures are used. In this case, however, the danger was the toxic nature of the vapors of carbon tetrachloride, even in small quantities. Mixed with other solvents in spotting or cleaning fluids, carbon tetrachloride should be used only in a well-ventilated room or out-of-doors, in order to avoid breathing the fumes for too long a period of time. The other chlorinated hydrocarbons are not used in this kind of household fabric cleaning product, for the reason that they are quite expensive and the householder has no way in which to distill and thus refresh the solvent between cleaning operations.

storage

A few simple rules for storage are as follows:

1 Never store a soiled or spotted article of clothing or household fabric.

2 If space permits, suits, coats, dresses, jackets, and other outerwear garments remain in better condition if hung in a well-ventilated storage space away from moisture and excessive heat and with the garments being protected against dust by means of plastic or fabric dust covers.

3 If they cannot be stored in a hanging position, they should be folded carefully and placed in large cartons or trunks without crushing. They must be protected against insect entry if any woolen articles are among those being stored (see 4).

4 Wool articles should be stored separately and should be protected against insect damage by sealing and also by using a satisfactory type of moth crystal, such as paradichlorobenzene.

5   Sweaters and other knitted wool articles should be stored in well-sealed and insect-proof boxes.

6   Sweaters and knitted garments of synthetic fibers or of cotton should be stored in boxes or drawers, so as not to cause any distortion of the knitted structure resulting from prolonged hanging.

7   Acetate garments should not be stored in contact with wool either in hanging or in folded condition, due to the fact that the acidity of wool is sufficiently great to cause the typical acid fading of acetates.

8   If a garment is to be stored and sealed with moth crystals, such as paradichlorobenzene, it might be advisable to remove fancy plastic buttons. On one occasion, a box of stored garments was referred to the author after six months' storage. An excess of paradichlorobenzene had been used, and the vapors had plasticized the plastic buttons on one coat in the box, causing the plastic to become soft and to flow down through several layers of fabric. When the garments were examined, at least three of them were ruined.

CONSUMER GUIDES

On many occasions throughout the chapters of this book, reference has been made to consumer guides of several types.

1   Legislative action pointed toward consumer protection.

2   Voluntary standards, such as those of the Federal government purchasing agencies.

3   Commercial standards developed by the United States Bureau of Standards through cooperation with industry.

4   Voluntary standards developed through the American Standards Association by all interested parties, including consumer representation.

5   Informative labeling developed by trade associations, standards promulgators, and individual retail establishments.

It cannot be over-emphasized, however, that none of these tools can be utilized to full advantage unless the consumer has some **basic knowledge** of textiles and textile materials, as well as of his own needs and habits.

textile legislation

On September 26, 1914, the Federal Trade Commission was created by an Act of Congress. This Act defined its powers and duties and its jurisdiction over commerce between states and between the United States and foreign nations. Briefly, its main function is to investigate and to prevent unfair methods of competition. Thus, the power and authority of the commission can be invoked most quickly when the question of unfair competition arises between two companies or associations whose business is competitive.

Five appointed commissioners generally specialize in specific fields of business. From time to time, the commission has issued fair trade practice regulations to correct some malpractice on the part of industry. The commission also draws up the specific rules and regulations described by Congress in its several labeling laws pertaining to textile and textile products and administers these laws.

trade practice conference rules

Silk Industry, November 4, 1938, revoked April 5, 1960; Linen Industry, February 4, 1941 revoked April 5, 1960; Rayon and Acetate Textile Industry, 1952, revoked April 5, 1960; Hosiery Industry, promulgated May 15, 1941, amended April 7, 1942, revised August 30, 1960; shrinkage of woven cotton yard goods, 1936.

federal labeling laws affecting textiles

1. *The Wool Products Labeling Act* of 1939 became effective July 15, 1941.

AN ACT

To protect producers, manufacturers, distributors, and consumers from the unrevealed presence of substitutes and mixtures in spun, woven, knitted, felted, or otherwise manufactured wool products and for other purposes.

One of the principal objectives of this law was to define the three types of fiber derived from sheep; that is, **wool,** meaning the new, virgin, or unused fiber from the fleece of sheep or lambs or the hair of angora or cashmere goats and to include also specialty fibers with the normal physical and chemical properties of wool; **reprocessed wool,** the fiber which had been spun into cloth or yarn but had never been worn or used by the ultimate consumer and had been reduced back to the fiber state; and **re-used wool,** resulting when wool or reprocessed wool had been spun, woven, knitted, or in other ways gone into wool products which had been used by the consumer and then subsequently been again reduced into a fiber. Any other textile fiber present must be identified also and the percentage of composition given. A 5 per cent tolerance was allowed for decorative yarns and fibers. The Wool Products Labeling Act specifically exempted from the law rugs, carpets, upholstery fabrics, and a few other specialty uses.

2. *The Fur Products Labeling Act* was passed August 8, 1951, and became effective August 9, 1952, and was amended March 15, 1961.

AN ACT

To protect consumers and others against misbranding, false advertising, and false invoicing of fur products and furs.

This is essentially a truth-in-advertising bill, designed to correct the prevalent mispractice of the time of giving all kinds of fictitious and misleading names to fibers and furs. The principal offender were those processing rabbit or lapin pelts which bore all kinds of romantic names suggesting that the original animal had been called almost anything from seal to mink. Not only must furs be correctly identified as to animal type, but the label also must disclose the country of origin and whether or not the furs had been dyed or in any other way had their color altered.

3. *Flammable Fabrics Act, 1953,* effective July 1, 1954, amended July 1, 1958.

AN ACT

To prohibit the introduction or movement in interstate commerce of articles of wearing apparel and fabrics which are so highly flammable as to be dangerous when worn by individuals and for other purposes.

This act is an example of textile law having a distinct health or safety point of view much as in the case of regulations under the Food, Drug, and Cosmetic Law. It has been discussed under fabric flammability, particularly under the cellulosic fibers, cotton and rayon, the two fibers most affected. Briefly, it sets a method of test and ground rules under which certain fabric constructions of dangerous flammability potential may be thrown out of interstate commerce unless these fabrics have been permanently treated with a satisfactory flammability-control chemical or compound.

4. *The Textile Fiber Products Identification Act,* approved 1958, effective March 3, 1960, of the FTC Rules amended and effective July 26, 1960.

AN ACT

To protect producers and consumers against misbranding and false advertising of the fiber content of textile fiber products and for other purposes. This law requires that the label disclose the name or registered number of the person or firm marketing the product in commerce. If the textile product is imported, the name of the country where the goods were processed or manufactured must appear on the label. The fiber name and the generic or family name of all fibers present in amounts above 5 per cent must be listed in the order of their predominance and giving the content of each as per cent by weight. The regulations provide also a system of 16 generic groups. These have appeared in each chapter with the fibers corresponding to that generic name group (i.e., nylon, Acrylic, glass, etc.). Thus, such terminology as 65 per cent Dacron polyester, 35 per cent wool; or 80 per cent silk, 20 per cent mink fiber; or 50 per cent wool, 30 per cent mink hair, 20 per cent nylon are all acceptable labels. This law does not include fabrics or end-use products exempted from the Wool Products Labeling Law, except carpets and rugs. Thus, upholstered fabrics and a few other specialty uses are still exempted from identification labeling.

american standards association

The American Standards Association was founded in 1918. It does not itself make standards but provides the climate in which standards may be developed by all those interested. It is essentially a clearing house for industrial, engineering,

TABLE 29-10 / AMERICAN STANDARD PERFORMANCE REQUIREMENTS FOR WOMEN'S AND GIRLS' WOVEN SPORTSWEAR FABRICS

(Other than Sport Suits)
L22.10.32-1960

MINIMUM REQUIREMENTS

Property	Identification:	L22.10.32-B Washable 160 F	L22.10.32-W Washable 160 F No Bleach	L22.10.32-C Washable 120 F No Bleach	L22.10.32-H Washable 105 F No Bleach	L22.10.32-D Dry Cleaning	Test Number (See Volume II)
Breaking Strength Dry (See Note 1)		35 lb	35 lb	35 lb	35 lb	35 lb	ASTM D 39-49, Grab Method (AS L14.68-1951)
Wet		20 lb	20 lb	20 lb	20 lb	20 lb	
Resistance to Yarn Slippage		15 lb	15 lb	15 lb	15 lb	15 lb	ASTM D 434-42 (AS L14.102-1957)
Tongue Tear Strength		1.5 lb	1.5 lb	1.5 lb	1.5 lb	1.5 lb	CCC-T-191b, Method No. 5134
Yarn Shifting Maximum Opening Satins		0.10 in.	0.10 in.	0.10 in.	0.10 in.	0.10 in.	ASTM D 1336-54T (AS L14.103-1957)
Others		0.05 in.	0.05 in.	0.05 in.	0.05 in.	0.05 in.	
Load Satins		2 lb	2 lb	2 lb	2 lb	2 lb	
Others		2 lb	2 lb	2 lb	2 lb	2 lb	
Maximum Dimensional Change—Each Direction (See Notes 2 and 3)		2.5%	2.5%	2.5%	25%	2%	AATCC 96-1960, Table II Test No. III Test No. II Test No. I CS 59-44, Section XVI (dry only)
Colorfastness to Atmospheric Fading After Washing (See Note 4)		Class 4	Class 4	Class 4	Class 4		AATCC 23-1957 (1 cycle alternate evaluation) (AS L14.54-1960)
Dry Cleaning (See Note 4)						Class 4	

	Test IVA (See Note 5)	Test IIIA (See Note 5)	Test IIA	Test IA	
Laundering					AATCC 61-1960
Alteration in Shade	Class 4	Class 4	Class 4	Class 4	
Staining	Class 4	Class 4	Class 4	Class 4	
Dry Cleaning (See Note 6)	Class 4	Class 4	Class 4	Class 4	AATCC 85-1960
Crocking					AATCC 8-1957 (AS L14.72-1960)
Dry	Class 4	Class 4	Class 4	Class 4	
Wet	Class 3	Class 3	Class 3	Class 3	
Perspiration					AATCC 15-1957 (AS L14.56-1960)
Alteration in Shade	Class 4	Class 4	Class 4	Class 3	
Staining	Class 4	Class 4	Class 4	Class 3	
Light	L5-40 hr	L5-40 hr	L5-40 hr	L5-40 hr	AATCC 16A-1957 (AS L14.53-1960)

ABRASION*
PILLING*
PRESSING

Whenever the pressing temperature specified in any testing procedure is too high for heat-sensitive fibers, pressing should be done at temperatures as high as possible without glazing or fusing.

RETENTION OF HAND, CHARACTER, AND APPEARANCE

A fabric shall not change substantially in hand, character, or appearance as a result of three launderings by the applicable shrinkage procedure or dry-cleaning by AATCC Test Method 86-1957. In addition, the fabric shall not lose more than 3 per cent of its weight as a result of this treatment.

COMPONENTS

All textile components and components other than textiles incorporated into the textile article shall conform to applicable performance requirements of this standard in order not to cause alteration in appearance of fabrics meeting these requirements after appropriate refreshing tests. If the provisions of this standard do not cover refreshing requirements suitable for removable components, other L22 end-use standards may be specified.

SPECIAL PERFORMANCE CHARACTERISTICS

When a claim is made for a special performance characteristic not covered by this standard. see Part IV of these standards.

SEAM STRENGTH (Garment or Textile Items)

Each original seam shall possess a breaking strength of at least 30 pounds (U.S. Testing Company Method).

RAVELING TEST (Seams in Garments or Textile Items)

Fabrics containing filament yarns shall be tested for seam strength after three launderings using the applicable shrinkage procedure, or after dry-cleaning by AATCC Test Method 86-1957. Seam failure due to excessive free-edge ravelling indicates the need for another type of seam.

Note 1: Fabrics known to exhibit a wet strength which is within 90 per cent of the dry strength need not be subjected to a wet test.
Note 2: Trade Practice Rule for Shrinkage of Woven Cotton Yard Goods as promulgated June 30, 1938, by the Federal Trade Commission.
Note 3: Use AATCC Test Method 41-1952 (AS L14.77-1956) when applicable.
Note 4: Use corresponding test methods as provided in the columns under laundering and dry-cleaning.
Note 5: If there is no nylon, wool, or silk in the fabric under test, staining of these fibers in the test cloth shall be disregarded.
Note 6: Under this standard, a washable fabric shall also be colorfast to dry-cleaning, unless specifically labeled: DO NOT DRY CLEAN. Dry-cleanable goods are dry-cleanable only.

* In the absence of completely satisfactory correlation between laboratory tests and end-use wear experience, a requirement for this factor is omitted until such correlation can be achieved.

From: American Standard Performance Requirements for Textile Fabrics, 1, American Standards Association, approved Feb. 11, 1960.

safety, and consumers' standards, with consumers' standards being by far the smallest part of its activities. These standards which are developed are not laws; they are voluntarily adopted and approved by the industries and by all organizations affected by them. Table 29-7 gives a typical page of a standard, from L-22. It is a rather tedious way of developing standards, but the vote of one interested group against ASA standards can prevent their passage. The original L-22 applied only to fabrics containing 50 per cent or more of rayon or/and acetate. This standard was published in 1953. In 1960, the new ASA All-Fiber Standard for ultimate consumer goods was promulgated. Between the two, the Institutional Buyers' Textile Standard, L-24, had been promulgated by the ASA and was in use by hotels, motels, hospitals, and other large users of textile products. The L-22 and the L-24 both have one section devoted to the standards themselves, of which the test table is representative, and another section dealing with the test methods. These are dealt with in Chapter 29, referring to each of the test methods in a brief manner.

CARE LABELING CODE FOR TEXTILE ARTICLES IN EUROPE [8]

The beginning of the Common Market in Europe added impetus to the gradual development of a common language and a common set of standards in the marketing of textile products. The very fast indanthrene colors developed principally in Germany were possibly the first to be identified as to fastness by means of an informative label. The public was willing to pay premium prices for these unusually wash-and-sun-fast dyes in fabrics, but disliked having the dyestuffs available from only one country, Germany. The International Association for the Fastness Label was propounded in 1952, but the problem of informative labels understood by salespersons, consumers, dry-cleaners, and laundry men, especially in a number of languages, led to the creation of what is referred to as "speaking images." The label should contain:

1   the washing temperature;
2   whether or not chlorine may be used;
3   whether the article may be ironed or not (if it can be ironed, the temperature at which the iron can be used);
4   whether solvents may be used in dry-cleaning and which solvent is suitable.

This is an elaboration of the graphic labels on washability now being used here (see Sure Care Labels, p. 493).

The washing temperature is indicated by an outline of a tub: green, for a

---

[8] P. J. Wood, *American Dyestuff Reporter*, 48, No. 16 (August 10, 1959), pp. 29–31 (translated from an article by M. Ringeissen, "Rayon et Fibres Synthetiques."

severe wash at 95° C. (203° F.); medium wash at 140° F. by a tub outline with a double line of amber and green; an all-amber tub indicating a light wash, 104° F. A green triangle indicates that chlorine bleach could be used, red that no bleach should be used. Three degrees of heat in ironing were expressed as follows: high heat, or cotton and linen, green L iron; amber iron for moderate ironing, acetate and some synthetics; red iron with a cross over it—"do not iron." A red tub with a cross over it similarly indicates "do not wash." As far as dry-cleaning is concerned, a green circle with a large A means all solvents including trichlorethylene can be used; a large circle with a P indicates perchlorethylene or benzene; and a large circle with an M in it, benzene only. A red circle with an A in it and a cross over it indicates "do not dry-clean."

It is proposed that this labeling shall be on a permanent woven textile label carrying at least three of the symbols in order to disclose completely the kind of washing, ironing, etc., suitable for the fabric. It is said to be necessary also that the type of fibers be disclosed, fastness of the color, the type of finish applied to the fabric, if any, and the type of trimmings and accessories used.

THE COMMON MARKET

From time to time, we have seen on the labels of merchandise in our stores foreign names, such as **Perlon,** the most common of the European names for nylon. Or we have seen **Terylene,** the British fiber made by the same process as our Dacron, as a result of the E. I. duPont de Nemours & Co., Inc., purchasing the patent rights to make this polymer in the United States. More confusing would be the name **Rhovil,** the French fiber made of 100 per cent vinyl chloride. Significant changes have taken place in world trade since the creation of the EEC—European Economic Community—in 1957. Progress of an ever-expanding market has been so rapid that the economic advisors of member and nonmember states alike must help most industries and merchandise firms to appraise the immediate and future effects of their world trade or their consumer selections and shifts in economic status.

At a treaty in Rome, six nations of Europe signed an agreement known popularly as "The Common Market" or the "Free Movement of Goods, Capital, Labor, and Services," within the borders of these six nations. This means that there will be a minimum of tariffs or other obstructions to the passage of the products from one nation to the other. It means that goods, textiles and other products, would be manufactured in that country where they could most economically be produced and distributed. Labor would be free to work within the borders of any of these six signatory countries, and the living conditions would be equalized as far as possible. The means of transportation, communication systems, credits, repairs, and similar services would be uniform throughout the area. So successful has this been to the original signatories—France, Italy, West Germany, Belgium, The Netherlands, and Luxemburg—that other

European countries are eagerly awaiting an opportunity to join; one of the great political issues facing Great Britain is whether she may eventually be able to join her continental European neighbors in this market. The Common Market is a consuming body of 170 million people, almost the same number as in the United States, whose population in 1961 was 187 million; but the new memberships being negotiated with the neighboring nations indicate that this total may swell to about 300 million people, producing annually almost as much total value in goods and services (usually referred to by economists as a *gross national product*) as that of the United States.

The issues are far too great and the potential influence on each of our industries, including textiles, is so far-reaching that even the briefest mention of its effect on our own buying habits must not be overlooked. It has forced our government into a re-appraisal of many of our own international policies regarding tariffs, which may be viewed as cushions protecting our home-made products against the importation of those of other countries, where cost of manufacture may be much less, as the result of low wages, lower standards of living, newer techniques, or some other element of economics. These tariffs are simply fees or charges which must be added to the cost of the goods coming into the United States, so that our own products may compete. Where there is danger of our products entering another country and seizing an appreciable portion of business, then tariffs are erected by that country against the United States. This is admittedly an over-simplification of the matter of tariffs, but we must view the potential effect of losing many of our best markets as our customers join this common market of Europe. If England joins, does she, in turn, bring favored terms to other members of the Commonwealth, such as Canada, a favorite customer of the United States, Australia, and New Zealand?

We have noted repeatedly as various fibers and products have been discussed that we produce not only for sale and consumption in the United States but also depend upon the sale abroad of many of our products of textile mills. It cannot be a one-way flow. We must import quantities of textiles also. For many years, we have looked upon silks and laces of France and Italy as being of unusual quality and value, and we have always felt that imported woolens and worsteds from England represented the highest quality available in fabrics from wool. We have closed our eyes to the fact that such products made of these fibers from the European countries and imported into the United States have generally been of the highest quality, but that we have not been interested in the large quantity of less expensive, lower-quality products being made of these same fibers, because we do not import them—*now*. Just as we in the United States have various grades of products made in our mills, so do the other nations. We have seen how much the quality of dyeing and of finishing influences the potential utility and serviceability of the textile garment or decorative fabric, but we know little of the finish on these imports.

In order to meet this competition, more and more American fiber producers and fabric manufacturers are moving some of their operations to Europe within this common market area. In some cases subsidiary companies have been established for the manufacture of products in Europe. In other cases, the manufacturing operation is a joint venture; that is, a well-established French company will affiliate with an American company. In other cases, a large American company may purchase outright a company in England or Belgium and then proceed to manufacture as before but with this European company in a position to operate under the economic and political rules of the common market and free from any existing barriers or red tape still involved between that market and our own manufacturing here. Likewise, the affiliated or subsidiary companies in Europe would enjoy perhaps a better reception in the United States than would commerce from another mill in that country endeavoring to break into the American market.

Eric Johnson, in the New York *Times Magazine,* March 11, 1962, said in part,

> United States business will have to launch a concerted well-planned effort to sell in foreign markets. It will have to toss out old ideas and come up with fresh skills. It will have to start designing for foreign markets right on the drawing board and follow through effectively in every area of merchandising. The export field is not a place to dump left-overs from the domestic market.

balance of textile imports vs. exports in 1961

Textile Organon reported that in 1961 the United States exported 302,281,-000 dollars worth of man-made fibers and manufacturers, a drop of 3 per cent from 1960.

United States imports of man-made fibers and of manufactures totaled 73,488,000 dollars in 1961, a drop of 7 per cent from 1960. Thus, the freedom of movement of our textile products into foreign markets is a very considerable part of our business in the field of all the man-made fibers. It points up the competitive position our manufacturers will meet when the Common Market in Europe has finally reached its full size.

The same source gives the following export range according to certain product categories. Cellulosic, 41,875,000 dollars; non-cellulosic and glass, 97,838,000 dollars; fabrics, 97,971,000 dollars; outerwear and underwear, 33,-191,000 dollars; house furnishing, etc., 26,090,000 dollars; hosiery, 5,300,000 dollars. Breaking down the import total, these categories show: cellulosic, 10,-772,000 dollars; non-cellulosic, 11,422,000 dollars; fabrics, 14,821,000 dollars; apparel, etc., 33,995,000 dollars; braids, 2,478,000 dollars.

TIRE CORD—A NEW USE FOR MANY SYNTHETICS

Figure 29-2 shows tire cord as being a major market for fibers, with the man-made fibers becoming increasingly significant. Since 1951, apparently, the tires for new cars and those for replacements on cars on the road have consumed approximately 400,000,000 pounds of fiber per year. Despite the fact that a major breakthrough in the use of polyesters in tire cord has recently been achieved, that is, permanently bonding it to rubber, the entry of this fiber with its many advantages has not yet been shown statistically to be very important. Dacron is currently being used in some of the premium tires, which can absorb the greater cost of Dacron tire cord.

From *C & E NEWS,* the price per pound of Dacron tire cord is about $1.40 to $1.50 per pound, compared to $0.92 for nylon and $0.57 for rayon. It must be remembered, however, that for the first few years of nylon tires, this was confined likewise to the premium tires, as well as the heavy-duty tires for truck and aircraft industry.

Improved nylons for tire cord and constant improvements in the tenacity of rayon assure these fibers of a continued place in tires of all qualities; in the meantime, cotton, once the fiber used in all tire cord, now accounts for only about one per cent of the textile fiber used in that industry in the United States.

SYNTHETIC FIBERS: THE STATUS OF SYNTHETIC FIBERS IN THE SOVIET UNION

Very likely, textile fiber products from the Soviet Union will never be of importance in our textile markets. However, some mention of the status of this industry should be of interest to students and to the public. The comments from observers from our side of the Iron Curtain have indicated for many years a relative shortage of textile products available to the citizens of Russia and its satellite countries. Therefore, any significant progress in development and production might reflect an improvement in the way of life of the citizens, and it might forecast the possibility of additional competition for our products in the import markets of the world. Buras[9] states that the present synthetic-fiber production in Russia is approximately that of the United States in the late 1940's and is about 6 per cent of today's production (1961).

A larger program of research development indicates that speed is the essence of their seven-year plan, by which time they expect to produce something over half of the amount of textiles presently produced in the United States. Most of this expansion is the result of new plants, either in operation or soon to be built by technologists from other countries, such as Germany, England, and Japan. The nylon-type fibers are **Capron,** a nylon 6; **Anid,** a nylon 66; **Lavsan,** a polyester similar to Dacron; and **Nitron,** an acrylic fiber. Considerable research has been devoted to the odd-numbered nylons, such as nylon 7, **Enant;** nylon 9, **Pelargon;** and nylon 11, **Rilsan.** A British chemical company is installing an acrylic-staple fiber plant in the Soviet Union which will about double their present production. Another plant, said to be installed soon by the Imperial Chemical Industry of England for the manufacture of polyester fibers **(Lavsan),** will cost 42 million

[9] Edmund M. Buras, "Synthetic Fibers, the Impatient Soviet Industry," *Chemical & Engineering News* (July 31, 1961), pp. 26–134.

dollars. Production of other types of fiber is of less immediate interest, but there are fibers similar to Saran, Nitron, and the vinyls being produced in the Soviet Union today.

This indicates that if the seven-year plan continues as it is now, the citizens will be dressed extensively in synthetic fibers, as well as rayon, which in 1960 was about 41 per cent of our production. However, as is the case in the United States, the production of rayon is not booming as is the production of synthetics.

Fig. 29-2   Tire Cord, a major market for synthetic fibers.

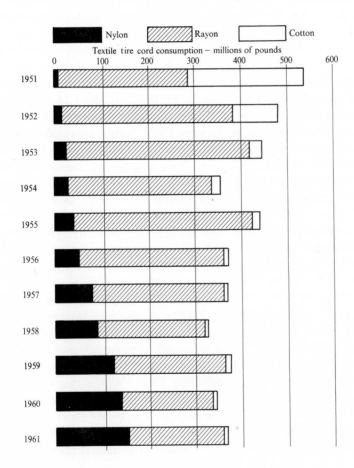

Sources: *Textile Organon* and *C. & E. N. estimates;*
Chem. and Eng. News, **40** (Aug. 20, 1962), p. 890.

FUTURE OF TEXTILES [10]

By the year 2000, less than 40 years from now, the world population is expected to double and reach the total of approximately 5 billion persons. If the standard of living in all parts of the world continues to rise at the rate of the last ten years and with the expected economic improvements in the new nations of Africa, the challenge to the textile industry to provide the clothing, shelter, and other fabrics appear to be staggering. The increase in population and the improved economic conditions of many of the so-called backward countries will require an equal challenge to the providers of foodstuffs. Doubtless, much land presently devoted to the growth of textile raw materials and the natural fibers will have to be curtailed in order that food may be grown. Thus, the acreage available for the growing of cotton, for the grazing of sheep and goats, and perhaps even for the growth of such fibers as hemp and jute for industrial purposes may have to be reduced. Slack then must be taken up by the man-made and synthetic fibers. The ever-expanding petroleum industry and the petro-chemicals derived from oil already produce the monomers on which many of our synthetic fibers are dependent. Thus, both oil and coal will continue to serve as clothing raw materials in addition to serving us as sources of heat, light, and power. The world textile production in the 1960's is about 16 million tons for a population of 2,800,000,000. Thus, the production of textiles will have to reach about 30 million tons in the year 2000. Today, approximately 3,180,000 tons of man-made fibers are produced annually. This amount is increasing at the rate of some 25 per cent each year. Such a fantastic increase can scarcely be expected to continue indefinitely. However, if it should, the production of man-made textiles would reach this desired figure of 20 to 25 million tons in ten years' time, approximately 24 million tons in 1972.

The man-made fibers have now reached their maturity. They are presented not as precocious infants but as fully-developed members of the economy of textiles. There are certain advantages possessed by individual members of this man-made family which are seized upon and used in promotion; most of these features arouse the interest of the public. The promotion of textiles must now be much more factual and less fanciful that it once was. New products must win their place in the market on their merit. The fiber identification law and the textile standards, combined with the public's thirst for more knowledge and facts about textiles, all contribute to the reduction of propaganda both for and against the synthetics and the cellulosic fibers. Within this competitive field, blending is sure to be truly significant, for it must help expand the use of available fibers in place of others which may be in relatively short supply from time to time. Blends must also provide the unique chemical and physical properties available through such mixtures, thus guiding the natural fibers and new mem-

[10] Largely taken from *American Fabrics,* No. 55 (Winter, 1961).

bers of the synthetic family into the more appropriate and necessary end-use items. And last, blends must be depended upon to help supply textiles at reasonable prices.

It is entirely possible that the blends now in use for fabric constructions common to many end-use items may be modified rather widely in percentage composition in order to accommodate other end-use fabrics. Textile-fiber compositions should not themselves become the significant base of selection of one fabric over another. In other words, selection should be based on the degree to which a fabric satisfies the needs of its end-use application rather than the exact mixture of fibers present in order to accomplish this. It is entirely possible that advertisers and copywriters may seize upon the presence of a slightly greater amount of a more desirable or newsworthy fiber in a mixture as a basis for its promotion without considering the construction and the end-use application for which that fabric has been devised.

forecast of the first step—to 1963

TABLE 29-11 / MAN-MADE TEXTILE FIBER CAPACITY OF THE UNITED STATES[1]

(Millions of Pounds)

		1961	1963 (Estimate)
Rayon	Regular filament	160	161
	High-tenacity	314	310
	Staple and tow	614	614
Acetate	Filament	317	317
	Staple and tow	92	92
Nylon	Yarn and monofilament	531	710
	Staple and tow	33	33
Olefins	Yarns and monofilaments	47	68
Acrylic and Modacrylic		215	223
Polyester and Vinyon		152	196
Textile Glass Fiber		246	296

[1] *Textile Organon.*

One cannot take such estimates as being more than the approximations arrived at by one group of economists, based on the study of the current textile industry capacity and reflecting current trends. Thus, the *Textile Organon* data reflect the following conclusions as to textile changes between 1961 and 1963.

1   The fibers derived from cellulose will continue in the same consumer-use items in the same total volume over this brief two-year span.

2   No significant improvements in these fibers seem imminent.

3   Nylon staple and tow fibers alone or in blends are expected just to hold their own.

4   Nylon filament is expected to expand with new uses in home and industrial fabrics. Much of this is probably based on the trend to nylon in automobile tires. This is indicated by the loss in volume forecast for H-T Rayons.

5   All the other synthetic fiber types are expected to expand as the engineering of superior tailor-made textile blends and the art of providing the desired textures and colors combine to perfect fabrics for specific end-uses.

6   The steady move to more free time or leisure adds impetus to this shift to esthetics above the utilitarian in wearing apparel.

Blending is a combination of art and science. It is a science in that it is designed and developed for the purpose of combining as fully as possible the individual advantages of each fiber constituent, and not only the physical and chemical properties of the fibers must be considered but also the engineering aspects of combining them into a yarn both stable and staple; that is, staple lengths must be compatible so as to produce a yarn of controlled twist and structure, and the fiber fineness and length must be easily seen and utilized for a durable yarn structure. The art of such blending is depended upon to produce a fiber composition which is appealing esthetically to the handle and touch, to the draping quality, to the texture, to the lustre, as well as its practical durability and its permanence in use and cleaning. Contributing also to this marriage of the fibers has been the development of special textured yarns (see Chapter 7). These textured yarns produce fabrics with greater loftiness and/or bulk with a great saving in actual fiber weight. Yarns such as Helanca, Agilon, and others are currently being used in knitted apparel, but woven goods will be using more of these specially-textured yarns in the future. These textured yarns and stretch yarns may be given still other desirable features when one realizes that thus far the greater part of the research and development has been using a single one of the synthetics as a base, nylon. When, therefore, the art of blending becomes even more sophisticated so that two or more of the synthetics can be blended together, these properties of bulking and stretchiness by a permanent crimp or other distortion may be applied to all-synthetic yarn, regardless of the material of which the fibers are composed.

It is expected that students of textiles will be required to do a certain amount of collateral reading. Therefore, a number of standard textbooks and references, including sources of abstracts of articles on textile technology, are listed. This list includes those books, encyclopedias, and technical journals most likely to be found in many college and university libraries.

A few suggestions may benefit the student before he embarks upon those outside reading assignments. At the basic level—that of students just beginning the study of textiles—the assignments will probably be to specific textbooks, wherein certain topics are discussed at greater length than in this volume, or to encyclopedias, such as *Encyclopedia Britannica, Encyclopedia Americana, Encyclopedia of Textiles,* or *Man-Made Textile Encyclopedia,* for elaboration on specific topics or facts already well established in the literature. One might say these reading assignments deal with "Whats," such as a description of a loom, information on batik prints, the history of silk, or from what materials rayon fiber is made.

The next group of reference materials would be the standard references in textiles, for example, Matthews' *Textile Fibers,* edited by H. R. Mauersberger, *Technology of Synthetic Fibers* by Sherman and Sherman, or *Man-Made Fibres* by Moncrieff, and other advanced books on textile technology. Other sources of information would be found in the technical information booklets and bulletins issued by some of the principal fiber-producing companies, such as du Pont,

Chemstrand, American Viscose, and Celanese. Generally, these resource materials will tell the student how a fiber is produced and how it is dyed or finished.

The more advanced student, especially one interested in textile research, must know the answers to questions as to "why" certain work was carried out as well as the results achieved. Specific projects, term papers, and similar requirements set up by the teacher in an advanced course require that the student study certain important primary sources of material, that is, original articles in the technical journals. Two principal sources of abstracts should be available in most libraries:

1   Tex-tracts, published monthly by J. B. Goldberg, 11 W. 42nd Street, New York 36, New York, and

2   Review of Textile Progress, a volume published annually by the Textile Institute, 10 Blackfriars Street, Manchester 3, England.

Among the journals probably to be found in most libraries would be *American Dyestuff Reporter, Modern Textiles, Textile World, Journal of the American Home Economics Association, Textile Research Journal,* and others. Faced by a shelf of unbound technical journals dating back several years, the uninitiated student is very likely simply to pick out two or three journals and thumb hopefully through them in search of information on the topic desired. All technical publications of this nature publish an Annual Index, which is generally in the last issue of the year, although sometimes the index is carried over to the January or even the February number. This is the place to look. Just as in the abstract sources previously mentioned, the student should concentrate only on those articles dealing with the topic at hand, beginning with the most recent issues of the journals and working backward. The bibliography following each article suggests other papers to be read and generally indicates the earliest date of significant publication in the field.

Very early in the experience of the student, he should become familiar with the technique of keeping an abstract card reference of each article he has read pertaining to his subject, and the teacher should acquaint the class early with the format of abstract he prefers. It may be argued that one's personal collection of abstracts on technical articles may be replaced sooner or latter by some giant memory machine; but unless these abstracts are fed into the machine originally in a clear, palatable form, the machine's information will be faulty. Judgment as to the significance of a discovery from a title can only be done by the human brain, even though we may be depending on the machine to do the memory work.

American Fabrics, the various magazines of fashion, the yearbooks of the technical societies (ASTM and ATCC), and numerous publications of the Federal Government, especially the Agricultural Experiment Stations and the Marketing Research Studies of the U.S.D.A. and the commercial standards now issued by the Department of Commerce, are interesting publications to which students may wish to refer on specific topics.

general bibliography

CHAPTERS 1 — 5

American Fabrics Magazine. *Encyclopedia of Textiles.* Englewood Cliffs, N.J.: Prentice-Hall, 1960.

Bendure, Zelma, and Pfeiffer, Gladys. *America's Fabrics.* New York: Macmillan, 1946.

Callaway's Textile Dictionary. La Grange, Ga.: Callaway Mills, 1959.

Denny, G. G. *Fabrics and How to Know Them.* Philadelphia: Lippincott, 1947.

Fairchild's Directory of Fabrics. New York: Fairchild Publications, 1959.

Goldberg, J. B. *Fabric Defects.* New York: McGraw-Hill, 1950.

Hall, A. J. *Standard Handbook of Textiles.* New York: Van Nostrand, 1947.

Haven, George. *Handbook of Industrial Fabrics.* New York: Wellington Sears Co., 1938.

Hess, K. P. *Textile Fibers and Their Use,* 5th ed. Philadelphia: Lippincott, 1949.

Hollen, N., and Saddler, J. *Modern Textiles.* Minneapolis: Burgess Publ. Co., 1952.

Linton, G. E., and Pizzuto, J. J. *Applied Textiles,* 5th ed. New York: Lifetime Editions, 1952.

Potter, M. D., and Corbman, B. F. *Fiber to Fabric.* New York: Gregg Publ. Div., McGraw-Hill, 1954.

Press, J. J. (ed.). *Man-Made Textile Encyclopedia.* New York: John Wiley, 1959.

Stout, Evelyn E. *Introduction to Textiles.* New York: Wiley, 1960.

Wingate, Isabel. *Textile Fabrics and Their Selection.* Englewood Cliffs, N.J.: Prentice-Hall, 1955.

CHAPTERS 6 — 9

Essentially, any of those previously listed, with the following additions.

Harris, J. C. *Detergency Evaluation and Testing.* New York: Interscience, 1953.

Harris, Milton. *Handbook of Textile Fibers.* Washington: Harris Research Laboratories, Inc., 1954.

Heyn, A. N. J. *Fiber Microscopy.* New York: Interscience, 1953.

Kaswell, Ernest R. *Textile Fibers, Yarns and Fabrics.* New York: Reinhold, 1953.

Matthews, J. M. *The Textile Fibers.* New York: Wiley, 1947.

Pizzuto, J. J., and D'Alessandro, P. L. *101 Fibers.* New York: Textile Press, 1952.

Schwartz, E. R. *Textiles and Microscope.* New York: McGraw-Hill, 1934.

Small, C. P. *How to Know Textiles.* New York: Ginn, 1932.

Staples, M. C. *Essentials of Textiles.* Boston: Ginn, 1932.

Taylor, L. *Know Your Fabrics.* New York: Wiley, 1951.

Textile Institute Staff. *Identification of Textile Materials.* Manchester, England: Textile Institute, 1951.

Von Bergen, Werner. *Textile Fiber Atlas.* New York: Textile Book Publishers, 1945.

Weiss, E. B., and Mermey, M. *The Shopping Guide.* New York: McGraw-Hill, 1937.

Woolman, M. S., and McGowan, E. B. *Textiles: A Handbook for the Student and the Consumer,* 3rd ed. New York: Macmillan, 1943.

CHAPTERS 10 — 14

Essentially, any of those previously mentioned, with the following important books dealing in greater depth with the natural fibers recommended for more serious study.

Evans, M. *Fundamentals of Clothing and Textiles.* New York: Prentice-Hall, 1949.

Higgins, A., and La Vault, R. *A Comprehensive Dictionary of Textile Terms.* Fall River, Mass.: Dover Press, 1948.

Matthews, J. M., and Mauersberger, H. R. *Textile Fabrics,* 6th ed. New York: Textile Book Publishers, 1954.

CHAPTERS 15 — 22

Though some information on material in these chapters is available in most of the textbooks previously mentioned, the most productive references, in addition to the *American Fabrics Encyclopedia of Textiles* and Press' *Man-Made Textile Encyclopedia,* are the following:

"Annual Man-Made Fiber Deskbook," *Modern Textiles Magazine,* **43**, No. 9 (Sept., 1962), pp. 41–56.

Du Pont Fiber Facts. Wilmington, Del.: Textile Fibers Dept., E. I. du Pont de Nemours & Co., 1962.

Hartsuch, P. E. *Introduction to Textile Chemistry.* New York: Wiley, 1950.

Johnson, George H. *Modern Fibers and Their Current Usage.* Special Report No. 207. Joliet, Mo.: American Institute of Laundering, (1953).

Moncrieff, R. W. *Man-Made Fibres.* New York: Wiley, 1959.

Sherman, J. V., and Sherman, S. L. *The New Fibers.* New York: Van Nostrand, 1946.

Speel, H. C. *Textile Chemicals and Auxiliaries.* New York: Reinhold, 1957.

CHAPTERS 24 — 29

consumership

Adams, Georgion. "Fifty Years of Home Economics Research," *J. Home Economics,* **51**, No. 1 (1959), pp. 12–18.

O'Toole, Lila, *et al.* "Responsibilities of Research," *J. Home Economics,* **52**, No. 3 (1960), pp. 159–60.

Personius, Catherine. "Objectives and Philosophy of Research," *J. Home Economics,* **51**, No. 2 (1959), pp. 94–96.

Swanson, Pearl. "New Resources for Research," *J. Home Economics,* **53**, No. 4 (1961), pp. 161–64.

United States Department of Agriculture, Marketing Research Division.

Report No. 153, "Women's Attitudes Toward Wool and Other Fibers" (Feb., 1957)
Part I—Suits, Skirts, Sweaters
Part II—Home Sewing, Knitting, Needlework

Report No. 155, "Teenage Girls Discuss Their Wardrobes and Their Attitudes Toward Cotton and Other Fibers" (1957)

Report No. 279, "Homemakers Appraise Cotton, Wool and Other Fibers in Household Furnishings" (July, 1959)

Report No. 338, "Consumers' Concepts of Fabric" (July, 1959)

Report No. 429, "Mothers' Opinions of Fibers in Children's Clothing" (September, 1960)

Report No. 493, "Women's Attitudes Toward Cotton and Other Fibers in Clothing" (July, 1961)

A M S-294, "Mothers Discuss Cotton and Other Fibers in Children's Clothes" (Feb., 1959)

A M S-378, "Selected Data in Women's Attitudes Toward Cotton and Other Fibers in Clothing" (June, 1960)

textile care

Barach, J. L., Stoll, R. G., and Tesi, A. F. "Predicting Commercial Acceptance of a Fiber," *Text. Res. J.,* **28**, No. 9 (Sept., 1958), pp. 747–54.

Better Wash Days. Cincinnati, O.: Proctor & Gamble, (1952).

Furry, M. S., *et al.* "Evaluating the Effectiveness of Fluorescent Whiteners and Oxidizing Bleaches on Cotton," *Am. Dyestuff Rep.,* **48** (1959), p. 59.

Horigan, F. D., and Sage, C. R. *The Serviceability of Fabrics.* Bibliographic Series, No. 13. Philadelphia: Q.M. Res. & Dev. Lab., 1950.

Leisure and Work Clothing—Trends and Outlook. Washington: U.S. Dept. of Commerce, Business & Defense Services Administration, 1961.

McLardon, Verda, and Richardson, Florence. "Residual Oily Soil as a Factor in Yellowing of Used and Laundered White Cotton Articles," *Am. Dyestuff Rep.,* **52** (1953), pp. 27–33.

Paper, H. "Soils, Stains and Modern Laundry Aids," *Proc. 15th National Home Laundry Conference* (1961), p. 69.

Retail Executives' Guide to Fibers and Finishes. Midland, Mich.: Dow Corning Corp.: 1960.

Stoll, R. G. *End Use Requirements vs. Material Properties of Textiles.* Res. & Dev. Report, Textile Series, No. 83. Washington: Dept. of the Army, 1953.

Weder, G. "Standardized Cleanliness," *Am. Dyestuff Rep.,* **51**, No. 5 (1962), pp. 154–57.

Weiner, L. J., and Kennedy, S. J. "Field Testing and Correlation of Laboratory and Field Test Data," *J. Textile Inst.,* **44**, No. 8 (Aug., 1953), pp. 433–74.

collateral reading lists
for specific chapters

C H A P T E R   1

Bayor, Stephania, and Wybourn, Marjory. "Third Clothing and Textile Seminar, Syracuse University," *J. Home Econ., 42* (Dec., 1950), p. 803.

Blair, Margaret. "Around the Table at the Syracuse Seminar," *J. Home Econ., 41* (Jan., 1949), p. 23.

Boettke, Eleanor, and Zook, Margaret. "Dress Design with Self-help Features for the Pre-School Child," *J. Home Econ., 48,* No. 8 (Aug., 1956), pp. 43–46.

Brandeau, Edna, and Myers, Doris E. "Second Syracuse Seminar," *J. Home Econ., 42* (Feb., 1950), p. 106.

Coles, Jessie, "Standards and Labels for Consumer Goods," in Lincoln Clarke, *Consumer Behavior*. New York: New York Univ. Press, 1955.

Douglas, Helen. "Easier Laundering for Wash and Wear Clothes," *J. Home Econ., 54,* No. 2, (Feb., 1962), p. 126.

Edwards, Alice. *Product Standards and Labeling for Consumers*. New York: Ronald, 1940.

Galbraith, Ruth L., Finch, Joan F., and Maclin, Janice. "The Laundering Stability of Elastic Fabrics," *J. Home Econ., 53,* No. 3 (March, 1961), pp. 206–11.

Grey, Edna. "Clothing Seminar Report Raises Timely Questions," *J. Home Econ., 43* (April, 1951), p. 228.

Hall, Katherine. "A Study of the Factors that Contribute to Satisfactions and Dissatisfactions in Clothing of 92 Urban Families," *J. Home Econ., 48,* No. 3 (March, 1956), pp. 214–5.

Hartman, George W. "Clothing: Personal Problem and Social Issue," *J. Home Econ., 41* (June, 1949), p. 295.

Illinois Work Conf. "Clothing and Textiles: Further Progress," *J. Home Econ., 53* (Oct., 1961), pp. 678–80.

Maryland Work Conf. "Clothing and Textiles Move Forward," *J. Home Econ., 48* (Oct., 1956), p. 635.

Reck, Dickson. *National Standards in a Modern Economy*. New York: Harper, 1956.

Rosencranz, Mary L. "Clothing Symbolism," *J. Home Econ., 54,* No. 1 (Jan., 1962), p. 62.

————. "Sociological Aspects of Clothing Studied," *J. Home Econ.*, **42** (March, 1950), p. 206.

Stout, Dorthy R., and Letzke, Alpha. "Values College Women Consider in Clothing Selection," *J. Home Econ.*, **50**, No. 1 (Jan., 1958), p. 43.

Sybers, Ruth, and Roach, Mary E. "Clothing and Human Behavior," *J. Home Econ.*, **54**, No. 3 (March, 1962), pp. 184–7.

Thompson, Henrietta M., Werden, Jane, and Stedman, Louise A. "Planning Ahead in Textiles and Clothing," *J. Home Econ.*, **48**, No. 6 (June, 1956), p. 409.

Warning, Margaret. "Clothing," *J. Home Econ.*, **52** (Oct., 1960), pp. 646–51.

Winaker, Geitel. "Time Lag Between High Fashion and Accepted Fashion," *J. Home Econ.*, **47**, No. 5 (May, 1955), pp. 343–4.

reference works

A.A.T.C.C. *1962 Yearbook.*

A.S.A. *Textile Standards (L-22).* New York: The Association, 1961.

————. *Textile Standards for Institutional Buyers (L-24).* New York: The Association, 1954.

CHAPTER 5

Papers of the American Association of Textile Technology. Published by *Modern Textiles Magazine,* **11**, No. 3 (Sept., 1956), pp. 56–65.

Moffitt, R. P. "New Bonding Techniques."

Probasco, D. V. "Processes, Problems and Prediction."

Riehl, H. V. "The Machines That Make Them."

Watkins, W. W. "Non-Woven Fabrics, Their Status Today."

Lauterbach, H. G. "Felt from Man-Made Fibres," *Text. Res. J.,* **25** (1955), pp. 143–49.

Leventhal, H. L. "Production and Utilization of Non-Woven Fabrics," *Am. Dyestuff Rep.,* **44** (1955), pp. 464–66.

Moncrieff, R. W. *Wool Shrinkage and Its Prevention.* London: National Trade Press, 1954.

"Non-Woven Fabrics—How Big, How Soon?" *Chem. & Eng. News,* **37**, No. 32 (Aug. 10, 1959), pp. 118–23.

Wente, V. A. "Superfine Thermoplastic Fibers," *Industrial Eng. Chem.,* **48** (1956), pp. 1342–46.

CHAPTER 6

fiber structure

Astbury, W. T., and Street, A. "X-ray Studies of the Structure of Hair, Wool and Related Fibres," *Phil. Trans. Royal Soc.,* **230A** (1931), pp. 75–101.

Harland, W. G. "Fractionation of Nitrated Rayons," *J. Text. Inst.,* **46** (1955), pp. T483–T499.

Howlett, F. "Fibres and Plastics," *J. Text. Inst.,* **40** (1948), p. 241.

Lovell, E. L., and Goldschmid, O. "Fiber Crystallinity" *Industrial Eng. Chem.,* **28** (1946), p. 811.

Moncrieff, R. W. "Crease Resistance in Textiles," *Text. Mercury and Argus,* **120** (1949), p. 1011.

Morley, D. V., and Martin, E. V. "Structural Orientation in Cellulose Acetate Filaments and Its Relation to the Dichroism of Adsorbed Dyes," *Text. Res. J.,* **21** (1951), p. 607.

Natta, G. "Isotactic Polymers," *J. Polymer Science,* **16** (1955), p. 143–45.

Preston, J. M. *Fibre Science.* Manchester, England: Textile Institute, 1949.

———. *Modern Textile Microscopy,* 1933

———. "Regain and Crystallinity," *Fibres,* **10** (1949), p. 218.

Simmens, L., and Urquhart, A. R. "The Structure of Textile Fibres," *J. Text. Inst.,* **40** (1949), p. 3.

"Textile Fibers Symposium," *Industrial Eng. Chem.,* **44** (1952), p. 2101.

fiber properties

A Look at the 1960's. A Seminar by Werner Textile Consultants, 1960.

Mauer, L., and Wechsler, H. *Man-Made Fibers.* Handbook of *Modern Textiles Magazine.* New York: Rayon Publ. Co., 1953.

Preston, J. M. *Fibre Science.* Manchester, England: Textile Institute, 1949.

Smith, H. DeWitt. "Textile Fibers: An Engineering Approach to Their Properties and Utilization," *Proc. A.S.T.M.,* **44** (1944), 543–92.

Textile Outlook for the Sixties. Washington: U.S. Dept. Commerce, Business and Defense Services Admin., 1960.

"Today's Fibers: Sure Ways to Identify Them," *Text. World,* **111** (Dec., 1961), pp. 47–59.

Turner, A. J. "Natural and Man-Made Fibres," *J. Text. Inst.,* **38** (1947), p. 411.

static

Henry, P. S. H. "Static—Notes on Its Causes and Prevention," *The Text. Institute and Industry,* **1** (Jan., 1963), pp. 8–10.

Silsbee, F. B. *Static Electricity.* N.B.S. Circular C-438. Washington: U.S. Dept. Commerce, 1942

Turer, Jack, and Smith, J. K. "Measurement of Static Electricity in Fabrics," *Am. Dyestuff Rep.,* **51** (Jan. 22, 1962), pp. 41–44.

CHAPTER 7

Eyre, N. *Testing of Yarns and Fabrics,* pp. 27–48. Textile Manufacturing Monograph No. 4., 1947.

Forward, M. V., and Smith, S. T. "Moisture Regain of 66 Nylon Continuous Filament Yarn," *J. Text. Inst.,* **46** (1955), pp. T158–T160.

stretch yarns

"A to Z Yarns," *Man-Made Textiles,* **39** (June, 1962), pp. 58–60.

Blore, J. H. *Text. World,* **105,** No. 6 (1955), p. 94.

Field, J. C. *Text. World,* **104,** No. 7 (1954), p. 75.

Hamilton, Joseph H. "Woven Stretch," *Modern Textiles Magazine,* **42** (June, 1961), pp. 57–60.

Hicks, E. M., Jr. "Lycra Staple Blends—A Route to Elasticity in Spun Yarn," *Text.*

Res. J., **32**, No. 10 (1962), pp. 791–98.

Kennedy, J. H. *Textile World*, **104**, No. 11 (1954), p. 140.

Noechel, Fred W. "New Yarns Widen Fabric Horizon," Papers A.A.T.T., *Modern Textiles Magazine*, **12**, No. 4 (Dec., 1957), pp. 124–30.

Ray, L. G. "Textured Filament Yarns," *The Textile Institute Report of 41st Annual Conference*, 1956, pp. 33–44.

CHAPTER 8

American Viscose Corp. *Rayon Technology*, pp. 190–251. New York: The Corporation, 1948.

"Aridye Process." British Patent 631,882.

Badertscher, Walter. "New Application Methods for Reactive Dyes in Printing," *Am. Dyestuff Rep.*, **52**, No. 1 (1963), pp. 38–42.

Boulton, J. "The Application of Dyes to Viscose Rayon Yarn and Staple," *J. Soc. Dyers and Col.*, **67** (1951), p. 522.

Boulton, J., and Morton, T. H. "The Dyeing of Cellulosic Materials," *J. Soc. Dyers and Col.*, **56** (1940), p. 145.

Edelstein, Sidney M. "Dyestuff and Dyeing in the 16th Century," *Am. Dyestuff.*, **52**, No. 1 (1963), pp. 15–18.

Elod, E. "Theory of the Dyeing Process," *Trans. Faraday Soc.*, **29** (1933), p. 327.

Furvik, N. B., Bernskold, A., and Gralen, N. "Heat Setting of Nylon Fabrics," *J. Text. Inst.*, **46** (1955), pp. T662–T667.

"Reports on the Dyeing Properties of Direct Dyes," *J. Soc. Dyers and Col.*, **62** (1946), p. 280, and **64** (1948), p. 145.

Thomas, H. A. *Technique of Dyeing Rayons*, rev. ed. Manchester, England: Textile Institute, 1949.

White, G. S. J., and Vickerstaff, T. "Colour," *J. Soc. Dyers and Col.*, **61** (1945), p. 213.

CHAPTER 9

Cole, P. M. "Barotor—Pressurized Fabric Dyeing Machine," *Am. Dyestuff Rep.*, **42** (Jan. 19, 1953), pp. 52–54.

Cole, P. M. "Barotor Loading Improvement," *Am. Dyestuff Rep.*, **43** (Oct. 25, 1954), pp. 673–675.

"Controlled Fiber Crimping," *Modern Textiles Magazine*, **42** (Oct., 1961), p. 38.

"Du Pont Offers New Stain Resistant Finish Zepel," *Modern Textiles Magazine*, **44** (Feb., 1963), p. 28.

Fern, A. S. "The Dyeing of Terylene Polyester Fibre with Disperse Dyes above 100°C." *J. Soc. Dyers and Col.*, **71** (1955), pp. 502–13.

Fowler, J. A. "The Dyeing of Textile Fibres above 100°C." *J. Soc. Dyers and Col.*, **71** (1955), pp. 443–50.

Hall, A. J. *The Standard Handbook of Textiles*, 4th ed. London:, 1954.

Hamburger, Walter J. "Dyeing and Finishing of New Cellulosic Fibers," *Am. Dyestuff Rep.*, **50**, No. 1 (Jan., 1961), p. 35.

Horsfall, R. S., and Lawrie, L. G. *The Dyeing of Textile Fibres*, 2nd ed. London: E Benn & Co., 1946.

"How to Pressure Dye Tufted Carpets," *Text. World*, **106** (Jan., 1956), pp.

McNeil, "Detection and Evaluation of Anti-Bacterial Activity of Treated Fabrics," *Am. Dyestuff Rep.,* **51**, No. 4 (Feb., 1962), pp. 121–24.

Meunier, P. L. "Practical Aspects of Dyeing in the Burlington Beam Machine," *Am. Dyestuff Rep.,* 45 (May 21, 1956), pp. 260–263.

"Piece Goods Can Be Dyed by Warp Dyeing Methods," *Text. World,* **105** (April, 1955), pp.

"Printing Dacron Top," *Text. World,* **110** (Dec., 1960), p. 80.

"Today's Trends in Dyeing and Finishing," *Modern Textiles Magazine,* **42** (Dec., 1960), p. 37.

Tomasino, U., *et al.* "A Study of Oil-and-Water Repellent Surfaces," *Am. Dyestuff Rep.,* **52** (Feb., 1963), pp. 25–33.

Young, Sanford P. "A Millman's Guide to Wash and Wear Finishes," *Modern Textiles Magazine,* **42** (Oct., 1961), p. 30.

CHAPTER 10

Arceneaux, R. L., Gautreaux, G. A., Reinhart, R. M., and Reid, J. D. "Studies of Wrinkle-Resistance Finishes for Cotton Textiles. Part III: An Accelerated Storage Test for 'Wash-and-Wear' Cotton Fabrics," *Am. Dyestuff Rep.,* **50** (1961), pp. 21–24.

Brown, H. B. *Cotton.* New York: McGraw-Hill, 1938.

Buras, E. M., *et al.* "Practical Partial Acetylation of Cotton," *Am. Dyestuff Rep.,* **43** (1954), pp. 203–08.

Cotton—The Great American Crop and Industry. Boston: Pepperell Mfg. Co., 1929.

Crawford, M. W. C. *Heritage of Cotton.* New York: Grosset & Dunlap, 1937.

"Cyanoethylation Moves Forward," *Chem. & Eng. News,* **34** (1956), p. 5058.

Dickson, Harris. *The Story of King Cotton.* New York: Funk & Wagnalls, 1937.

Dockray, G. H., Meadows, B., and Smith, L. "Cotton Waste," *Text. Res. J.,* **20** (Oct., 1950), p. 10.

Facts About Cotton. Leaflet No. 167. Washington: U.S. Department of Agriculture, 1938.

Gagliardi, D. D. "Cotton Finishing: Where It Stands, and What's Ahead," *Text. World,* **112** (1962), pp. 86–94.

Greathouse, L. H., *et al.* "Cyanoethylation of Cotton," *Industrial Eng. Chem.,* **48** (1956), pp. 1263–67.

Hall, Laura T., and Elting, John P. "Cavitomic Cotton—A Progress Report," *Text. Res. J.,* **21** (1951), pp. 580–86.

Harwell, J. T., Jr., and Russell, C. W. *Cotton in Rubber Gloves.* Washington: National Cotton Council of America (hereafter referred to as NCCA), 1961

Haynes, Williams. *The Fiber That Grows.* New York: Doubleday, 1953.

Hessler, L. E. "The Relationship Between Cotton Fiber Development and Fiber Properties," *Text. Res. J.,* **31** (1961), pp. 38–51.

Howell, J. T., Jr. *Cotton in the Paper Industry.* Washington: NCCA, 1962.

Hoye, John. *Staple Cotton Fabrics.* New York: McGraw-Hill, 1947.

"Making Good Cotton Better," *Pacific Gas & Electric Progress,* **38**, No. 3 (March, 1961), pp. 1.

McCord, F. A., and Dikeman, Neil J., Jr. *Cotton Linters.* Memphis, Tenn.: Utilization Research Div., NCCA, 1952.

McCord, F. A., and Getchell, Nelson F. "Cotton—Improving Its Properties Spurs

Demand for Chemicals," *Chem. & Eng. News,* **38**, No. 46 (Nov., 1960), pp. 106–12.

McCord, F. A., and Steinbach, R., Jr. *Cotton Fabrics in Upholstery, Drapes and Slipcovers.* Washington: NCCA, 1958.

———. *Cotton in Non-Woven Fabrics.* Washington, NCCA, 1949.

———. *Cotton in Retail Piece Goods.* Washington, NCCA, 1952.

Merrill, G. R., Macormac, A. R., and Mauersberger, H. R. *American Cotton Handbook.* New York: Textile Book Publishers, 1949.

Michl, H. E. *Textile Industries: An Economical Analysis.* Washington: Textile Foundation, 1938.

Murro, W. P., Williams, C. R., Rossin, E. H., and Huskbeck, H. R. "Symposium of 'Cellulose Reactants.' Part I: Cellulose Reactants. Part II: The Performance Characteristics of Cotton Finished with a Sulfone Reactant. Part III: Cellulose Reactants," *Am. Dyestuff Rep.,* **51** (1962), pp. 30–34.

Nickerson, R. F. "Cotton Fibers—Constitution, Structure and Mechanical Properties," *Industrial Eng. Chem.,* **32** (1940), pp. 1454–62.

Robinson, Helen M., and Reeves, Wilson A. "Survey of the Effect of Light on Cotton and Other Cellulosic Fabrics," *Am. Dyestuff Rep.,* **50** (Jan. 9, 1961), p. 17.

Russell, C. W. *Cotton in the Laundry and Dry Cleaning Industry.* Washington, NCCA, 1961.

Story of Cotton. Macon, Ga.: Bibb Mfg. Co., 1954.

Strong, Peter M. "Cotton Manufacture, Cotton Growing and the National Economy," *Am. Text. Rep.,* **76**, Nos. 2, 3, 4, and 5 (Jan. 11, 18, and 25, and Feb. 1, 1962).

Texas Cotton—From Seed to Mill. Houston, Texas: Anderson, Clayton & Co., 1937.

Ward, Kyle, Jr. *Chemistry and the Chemical Technology of Cotton.* New York: Interscience, 1955.

Washington, D.C., Section, A.A.T.C.C. "Achieving Accuracy in Measurements of Textiles for Reflectance and Whiteness," *Am. Dyestuff Rep.,* **50**, No. 2 (Oct. 16, 1961), pp. 45–55.

Williams, J. F., and McCord, F. A. *Easy Care Cottons.* Washington: NCCA, 1960.

CHAPTER 11

linen

Caplin, J. F. *Linen Fabrics.* St. Paul, Minn.: Riverside Press, 1939.

Gibson, W. H. *Linen and Human Welfare.* Belfast, Ireland: Linen Industry Research Association, 1945.

Leggett, W. F. *The Story of Linen.* New York: Chemical Publ. Co., 1945.

Moore, A. S. *Linen.* New York: Wiley, 1951.

other cellulosic fibers

Anderer, Joseph W. "Polyesters and Modified Rayons in Lightweight Fabrics," *Modern Textiles Magazine,* **41** (Dec., 1960), p. 54.

Asaedo, T. "Torancomen-61: A New Polymerized Cellulosic Fiber," *Modern Textiles Magazine,* **44** (1963), pp. 23–24.

Compton, J. "New Textile Fibres with the Structural Elements of Natural Cellulosic Fibres," *Am. Dyestuff Rep.,* **43** (1954), pp. 103–11.

Lund, G. V. "Elements of Fabric Stability—The New High Modulus Cellulosic

Fibers," *Modern Textiles Magazine,* **40** (April, 1959), pp. 8–14.

Smith, B. F., Davidson, S., and Smith, F. "Determination of Cellulose in Textile Fibers," *Text. Res. J.,* **32,** No. 1 (1962), pp. 29–38.

CHAPTER 12

Biological Aspects of Insect Damage to Wool. New York: Mitin Dept., Geigy Dyestuff, 1954.

Boerg, W. J., and Warren, L. O. *Biology and Control of the Webbing Clothes Moth.* Bull. 544. Fayetteville, Ark.: Agr. Expt. Sta., Univ. of Arkansas, College of Agriculture, 1954.

Fairservis, W. A., Jr. *Wool Through the Ages.* New York: The Wool Bureau, 1955.

Farnsworth, A. J. "The Permanent Setting of Wool," *Am. Dyestuff Rep.,* **49,** No. 26 (Dec. 26, 1960), pp. 996–1006.

Hopkins, Giles E. *Wool as an Apparel Fiber.* New York: Rinehart, 1953.

————. "Wool as an Apparel Fiber," *Text. Res. J.,* **20,** No. 8 (Aug., 1950).

Leggett, W. F. *The Story of Wool.* New York: Chemical Publ. Co., 1947.

"Mechanical Properties of the Wool Fiber and Their Relation to Structure," *Wool Science Review,* **21** (Aug., 1962), pp. 14–26.

Men's Preferences Among Wool Suits, Coats, and Jackets. Agr. Inf. Bull. No. 64. Washington: U.S. Dept. of Agriculture, 1951.

The Mothproofing of Wool. London: International Wool Secretariat, 1955.

Pendleton Blankets—Always Virgin Wool. Portland, Oregon: Pendleton Woolen Mills, 1959.

Pendleton Sweater Sense. Portland, Oregon: Pendleton Woolen Mills, 1959.

"Physical Properties of Wool Fibers," *Wool Science Review,* **17** (July, 1957), pp. 33–49.

"The Physiological Properties of Wool Clothing," *Wool Science Review,* **21** (Aug., 1962), pp. 40–50.

The Romantic Story of Man and Sheep. Portland, Oregon: Pendleton Woolen Mills, 1958.

Rules and Regulations Under the Wool Products Labeling Act of 1939. Washington: Federal Trade Comm., 1941.

Scott, C. L. *When a Woman Buys a Coat.* Leaflet No. 117. Washington: U.S. Dept. of Agriculture, 1938.

The Story of Wool. Bull. No. 17. New York: *Good Housekeeping Magazine,* 1940.

Von Bergen, W., *American Wool Handbook,* 3rd ed. New York: Interscience 1963.

The Wool Bureau. *Durable Mothproofing of Wool—New and Inexpensive Method Using Dieldrin.* Wool Science and Technology Report No. 2. New York: The Wool Bureau, 1958.

————. *Durable Pleating and Weaving of All-Wool Apparel with Si-Ro-Set Solution.* Wool Science and Technology Report No. 4. New York: The Wool Bureau, 1959.

CHAPTER 15

Biefeld, L. P., and Philipps, T. E. "Sizes for Glass Textiles for Reinforcing Polyester Fabrics," *Am. Dyestuff Rep.,* **42** (Aug. 18, 1952), pp.

Fiberglas Bibliography, 3rd ed. Toledo, O.: Dow Corning Corp., 1950.

Mennerich, F. G. "New Textile Uses for Glass Fiber Yarns," Papers A.A.T.T.,

Modern Textiles Magazine, **43** (Dec., 1962), pp. 43–45, 67.

Owens-Corning Fiberglas Corp. "Fiberglas, An Engineering Material," *British Rayon Manual,* pp. 39–40. Manchester, England: Jgn., 1947.

CHAPTER 16

general

Mauersberger, H. R. *American Handbook of Synthetic Textiles.* New York: Textile Book Publ., 1952.

Schwartz, E. W. K., and Mauersberger, H. R. *Rayon and Synthetic Yarn Handbook,* 2nd ed. New York: Textile Book Publ., 1936.

rayon

Barker, S. W., and Alleston, R. "Continuous Spinning of Rayon" *J. Text. Inst.,* **39** (1948), pp. 1, 3.

British Rayon Manual, pp. 15–26. Manchester, England: Textile Inst., 1947.

Crawford, M. D. C. *5,000 Years of Fibres and Fabrics.* Brooklyn: The Brooklyn Museum, 1946.

Dorée, C. *The Methods of Cellulose Chemistry,* 2nd ed. New York: D. Van Nostrand, 1947.

Frisk, P. W. "Review of Continuous Viscose Spinning," *Rayon and Synthetic Textiles,* **30,** No. 9 (1952), p. 49.

Hegan, H. J. *et. al., Talks on Rayon,* pp. 1–22. Manchester, England: The Cotton and Rayon Merchants Assn., 1944.

Knight, A. R. *et. al., Talks on Rayon,* pp. 43–55. Manchester, England: The Cotton and Rayon Merchants Assn., 1944.

Moncrieff, R. W. "The Genesis of Synthetic Fibre," *Textile Manufacturer,* **75** (1949), p. 285.

cellulose

Dreyfus, H. "The Birth, Development and Present Position of the Cellulose Acetate Artificial Silk Industry in the Country," *J. Soc. Dyers and Col.,* **55** (1939), p. 116.

Ellis, G. H. "The Dyeing of Cellulose Acetate" *J. Soc. Dyers and Col.,* **57** (1941), p. 353.

cellulose triacetate

Arnel. Technical Bull. TD-12A. New York: Celanese Corp. of America, 1960.

Boulton, J. "Courpleta—The Dyeing and Other Properties of Cellulose Triacetate Yarn and Staple," *J. Soc. Dyers and Col.,* **71** (1955), pp. 451–64.

Fortess, F. "Dyeing, Finishing and Heat-Treating Arnel Triacetate," *Am. Dyestuff Rep.,* **44** (1955), pp. 524–37.

Harrington, R. C., and Jarett, C. A. "A New Dull Acetate for Decorative Fabrics," Papers A.A.T.T., *Modern Textiles Magazine,* **44** (April, 1963), pp. 67–70.

Mellor, A., and Olpin, H. C. "The Dyeing and Finishing of Cellulose Triacetate Yarns and Fabrics," *J. Soc. Dyers and Col.,* **71** (1955), pp. 817–29.

high-tenacity cellulosic fibers

Berry, J. K. "The Chemical and Physical Properties of Modern Textile Fibres," *J.*

Roy. Soc. Arts., **94** (1946), pp. 403–17.

Mellor, A. "Celanese-Fortisan Dyeing and Printing," *J. Soc. Dyers and Col.,* **62** (1946), p. 168.

Rose, L. "High Tenacity Viscose Rayon," *J. Soc. Dyers and Col.,* **61** (1945), p. 113.

Sherman, J. V., and Sherman, S. L. *The New Fibers,* pp. 279–85. New York: D. Van Nostrand, 1946.

Sisson, W. A., and Morehead, F. F. "The Skin Effect of Crimped Rayon," *Text. Res. J.,* **23** (1953), pp. 152–57.

"*Tenasco.*" History & Development: Courtaulds, Ltd., London, England, 1952.

Wilcock, C. C. "Dyeing of Tenasco and Durafil," *Dyer,* **93** (1945), p. 127.

staple fibers

Ashton, H. "Greenfield Top—Rayon Tow to Top," *Textile Manufacturer,* **69** (1943), p. 259.

Baird, M. E., Hatfield, P., and Morris, G. J. "Pilling of Fabrics," *J. Text. Inst.,* **47** (1956), pp. T181–T201.

British Rayon Manual, pp. 76–91. Manchester, England: Textile Inst., 1947.

Dennison, R. W., and Leach, L. L. "Blends Containing the New Man-Made Fibres," *J. Text. Inst.,* **43** (1953), p. 473.

Electrical Safety in Hospitals. Min. of Health, interim note (June 19, 1953).

"Rayon Staple, Its Manufacture, Handling and Uses," *Rayon Text. Monthly,* **28** (1947), p. 68.

"Perlock Systems," *Rayon Text. Monthly,* **25** (1944), p. 437.

"Processing of Rayon Cut Staple," *Text. Mercury and Argus,* **120** (1949), p. 959.

Quig, J. B., and Dennison, R. W. "Functional Properties of Synthetics," *Industrial Eng. Chem.,* **44** (1952), p. 2176.

Rayon Lint. Min. of Health, Prescriber's Notes (Dec., 1952).

Rayon Technology, pp. 2–84. New York: American Viscose Corp., 1948.

Textile Institute Annual Conference on Fibre Blends, Edinburgh, 1952. *J. Text. Inst.,* **43**, No. 8 (1953).

"Tow to Yarn Spinning Frame, *Textile Recorder,* **65** (Dec., 1943), p. 43.

CHAPTER 17

azlons

Arend, A. G. "Hats of Casein Fibre" *Fibres,* **7** (1946), p. 194.

Boyer, R. A. "Soybean Protein Fibres," *Industrial Eng. Chem.,* **32** (1940), p. 1549.

Brown, A. E., Gordon, W. G., Gall, E. C., and Jackson, R. W. "The Acetylation of Casein Fibre" *Industrial Eng. Chem.,* **36** (1944), p. 1171.

Cassie, A. D. B. "Physical Properties of Fibres and Textile Performance," *J. Text. Inst.,* **37** (1946), pp. 154–165.

Cheetham, R. C. "The Dyeing of a Blend of Wool and Fibrolane for the Hand Knitting Trade," *J. Soc. Dyers and Col.,* **69** (1953), p. 76.

Hock, C. W., Sookne, A. M., and Harris, M. "Thermal Properties of Moist Fabrics," *J. Res. Nat. Bur. Stds.,* **32** (1944), p. 229.

Jenkins, H. S. *Proteins as Fiber-Forming Materials.* Paper presented at the ACS Symposium on Fibrous Proteins, New York, Sept. 16, 1954.

Kenchington, K. W. L. "Clothing and Climate," *Texture,* **3** (1956), pp. 11–17.

Matthews, J. M. *Textile Fibres*, 6th ed. London: Wiley, 1954.

Speakman, J. B. "The Chemistry of Wool and Related Fibres," *J. Text. Inst.*, **32,** No. 7 (1941), p. 540.

Sutermeister, E., and Browne, F. L. *Casein and Its Industrial Application*. New York: Reinhold, 1939.

Traill, D. "Some Trials by Ingenious Inquisitive Persons; Regenerated Fibres," *J. Soc. Dyers and Col.*, **67** (1951), pp. 257–70.

W.I.R.A. "The Warmth of Clothing," *Wool Research*, **2** (1955), pp. 43–70.

Wormell, R. L. "Milk Casein and Peanut Protein Fibres," *J. Text. Inst.*, **44** (1953), p. 258.

alginates

Bashford, L. A., *et al.* "Alginate Hessian," *J. Soc. Dyers and Col.*, **73** (1957), p. 203.

Percival, E. G. V., and Ross, A. G., "Comparison of Seaweed Cellulose and Land Plant Cellulose" *Nature*, **162** (1948), p. 895.

Reinhardt, R. M., Fenner, T. W., and Reid, J. D. "New Methods for the Preparation of Alkali-Soluble Textile Materials," *Am. Dyestuff Rep.*, **50,** No. 19 (1961), pp. 694–709.

Speakman, J. B., and Chamberlain, N. H. "Formaldehyde Treatment of Alginates," *J. Soc. Dyers and Col.*, **60** (1944), p. 264.

Tseng, C. K. "Alginates Fibres Compared," *Text. World*, **95** (Dec., 1945), p. 113.

CHAPTER 18

Bawn, C. E. H. *The Chemistry of High Polymers*. London: Richard Clay & Co. Ltd., 1948.

Carothers, W. H., and Hill, J. W. "Collected Papers on Polymer Formation" *J. Am. Chem. Soc.*, **54** (1932), pp. 1559–87.

Embossed Fabrics. Service Bull. 451–B. Joliet, Mo.: Am. Inst. Laundering, 1953.

Feild, T. A. "Dyeing and Wet-Finishing Dynel Fabrics," *Am. Dyestuff Rep.*, **40** (1951), p. 737.

Handling Resin-Finished Fabrics. Service Bulls. 419 and 441–B. Joliet, Mo.: Am. Inst. Laundering, 1953.

Housmon, J. A. "Recent Progress in Cellulose and Acetate Fibers," *Annals N.Y. Acad. Sciences*, **67,** No. 11 (1957), pp. 901–09.

Laundering and Finishing of Sport Shirts. Service Bull. 445. Joliet, Mo.: Am. Inst. Laundering, 1953.

Laundering Properties of Dynel. Service Bull. 424. Joliet, Mo.: Am. Inst. Laundering, 1951.

Milestones in the du Pont Company's Textile Fibers History and Some Important Industry Dates. Wilmington, Del.: Products Information Section, Text. Fibers Dept., E. I. du Pont de Nemours & Co., 1962.

Moncrieff, R. W. "The Genesis of Synthetic Fibre," *Text. Manufacturer*, **75** (1949), p. 285.

Mosher, H. "The Use of Resins and Plastics in Textile Finishes," *Am. Dyestuff Rep.*, **42** (1953), p. 402.

"New Man-Made Fibers to Boom," *Chem. & Eng. News*, **37,** No. 13 (March 30, 1959), pp. 86–96.

Preston, R., and Warburton, N. "A Method for the Quantitative Determination of

Ardil in Admixture with Wool," *J. Text. Inst.,* **44** (1953), p. T298.

Richardson, G. W., Stanley, H. E., and Heckert, W. W. "Recent Progress in Polyamide and Polyesters," *Annals N.Y. Acad. Sciences,* **67,** No. 11 (1957), pp. 910–31.

Sheehan, Charles R. "Rovana—Versatile New Yarn," *Am. Dyestuff Rep.,* **50,** No. 4 (Feb. 20, 1961), pp. 139–41.

Soday, Frank J. "Synthetic Fiber Developments," *Quarterly Bull. of Southern Research Inst.,* **6** (1953), p. 29.

Solomon, Goody. "New Uses of Man-Made Fibers in Apparel Fabrics," *Modern Textiles Magazine,* **42** (June, 1961), pp. 49–56.

"Standard Method of Test for the Quantitative Chemical Analysis of Mixtures of Protein and Non-Protein Fibres (Tentative Textile Standard No. 39, 1956)," *J. Text. Inst.,* **47** (1956), pp. 278–79.

Szlosberg, M. "Problems in Dyeing Synthetic Fiber Blends," *Am. Dyestuff Rep.,* **42** (1953), p. 431.

Trademark Glossary of Manufactured Fibers. Marcus Hook, Pa.: Tech. Svc. Dept., Product Info. Div., Am. Viscose Corp., 1960.

CHAPTER 19

Frey-Wyssling, A. "Optical Properties," *Nature,* **145** (1940), p. 82.

Loasby, G. "The Development of the Synthetic Fibers, *J. Text. Inst.,* **42** (1951), pp. 422–430.

"Nylon Moves Ahead in Upholstery," *Modern Textiles Magazine,* **42** (1961), pp. 33, 36.

Talliss, H. C. H. "Developments in Nylon 66 and 610 Fibres," *The Textile Institute Report of 41st Annual Conference,* 1956, pp. 45–58.

Waltz, J. E., and Taylor, G. A. "Determination of Molecular Weight of Nylon," *Anal. Chem.,* **19** (1947), p. 448.

CHAPTER 20

Demme, G. S., Thompson, C., and Hicks, E. M. "Where Orlon Stands Today," *Modern Textiles Magazine,* **42** (Feb., 1961), pp. 39–45.

"Enter Zefran," *Man-Made Textiles,* **39** (Dec., 1962), pp. 68–69.

Feild, T. A. "The Dyeing of Dynel and Related Products," *Am. Dyestuff Rep.,* **41** (1952), p. 475.

Haller, H. C. "Maximum Construction Tables for Fabrics of Creslan Acrylic Fiber and Other Fibers," *Am. Dyestuff Rep.,* **50** (1961), pp. 31–34.

Houtz, R. C. "Orlon Acrylic Fibre, Chemistry and Properties," *Text. Res. J.,* **20** (1950), p. 11.

McIntire, O. R. "How Zefran Performs in Fabrics," Papers A.A.T.T., *Modern Textiles Magazine,* **12,** No. 3 (Sept., 1957), pp. 80–86.

Papers of the American Association of Textile Technology. Published by *Modern Textiles Magazine,* **11,** No. 4 (Dec., 1956), pp. 120–141.
Coover, H. W., Jr. "Verel, Acrylic Fiber, Physical and Chemical Aspects."
Crawford, R. T. "Applications and Possibilities."
Ivey, W. R., Jr. "Dyeing and Finishing Properties."

Papers of the American Association of Textile Technology. Published by *Modern*

Textiles Magazine, **43,** No. 11 (1962), pp. 45–58.

Loosli, A. R. "American Cyanamid's New Acrylic Filament Yarn. Part I: Why Offered."

Marsh, N. H. "Part II: Properties."

Keefer, W. H. "Part III: The Marketing Approach."

Papers Presented at the Technical Conference on Dyeing of Orlon Acrylic Fiber and Dacron Polyester Fiber, Aug. 5, 1952. Wilmington, Del.: E. I. du Pont de Nemours & Co., 1952.

Quig, J. B. "Orlon Acrylic Fiber," Papers A.A.T.T., *Modern Textiles Magazine,* **4** (1949), pp. 61–70.

Walls, I. M. S. "The Dyeing of Orlon and Orlon Mixtures," *J. Soc. Dyers and Col.,* **72** (1956), pp. 261–66.

Woodruff, J. A. "Introduction to the Dyeing of Chemstrand Acrylic Fiber," *Am. Dyestuff Rep.,* **40** (1951), p. 402.

CHAPTER 21

Faris, B. T. "Properties of Synthetic Fibers with Respect to Wet Processing Conditions and End-Use Performance—Dacron Polyester Fiber," *Am. Dyestuff Rep.,* **51** (1962), pp. 41–44.

Lacy, R. E., Salvin, V. S., and Schoenberg, W. A. "Optimum Dyeing and Finishing of Specific Polyester Blend Fabrics," *Am. Dyestuff Rep.,* **50** (1961), pp. 39–43, 99–101.

Martin, E. V. "Structure and Properties of a New Polyester Fiber," *Text. Res. J.,* **32** (Aug. 1962), pp. 619–27.

Thomas, P. M. "Woven Stretch Fabrics," *Modern Textiles Magazine,* **42** (1961), p. 22.

Whinfield, J. R. "The Development of Terylene," *Text. Res. J.,* **23** (1953), p. 289.

Woodruff, J. "The Dyeing of Vinyon," *Am. Dyestuff Rep.,* **33** (April 22, 1946), pp. 290–93.

CHAPTER 22

polyvinyl chloride fibers

Mouchiroud, G. "The Blending of Polyvinyl Chloride Fibres with Other Fibres," *J. Text. Inst.,* **43** (1952), p. 466.

Synthetic Fibre Developments in Germany. File XXXIII—50, BIOS, H.M.S.O., 1946.

dynel fibers

Denbridge, C. R. "Dynel," *Fibres,* **9** (1948), p. 335.

Feild, T. A. "The Dyeing of Dynel and Related Products," *Am. Dyestuff Rep.,* **41** (1952), p. 475.

propylene

Erlich, Victor L. "Propylene's Future," *Modern Textiles Magazine,* **43** (Dec., 1962), pp. 46–48.

saran fibers

Goggin, W. C., and Lowry, R. D. "The Manufacture of Saran," *Industrial Eng. Chem.*, **34** (1942), p. 327.
Saran. Midland, Mich. The Dow Chemical Co., 1942.

spandex

Faris, B. F. "Dyeing and Finishing of Hosiery Containing Lycra Spandex Fibers," *Am. Dyestuff Rep.*, **52**, No. 1 (1963), pp. 35–37.
Hicks, E. M., Jr. "Lycra Spandex Fiber—Structure and Properties," *Am. Dyestuff Rep.*, **52**, No. 1 (1963), pp. 33–35.

polyethylene fibers

Clark, A., Logan, J. P., Banks, R. L., and Lanning, W. C. "Marlex Catalyst Systems," *Industrial Eng. Chem.*, **48** (1956), pp. 1152–54.
Jones, R. V., and Boeke, P. J. "Properties of Marlex 50 Ethylene Polymer," *Industrial Eng. Chem.*, **48** (1956), pp. 1155–61.
Preston, J. M. *Fibre Science*, pp. 327–28. Manchester, England: Textile Institute, 1949.

teflon fiber

Rivers, J. T., and Franklin, R. L. "Teflon," *Text. Res. J.*, 26 (1956), pp. 805–11.

foam and laminates

Erlich, V. L. "Fabric Foam Laminates—Their Status Today," *Modern Textiles Magazine*, **43** (Feb. 20, 1962), pp. 37–40.
Monego, Constantin J., *et al.* "Insulating Values of Fabrics, Foams and Laminates," *Am. Dyestuff Rep.*, **52**, No. 1 (1963), pp. 21–32.
Papers of the American Association for Textile Technology. Published by *Modern Textiles Magazine*, **12**, No. 4 (Dec., 1957), pp. 132–40.
  Lynn, J. E., "Plastic Foams—A New Textile Material."
  Singer, R. A. "Urethane in Clothing—Warmth Without Weight."
  Tompkins, T. G. "Expanded Vinyls in Special Purpose Garments."

CHAPTER 23

Baker, Cameron, Burston, W., Lovell, M. J., Fri, J. M., McNair, J. W., and Layer, R. H. "An Examination of Fabric Performance Standards," *Modern Textiles Magazine*, **42**, No. 1 (Jan., 1961), p. 39.
Bostwick, C. O. "Comparison of Some Methods for Testing Wrinkle Recovery," *Am. Dyestuff Rep.*, **51**, No. 11 (May 28, 1962), pp. 386–93.
Fisher, C. H. "Improved Warmth Qualities for Cotton Could Boost Consumption," *Am. Textile Rep.*, **75**, No. 48 (Nov. 30, 1961), 560–64.
Freedman, Ephraim. "American Standard Performance Requirements for Textile Fabrics," *Am. Dyestuff Rep.*, **50**, No. 15 (July 24, 1961), pp. 557–66.
Labarthe, Jules. "What the Textile Consumer Expects from Science," *Annals N.Y. Acad. Sciences*, **67**, No. 11 (1957), pp. 975–82.
Meyers, S. L. "Consumer Complaints: A Source of Information for Producers," *Am.*

Dyestuff Rep., **50** (1961), pp. 25–28.

Morrill, E. "The Textile Consumer Looks at A.A.T.C.C." *Am. Dyestuff Rep.*, **50** (March 20, 1961), pp. 209–10.

Steele, Richard. "Factors Affecting the Drying of Apparel Fabrics," Sixth Chem. Finishing Conf., Nat'l. Cotton Council of America, 1957, pp. 2–14.

Tovey, Henry. "Wrinkle Resistance and Recovery from Deformation," *Text. Res. J.*, **31,** No. 3 (1961), pp. 185–252.

Tremaine, B. K. "The Importance of Odor Control in Textile Processing," *Am. Dyestuff Rep.*, **50** (1961), pp. 35–40.

CHAPTER 29

articles

Brew, M. L. "Development of Clothing Budgets," *J. Home Econ.*, **46** (Oct., 1954), pp. 578–82.

Ebeling, M., and Rosencranz, M. L. "Social and Personal Aspects of Clothing for Older Women," *J. Home Econ.*, **53** (June, 1961), pp. 464–65.

Getchell, N. F. "New Finishes on Cotton," *J. Home Econ.*, **50** (Jan., 1958), pp. 12–14.

Gilbert, P. D. "Men's Wear Is Important," *J. Home Econ.*, **46** (Feb., 1954), pp. 76–78.

Hoffman, A. M. "College Clothing Expenditures," *J. Home Econ.*, **52** (Oct., 1960), pp. 665–66.

Ingalls, I. "Factors Influencing Wear of Girls' Dresses," *J. Home Econ.*, **50** (Feb., 1958), p. 104.

Labarthe, J. "Your Money's Worth in Clothing and Textiles," *J. Home Econ.*, **46** (Nov., 1954), pp. 640–44.

Petzel, F. "Mandatory Textile Labeling," *J. Home Econ.*, **50** (June, 1958), pp. 410–13.

Phillips, V. "College Students Study Their Own Buying Habits," *J. Home Econ.*, **46** (Nov., 1954), pp. 665–66.

Quinn, F. R. "Significance of Consumers' Textile Complaints," *J. Home Econ.*, **52** (April, 1960), pp. 253–55.

Ryan, M. S. "Effect on a College Girl of Feeling Well Dressed," *J. Home Econ.*, **43** (Dec., 1951), p. 799.

––––––. "A Study of Factors in the Selection and Care of Blouses Which Relate to Consumer Satisfactions," *J. Home Econ.*, **46** (March, 1954), pp. 149–54.

Ryan, M. S., and Miller, M. S. "Mothers and Daughters Select School Dresses," *J. Home Econ.*, **52** (June, 1960), pp. 455–56.

Shively, A. E., and Roseberry, E. D. "Adequacy of College Wardrobes Judged," *J. Home Econ.*, **40** (Feb., 1948), pp. 81–82.

Stone, G. P., Form, W. H., and Straham, H. B. "The Social Climate of Decision in Shopping for Clothes," *J. Home Econ.*, **46** (Feb., 1954), pp. 86–88.

Stout, D. R., and Latzke, A. "Values College Women Consider in Clothing Selection, *J. Home Econ.*, **50** (Jan., 1958), pp. 43–44.

Thompson, H. M., and Edmonds, M. N. "A Minimum College Wardrobe for a Freshman," *J. Home Econ.*, **52** (Oct., 1960), pp. 662–64.

Warden, J. A. "Some Desires or Goals for Clothing of College Women," *J. Home*

Econ., **49** (Dec., 1957), p. 795.

Waters, B. J. "Wash-and-Wear Dresses—A Pilot Study," *J. Home Econ.*, **53** (Oct., 1961), pp. 694–95.

Wham, G. "Today's Issue on Clothing Care," *J. Home Econ.*, **51** (Dec., 1959), pp. 864–66.

White, R. V. "Standards for the Consumer," *J. Home Econ.*, **53** (Sept., 1961), pp. 532–37.

Whitlock, M. C. "Adjustment Guide for Consumers of Textile Products," *J. Home Econ.*, **54** (Feb., 1962), pp. 109–11.

Winakor, Geitel. "Consumer Expenditures for Clothing in the United States, 1929–1958," *J. Home Econ.*, **54** (Feb., 1962), pp. 115–18.

studies

Clothing Fabrics. Home Economics Research Report No. 1. Washington: U.S. Dept. Agriculture,

"Consumer Expenditures," *Life* Magazine, 1957.

Family Clothing Inventories and Purchases (1949–1950). Bull. No. 148. Washington: U.S. Dept. Agriculture, 1956.

Heller Committee. *Quantity and Cost Budgets for Two Income Levels.* Berkeley: Univ. of Calif., 1960.

How American Buying Habits Change. Washington: U.S. Dept. Labor, 1957.

Stone, G. B., and Form, William. *Clothing Inventories and Preferences Among Rural and Urban Families.*

U.S. Department of Agriculture. Preliminary Reports.
No. 1: "Family Clothing Inventories by Income."
No. 2: "Family Clothing Purchases by Income."
No. 3: "Family Clothing Inventories by Age."
No. 6: "Farm Family Clothing Inventories and a Farm-City Comparison."
No. 7: "Farm Family Clothing Purchases and a Farm-City Comparison."

Your Clothing Dollar. Chicago: Household Finance Corp., 1961.

references

Statistical Abstract of the U.S., 1961. Washington: Bureau of the Census,

Woytinski, W. S., and Woytinski, E. S. *World Population and Production, 1953.* Supt. of Documents. Washington.

TABLE 1 / A FEW CONVERSION FACTORS OF IMPORTANCE TO TEXTILE STUDY

	Multiply by
Meters to yards	1.0936
Meters to feet	3.28084
Meters to inches	39.370
Square meters to square yards	1.196
Square meters to square feet	10.764
Square inches to square centimeters	6.4516
Cubic inches to cubic centimeters	16.387
Cubic inches to liters	0.0164
Cubic feet to liters	28.339
Gallons (US) to liters	3.785
Liters of water to pounds	2.2046
Pounds to kilograms	0.45359
Ounces to grams	28.349
Grains to grams	0.0648
Grams per meter to ounces per yard	0.03226
Grams per square meter to ounces per square yard	0.0295
Pounds per square inch to grams per square centimeter	70.31

For the reverse conversion, divide by the constant.

T A B L E   2   /   S E R V I C E - U S E   R A T I N G S   O F   T E X T I L E S   (A V E R A G E   R A T I N G S)

1—Excellent
2—Good
3—Fair
4—Poor

	Synthetic Fibers								
	Nylon and Perlon	Orlon	Dacron and Terylene	Dynel	Acrilan	Creslan*	Vicara	Saran	Verel
Durability Factors									
Wear or abrasion	1	2	1–2	2	2	2	3	2	2
Breaking Strength, dry	1	2	2	2	2	2	4	3	2
Breaking Strength, wet	1	2	2	2	2	2	4	3	2
Tearing resistance, dry	1	2	2	2	2	2	4	3	2
Tearing resistance, wet	1	2	2	2	2	2	4	3	2
Sun resistance (fabric not color)	4	1	2	2	1	2	3	3	1
Insect resistance (moth and carpet beetle)	1	1	1	1	1	1	1	1	1
Mildew resistance	1	2	1	1	2	1	2	1	1
Acid resistance	4	2	2	1	2	2	2	1	1
Alkali resistance	1	3	2	1	3	3	2	1	1
Bleach resistance	3	3	3	3	3	3	2	2	1
Burning resistance	2	2–4	1–2	1	2	2	2	1	1
Iron damage resistance	3	4	4	4	4	4	3	3	3
Appearance and Comfort Factors									
Draping quality	3	2	2	2	2	2	1	2	1
Crease retention	1–2	1	1	2	1	2	2¹	2	2
Wrinkle resistance (and recovery)	1–2	2	1	2	2	2	2¹	3	2
Softness of hand	3	2	2	2	2	2	1	4	1
Ease of dyeing	2	4	3	3	2	4	1	2	4
Bulk and warmth	2	1	3	2	1	1	2	3	1
Warmth retention after prolonged use	2	1	3	1	1	1	3	3	1
Comfort in all weather	4	1–2	3	1	3	1–2	1–2	3	1

* Estimated from chemical origin.
¹ Dry rating—4 when wet.

1—Excellent
2—Good
3—Fair
4—Poor

	Glass Fiber	Other Man-Made Fibers				Natural Fibers		
		Rayon	Acetate	Fortisan	Arnel	Cotton	Wool	Silk
Durability Factors								
Wear or abrasion	3	3	3	2	3	2	2	2
Breaking Strength, dry	1	3	4	1	3	2	4	2
Breaking Strength, wet	1	4	4	2	3	1	4	3
Tearing resistance, dry	1	3	4	1	3	1	4	2
Tearing resistance, wet	1	4	3	2	3	1	4	3
Sun resistance (fabric not color)	1	4	1	2	3	3	3	4
Insect resistance (moth and carpet beetle)	1	1	1	1	1	1	4	4
Mildew resistance	1	4	2	3	2	4	2	2
Acid resistance	3	4	3	3	3	4	3	3
Alkali resistance	2	4	4	2	4	2	4	4
Bleach resistance	1	4	2	2	2	2	2	2
Burning resistance	1	4	3	4	2	4	2	2
Iron damage resistance	1	2	4	3	3	1	3	3
Appearance and Comfort Factors								
Draping quality	1	4	1	1	2	4	1	1
Crease retention	1	4	3	2[1]	2	4	2[1]	2[1]
Wrinkle resistance (and recovery)	1	4	3	3	1	4	1[1]	2[1]
Softness of hand	2	2	2	2	3	3	1	2
Ease of dyeing	4[2]	1	2	1	1	1	2	2
Bulk and warmth	1	4	3	2	3	4	2	2
Warmth retention after prolonged use	2	4	3	—	3	4	2	2
Comfort in all weather	4	3	3	—	3	2	1	1

[1] Dry rating—4 when wet.
[2] Colored by other methods.

543

TABLE 3 / THE BURNING CHARACTERISTICS OF FIBERS

Fiber	Before Touching Flame	In Flame	After Leaving Flame	Odor	Ash
Cellulose					
Cotton	Burns just as flame touches fiber.	Burns.	Supports combustion, burns rapidly, has afterglow.	Burning paper.	Very small, soft, and grey.
Viscose	Burns as fiber touches flame.	Burns.	Supports combustion, burns very rapidly, no afterglow.	Burning paper.	No ash unless dulled.
Cuprammonium (Bemberg)	Burns just as fiber touches flame.	Burns.	Supports combustion, burns very rapidly, no afterglow.	Burning paper.	No ash unless dulled.
Fortisan (regular and 36)	Burns as fiber touches flame.	Burns.	Supports combustion, burns very rapidly, no afterglow.	Burning paper not as strong as others.	No ash unless dulled.
Cross-linked cellulose					
Corvel	Burns as fiber touches flame.	Burns.	Supports combustion, burns rapidly, no afterglow.	Faintly like burning paper, very sharp.	Very fine grey.
Topel	Burns as fiber touches flame.	Burns.	Supports combustion, burns rapidly, no afterglow.	Faintly like burning paper, very sharp.	Very fine grey.
Acetates					
Acetate	Melts and turns black about ¼ in. from flame.	Melts and burns.	Supports combustion, melts ahead of flame.	Acrid, resembles vinegar.	Hard, brittle, black, and irregular.
Arnel	Melts and turns black about ⅛ in. from flame.	Melts and burns.	Supports combustion, melts ahead of flame.	Acrid.	Hard, brittle, black, and irregular.
Protein					
Wool	Melts away from flame.	Melts and burns.	Supports combustion with difficulty, melts ahead as it burns.	Burning feathers.	Easily crushable, brittle, puffy, black.
Silk	Melts away from flame.	Melts and burns.	Supports combustion with difficulty, melts ahead of flame, sputters as it burns.	Burning feathers.	Easily crushable, brittle, puffy, black.
Vicara	Melts away from flame.	Melts and burns.	Supports combustion with difficulty, melts ahead of flame.	Burning feathers, fainter than wool.	Easily crushable, brittle, puffy, black.
Fibrolane Merinova	Melts away from flame.	Melts and burns.	Supports combustion with difficulty, melts ahead of flame.	Burning feathers, stronger than wool.	Crushable, brittle, puffy, black.
Ardil	Melts away from flame.	Melts and burns.	Supports combustion with difficulty, melts ahead of flame, sputters as it burns.	Burning feathers.	Easily crushable, brittle, puffy, black.
Nylon 66	Melts before touching flame.	Melts and burns.	Does not readily support combustion.	Celery-like.	Hard, round, light, brow to grey bead.
Nylon 6	Melts before touching flame.	Melts and burns.	Supports combustion with difficulty.	Celery-like, fainter than 66.	Hard, round, grey bead.

Fiber	Approaching flame	In flame	Combustion	Odor	Residue
Dacron	Melts before touching flame.	Melts and burns.	Burns readily.	Very faint sweet.	Hard, round, black.
Kodel	Melts before touching flame.	Melts and burns.	Burns readily, produces some soot.	Faintly like burning pine tar.	Hard, round, black.
Vinyon HH	Shrinks away from flame and melts.	Melts and burns.	Does not support combustion.	Sweet.	Hard, black, irregular.
Dynel	Shrinks away from flame and melts.	Melts and burns slowly.	Does not support combustion.	Sharp sweet.	Hard, black, irregular.
Verel	Melts.	Melts and burns slowly.	Does not support combustion.	Sharp, similar to burning gun.	Hard, black, irregular.
Darvan (Darlan)	Melts before reaching flame.	Melts and burns readily.	Burns readily.	Sweet, nitrogenous.	Hard, black, irregular.
Acrilan	Melts, ignites before reaching flame.	Melts and burns rapidly.	Burns readily with sputtering.	Burning steak.	Hard, black, irregular.
Creslan	Melts.	Melts and burns.	Supports combustion.	Sweet.	Hard, black, irregular.
Orlon (81 and 42)	Melts and ignites before reaching flame.	Melts and burns.	Burns rapidly with sputtering.	Faintly like burning flesh.	Hard, black, irregular.
Zefran	Melts away from flame.	Melts and burns.	Supports combustion, burns readily.	Tumeric-like.	Brittle, black, irregular.
Saran Velon	Melts before reaching flame.	Melts and burns.	Does not support combustion.	Acrid, sweet.	Crushable, hard, black, irregular.
Teflon	Melts when almost in flame.	Melts and decomposes.	Does not support combustion.	GASES POISON, DO NOT INHALE.	Hard, round, black bead.
Rhovyl	Shrinks from flame.	Melts and burns.	Does not support combustion.	Sharp, sweet.	Hard, black, irregular.
Polyethylene	Melts, shrinks, and curls from flame.	Melts and burns.	Burns rapidly.	Burning paraffin.	Soft, round, same color as fiber.
Polypropylene	Shrinks rapidly from flame, curls, and melts.	Melts, ignites with difficulty.	Burns slowly.	Faintly like burning asphalt.	Hard, round, light tan.
Polystyrene	Melts, shrinks, and curls from flame.	Melts and burns.	Burns rapidly with production of great deal soot.	Benzene hyacinth.	Soft, round, same color as fiber.
Kuralon Vinylon	Melts.	Burns.	Supports combustion.	Sweet, flower-like.	Hard, brown or black, round bead.
Mineral					
Asbestos	No effect.	Glows.	Does not burn.	None.	Powder if flame is hot.
Glass	No effect.	Glows.	Does not burn.	None.	None.
Metallized yarns	Curls from flame.	Burns.	Depends upon supporting material.	Depends upon supporting material.	Metallic ribbon.

From: J. J. Press (ed.), *Man-Made Textile Encyclopedia* (New York: John Wiley & Sons, Inc., 1959), pp. 143–144, Table 1.

TABLE 4 / YARN NUMBERING AND COUNT SYSTEMS

indirect or length per unit weight

Asbestos and glass fiber (American cut)	the number of 100-yard hanks per pound
Cotton count	the number of 840-yard hanks per pound
Spun silk	the number of 840-yard hanks per pound
Spun rayon staple	the number of 840-yard hanks per pound
Linen count (wet spun)	the number of 300-yard hanks per pound
Worsted count (and special wools)	the number of 560-yard hanks per pound
Woolen count (American cut)	the number of 300-yard hanks per pound
Typp* (a proposed universal system)	the number of 1000-yard hanks per pound

direct or weight per unit length

Denier—silk & all filaments—The weight in grams of 9000 meters of yarn.

Grex (a proposed universal unit)—The weight in grams of 10,000 meters of yarn.

conversion from one count to another

Assume we have a 1's cotton yarn. By definition, 840 yards weigh one pound.

From the conversion table, 1 lb. = 0.453.6 Kg. or 453.6 grams. 1 meter is 39.37 inches.

$$840 \text{ meters weigh } 453.6 \times \frac{39.37}{36} \text{ grams.}$$

The ratio for determining the denier of 1's cotton is therefore:

$$\frac{9000}{840} = \frac{x}{\dfrac{453.6 \times 39.37}{36}} \text{ or } x = \frac{9000 \times 453.6 \times \dfrac{39.37}{36}}{840}$$

$$\therefore x = 5315 \text{ grams}$$

so 1's cotton yarn is 5315 denier in size.

Thus, for any cotton count such as 40's, the constant conversion factor for 1's would be used and this is divided by the cotton count to give the denier. For example, 40's cotton would be $\frac{5315}{40} = 133$ denier.

Knowing the denier and wishing to calculate the equivalent cotton count, the same constant is used and the denier is divided into 5315. For example, a 150 denier yarn would be equivalent to $\frac{5315}{150}$ or 35.4's cotton yarn. This would properly be rounded out to the nearest whole number, 35's.

One might wish to compare the fineness of cashmere, calculated by the worsted count with that of a synthetic reported by the denier system. A new conversion factor is required because the worsted system uses the 560 yard hank units to weigh one pound. Following the same procedure, the conversion factor or constant is found to be 7972.

Thus, a 60's cashmere count $= \frac{7972}{60}$ or **133 denier** (approximately), and a 200 denier yarn would $= \frac{7972}{200}$ or 40's worsted count (almost).

* Typp—the letters stand for *Thousands of Yards Per Pound.*

FIGURE 1 PHOTOMICROGRAPHS OF IMPORT TEXTILE FIBERS [X350 (APPROXIMATELY) UNLESS NOTED OTHERWISE]

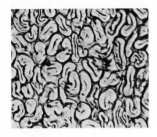

(1) Cotton Fibers not Mercerized.

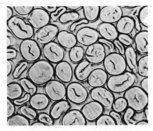

(2) Cotton Fibers Mercerized.

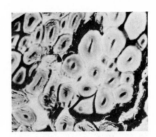

(3) Flax (linen) Fibers.

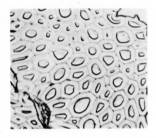

(7) Sisal Fibers Java X

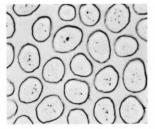

(8) Wool Fibers Merino.

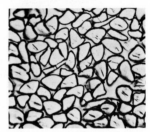

(16) Silk Fibers.

(18) Asbestos Fiber X7500).

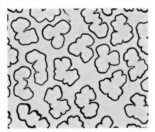

(19) Acetate Fibers, 3.8 d. per Filament, Lustrous (Typical of Estron, Acele, Avisco and Celanese).

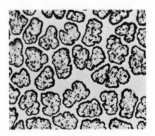

(20) Triacetate Fibers, 2.5 d. per Filament, Dull Luster Typical of Arnel.

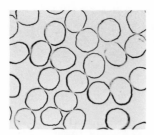

(21) Wet Spun Acrylic Fibers, 3.0 d. Semi-dull. Typical of Acrilan, Creslan, Zefran and a Few Foreign Fibers.

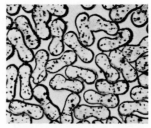

(23) Regular Solvent Spun Acrylic Fibers, 3.0 d. per Filament. Semi-dull Luster. Typical of Orlon.

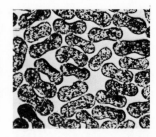

(25) Modacrylic Fibers. Typical of Dynel 97.

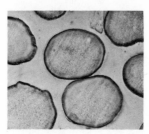

(27) Modacrylic Fibers, 3.0 d. per Filament. Dull Luster. Typical of Verel.

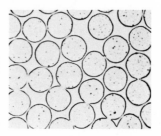

(28) Regular Nylon (Melt Spun) Fibers, 3.0 d. Semi-dull. Typical of Nylon 6, Nylon 66 and Nylon 11.

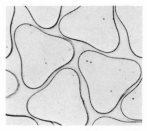

(29) Trilobal Nylon Fibers, 15 d. per Filament. Bright Luster. Typical of Antron.

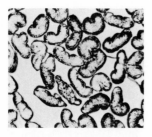

(31) Nytril Fibers, 2.0 d. per Filament. Dull Luster. Typical of Darvan.

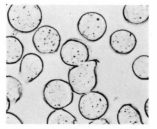

(33) Olefin Fibers, 3.0 d. per Filament. Bright Luster. Typical of Polypropylene.

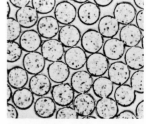

(34) Regular Polyester (Melt Spun) Fibers, 3.0 d. per Filament. Semi-dull. Typical of Dacron, Kodel, Vycron and Fortrel.

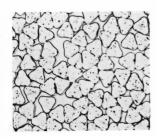

(35) Low Modification Ratio Trilobal Polyester Fibers, 1.4 d. per Filament.

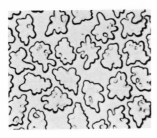

(36) Rayon Regenerated Acetate Fibers, 0.8 d. per Filament. Bright Luster. Typical of Fortisan.

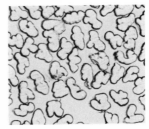

(37) Viscose Rayon Fibers. High Tenacity.

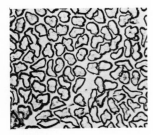

(39) Rayon Regenerated Acetate 0.8 d. per Filament. Bright Luster. Typical of Fortisan.

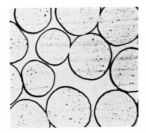

(44) Saran Fibers, 16 d. per Filament. Bright Luster.

(46) Spandex Adhering Filaments, 12 d. per Filament. Dull Luster. Typical of Lycra.

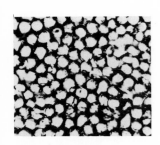

(48) Glass Fibers.

(Courtesy American Society for Testing and Materials [Philadelphia, Com. D-13 Standards for Textiles, 1962].)

Folios in **boldface** refer specifically to terms in the text also in boldface.